Management of
WILD MAMMALS IN CAPTIVITY

The Management of
WILD MAMMALS

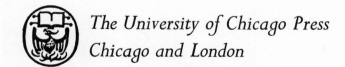

The University of Chicago Press
Chicago and London

IN CAPTIVITY

By LEE S. CRANDALL

General Curator Emeritus / New York Zoological Park

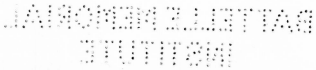

Library of Congress Catalog Card Number: 64-10498

THE UNIVERSITY OF CHICAGO PRESS, CHICAGO & LONDON
The University of Toronto Press, Toronto 5, Canada

FOREWORD

It is rarely that one is justified in saying, "This is the first book of its kind and scope that has ever been published." The statement would not be so noteworthy if the book happened to deal with a subject of remote or specialized interest to a limited coterie. But *The Management of Wild Mammals in Captivity* is not a book of this kind. The whole subject of wild animals, including methods of keeping them under captive conditions, has been of engrossing interest throughout the world for many centuries, even, one might say, since those earliest days when man captured wild animals and attempted to domesticate them. Today the exhibition of wild animals is world-wide and of universal appeal, evidenced by the constant increase in zoological parks in many countries and the great numbers of people attracted to them. In the United States, for instance, the annual number of visitors to zoos and aquariums aggregates not less then 60 million persons (or about a third of our total national population). This same intense interest prevails throughout Europe and other parts of the world where people can go and gaze upon the creatures of the sky, the earth, and the sea.

The arts and techniques required to maintain the health and welfare of captive wild animals have developed rapidly, particularly within the last half century. As a consequence, many kinds of animals—not only mammals but birds and reptiles as well—are now found in zoos in good health, and even breeding, that in earlier days could not be kept at all.

Several years ago the need for a book such as this became evident, and the New York Zoological Society grasped the opportunity of giving it sponsorship and financing the work entailed in its preparation. Fortunately, the ideal author was at hand in the person of Lee S. Crandall, who had had some fifty years of experience in keeping wild animals in the New York Zoological Park, and who was conversant with the practices of other zoos both in this country and abroad. As for the scope of the book, it was decided that it should contain information about as many as possible of the mammals that have been kept in the zoological parks of the world. This has proved to be a task of great magnitude which the author has accomplished only after sustained and arduous work throughout the last seven years.

Because so many aspects of wild animal care are included, it is expected that this book will be of significant value to all who are involved in the management of zoos and, in addition, that it may be of interest and use to an extensive number of others who, in one way or another, are involved in the management of wild animals—including veterinarians, animal nutritionists, medical and research laboratories maintaining animals, students of animal behavior, professional mammalogists, wildlife management experts, zoology students, and conservationists.

Many years of personal association with the author serve to corroborate the statement made above, "Fortunately, the ideal author was at hand." His extreme caution in avoiding any statement unless certain of its validity is especially characteristic. Occasionally, those of us who work with him have been tempted to try to prove him wrong, but without success. His modesty has resulted in his making occasional complaints to the effect that this book cannot be "the last word," as new knowledge is always to be gained. He seems to fail to recognize that this is true of any book on any subject. In completing this volume he has accomplished a monumental task that will serve as a foundation for future literature on this entire subject—a volume that will be invaluable to all who are interested in wild animals over an indefinite period in the future.

FAIRFIELD OSBORN
President
New York Zoological Society

OCTOBER 1963

INTRODUCTION

•

The zoological garden of today has progressed far beyond the scope and status of the mere menagerie. Within the present century great strides have been made in the development of maintenance methods that will satisfy the physical and psychological needs of the animals and at the same time allow them to be so shown that at least some segments of natural habitats and life cycles are illustrated. Changing world conditions that endanger the wild life of many areas have brought the zoological garden into new prominence in the field of propagation of threatened species. This book is written in the interests of those charged with the operation of living mammals in zoological gardens and is devoted, mainly, to the special problems involved.

Exhibition areas, whether indoors or outside, have been considered rather broadly, for as long as the basic requirements of the animals are met and suitable methods for both restraint and viewing are provided, details of elaboration become architectural devices. As for specific treatment, each form has been assigned to its generally accepted position in zoological sequence, the system followed being that of Simpson (1945) except as noted in the text. Only forms having definite captivity histories have been included, and some groups, such as the Cetacea (whales, etc.) have been omitted entirely as not usually considered as proper zoological-garden subjects. Common names given are those in general use, and technical designations have been derived from accepted authorities. Habits in nature, as they affect treatment in captivity, have usually been given. Since identification of living animals must depend almost entirely on external characters, descriptions are mainly of general appearance and coloration, with shoulder height and weight when the latter two are available. Food, care, and management coverage is largely from our own experience in the New York Zoological Park, although practice elsewhere has frequently been incorporated. Breeding, of course, is becoming more and more a major objective of the zoological garden, and methods followed, results obtained, gestation periods, and similar data, when available, have been recounted. Longevities of captive animals are of paramount interest, and records have been extensively sought.

An attempt has been made to scan the immense but scattered literature devoted to the subject and to combine the results, as far as possible, with present practice. Undoubtedly, much has been missed and certainly much remains to be learned. The effort to amass the detailed information required has often led far afield—sometimes, no doubt, too far and surely, too often, not far enough. References listed after each section include text citations only.

More and more, as the work progressed, I became impressed with the futility of attempting to present a total picture. No book of this nature can ever be final, for the zoological garden is a fluid, moving entity, changing so constantly in concept and execution that any statement of existing conditions may be quickly outmoded. But at least the past is unchangeable, and much that I have missed will be made known by future researchers.

Acknowledgment must be made of the generous support and assistance that have been accorded me. The New York Zoological Society, through its president, Dr. Fairfield Osborn, and Mr. Laurance Rockefeller, chairman of its Executive Committee, as well as the members of that body, have been most forbearing in the maintenance of a project long in reaching completion. Hardly a zoological-garden worker in this country or elsewhere has escaped my persistent pursuit of information; cessation, I am sure, will bring a feeling of relief to many. I am most grateful to them all, and credits given in the text do not express fully my appreciation of their complete co-operation. My thanks are due, also, to the many typists who have labored to make legible my often undecipherable copy.

This acknowledgment of obligation would be incomplete without mention of the members of the staff of the New York Zoological Park who have been especially helpful. These include William Bridges, William G. Conway, Grace Davall, Joseph A. Davis, Jr., Charles P. Gandal, and John Tee-Van. All users of the book will have occasion to be grateful to James W. Atz, for the completeness of the index.

L. S. C.

CONTENTS

·

ORDER LAGOMORPHA—(*Continued*)

•

ORDER RODENTIA. 207

Rodents

ORDER ARTIODACTYLA—*(Continued)*

PLATES
following page 16

Weighing the young Atlantic walrus "Herbert"

"Alice," an Indian elephant, mothering the African forest elephant "Tiny"

The platypusary being packed with hay by a keeper

The African Plains and the Lion Rock

"Malamba," a young white rhinoceros from Zululand

Keeper M. Quinn with the female lowland gorilla "Oka"

Keepers M. Quinn and Mrs. Helen Martini with the male lowland gorilla
   "Mambo"

"Oka" builds a nest of leaves

White-handed gibbons on Gibbon Island, New York Zoological Park, showing
   their method of drinking

Two of our keepers bottle-feeding pronghorn antelopes

A lion family on the Lion Rock

ORDER MONOTREMATA

.

Echidnas and Platypus

Because of normally crepuscular or even nocturnal habits, the members of this order cannot be considered as entirely satisfactory for public exhibition, the basic purpose of the zoological garden. Nevertheless, their primitive egg-laying method of reproduction, unique among mammals, and numerous other peculiarities are of such great general interest that their occasional presence in collections is fully justified.

FAMILY TACHYGLOSSIDAE

Echidnas or Spiny Anteaters

The echidnas have a fairly long history in captivity. According to Flower (1929:381), a specimen of the Australian echidna or spiny anteater (*Tachyglossus aculeatus*) received at the Zoological Gardens of London on April 26, 1845, was "the first individual ever brought alive to Europe." It lived for only 4 days, a precedent closely followed, it must be said, by most of its successors.

During the following years and up to the present time a considerable number of echidnas have arrived sporadically at many of the zoological gardens of Europe and America. For most of these animals longevity results were not good, so that some zoo officials are now inclined to take a rather dim view of their desirability.

The first echidna to arrive at the New York Zoological Park was a representative of the Australian species, received here on July 23, 1913. It survived for only 24 days. Nine specimens received in following years showed improved longevities, the best of which was a few days short of 6 years. This rather unimpressive record checks fairly closely with general zoological-garden experience, although Flower (1931:230) notes a specimen of *T. aculeatus* that lived for 14 years, 9 months, 15 days in Artis, the zoological gardens of Amsterdam.

Experiences with the large, curved-beaked Bruijn's echidna or spiny anteater (*Zaglossus bruijni*) of New Guinea, while few in number, have been of quite a different order. According to Flower (1931:230), a small shipment of these animals reached Europe in 1911, two of them finally achieving notable longevities. One was received at the Zoological Gardens of London on November 27, 1912, and G. S. Cansdale, former superintendent, informs me (*in litt.*) that this specimen died on August 4, 1943. It had therefore lived in the Gardens for 30 years, 8 months, 8 days, just short of the approximation of 30 years, 9 months given by Hamerton (1944:315) in his post mortem report.

The second outstanding record was established by an echidna, presumably from the same importation, stated by Flower (1931:230) to have arrived at the Zoological Gardens of Berlin at an unspecified date in 1911. Dr. Katherine Heinroth, former director of the Zoological Gardens of Berlin, states (*in litt.*) that "the *Zaglossus* male died on August 10, 1943." On the basis of arrival in 1911, this animal lived for something in excess of 31 years. However, it appears that nothing more definite can be established in the light of a further quotation from Dr. Heinroth's letter: "Unfortunately, the record card of *Zaglossus bruijni* was destroyed through the war's confusion. Its date of arrival in 1911 is probably not correct, since my man himself went to Tübingen for it and has given 1906 as the date."

There is the possibility, therefore, that this specimen may actually have endured for more than 36 years. However, as compared with the remarkable record quietly being established at the Philadelphia Zoological Garden, the questions concerning *Zaglossus* become of less importance. For a specimen of the Australian echidna, *T. a. aculeatus*, received there in 1903, lived until March 18, 1953, a span in several ways remarkable.

The date of arrival of this animal at Philadelphia is given by Flower (1931:230) as September 3, 1903, but Frederick A. Ulmer, Jr., curator of mammals at the Philadelphia Zoological Garden, informs me (*in litt.*) that the correct date is October 3, 1903. Acceptance of this change results in definite longevity of 49 years, 5 months, 15 days. This is not only important as the outstanding record for an echidna but takes a position near the top of the list of mammalian life spans. Flower (1931:230) says: "The only mammals besides man that are known to exceed fifty years are the Asiatic elephant, and in very rare cases, the horse." Since this echidna must have been more than 7 months old when it reached Philadelphia, its actual age at death was certainly in excess of 50 years.

The manner in which this remarkably tenacious animal was kept is of particular interest and has been broadly outlined in two articles (Anon., 1953*a*, 1953*b*). However, the details are of such importance that the following excerpts are taken from a letter received from Frederick A. Ulmer, Jr., the curator in charge of the animal during its later years:

> The cage is three feet deep, three and a half feet wide, and five feet high and has a wooden floor, covered with earth. The animal also sleeps on earth in the nest box, which is quite roomy—approximately three feet long, sixteen inches deep and ten inches high. The Echidna can and does climb up on top of the box at night. It cannot climb up the cage front for it is made of vertical bars not wire mesh. . . .
>
> Our Echidna is fed daily, the very last thing in the afternoon. It receives a half pint of whole milk and a raw egg in separate dishes. Lime water [in the milk] has not been used for many years—at least ten. Our animal occasionally fasts for periods up to eighteen days and apparently this is quite normal. . . .
>
> Our specimen is normally active at night but can often be seen late in the afternoon during the winter months, when dusk is falling. Normally the animal is very shy and will run back into its box at the slightest noise or upon sighting a person. However, there have been rare, isolated occasions when it came out in broad daylight, roamed all over its cage and did not scare easily. The building was always empty [of visitors] at the time.
>
> I was right about the Echidna's sex—it was a female.

This account provides a classic example of an animal completing a maximum life span in captivity under conditions to which it could accommodate completely. No attempt was ever made to beautify the exhibit or to compel the inmate to be visible to the public. I saw this echidna first in 1909, a feat accomplished by inserting my index finger through the cage bars and gently lifting the lid of the sleeping-box. I repeated the act for the last time on April 13, 1951, the only noticeable change during the 42-year interval being the slightly increased resistance of the rusting lid hinges. Few zoo animals can enjoy such prolonged seclusion.

Unfortunately, accounts of the housing arrangements under which the long-lived London and Berlin specimens of *Zaglossus* were kept have not been available, but on the basis of the Philadelphia experience it must be presumed that the animals were little disturbed. It seems reasonable, also, to suppose that efforts to enforce some degree of exhibition value have resulted in shortening the lives of most specimens of *Tachyglossus* shown elsewhere. There is always the possibility, of course, that *Zaglossus* adapts itself more readily than *Tachyglossus* to the conditions of captivity, since most of the individuals in the 1911 shipment appear to have done well.

The feeding regimen followed for the Philadelphia echidna has many implications of special interest. As a basic premise, it must be taken for granted that the food provided was adequate, and that all elements necessary for the nutrition of the animal were present. In general, the system is in accord with usual practice, except for the points that it is customary to stir milk and eggs together and to add finely shredded raw meat to the mixture. In the earlier days one teaspoonful of limewater, thought to make smaller milk curds in the stomach, was added to the milk of the Philadelphia echidna. This was later discontinued, as noted in the above quotation from Mr. Ulmer; since the animal lived for many years after discontinuance, limewater is obviously not essential.

It is the question of the egg used that is of paramount importance. It has been found by various workers and well summarized by McCay (1943:33–35) that in certain mammals and birds raw egg white is not only poorly digested but inhibits the action of an organic substance known as biotin, present in the yolk and essential in fat and carbohydrate metabolism. When cooked, egg white loses this ability and is also much more fully digested. Another characteristic of raw egg white is that it passes so rapidly through the intestinal tract that diarrhea may result.

For these reasons, during recent years we have been coddling eggs fed to both echidnas and anteaters sufficiently to set the whites but not the yolks, with resultant reduction of the looseness and offensive odor usually noticeable in the stools of these animals. While we cannot say that this change resulted in longevities approaching that of the Philadelphia echidna, a definite improvement in the spans of our specimens occurred during the period when coddled egg was used.

Ordinarily, the Australian echidna does not present itself as an animal of particular individuality. However, Coleman (1934, 1935a, 1935b, 1936, 1938a, 1938b) has recorded intimate experiences with tame captive animals in Australia that indicate much greater adaptive ability than might be expected. Climbing, seasonal dormancy, molting, digging, and sense of smell are included with general observations. Of particular interest is a note (1936:127) that one specimen became dormant during the Australian winter for a continuous period of 51 days. Ulmer, as quoted above, reports occasional lapses in feeding, which could be interpreted as incipient dormancy. Neither condition has ever been noted in animals kept in the New York Zoological Park.

Up to this time no workable means for exhibiting the echidna attractively and at the same time in accord with its living requirements seems to have been devised. The closest approach I have seen was in the Zoological Garden of Melbourne, Australia. Here, in 1929, a conventional, circular prairie dog exhibit, surrounded by a low fence with an interior overhang, was inhabited by "dogs" and echidnas. While the echidna is said not to tunnel (Troughton, 1951:9) it certainly is ready to take advantage of burrows already made, for a constant procession of alternating animals emerged from one hole and disappeared into the next. I could not avoid the impression that each species annoyed or disturbed the other, causing the continuous flow, and I should suppose that such an exhibit could not be permanent. Nevertheless, the echidnas were moving, in broad daylight!

In the New York Zoological Park we have tried various expedients. On the assumption that the Australian echidna would not be hardy at this latitude in spite of its ability to become dormant during cold weather, we have always kept our specimens in heated quarters. Since the echidna can climb up wire netting with surprising facility but seems quite unable to reverse the process—we once lost an animal through an injury received in falling after a climb—we have used solid or at least unclimbable walls at the sides and back of inclosures. At one time we installed a glass plate 2 feet high across the bottom of the cage front, which prevented the echidna from reaching the wire above. Since an echidna exposed to view with no place of retreat is likely to injure itself in its efforts to find a hiding place, we provided a 2-foot length of hollow log, perhaps 18 inches in diameter, to which the animal resorted at once. Placed at right angles to the front, the log afforded an excellent view of the recumbent echidna, which lived for several years. Later we provided a larger cage with opaque guards extending 3 feet upward on all sides. A low heap of sand at the rear was used for sleeping and insured that the animals' backs, at least, were always visible to visitors.

None of these efforts, certainly, was completely satisfactory, and the problem of how to get the echidna out of its box and into the public view without destroying the sense of security essential to its welfare still remains to be resolved. It is possible that the use of red light to simulate darkness, as developed here by Davis (1961), may bring the solution.

Because of the strong, barbless spines and their defensive use, the echidna is one of the most difficult animals to handle physically. When threatened, the echidna can press itself to the ground or into a corner so tenaciously that it is next to impossible to dislodge it. At such times, the lower quills are turned strongly downward, so that an unwary hand may be severely injured. At the same time, force applied by a tool, such as a shovel, may cause damage to the animal.

I well remember two echidnas which I was taking to New York from Sydney by steamer. These animals were incased in a strong wooden box with a stout wire top in which they traveled perfectly. However, a daily struggle was involved in getting them to move so that the box could be cleaned. I finally discovered that the only successful method was to tip the box so that the animals would slide to the opposite side, they being unable to cling to the smooth boards of the bottom. There is no reason for supposing, of course, that the production of a vacuum is in any way involved in this clinging ability.

Lucas and Le Souef (1909:147) suggest that when an echidna has rolled itself up in defensive position it "can be handled by seizing one of the projecting toes of the hind foot and can then be carried by the foot with the head hanging down." It is true that this can be accomplished without much difficulty, but the hind legs of the echidna are so frail that this means of transportation entails such risk of injury to the animal that few would care to undertake it. The sharp spurs on the heels of the males also might function as a further deterrent! Actually, the protection of a pair of stout leather gloves will permit handling with little risk of mutual injury.

Besides this effective means of defense, the echidna has in its digging ability a fairly efficient escape method. Placed on an ordinary earth surface, even a fairly hard one, an echidna, using the front feet with some assistance from its snout, can work itself below the surface in a remarkably short time. A series of photographs printed in *Animal Kingdom* (Anon., 1947) well illustrates the digging ability of the animal which, in this case, disappeared from sight in hard-packed earth in exactly 9 minutes.

This excavating action, of course, has no relation to the breeding habits of the echidna, which lives primarily above ground. The single egg is carried in a pouch, and the succeeding young animal is similarly transported until it becomes too large and troublesome. It is then deposited in some convenient hiding place, where it is visited periodically (Troughton, 1951).

Echidnas certainly have seldom bred in captivity, yet such events have been recorded. Heck (1908) gives an account of a young Australian echidna discovered in the pouch of a female in the Zoological Gardens of Berlin on May 7, 1908. It lived until August 15 of the same year. Lang (1958) reports that following the observation of an egg in the pouch of a female Australian echidna in the Zoological Gardens of Basel, a young animal which apparently had emerged prematurely was found on the floor of the cage on March 4, 1955. It was warmed and returned to the pouch, but 2 days later was found dead in the sand.

FAMILY ORNITHORHYNCHIDAE

PLATYPUS OR DUCKBILL

Well distributed in eastern Australia and Tasmania, the semiaquatic platypus (*Ornithorhynchus anatinus*) seeks its food of small crayfish or "yabbies," aquatic insects and worms, in the water. Burrows in the banks of streams provide shelter and nesting areas. Three mainland races, distinguished chiefly by differences in size, have been named, with a possible fourth in Tasmania (Troughton, 1951).

Following the arrival of the first skin of a platypus at the British Museum in 1798 and its subsequent description by Shaw, a long period of doubt and controversy concerning the nature of the animal ensued. It was not until 1884, when the English zoologist Caldwell obtained eggs of both the platypus and the echidna in Australia, that the little duckbill was finally acknowledged as a primitive, egg-laying mammal.

Considering the immense interest that had been aroused during this long span of years, it is not remarkable that efforts were made to keep the platypus in captivity. However, knowledge of the animal's requirements was so slim and the difficulties, as reported by Burrell (1927), were so great, that early attempts came to nothing. In fact, it was not until 1910 that Burrell (1927:207) began the experiments that laid the foundation of our present knowledge and finally resulted in the successful transportations of living platypuses to America. Burrell's first subject escaped after living in his primitive "platypusary" for 68 days but left her owner with a realization of the appalling amount of food required daily and with ideas for the improvement of platypus quarters. Putting these into effect, Burrell constructed a portable contraption, consisting of a small tank and an attached labyrinth of tunnels, through which the animal had to pass to reach its nest. The cardinal point lay in the rubber gaskets placed in the tunnels which served to squeeze the water out of the platypus's fur as it passed through. Otherwise the nest would become wet; the animal could not dry its coat and would be in risk of pneumonia. Without this contrivance it seems doubtful that success could have been attained.

After exhibiting a living platypus for 3 months in the Zoological Gardens of Sydney, in 1910, Burrell became discouraged by what he considered to be lack of interest and abandoned the project. It seems quite possible that "lack of interest" may have been engendered by the great cost and difficulty of securing sufficient food for the animal. Burrell (1927:208) says, "I worked six hours daily with mattock and shrimping net. . . . But my utmost endeavors succeeded in producing only about two pounds of animal food a day." This food, consisting of earthworms, shrimps, beetle larvae, and pond snails, was provided for five platypuses. But when the number of animals had been reduced to one, Burrell found that the survivor had no difficulty in consuming the lot!

Some years later Burrell was encouraged by the late Ellis S. Joseph, a well-known dealer in animals, to renew his efforts. Joseph, a man of great skill and determination, had a compelling desire to transport a living platypus to America. As a result of this joining of forces, Joseph embarked on May 12, 1922, aboard the *U.S.S. West Henshaw*, bound for San Francisco. Included in the large transport of animals usually carried by Joseph were five male platypuses ensconced in Burrell's "contraption" and a large supply of earthworms for use as food for the animals.

The difficulties of this pioneer project have been recounted in detail by Joseph (1922). After a rough voyage of 49 days' duration the ship arrived at San Francisco on June 30, with one vigorous platypus but no earthworms. After a stop to renew the food supply, Joseph proceeded to New York by train and reached the Zoological Park on July 14. I well remember that momentous day and Joseph's remark that the few days of travel by rail were far more trying than the long ocean voyage.

This event, of course, aroused the most intense general interest. William T. Hornaday (1922), then director of the New York Zoological Park, wrote of it: "The most wonderful of all living mammals has been carried alive from the insular confines of its far-too-distant native land and introduced abroad. Through a combination of favoring circumstances it has been the good fortune of New York to give hospitality and appreciation to the first platypus that ever left Australia and landed alive on a foreign shore. . . ."

The difficulties of maintaining the food supply immediately came to the front with the arrival of the first New York platypus. Dr. Hornaday complains that the cost was from $4.00 to $5.00 per day, giving one day's ration as $\frac{1}{2}$-pound of earthworms, 40 shrimps, and 40 grubs—an amount that in the light of more recent experience seems hardly adequate. In summing up, he says: "Really, it seems incredible that an animal so small could chamber a food supply so large. I know of nothing to equal it among other mammals."

Each afternoon during its sojourn here the platypus was exhibited daily for one hour, long lines of visitors filing slowly past the open tank of the platypusary. The highly nervous temperament of the animal caused it to swim, scramble, and climb incessantly. On occasion, the keeper in charge did not hesitate to pick up the platypus and hold it—as long as he could—for the closer inspection of special guests. All of this, at the time, seemed perfectly reasonable, and the endurance of the animal until August 30, 1922, after 47 days with us, was considered to be an unexpectedly good result.

Progress in advancing knowledge of the platypus in captivity continued, of course, in Australia. Robert Eadie (1934, 1935), director of the Sir Colin Mackenzie Sanctuary for Native Fauna at Healesville, Victoria, maintained the famous "Splash" in a platypusary of the conventional Burrell type. Splash lived there from 1933 to 1937, a period of 4 years, 1 month (Fleay, 1944:15), a feat that firmly established the viability of the species.

In 1937, when David Fleay (1944:16) was in charge of the Australian Section at the Melbourne Zoo, he kept there a female platypus known as "Barwon," which lived for "four years, ten and three-quarter months." Following his transfer to the position of director of the Healesville Sanctuary, Fleay's interest in the platypus had full play and culminated in the breeding of the species in captivity for the first—and so far—the only time. The following is a brief summary of events, as recorded by Fleay (1944):

"Jill," the female of the breeding pair, was picked up on a road on February 19, 1938, while "Jack" was plucked out of shallow water in January, 1939, both less than fully grown. Established in a platypusary provided with an earth bank in which the female was allowed to burrow, the animals did exceptionally well and were exhibited to the public for short periods almost daily. In mid-September, 1943, when Jill was approximately 6 years old and Jack about 5, the typical circling courtship was observed. This continued until mid-October, when copulation was noticed, followed by the retirement of Jill to her nesting burrow on the evening of October 25. As she did not appear again until the thirty-first, it was assumed that the eggs had been laid and hatched and that the incubation period was approximately 6–10 days. This checks reasonably well with Burrell's (1927:182) excellent but purely conjectural estimate of 14 days.

On January 3, 1944, after a period of very heavy feeding on the part of Jill, the mound was opened and a nest containing a well-developed youngster, presumed to be $8\frac{1}{2}$–9 weeks old, was disclosed. This infant, named "Corrie," entered the water and fed lightly for the first time on February 26, 1944, when about 17 weeks old.

Encouraged by this triumph, the New York Zoological Society decided to attempt another platypus importation. After a long delay for the construction of traveling platypusaries, the accumulation of the necessary supply of earthworms, and, most important of all, the securing of official sanctions, Mr. and Mrs. Fleay embarked for Boston aboard the *S.S. Pioneer Glen* on March 29, 1947, with one male and two female platypuses. After an arduous journey of 27 days, during which the food supply was reinforced by the addition of fresh worms at Pitcairn and Panama, the ship reached its destination, and the platypuses were conveyed to New York by motor. Three days later, on April 28, 1947, the animals were exhibited to the public in the permanent platypusary we had constructed for them (Fleay, 1947).

This concrete structure, 46 feet, 2 inches in length and 8 feet, 6 inches wide (outside measurements), was based on specifications furnished by Mr. Fleay. At each end of a 20-foot, wire-covered, wood-lined swimming pool, a 6-foot compartment was devoted to a series of connecting wooden "tunnels" with hinged lids. These tunnels, raised a foot above ground level, were provided with numerous wooden squeegees (rubber ones being considered too yielding) alternating with 2-inch upright strips over which the animal had to crawl, the whole serving to rid the fur of most of its water. The squeegee apertures were roughly semicircular, the base measuring $3\frac{3}{4}$ inches and the upright radius $2\frac{1}{8}$ inches for the male, with a $3\frac{1}{4}$-inch base and an upright of $1\frac{7}{8}$ inches for the females. Close supervision was necessary to make certain that the apertures were in accord with variations in the condition of the animals. The tunnels were kept packed with fine marsh hay, changed frequently to avoid dampness. The quality of the hay used is important, since harsh seeding heads are annoying and perhaps dangerous to the animals. A narrow landing board just above water level provided a convenient scratching and combing ledge as well as access to the tunnels. This tunnel area was provided with a folding, water-tight wooden cover, easily opened for service and insuring darkness and seclusion in the tunnels.

The sleeping sections were practically identical at each end, but for the optimistic reason that breeding might some time be undertaken, a further section of 9 feet in length was added to the quarters of the females. While the remainder of the structure was floored throughout with concrete, two layers of copper-bearing wire netting of 1-inch mesh were placed at the bottom of the nursery to insure drainage and the whole was filled with heavy clay soil to a depth of 4 feet. The top was then provided with removable wire netting screens and a canvas sheet for controlling rainfall. Access to this earth bank could be had through the side tunnels, but the entrances were blocked with wooden slides during periods when the platypuses were being exhibited.

With the construction of three-level wooden ramps along the sides to provide viewing areas for the public and the addition of a high wire fence around the entire area, the platypusary was ready for occupancy. We soon found that 60° F. was the critical temperature for the water in the tank. The platypuses entered more freely and were more active when the water was warmer than 60° F. Below this point they became increasingly reluctant to enter the water and at 50° F. might refuse altogether. To maintain some control, a small electrical water-heating unit was set up in the tunnel section at one end of the installation. During spring and autumn months, when water temperatures might be low, at least partial regulation was essential, as the animals fed only in the water.

When first allowed to enter the tank, the platypuses gave the usual indications of discontent, rolling over and over in the water and trying frantically to climb the corners. David Fleay, who had undertaken to remain with us for 3 months to get the animals established, considered that the disturbance was caused by lack of overhead cover. We then arranged a green canvas, lined with white, above the pool to reduce the light, but the white lining had to be replaced with green before the animals were satisfied.

Because of a previous experience of Fleay's (1950:49), when Jill's life was endangered by an injection of poison from Jack's spurs, our two females, "Betty" and "Penelope," were kept together at one end of the platypusary, the male, known as "Cecil," at the other. Following the system originally put into effect by Fleay while he was at Melbourne, the male and the two females were shown on alternate afternoons from 3:00 to 4:00, so that each animal was exposed for only 1 hour every other day. Cecil was fairly indifferent and seldom showed distress, but Betty and Penelope were far more nervous, and sometimes the exhibition period had to be curtailed because of their excitement.

At 4:00 P.M. the slides that closed the burrow openings were opened so that the animals could leave or enter at will, and their food was placed in the water. From dusk to dawn the platypuses were almost continually active, filling their cheek pouches under water and floating on the surface to break up and swallow the prodigious quantities of food consumed.

Providing food for a platypus on a continuing basis is no small matter. When it was definitely determined that the animals would be brought from Australia, we set about the construction of a "wormery." Small wooden breeding boxes and large cinder-block holding bins measuring 4 by 10 feet were installed in the warm basement of the Lion House. Having then secured a breeding stock of the brandling or manure worm (*Eisenia foetida*), commonly cultivated by commercial breeders and known usually as "red worm," it was not long before a large supply was available. Unfortunately, it soon turned out that the platypuses would eat these worms only under great stress, so that other means for satisfying their needs had to be found. The large earthworm, *Lumbricus terrestris*, known generally in America as "night crawler," was taken avidly. While these worms can be purchased from bait purveyors and dealers in biological materials, we found that our own people could obtain them more economically. In our searching for night crawlers we soon turned up another species, very similar in size but firmer in body and much more active, of which the platypuses were particularly fond. These worms, unknown to us, were termed "fighters" or "leaf worms." Samples from nearby localities were finally submitted to G. E. Gates, an expert in the taxonomy of earthworms, who was able to determine three species of *Pheretima*, an Oriental genus, among them. Later, a fourth species of the same genus was identified from a shipment of worms received from Florida (Atz, 1951).

Having thus determined the preferences of the platypuses, our stocks of red worms were allowed to recede and the bins devoted to holding supplies of the preferred species. Since these are unobtainable locally during the winter, large numbers were accumulated in the autumn and sometimes augmented by shipments of *Pheretima* from Florida. In deep beds of leaf mold and earth alternating with layers of leaves (chiefly elm), kept cool and regularly moistened and fed with carefully selected soft fruits and vegetables, grass clippings, and meal, the worms were easily maintained, although it was not definitely established that they bred.

Normal daily rations for one platypus consisted of 1 pound of earthworms (about two hundred adults of *Lumbricus* or *Pheretima*), two dozen live crayfish (*Cambarus*), one or two leopard frogs (*Rana pipiens*)—Cecil ate frogs regularly, but the females seldom took them—two eggs steamed in a double boiler, and perhaps a handful of cockroaches (*Blatta*) or mealworms (*Tenebrio*). Quantities were varied constantly, of course, to suit the animals' variation in condition, vagaries of appetite and individual whims.

In addition to the items listed above, the platypus will take tadpoles, beetle grubs, and some insects. However, these are either seasonal or too difficult to obtain in sufficient quantity to be included in the regular diet. As far as our experience here goes, platypuses will not take fish, but I have been assured by the late J. E. Ward of Sydney (*in litt.*) that freshly caught animals will not only eat both fish and beef if it is finely scraped but will thrive on them as part of a general diet. With animals as far from home as platypuses in New York, dietary experiments did not seem to be in order.

Worms were furnished in a tin also containing earth, sunk to the bottom of the tank. Earth was always provided because, as suggested by Burrell (1927:13–14), it appears to serve an essential function in the digestive process. Crayfish and frogs were liberated in the tank, where they were readily captured by the animals. The steamed egg was scattered over the bottom of the tank. Because of the method of feeding and the animals' habit of defecating in the water, it was necessary that the tank be drained and thoroughly scrubbed daily.

On this regime our three platypuses throve during the summer of 1947 and, by turnstile count, were viewed by just over 200,000 of our visitors. With the approach of autumn plans for winter quarters had to be expedited. Our previous experience with the species had not led us to expect a duration of more than a few months. In fact, we had even entertained the thought that it might be expedient for Fleay to take the animals back to Australia at the close of the season, a suggestion to which he, quite naturally, was strongly resistant. Since it now became obvious that winter quarters would actually be required, the two traveling platypusaries were set up in a wire-inclosed room in the basement of the Large Bird House. On October 27 the three platypuses were transferred. They settled down quickly and passed the winter without incident, except for a shortage of both crayfish and earthworms that occurred late in the season.

While this period of short rations endured, Cecil and Penelope made up with extra frogs and cooked eggs, but Betty was less pliable in changing her dietary preferences. When exhibition in the outdoor platypusary was resumed in the spring of 1948, Betty was obviously out of condition, although her weight remained at 1.98 pounds, her apparent normal. Gradually, however, she began to lose and finally was isolated in winter quarters, where she died of pneumonia on September 6. Her weight was then found to be only 1.56 pounds, a loss of 21.2 per cent. We attributed her death to our failure to realize that her reduced girth permitted her to pass through the burrow barriers without her fur being sufficiently squeezed (Crandall, 1951).

Cecil and Penelope continued in the alternation of summers out of doors and winters indoors until the spring of 1951, when it appeared that we should give serious thought to breeding possibilities. During the winter both animals had managed to leave their inclosures through chance crevices and enjoyed nocturnal prowls inside the wire walls. When they were found one morning to have reversed homes, friendly relations seemed obvious. In Victoria the normal breeding season is September and October (Burrell, 1927:172), followed by a molt in January (Fleay, 1944:19). Our

platypuses molted regularly in August (Blair, 1952) and it seemed reasonable to wonder if their potential breeding cycle might have undergone a
corresponding change.

Consequently, when the animals were returned to summer quarters on May
13, 1951, the public was excluded for the season in order to maintain privacy.
The wooden division of the pool was removed for common use and Penelope
was given access to the earth mound, Cecil being excluded by the small
opening in the baffle. The nocturnal actions of the animals were closely
watched by Keeper John Blair, who found that whenever they met in
the water Penelope showed fear reactions and if pursued, returned to her
burrow. With the coming of August, wisps of hair floating on the surface of
the water indicated the beginning of the annual molt. Without further hopes
for breeding but in order to round out the season, the animals were allowed
to remain out of doors until October 9, when they were removed to winter
quarters.

The following spring (1952), favored by good weather and determined
on an early date, we returned the platypuses to the outdoor installation on
April 21. Their reactions, however, were similar to those of the previous
season and abandoning hope of their breeding even in outdoor seclusion,
we opened the platypusary to visitors on June 27. That winter Penelope
found a nesting box included in her tunnel maze but she used it only as a
comfortable sleeping cubicle.

By spring, 1953, we had given up all thought of duplicating the feat of
David Fleay and embarked on the platypuses' seventh summer with us as a
routine affair. However, on May 21, at the close of Penelope's exhibition
hour, she refused to return to her burrow as she customarily did. Cecil was
then liberated into his side, in preparation for feeding, when Keeper Blair
noticed that Penelope was scratching desperately at a corner of the wooden
partition of the pool. Blair then removed the partition and the two animals
almost immediately went into the circular mating maneuver described by
Fleay (1944:24), the male grasping the female's tail firmly with his bill.
When the grip was finally loosened there was a brief pursuit, ending with
Penelope floating quietly on the surface while Cecil preened her fur with
his bill. This cycle was repeated four times up to 10:30 P.M. as observed
by Blair, but no actual copulation was seen. For several days following,
with the exhibit open to the public for 2 hours daily, the animals were left
together, but while Cecil continued courting and Penelope showed no
fright reactions, the circling maneuver was not seen to be repeated.

On June 26 the entrance to the earth bank was opened and Penelope
immediately began excavating. On the next day she evidenced disturbance

by Cecil's company, and the separating panel was replaced, leaving Penelope in solitude. Dried eucalyptus leaves, a favorite nest-building material, were floated on the water, and on the nights of July 6, 7, and 8 a considerable number were taken by the animal, dry grass and maple leaves being rejected. On the night of July 9 Penelope retired to her burrow and did not emerge again until the night of July 15, when she ate 8 crayfish. It was now found that the animal carefully plugged the tunnel entrance with earth when she was inside, replacing it regularly after each nightly foray. Her appetite slowly increased, but on the nights of August 10 and 11 she failed to emerge. On the possibility that some internal block might have occurred, the alternative tunnel entrance was opened. Through this, Penelope entered the pool on the night of August 12 and fed normally. The usual food supplied from this time on was as follows:

Cecil	Penelope
25 crayfish	65 crayfish
$\frac{1}{2}$ lb. earthworms	$1\frac{1}{2}$ lbs. earthworms
2 or 3 frogs	$\frac{1}{2}$ of 4–5 eggs
$\frac{1}{2}$ of 4–5 eggs	

Cecil ate all food supplied him, but Penelope occasionally left some bits untaken. On September 22 Penelope received a test feeding of $2\frac{1}{2}$ pounds of earthworms, 2 frogs, and 2 cooked eggs, no crayfish being available. This prodigious meal was completely consumed.

The first molted hairs from Cecil's coat were observed on August 1, but Penelope did not begin to shed until August 30. Otherwise, a careful charting showed that the data gathered for Jill by Fleay (1944:28; 31) were closely approximated by Penelope (McClung, 1953a).

In order to give the hoped-for young as much time as possible to develop, removal to winter quarters was delayed as long as weather conditions permitted. However, a deadline was set at November 5, when a youngster hatched on July 16 would be 16 weeks old, a week short of the age at which the animal bred by Fleay (1944:40) emerged from the nest. On that day the mound was carefully and methodically excavated. At the end of 2 hours of digging, Penelope alone was unearthed, with no sign of young, no proper nest, or even remains of the many leaves that had been removed from the pool (McClung, 1953b). Why she should have paralleled the cycle of Jill without result remains unexplained. The platypus is known to hibernate in Victoria, Fleay (1944: 20–23) giving the season when this may occur as May–September. It is possible that Jill's retirement in July may have been spent in hibernation rather than in incubation (Crandall, 1958).

At the end of nearly 4 months of ingesting what would seem to be an excessive quantity of food, Penelope's weight had fallen from 1.738 pounds in the preceding spring to 1.56 pounds (− 10.2 per cent). Cecil, on a much more restricted diet, had dropped from 3.562 to 3.146 pounds (− 11.6 per cent). These lower weights are the minima recorded for each animal. Cecil's maximum was 4.07 pounds on October 25, 1949; Penelope's was 1.99 pounds on November 3, 1950.

Little is known concerning the potential life span of the platypus, either under natural conditions or in captivity. David Fleay has furnished me the following data concerning Jack, Jill, and Corrie, all kept by him during his tenure at Healesville and still there when he left:

> Jack, captured in January, 1939, died sometime in 1956, after at least 17 years in captivity, save for 5 months at liberty in 1948 before recapture by Fleay.
> Jill, captured on February 19, 1938, died at the end of December, 1947, after at least 9 years and 10 months.
> Corrie, hatched at Healesville in November, 1943, escaped in the autumn of 1955, when she would have been approximately 12 years old.

Our own specimens, Cecil and Penelope, provided dates more exact, if not more satisfactory. Penelope was found to be missing from the platypusary on August 1, 1957, when she had been with us for 10 years, 3 months, 7 days. She was captured by Fleay in April, 1946, so that her captivity span was well over 11 years. Cecil died on September 18, 1957, after 10 years, 4 months, 24 days here. Since he, too, had been captured in April, 1946, at least another year must be added to his captivity record.

Three further platypuses, a male and two females, were brought to us by David Fleay on June 7, 1958. A full account of the capture, transport, and installation of these animals is given by Fleay (1958). Although kept under the same conditions as our previous specimens, these later arrivals failed to adapt, the survivor living only to March 25, 1959.

That animals of such intense activity, huge food intake, and presumably high rate of metabolism should live even for a few months in captivity seems extraordinary. Yet it appears probable that the much greater longevities noted do not represent the maximum potential of this remarkable species.

· REFERENCES

ANON.
>   1947.   Digger from Down Under. Animal Kingdom, 50 (5):151–53.
>   1953a. Record breaker dies at Philadelphia. Parks and Recreation, 36 (4):31.
>   1953b. A record breaker dies. America's First Zoo, 5 (2):4.

Weighing the young Atlantic walrus "Herbert."

(New York Zoological Society photo.)

"Alice," a female Indian elephant, mothering the young African forest elephant "Tiny."
When this picture was taken, "Tiny" stood 3 feet, 2 inches tall.

(New York Zoological Society photo.)

The platypusary (p. 10) being packed with hay by a keeper.
(New York Zoological Society photo.)

The waterhole at the African Plains exhibit, with the Lion Rock in the background.
(New York Zoological Society photo.)

"Malamba," one of two young white rhinoceroses brought from the *Umfolozi Game Reserve in Zululand,* steps into his new quarters.

(New York Times photo.)

*Keeper M. Quinn with
the female lowland
gorilla "Oka."*

(New York Zoological Society photo.)

*Keepers M. Quinn and Mrs. Helen Martini with the young male lowland gorilla
"Mambo."*

(New York Zoological Society photo.)

"Oka," the female lowland gorilla, builds a nest of leaves.
(New York Zoological Society photo.)

White-handed gibbons on Gibbon Island, New York Zoological Park, showing their method of drinking.

(Photo by Lilo Hess.)

Two of our keepers bottle-feeding pronghorn antelopes.

(New York Zoological Society photo.)

A lion and his mate stare over the moat edge while their well-trained cubs stay behind.
(New York Zoological Society photo.)

A[TZ], J[AMES] W.
1951. There is a difference in the taste of earthworms—to platypuses. Animal Kingdom, **54** (3):95.

BLAIR, JOHN P.
1952. Our duckbills molt by "American time." Animal Kingdom, **55** (5):163–64.

BURRELL, HARRY.
1927. The platypus. Angus & Robertson, Ltd., Sydney. 227 pp.

COLEMAN, EDITH.
1934. The echidna under domestication. Victorian Nat., **51**:12–21.
1935a. Hibernation and other habits of the echidna under domestication. *Ibid.*, **52**:55–61.
1935b. The echidna under domestication. *Ibid.*, pp. 151–54.
1936. Climbing habits and further notes on the hibernation of the echidna. *Ibid.*, **53**:124–28.
1938a. Notes on hibernation, ecdysis and sense of smell of the echidna under domestication. *Ibid.*, **55**:105–7.
1938b. Further notes on the hibernation of the echidna. *Ibid.*, **54**:178–79.

CRANDALL, LEE S.
1951. We are attempting to breed the platypus. Animal Kingdom, **54** (3):89.
1958. Notizen über das Verhalten des Schnabeltieres (*Ornithorhynchus anatinus*) in Gefangenschaft. Trans. from English by H. HEDIGER. Handbuch d. Zool., **8**, **10** (8):1–8. Walter deGruyter & Co., Berlin.

DAVIS, JOSEPH A., JR.
1961. Red means go! Animal Kingdom, **64** (4):114–18.

EADIE, ROBERT.
1934. The platypus in captivity. Victorian Nat., **51**:3–11.
1935. The life and habits of the platypus. Stillwell and Stephens, Melbourne. 78 pp.

FLEAY, DAVID.
1944. We breed the platypus. Robertson & Mullens, Melbourne. 44 pp.
1947. How the duck-billed platypuses came to New York. Animal Kingdom, **50** (3):66–80.
1950. New facts about the family life of the Australian platypus. Zoo Life (London), **5** (2):49–51.
1958. Platypuses in the zoo again! Animal Kingdom, **61** (4):98–108.

FLOWER, S. S.
1929. List of the vertebrated animals exhibited in the gardens of the Zoological Society of London, 1828–1927. 1. Mammals. Zoological Society of London. 419 pp.
1931. Contribution to our knowledge of the duration of life in vertebrate animals. 5. Mammals. Proc. Zool. Soc. London, pp. 145–234.

HAMERTON, A. E.
1944. Report on the deaths occurring in the Society's gardens during the year 1943. Proc. Zool. Soc. London, **114**:307–19.

HECK, L.
  1908. Echidna-Zuchtung im Berliner Zoologischen Garten. Sitzungsber. Gesell. Naturforsch. Freunde Berlin, 1908:187–89.

HORNADAY, WILLIAM T.
  1922. New York's duck-billed platypus. Bull. New York Zool. Soc., 25 (5):99–104.

JOSEPH, ELLIS S.
  1922. My experience with the platypus in captivity. Bull. New York Zool. Soc., 25 (5):105–11.

LANG, E. M.
  1958. Nachtliches Leben im Zoo. Im Schatten der Nacht, 3. J. R. Geigy S.A., Basle. 13 pp.

LUCAS, A. H. S., and W. H. DUDLEY LE SOUEF
  1909. The animals of Australia. Whitcomb & Tombs, Ltd., Melbourne. 327 pp.

McCAY, CLIVE M.
  1943. Nutrition of the dog. Comstock Publishing Co., Ithaca, N.Y. 140 pp.

McCLUNG, ROBERT M.
  1953a. The outlook for a baby platypus. Animal Kingdom, 56 (5):146–50.
  1953b. No baby platypus! Ibid., pp. 162–66.

SIMPSON, GEORGE GAYLORD.
  1945. The principles of classification and a classification of mammals. Bull. Amer. Mus. Nat. Hist., 85. 350 pp.

TROUGHTON, ELLIS.
  1951. Furred animals of Australia. Angus & Robertson, Ltd., Sydney. 376 pp.

ORDER MARSUPIALIA

.

American Opossums, Dasyures, Bandicoots, Phalangers, Wombats, and Kangaroos

The distinguishing character of the members of this order, of course, is the fact that the young are born at an early stage of development and are usually, although not always, carried by the mother in an external pouch low on the abdomen. In spite of great diversity in structure and habits, the marsupials provide many subjects eminently well suited to the purposes of the zoological garden. It is true that some species, notably the koala, have become so specialized in food requirements and are so resistant to deviation that their keeping is possible only for the favored few. In general, however, suitable conditions are fairly easily supplied, and most members of the order respond well. While some species are largely nocturnal and not readily observed by day, the diurnal kangaroos amply compensate for the drawbacks of their small relations.

FAMILY DIDELPHIDAE

American Opossums

The American opossums and the opossum-rats or pouched rats of the family Caenolestidae are the only marsupial animals found in the New World. The small, little-known members of the latter group are confined almost entirely to restricted areas in the western slopes of the Andes of South America, and I find no record of any of the several recognized forms having been kept in captivity.

The opossums, on the other hand, are well known as zoological-garden denizens, at least in America. Most, if not all, of the species are largely nocturnal in habit, so that their general exhibition value is low. However, the fact that they are marsupials, coupled with the handsome appearance of many of the numerous species, insures them a place in most collections.

Housing of opossums presents no particular difficulties. It must be kept in mind that all can climb to some degree and that certain forms, notably the woolly opossums (*Caluromys*), are essentially arboreal. All but the Virginia opossum (*Didelphis marsupialis virginiana*) require heated quarters in cold weather, of course, and even the sturdy native of the eastern United States will be happier with it. For any of the larger species, an inclosure approximating 4 by 4 feet is adequate, since it is usually impossible to keep two or more specimens together without risk of serious injury. A sleeping shelter of some sort is essential, and for this purpose we have found a short section of hollow log, laid on its side, most satisfactory. Like most nocturnals, the opossums are extremely sensitive to strong light (Hediger, 1950:84), so that, in addition to the sleeping log, blue fluorescent tubes have been used here to reduce intensity. Opossums have reacted well here under the simulation of darkness by red light, as developed by Davis (1961).

Smaller creatures will do, of course, with very much less space, provided the essentials of secluded sleeping quarters and protection from bright light are kept in mind. The mouse opossum (*Marmosa*) is incredibly facile in squeezing itself through the tiniest opening, so that its inclosure must be completely tight.

The rare and aberrant yapock, or Central American water opossum (*Chironectes p. panamensis*), of which we have been so fortunate as to possess two specimens, requires special treatment. Because of our eagerness to allow this little-known creature to be seen by the public, our first specimen was housed in a spacious, glass-fronted cage with a swimming pool but with partly exposed sleeping chamber, inadequately drained. Although the animal survived for 3 months, it was obvious that more suitable means for housing it must be devised. On May 4, 1949, a second specimen, consigned to us as a "fox," arrived by air from Costa Rica. Based on our previous experience, a new plan for proper quarters was quickly devised. We inclosed a large aquarium tank, 4 by 2 by 2 feet, in a frame covered with ½-inch wire cloth and attached to it an elevated chamber provided with drainboards and inclosing a sleeping box 18 inches in each dimension. This sleeping box was filled with paper strips, changed daily to insure dryness. In this box the yapock spent its days, presumably in sleep, coming out at night to feed and swim. In the latter action, the force was supplied almost entirely by the strongly webbed hind feet. When drawn out of its box for inspection, as frequently happened, the animal was entirely amenable and never showed any inclination to bite.

The more typical opossums are practically omnivorous in feeding habits and present no special dietary problems. In reporting on the extensive investigations of the suitability of various opossums for use as laboratory animals conducted at the Wistar Institute of Philadelphia, Farris (1950) gives complete details of successful feeding of a large colony under laboratory conditions. In zoological-garden practice, more specialized treatment seems desirable. The larger species, such as the Virginia (*D. m. virginiana*) and Azara's (*D. azarae*), thrive on a mixture of dog biscuit or canned dog food, with raw chopped meat, fine bone meal, and cod-liver oil added, and milk and coddled egg and any raw fruits and vegetables that may be available.

For the medium-sized forms, such as the brown (*Metachirus nudicaudatus*) and the woolly (*Caluromys*), the following daily regimen has proved successful here: 1 ounce of orange juice, sweetened with sugar, 2 drops of multiple vitamin concentrate added; 1 ounce of reconstituted evaporated milk (given separately); 1 diced hard-boiled egg; 1 banana, partly peeled; 1 ounce of dog biscuit or canned dog food, sprinkled with fine bone meal. Most species will take American "chameleons" (*Anolis*) eagerly, when available.

The tiny mouse opossums (*Marmosa*) seem to prefer bananas, which are offered partly peeled. In addition, we furnish milk, dog food, and hard-boiled egg, although these are not always fully consumed. "Chameleons" are a special delicacy with this group.

The yapock is sharply differentiated in feeding habits. Its principal food here has been chopped raw meat with finely ground bone meal and cod-liver oil added. In addition, it received filleted smelts (*Osmerus*) and also drank milk freely. In spite of the fact that fresh-water crustaceans are said to enter largely into the natural diet (Cabrera and Yepes, 1940:27), neither of our specimens would eat crayfish (*Cambarus*). The only exception occurred when a crayfish, offered to a newly arrived yapock, nipped the animal's nose with a claw. Thus stimulated, the yapok promptly ate its assailant and followed it with two more. It could never be induced to repeat the act. No fruits or vegetables were ever taken. Because of the nocturnal habits of opossums, all feeding should be postponed until late evening.

A particular difficulty with opossums in captivity is swelling and cracking of the skin of the tail. Farris (1950:266) attributes this trouble to low humidity and states that when humidity is increased to 50–60 per cent, difficulty disappears. He recommends applications of sulphur ointment or vaseline. We have used the latter with some success. Rather curiously, our yapocks were particularly susceptible, in spite of regular immersion in swimming tanks.

In general, opossums are not easily bred in captivity, and the infrequent births recorded in zoological gardens are ordinarily the result of impregnation before capture. Zoological gardens sometimes receive female opossums carrying young in the pouch, attached to the mammae, or clinging to the abdominal hair in the pouchless forms such as the mouse opossums (*Marmosa*). Strange to say, members of this latter group are temperamentally resistant, and while the young are sometimes reared they are difficult to tame (Beach, 1939; Farris, 1950:260). The classic observations of Hartman (1920, 1952), which definitely established the fact that the newborn young find their way to the mother's pouch unassisted, were made (with the aid of red light) on a female opossum impregnated before capture.

On the other hand, pouch litters of the Virginia opossum (*D. m. virginiana*) have frequently been reared here. One such litter, in particular, was notable in that of nine young reared, six were normal in coloration, one was of the black-tipped white type mentioned by Cahalane (1947:107), and two were pink-eyed albinos. One of the latter was sent to Australia when just over 2 years old. Of a litter of five brown opossums (*Metachirus n. dentaneus*) carried by the mother when she arrived from Panama in 1947, all were fully reared. One lived here for 1 year and 5 months.

In such rearing operations, the basic difficulties of establishing opossum groups under zoological-garden conditions quickly became apparent. As soon as the young animals have been weaned and begin feeding for themselves, quarreling develops, which soon assumes serious proportions. When only a few months old, they must be removed and caged singly to avoid injury or even death.

At the Wistar Institute extensive efforts have been made to establish various kinds of opossums as laboratory animals. Success to a reasonable degree was obtained with at least one species, the gray-masked or "four-eyed," *Metachirops fuscogriseus*, known currently as *Philander opossum fuscogriseus*. However, even with established specimens, there is always some risk that one animal or the other may be maimed or killed when introductions for mating purposes are made (Farris, 1950).

The rather scanty information available indicates a comparatively short life span for the group. Farris (1950:258) gives "about three-and-a-half years" for the gray-masked or "four-eyed" and indicates 3 years for the Virginia. Mann (1930:284) records 4 years, 5 months and still living for this species. Unfortunately, the rapid turnover of Virginia opossums in the

New York Zoological Park has made definite longevity records for the species difficult to decipher, although they do appear, in general, to confirm the findings of Farris. However, the following spans established here are definite: a form of the Mexican mouse opossum, *Marmosa mexicana*, 1 year, 7 months; brown opossum, *Metachirus n. dentaneus*, 1 year, 5 months; yapock, *Chironectes p. panamensis*, 2 years, 11 months; woolly opossum, *Caluromys derbianus*, 5 years, 2 months. The latter is the longest record known to me for any opossum.

FAMILY DASYURIDAE

MARSUPIAL MICE, NATIVE CATS, TASMANIAN DEVIL, AND THYLACINE

This apparently heterogeneous group contains a number of species of very special interest. One common character is found in the fact that the pouch, if present (it is absent in some members), has its opening directed backward or toward the tail and not toward the head as in the kangaroos. The family includes the smallest of the marsupials, the marsupial "mice," as well as the largest carnivorous form, the thylacine. All are insect or flesh eaters.

The marsupial mice are small, secretive, chiefly nocturnal creatures, found over most of Australia, with extensions into New Guinea and Tasmania. Of the numerous known forms, only a fraction seem to have found their way into collections outside Australia. Here, we have shown the fat-tailed marsupial mouse (*Sminthopsis crassicaudata*) and the red-tailed phascogale (*Phascogale calura*), none of which survived for as long as two years.

The marsupial mice are shrewlike in feeding habits, consuming anything in the way of insects or other small creatures that they can capture and overcome. Apparently, some vegetable matter is taken also (Troughton, 1951:23, 24). Unfortunately, experience here is too slight and too remote to be of any special value. However, an excellent account of the keeping and breeding in captivity of the brush-tailed phascogale or tuan (*P. tapoatafa*) has been provided by Fleay (1950a), and a similar record of the yellow-footed marsupial mouse (*Antechinus flavipes*) has been published by the same author (1950b).

The dasyures or native cats are the largest of the carnivorous marsupials surviving on the mainland of Australia. Climbing and leaping with agility, they are at home in the trees or on the ground. Because of their blood-thirsty raids on poultry and small stock, their numbers have become greatly decreased with the settling of the country, so that they have now disappeared from many areas.

Only the spotted dasyure or eastern native cat (*Dasyurus viverrinus*) has been kept here, maximum survival being 2 days under one year. Mitchell (1911) gives 6 years, 10 months as maximum duration of this species in the Zoological Gardens of London. The animals were kept on a diet of raw beef, alternating with such "fur and feather" as might be available. Throughout they remained savage and unfriendly, although Troughton (1951:43) states that in captivity they are "attractive" and "familiar." The considerably larger spotted-tailed dasyure or Australian tiger cat (*Dasyurops maculatus*) has been kept in the Zoological Gardens of London (Flower, 1929) and doubtless elsewhere. Fleay (1948a) gives an excellent account of collecting, maintaining, and breeding this species in captivity.

Second largest of the carnivorous marsupials (granting the possible existence of the nearly extinct thylacine) is the Tasmanian devil (*Sarcophilus harrisii*), now apparently confined to the island for which it is named. In its feeding habits (Fleay, 1948b) and in its powerful cranial structure (Tate, 1947) it is strongly suggestive of the hyena.

Because of its unattractive appearance and strongly nocturnal habits, the Tasmanian devil certainly is not an ideal zoological-garden subject. On the other hand, the sinister implications of its name, more or less justified by tales of ferocity, carry great weight.

Of a total of nineteen Tasmanian devils kept here between 1909 and 1954, the best duration was just over 4 years. Flower (1931) gives 5 years, 9 months, 6 days in the Zoological Gardens of London as the longest then known to him. Mann (1930) reports 5 years, 7 months in the National Zoological Park, Washington, while Jones (1958) lists 6 years, 10 days in London and 6 years, 15 days in the Zoological Gardens of Basel.

Since this species, if provided with an unheated nesting shelter, is quite hardy at the latitude of New York and presumably at least somewhat farther north, it should be provided with a moated or wired outdoor inclosure. Its leaping ability is very limited, but young animals climb well, while adults retain some faculty in this direction. The only food our animals have taken has been flesh in some form: beef, horse meat, fowl, pigeons, rabbits, etc.

Here, Tasmanian devils have invariably remained truculent and un-responsive. However, an entirely different picture is drawn by Roberts (1915) in her classic account of the keeping and breeding in captivity of the species in Tasmania. When captured while young or reared in captivity, individuals become both playful and friendly. Fleay (1935, 1948*b*) has contributed illuminating reports on breeding and maintaining the Tasmanian devil in captivity in Australia.

The creature known variously as Tasmanian wolf, Tasmanian tiger, or thylacine (*Thylacinus cynocephalus*), if indeed it still survives, is much the largest of present-day carnivorous marsupials. Although proportionately short-legged, its general appearance is somewhat wolflike, while the body stripes, of course, are suggestive of the tiger. Once apparently widely spread over the Australian continent, as indicated by discoveries of skeletal remains, it has now become extremely rare in its last stronghold in Tasmania, although there remains the hope that it still exists and can be preserved in the remote parts of that island (Sharland, 1941).

While never really common in captivity, the thylacine has been seen in many zoological gardens since 1850, at least, when the London Zoological Society received its first pair (Flower, 1929). Specimens are reported as seen in continental zoological gardens at Cologne, 1909, and Antwerp, 1913 (Renshaw, 1914). According to Harman (1949) "at least a dozen" have been shown in London. The final survivor died there on August 9, 1931, and may very well have been the last living specimen seen outside the Antipodes.

Between 1908 and 1919, four specimens of the thylacine were exhibited here. In spite of the immensely powerful jaws and undoubtedly ferocious nature, all of these animals were phlegmatic and docile, if not actually friendly, and showed none of the indomitably savage reactions of the Tasmanian devil. Much less strongly nocturnal than the latter, they were often seen moving sluggishly about their inclosures during daylight hours. They were indifferent to cold. All were fed exclusively on beef or horseflesh, with such small game as might be available.

The best longevity achieved here was 5 years, 7 months, 29 days. Mann (1930:218) records 7 years, 1 month in the National Zoological Park, and Flower (1931) reports 8 years, 4 months, 18 days in the Zoological Gardens of London. I find no record of the breeding of this species in captivity.

FAMILY PERAMELIDAE

BANDICOOTS

The rabbit-eared bandicoot, rabbit bandicoot, or bilby (*Macrotis lagotis*) is the only member of this group to have been kept here. Of a total of eleven specimens, none survived for more than a few months. However, very much better results have been obtained elsewhere, Flower (1931) recording 5 years, 6 days in the Zoological Gardens of London and 7 years, 2 months in Frankfurt.

In spite of fairly large size—that of a small rabbit—this bandicoot is shy, furtive, and delicate. Nocturnal in habit, it is not especially useful as a zoo exhibit. It is almost entirely carnivorous and was fed here on chopped raw beef, mice, mealworms, and any other available insects.

FAMILY PHALANGERIDAE

Cuscuses, Phalangers, Flying Phalangers, and Koala

All of the members of this group, many of which are well-known zoological-garden figures, are arboreal in habit and feed on foliage, blossoms, and nectar, sometimes adding insects and other small creatures to the diet. In all but the koala, the pouch opens forward as in the kangaroos.

The cuscus (*Phalanger*), in all its numerous forms, is a slow-moving, strongly nocturnal creature, not unlike the lorises in general habit. It has the advantage, however, of a long, powerfully prehensile tail. It is this creature, of course, which is frequently mistaken for a monkey by visitors to northeastern Australia and the islands to the north, where no primates exist.

The cuscus has always been considered as most difficult in captivity and has almost invariably proved to be short-lived. However, Fleay (1949*a*) reports that a young male in white, dark-spotted pelage, picked up at Port Moresby in 1939, was still living in Australia 10 years later.

Our only experience here had to do with two dark-brown females of an undetermined race of the spotted cuscus (*Phalanger maculatus*) brought from the island of Manus and received here on July 14, 1953. These animals lived together peacefully with no indication of the evil tempers commonly attributed to cuscuses. The typical strong odor, however, was very noticeable, but since the animals were kept behind glass with forced ventilation, this was not distressing to our visitors. With a hollow log for a sleeping-den and protected from bright light by the use of blue fluorescent tubes, these cuscuses maintained excellent condition. Bananas were the most favored food. Oranges, apples, and carrots were also eaten but lettuce was refused. A mixture of dog biscuit, chopped raw horseflesh, and finely ground bone meal, with a few drops of vitamin concentrate added, was taken well. Food to which cod-liver oil had been added was refused. One of these animals died on January 18, 1955, but the other lived until May 13, 1959, or 5 years, 9 months, 29 days.

The brush-tailed phalangers or possums, as they are called in Australia, probably are the best known members of the family, at least as far as captivity is concerned. Most institutions have shown the gray phalanger (*Trichosurus v. vulpecula*) of southeastern Australia and possibly some other forms of this species. The tail is heavily haired to the tip, beneath which is a bare, rather weakly prehensile area. While the gray phalanger, like its close relatives, is largely nocturnal, it is often at least awake by day if protected from bright light and hence is an attractive zoological-garden exhibit. Here it is fed bananas, oranges, apples, carrots, raw sweet potatoes, and lettuce, with small amounts of mixed dog biscuit, chopped raw horseflesh, and bone meal. To this mixture are added a few drops of vitamin concentrate—like the cuscus, the gray phalanger refuses cod-liver oil. The animal seems to have a special fondness for bread soaked in water, then squeezed. It consistently refuses cabbage. The taking of meat, of course, is not entirely in accord with the mainly vegetarian diet attributed to the species in nature. During the summer months, edible foliage, especially that of the Russian mulberry (*Morus alba tatarica*), is always welcome.

The gray phalanger breeds well in captivity and has reproduced here as well as elsewhere. Only single young have been born here, but Zuckerman (1953:914) reports that of sixty births in the Zoological Gardens of London between 1857 and 1924, six resulted in twins and one in triplets.

A male received here on May 2, 1947, lived until August 9, 1957, or 10 years, 3 months, 7 days. Jones (1958) reports 11 years, 11 months, 19 days for a specimen in the Zoological Gardens of London. Two other species of the brush-tailed group have been shown here: the Tasmanian or dusky phalanger (*T. fuliginosus*) and the short-eared phalanger (*T. caninus*).

Of the flying phalangers or gliders, only one species has been shown here regularly: the short-headed flying phalanger or sugar glider (*Petaurus b. breviceps*). In Australia this delightful little creature is known commonly as the "flying squirrel." There is some reason for this, as the general appearance, soft velvety fur, and the lateral skin folds by means of which long-distance scaling is accomplished are remarkably like those of the rodents to which the name properly belongs.

If left to follow its natural inclination, the flying phalanger will spend the daylight hours in sleep, so that it can be seen by the zoological-garden visitor only as it is curled up in a shallow receptacle in its semi-darkened cage. However, tame individuals do not in the least mind being disturbed nor are they then distressed by exposure to moderate light. The use of red light, as outlined by Davis (1961), seems to offer great possibilities in the exhibition of this attractive species.

The species has not been bred here but has frequently produced young elsewhere. Zuckerman (1953:913) reports twenty-two births in the Zoological Gardens of London between 1865 and 1937. Fleay (1949*b*) gives an excellent account of the life habits of the sugar glider.

Our greatest longevity here is 8 years, 2 months, 18 days. Flower (1931:229) gives "over ten years" in the Zoological Gardens of London.

In nature the flying phalanger is said to feed chiefly on insects, flowers, buds, and fruits (Troughton, 1951:96). It has been our experience that, at least in captivity, the favored diet is considerably more inclusive. Its principal volume is made up of canned dog food, containing a high protein ratio. In addition, it will take milk, orange juice, diced fruits, and hard-boiled egg. Rather curiously, it drills through the hardest nut shells with great skill and is especially fond of walnuts and peanuts. Sunflower seeds, of course, offer no obstacle. All of these items, naturally, are taken in minute quantities. Vitamin concentrate drops are added to the orange juice.

Two specimens of the beautiful little feather-tailed glider (*Acrobates p. pygmaeus*) were brought to us from Australia in 1920 by Ellis S. Joseph. On a diet of evaporated milk diluted with honey, orange juice, and diced fruits, both lived for just under a year. Flower (1931) reports a specimen of this delicate species as having lived in the Zoological Gardens of London for 3 years, 11 months, 22 days.

Easily ranking among the most appealing mammals known to man, the koala (*Phascolarctos cinereus*), unfortunately, will presumably never become well known as a zoo animal outside Australia. Because of the extreme specialization of its feeding habits, depending as it does upon the leaves and shoots of various gum trees (*Eucalyptus*), it is obvious that only a well-established and constant supply will assure maintaining this quaint creature in health.

Aside from its more patent and endearing characteristics, the koala has greatly puzzled systematists because of the fact that the pouch opens toward the rear, as opposed to the forward direction customary in members of this family. Actually, the true relationships of this unique species have not yet been fully determined.

The first koala known to have been seen alive outside Australia is one that was "purchased of a dealer" by the London Zoological Society on

April 28, 1880 (Sclater, 1880). Fed at first on dried eucalyptus leaves brought from Australia, it was later supplied with fresh leaves. After doing remarkably well for nearly 14 months, the animal was accidentally strangled when its head was caught between the upper and lower parts of a heavy washstand in the office of the superintendent, where it was allowed to roam (Forbes, 1881). Another specimen was received at the Zoological Gardens of London on May 23, 1882 (Sclater, 1882). This animal was fed on the leaves of *E. globulus* and also "a little bread and milk."

In addition to these events of record, I am indebted to L. Harrison Matthews, director of the Zoological Gardens of London, who (*in litt.*) fills in the history of the koala in London as follows:

> A male purchased on the 5th February, 1881, died on the 6th October, 1881. . . . Two more were purchased on the 10th November, 1927, but these survived for little more than a month, the first dying of broncho-pneumonia on the 13th December, 1927, and the second on the 15th December, 1927. . . . Some more specimens started on their way from Australia in the care of Mr. Vinall, now the Curator of the Aquarium here, but at that time (1908), a Keeper. He found that once the Eucalyptus leaves wither, the animals refuse to eat them but he was doing very well with them on a diet of bread and milk and honey. He also offered them Eucalyptus throat pastilles which they ate with every appearance of joy! Unfortunately, however, the ship ran into extremely cold weather in the Australian Bight with the result that they caught cold and died.

The only koala so far received at the New York Zoological Park was brought to us from Australia by the late Ellis S. Joseph and arrived here on October 30, 1920. It had been fed during the journey on eucalyptus leaves, both dried and refrigerated, but the supply was already exhausted when the animal was received. Fresh foliage of many sorts was offered and refused. As eucalyptus leaves were not then available, the koala died five days later, on November 4.

Results in California, blessed with an abundance of naturalized eucalyptus in wide variety, have been very much more favorable. At least one specimen arrived there before 1918 (Hornaday, 1918), but its history is not presently available.

In 1925 two koalas were received by the Zoological Society of San Diego. On March 20, 1954, Belle J. Benchley, then executive secretary of that organization, supplied me with information concerning these animals which is summarized as follows:

On May 10, 1925, Mr. Faulconer, then director of the Zoological Garden of San Diego, arrived from Australia with two koalas. One of these animals, the personal property of the director, was taken to his home, where it lived until October. The second specimen was retained at the Zoological Garden, where it was kept in a cage in the Reptile House at night and in an inclosure containing a decrepit eucalyptus of acceptable but unknown species. Each day she was supplied with a variety of eucalyptus clippings, standing in a tin of water. Under these rather unfavorable conditions, this koala persisted until late March, 1927, or nearly 2 years. At autopsy, the long appendix was found to contain numerous undigested eucalyptus leaves which appeared to have been eaten when withered and dry.

On January 7, 1952, four further koalas were received by the Zoological Society of San Diego (Benchley, 1952). These animals, two males and two females, came from the private preserve of Sir Edward Hallstrom near Sydney and quickly accommodated themselves to the change. The grounds of the San Diego Garden are heavily populated with a wide variety of eucalyptus, so that no difficulty in finding acceptable food was experienced, and excellent results were obtained. Two males lived until February 21, 1957, and December 28, 1957, respectively. The survivor, a female, was placed in the Children's Zoo (Moxley, 1958) where she died on November 17, 1958, after 6 years, 10 months, 10 days (Anon., 1958).

On April 14, 1959, trios of koalas consisting of a male and two females were received by the zoological gardens of San Diego and San Francisco. In each group one of the females carried single young in the pouch, both of which were fully reared. Early in September, 1960, young were reported to have been born at both San Diego and San Francisco, in each case to the female that had arrived with pouch young. Accounts of these births, the first to occur outside Australia, are given by Pournelle (1961). The San Diego baby was safely reared, leaving the pouch for the first time on December 9, but the young koala at San Francisco was lost, reportedly following a fall from the pouch (*What's New at the San Francisco Zoo*, December, 1960). The adult male at San Diego died from acute leukemia in September, 1960 (Pournelle, *loc. cit.*), leaving that institution with four females only; at the same time, San Francisco possessed two males and two females. The obvious exchange of male for female was accomplished in April, 1961 (Anon., 1961), resulting in two thriving colonies, each consisting of one male and three females.

In Australia, of course, much has been done with the koala in restrained captivity and at semi-liberty in preserves. For the survival of the species, it is most fortunate that it is amenable to the conditions of semi-captivity, for its lethargic habits, lack of fear and means of protection, and particular food requirements all militate against survival in the face of increasing settlement and development of its territory.

The koala has been bred successfully in at least two Australian zoological gardens: Sydney (Patten, 1938) and Melbourne (Fleay, 1937). As a result of observations on captive animals, a most remarkable habit was brought to light. Minchin (1937) reported that a young koala at the Koala Farm, Adelaide, just approaching the end of its 6 months' sojourn in its mother's pouch, was seen to have extended its head and forelimbs and to have been feeding upon soft matter extruded from the mother's anal opening. Later observations by Fleay (1937:77–79) confirmed this presumably unique means of gapping the break between mother's milk and solid food.

The particular eucalyptus leaves taken by the koala at a given time seem to depend on two factors: species and state of growth. Young, terminal tips of preferred kinds of eucalyptus are favored, but it has been established that shoots arising from suckers may contain lethal quantities of prussic acid (Troughton, 1951:136). Leaves of this sort are rejected by the animals.

Acceptable species of eucalyptus vary, of course, over broad areas. For Victoria, Fleay (1937) gives the most acceptable as *viminalis, elaeophora, tereticornis, globulus,* and *rostrata.* For New South Wales, Patten (1938) lists *punctata, tereticornis, rostrata,* and *viminalis.* It is noteworthy that the foliage of even these favored kinds is eaten only when it is in the proper stage of growth; that of some others is taken sparingly on occasion, while others are consistently rejected.

It is commonly stated that in nature the koala does not drink water, deriving all necessary moisture from its food. However, Faulkner (1923) reared a young koala largely on cow's milk which it "lapped very slowly in the same manner as a kitten." At the age of $8\frac{1}{2}$ years this animal was still taking $\frac{1}{2}$ pint of milk daily. Incidentally, Troughton (1951:138) reports this koala to have lived for 12 years as a family pet, a presumed longevity record for the species in captivity. Other efforts to maintain the koala on a purely artificial diet have not been fully successful. The eating of earth by the koala, as an apparent source of minerals otherwise lacking in the diet, is mentioned by Faulkner (1923) but Fleay (1937:79) states that he has never observed it.

The ring-tailed phalangers or possums are small, markedly nocturnal creatures with strongly prehensile tails. For some reason—perhaps merely because they are not particularly well adapted to the purposes of the zoological garden—they are seldom seen in collections. Only one form— the Victorian ring-tail (*Pseudocheirus laniginosus victoriae*)—has been seen here. This animal, received in 1953, was in poor condition and survived for only a short time. In spite of an attributed vegetarian habit even more strict than that of the brush-tailed phalangers, our ring-tail ate the same food as that supplied for our brush-tails, including the meat mixture. It would appear that the London Zoological Society's record of 5 years, 8 months, 2 days (Flower, 1931) for the Queensland gray ring-tail (*Pseudocheirus peregrinus*) is a very creditable one.

FAMILY PHASCOLOMIDAE

WOMBATS

These large, squat, unlovely marsupials are strongly suggestive of giant woodchucks and carry the resemblance further by their burrowing habits and the rodent-like arrangement of the incisor teeth. Thoroughly nocturnal, they are seldom seen outside their burrows by daylight, unless occasionally to sun themselves. A pair kept in a large outdoor inclosure at Whipsnade Park could frequently be seen basking—when the sun shone!

Under ordinary zoological-garden conditions, wombats are not only unattractive but sometimes truculent. One male kept here was especially aggressive and frequently charged the broom wielded by a cautious keeper. This aggressive action is not reserved for human intruders alone, and at anything like close quarters even male and female usually will not live quietly together, except at the mating season. These rather unpleasant characteristics, of course, presumably apply to the wild-caught animal most usually available. Le Souef and Burrell (1926:294) give an account of a tame specimen which was a playful and engaging pet.

As the tooth arrangement indicates, the wombats are herbivorous, feeding largely on grasses, bark, and roots (Troughton, 1951). In captivity, timothy or clover hay, mixed grain, vegetables, and available greens make acceptable substitutes.

The only form that has been kept here is the common wombat (*Phascolomis hirsutus*). The hairy-nosed wombat (*Lasiorhinus latifrons*) has been kept at the San Diego Zoological Garden and at various European institutions. Our best longevity here is just under 15 years for the common wombat, but Flower (1931) reports 17 years, 8 months, 17 days for the hairy-nosed and 26 years, 21 days for the common, both in the Zoological Gardens of London.

Wombats are not easily or frequently bred in captivity, but there are at least two records. One quoted by Mohr (1942) describes the breeding of the common wombat at the Zoological Gardens of Halle, Germany, in 1914, and Zuckerman (1953) lists a birth at Whipsnade in 1931.

FAMILY MACROPODIDAE

KANGAROOS AND WALLABIES

Of all the marsupials, certainly most useful to the zoological garden are the members of this family. Herbivorous and diurnal in habit, their housing and care are relatively simple, while their exhibition and interest values are very high. Most of the species breed readily in captivity, and from the moment the young animal first peeps from its mother's pouch until it is fully weaned, its development is easily observed by the visiting public.

Of the rat-kangaroos, diminutive representatives of the Macropodidae, only two species have been shown here: Lesueur's (*Bettongia lesueur*) and the long-nosed (*Potorous tridactylus*). Various others of this rather extensive group have been kept elsewhere, of course, and in the Zoological Gardens of London especially have been bred remarkably well (Zuckerman, 1953). A specimen of the long-nosed rat-kangaroo born in the New York Zoological Park in 1901 lived for 9 years, 6 months, 16 days, a very long span for the group.

The rat-kangaroos are more nearly nocturnal than other members of the Macropodidae and usually spend the day in nest or burrow. They are more active at night, when they feed on grasses and roots. Consequently, a nesting shelter or at least protection from bright light should be provided. The tail is partially prehensile and is used for carrying nesting material (Le Souef and Burrell, 1926). Most of the species are notoriously quarrelsome, so that two males, at least, cannot be kept together. Clover or alfalfa hay, cut vegetables, and rolled oats make a satisfactory diet.

The climbing ability of the tree kangaroos presents a characteristic not found in others and is supported by various specializations, such as the strongly developed claws and long, pensile tail which must be important as a balancing organ. In nature they are said to spend much time on the ground and to take to the trees only to feed on the foliage or to escape enemies (Le Souef and Burrell, 1926). This habit is confirmed by the actions of animals in captivity.

The tree kangaroos are unattractive creatures, lacking the grace of terrestrial species. Also, while they accept readily the conditions of captivity, they ordinarily do not live for long. Of the three species that have been kept here—the black (*Dendrolagus ursinus*), Bennett's (*D. bennettianus*) and Doria's (*D. dorianus*), the greatest longevity—2 years, 13 days—was established by a female black.

On the other hand, some very remarkable results have been obtained elsewhere. Schneider (1954) records 16 years for a female of the black tree kangaroo in the Zoological Gardens of Leipzig. Of a pair of grizzled-gray tree kangaroos (*D. inustus*) received at the National Zoological Park, Washington, on September 28, 1937, the female lived until 1943 but the male, when seen in 1956, was still in good condition. Theodore H. Reed, director (*in litt.*), reports the animal's death on November 19, 1957. This span of 20 years, 1 month, 22 days is the greatest known to me for any kangaroo. Two young produced by this pair failed to survive their sire.

Tree kangaroos in captivity are usually fed in the same way as are the terrestrial forms, with hay, rolled oats, or feeding pellets, and any available vegetables and greens. An excellent insight into this situation has been given me by George Scott, former head keeper of birds in the New York Zoological Park. Early in 1953 Mr. Scott visited the experimental farm at Nondugl, in the Wahgi Valley of northeastern New Guinea, owned by Sir Edward Hallstrom of Sydney. While Mr. Scott's basic interest was in birds of paradise, he made the following observations on a group of Matschie's tree kangaroos (*D. matschiei*) that were in the care of Fred Shaw Mayer, the well-known collector. A wire netting inclosure approximately 12 feet long, 6 feet wide, and 9 feet high, with the netting extending over the top, contained an adult male, two adult females, and the offspring of one of the females, born in captivity. An open shelter, raised perhaps 5 feet from the ground and reached by means of inclined branches, provided protection from the rain. The adults had been in captivity about 2 years, and the group lived peaceably together.

It is true, of course, that these animals were living under natural climatic conditions not possible to duplicate completely in colder latitudes, but it appears possible that the food factor might be even more important. Scott reports that what seemed to him immense quantities of native greens (not identified), fresh carrots with tops, and sweet potato vines were placed in the cage daily and usually were completely consumed, the carrot tops being most favored. It is impossible to escape the conclusion that, like other leaf-eating species, the tree kangaroos require greater food bulk than that afforded by the comparatively concentrated diets usually provided.

Although tree kangaroos do not breed in captivity as freely as the more essentially terrestrial species, there are a number of records, including those at Nondugl and Washington. Schneider (1954) gives an account of births of the black tree kangaroo at Leipzig and Zuckerman (1953) reports young of black and Matschie's in the Zoological Gardens of London. Both females of a trio of Matschie's received at the San Diego

Zoological Garden in 1960 as the gift of Sir Edward Hallstrom produced young in 1961 (Hill, 1962).

The true kangaroos and wallabies, from the point of view of the zoological garden, are the really important members of the Macropodidae. Name distinctions in this group are purely arbitrary, "kangaroo" applying to the larger species and "wallaby" to the smaller, as in the case of "pigeons" and "doves." Smallest are the charming and gentle gray wallabies (*Dorcopsis*), of New Guinea, barely exceeding two feet in total length, while probably largest is the gray kangaroo (*Macropus canguru*), for which Lydekker (1893-96, 3:241) records 9 feet, 7 inches over-all length, although the red (*M. rufus*) presses hard for the honor. Male kangaroos are greatly superior to females in size and have the further rather curious characteristic pointed out by Troughton (1951) of continuing to grow long after they have reached maturity. Consequently, some huge old males of both gray and red fully deserve the common appellation of "Old Man." Such an animal, of course, is usually not only truculent but actually dangerous, since the powerful hind legs can deliver a blow of crushing impact.

In western Europe the acclimatization of the hardy Bennett's wallaby (*Protemnodon rufogrisea frutica*) at semi-liberty in large inclosed areas, often in company with blackbuck (*Antilope cervicapra*) and Chinese water deer (*Hydropotes inermis*), has been accomplished with great success. This sort of thing, however, is more properly the province of the private estate than of the zoological garden, where suitable space is not ordinarily available.

In most institutions kangaroos are kept on the conventional cage-and-yard system. But in at least two American zoological gardens the group basis, as generally seen in Australia, is used. Both the St. Louis Zoological Park and the Chicago Zoological Park, at Brookfield, Illinois, maintain large herds, each consisting of a number of species. At Brookfield the animals are confined in winter to an indoor shelter where they may be viewed by the public. This consists of a single huge compartment, perhaps 100 feet long by 40 feet wide. In it are arranged low, broad benches or tables, on which groups of resting animals often lie. During the summer months the kangaroos have access to a large outdoor inclosure.

An account of the history of this exhibit (Anon., 1949) states that because of supposed dietary deficiencies, an importation of fifty-two kangaroos in 1934 became reduced to three specimens of the black-faced gray (*M. c. melanops*). Following the addition of calcium and other minerals and subsoil clay to the usual diet of alfalfa hay, rolled oats, fruits,

vegetables, greens, and rock salt, the animals improved in condition, and
by 1949 the herd had increased to forty-seven, all descendants of the
original three. At intervals, also, other kinds had been introduced, and
when seen in 1947 the group included red kangaroos (*M. rufus rufus*),
Woodward's wallaroos (*M. robustus antilopinus*), and wallaroos (*M. r.
robustus*). I was informed by Robert Bean, the director, that the only
operational difficulty was the necessity for constant vigilance in the removal
of aggressive young males as they developed to the point where they might
challenge the established larger males or arouse their animosity. It is of
interest to note that there appeared to be no evidence of hybridizing
except, as might be expected, between forms of the same species.

In the New York Zoological Park, as in most other institutions, our
kangaroos are kept in individual compartments, each usually containing
a single animal or a female with her most recent offspring. These indoor
cages extend along each side of a building intended primarily for marsupials.
All cage floors are of concrete. Each measures 10 by 10 feet, with front and
partitions 7 feet high. The partitions are made of sheet metal for half their
height, topped by $\frac{5}{8}$-inch bars set on $3\frac{1}{2}$-inch centers. This allows desirable
seclusion but does not inforce complete solitude. In most cases the cage
tops are open, but no kangaroo has ever leaped over a partition. Broad
jumps of 27 feet and vertical leaps over barriers 9 and $10\frac{1}{2}$ feet are reported
by Troughton (1951:216). Such feats, of course, are accomplished only
under great pressure, not likely to be experienced in zoological-garden
practice.

For every two cages there is an outside run approximately 75 feet long
by 20 feet wide, inclosed with 2-inch-square mesh wire netting, 7 feet,
6 inches high. The floors of the runs are paved with a mixture of asphalt
and crushed stone, the only bare earth areas being very small ones, covered
with sand, around occasional shade trees. Both indoor cages and outside
runs are provided with connecting shift doors in partitions, so that animals
are readily moved from one compartment to another.

While the keeping of kangaroos in this manner has many operational
advantages, there is one serious drawback: the extreme nervousness of most
species. Ordinarily, kangaroos are calm enough at close quarters but, like
most animals which rely on running for escape from danger, are likely to
panic if suddenly frightened. We have lost several animals which have run
into fences at top speed when startled by sudden claps of thunder. There is
danger, too, if a vehicle or other noisemaking apparatus should come
suddenly upon the scene. In our experience the euro (*M. robustus erubescens*)
and the agile wallaby (*Protemnodon agilis*) are the most susceptible.

Kangaroos here are fed clover hay, rolled oats, feeding pellets, a mixture of ground grains to which salt and various minerals have been added, bread, cut potatoes, carrots, apples and bananas, and any greens available. Since only the more leafy portions of the hay are eaten, the rejected stems, spread in one corner, make excellent bedding for the night. This, of course, is changed daily.

As already noted in the feeding regime followed at Brookfield, clay is eaten freely there, a habit that has been reported by others. However, clay has never been furnished our animals, and since they maintain themselves in excellent condition with no access to natural soil, we feel safe in assuming that their mineral requirements are satisfied by the food mixture provided.

Under such conditions of control, breeding becomes a matter of calculation. At the chosen time or when adjoining male and female give evidence of special interest in each other, the door between the cages is opened, and the animals are allowed to run together until the female is known to have been bred. Various authorities quoted by Asdell (1946) give the gestation periods of species listed as from 30 days to 6 weeks. We have kept no exact records here but have found the period for the larger species to correspond approximately with the latter figure. Because of the short span before the embryonic young emerges to enter the pouch, it is advisable to remove the male as soon as the female has ceased to be receptive. If closely confined with the mother following the birth, his attentions will almost certainly result in forcing the helpless young animal from the pouch, so that it will dangle from the nipple to which it is attached until it perishes, unless promptly discovered.

When kangaroos are kept in groups in spacious quarters, as at Brookfield, losses through the activities of overambitious males are less likely to occur. Even then, it is important that maturing young males be kept at a minimum.

After many years of controversy and misunderstanding, a gradual accumulation of observations finally culminated in the brief illustrated paper by Dathe (1934), with later confirmation by Matthews (1943), which established the facts of kangaroo birth beyond question—facts which presumably apply, in general, to all marsupials. The course of these investigations has been ably summarized by Matthews (1943), Troughton (1951), and Hartman (1952).

Briefly stated, the expectant mother sits low on her spine, with her tail extending forward between her hind legs, the upper level of the abdomen being nearly horizontal. The inch-long embyro emerges from the cloaca, climbs hand over hand along a strip moistened with saliva by the mother, and enters the pouch unaided. Once it has found a nipple, the latter enlarges within its mouth, so that the embyro cannot be removed without damage.

Close observation by an interested keeper will detect the small blood spots that indicate a birth, if cage floors are as clean as they should be, so that exact dates are often determinable. For this reason, I can vouch for the accuracy of a note (Anon., 1944a) concerning a hybrid wallaroo (*M. r. robustus*) by euro (*M. r. erubescens*) which, born in our Kangaroo House, was seen to project its head from the pouch for the first time 5 months and 11 days after birth. For the next several weeks this young animal was in and out of the pouch until it had grown so large it could no longer enter. Even then, it inserted its head to draw the nourishment necessary to sustain it until it could adapt itself entirely to the use of solid food. This schedule, in general, is that of all of the larger species. Asdell (1946: 51) quoting Wood-Jones, gives "a pouch life of nearly four months" for *B. lesueur*. A period in this order will presumably be found to apply to the smaller Macropodidae.

During the period of pouch occupancy, the mother cleans the pouch assiduously with her lips, often holding it open with her forefeet while she inserts her head. Even when blood spots have gone unobserved, this action will draw attention to the event.

Delayed implantation in the Macropodidae has long been suspected and was definitely established through extensive investigation of the reproductive process in the short-tailed wallaby or pademelon (*Setonix brachyurus*), by Sharman (1955). Further studies reported by Sadleir and Shield (1960) disclosed the presence of free blastocysts in the uteri of females of several species while carrying young in the pouch. There appears to be no doubt that at least some of the puzzling births occurring in this group are now explainable.

As already stated, well-kept kangaroos, when adult pairs are available, breed well in captivity. Of the twenty-six forms of the family that have been kept here, seventeen have produced young, to a total of eighty-nine. Exact dates were determined for thirty-eight of these births, establishing the occurrence of at least one in each month of the year, the greatest number (6) occurring in September, with one each in February and July. From a total of forty-two births each for the gray and the red, Zuckerman (1953) is able to establish that at the Zoological Gardens of London gray births occur from February to October, while the red breeds the year around.

While the usual rule is for a single young at a birth, multiple births sometimes occur. Among the 219 births of kangaroos and wallabies in the Zoological Gardens of London and at Whipsnade, Zuckerman (1953) records eleven pairs of twins and one set of triplets. A birth of twin gray kangaroos in the Philadelphia Zoological Garden resulted in one of the youngsters being ejected from the pouch (Anon., 1944*b*). This animal was successfully bottle-reared on cow's milk with a vitamin supplement.

In discussing the age which kangaroos and wallabies may reach in captivity, Flower (1931:227) considers the extreme for kangaroos to be 17 years and for wallabies 12. As for wallabies, our best records here are in accord: 12 years, 2 months, 11 days for the ringtailed rock wallaby (*Petrogale xanthopus*) and 12 years, 5 months, 9 days for the swamp wallaby (*Protemnodon bicolor*). Longevities established here for kangaroos are somewhat in excess of those recorded by Flower. A female black-faced gray (*M. c. melanops*) received on July 14, 1917, with young in pouch, lived until July 11, 1936, just 3 days short of 19 years. Another female of the same form, born here on December 18, 1931, died on March 7, 1950, a period of 18 years, 2 months, 17 days. A female euro born in April, 1941, died November 23, 1960, after approximately 19 years, 7 months. Various other members of the genus *Macropus* have lived here for periods of 17 and 18 years.

The greatest obstacle to the successful keeping of kangaroos in captivity, under whatever conditions, has been the disease commonly known as "lumpy jaw." It has been considered that infective agents enter through injury caused by sharp food particles (Fox, 1923:572). It is for this reason that rolled oats, rather than whole or crushed, or feeding pellets are recommended for kangaroos. Two conditions seem to be involved: actinomycosis, caused by the mold *Actinomyces*, which affects bony structures of the jaw, and a mixed infection resulting from a general invasion of bacteria and molds, causing swelling and abscesses of the soft tissues of the head and mouth (see Fox, 1923; Hagan, 1943; and Udall, 1943). L. J. Goss, former veterinarian of the New York Zoological Park, reports (*in litt.*) favorable results in the treatment of actinomycosis with sulfonamides and antibiotics. The soft-tissue infection seems to develop from the impaction of food materials about the teeth and gums to which kangaroos, perhaps because of the narrowness of their jaws, are particularly subject. In initial stages, direct local treatment is recommended. Under the conditions of proper sanitation, correct feeding, close supervision, and prompt treatment, neither form of "lumpy jaw" is the menace it once was.

Incidentally, the brownish or reddish urine common to kangaroos and wallabies is perfectly normal and not an indication of ill health. The reddish exudate sometimes seen on the throats and chests of adult male red kangaroos (*M. rufus*) appears to be a glandular secretion (Troughton, 1951:226).

· REFERENCES

ANON.
1944a. Checking up on Joey. Animal Kingdom, 47 (2):45.
1944b. The kangaroo twins. Fauna, 6 (2):61.
1949. Kangaroos. Bandar-log, 3:2–3.
1958. Note. Zoo Bell (San Diego), 5 (12):4.
1961. Koala trade. Zoonooz, 34 (8):7.

ASDELL, S. A.
1946. Patterns of mammalian reproduction. Comstock Publishing Co., Ithaca, N.Y. 437 pp.

BEACH, FRANK A.
1939. Maternal behavior of the pouchless marsupial *Marmosa cinerea*. Jour. Mammal., 20 (3):315–22.

BENCHLEY, BELLE J.
1952. Note. Zoonooz, 25 (3):2–4.

CABRERA, ANGEL, and JOSÉ YEPES.
1940. Historia Natural Ediar: Mammiferos Sud-Americanos. Compañia Argentina de Editores, Buenos Aires. 370 pp.

CAHALANE, VICTOR H.
1947. Mammals of North America. The Macmillan Co., N.Y. 682 pp.

DATHE, H.
1934. Eine neue Beobachtung des Känguruhgeburtsaktes. Zool. Garten, Leipzig (N.F.), 7 (7/9):223–24.

DAVIS, JOSEPH A., JR.
1961. Red means go! Animal Kingdom, 64 (4):114–18.

FARRIS, EDMOND J.
1950. In The care and breeding of laboratory animals. John Wiley & Sons, Inc., N.Y. 515 pp.

FAULKNER, A. S.
1923. Note. Australian Zool., 3 (3):112–13.

FLEAY, David.
1935. Notes on the breeding of Tasmanian devils. Victorian Nat., 52:100–105.
1937. Observations on the koala in captivity. Australian Zoologist, 9:68–80.
1948a. Australia's marsupial tiger cat. Animal Kingdom, 51 (2):36–41.
1948b. The marsupial devil of Tasmania. *Ibid.*, No. 3, pp. 86–91.
1949a. That curious marsupial, the cuscus. *Ibid.*, 52 (1):22–25.
1949b. Australia's vivacious sugar-glider. *Ibid.*, No. 3, pp. 70–75; 95.

1950a. Experiences with Australia's brush-tailed tuan. *Ibid.*, **53** (5):152–57.

1950b. Australia's yellow-footed marsupial mouse. *Ibid.*, No. 1, pp. 20–24.

FLOWER, S. S.

1929. List of the vertebrated animals exhibited in the gardens of the Zoological Society of London, 1828–1927. 1. Mammals. Zoological Society of London. 419 pp.

1931. Contributions to our knowledge of the duration of life in vertebrate animals. 5. Mammals. Proc. Zool. Soc. London, pp. 145–234.

FORBES, W. A.

1881. On some points in the anatomy of the koala (*Phascolarctos cinereus*). Proc. Zool. Soc. London, pp. 180–94.

FOX, HERBERT.

1923. Disease in captive wild mammals and birds. J. B. Lippincott Co., Philadelphia. 665 pp.

HAGAN, W. A.

1943. The infectious diseases of domestic animals. Comstock Publishing Co., Inc., Ithaca, N.Y. 665 pp.

HARMAN, IAN.

1949. Tasmania's wolf and devil. Zoo Life, **4** (3):87–89.

HARTMAN, CARL.

1920. Studies in the development of the opossum. V. The phenomena of parturition and the method of transfer of young to the pouch. Anat. Record, **19**:1–11.

1952. Possums. Univ. of Texas Press, Austin. 174 pp.

HEDIGER, H.

1950. Wild animals in captivity. Butterworth's Scientific Publications, London. 207 pp.

HILL, CLYDE A.

1962. Pouch perils of a tree kangaroo. Zoonooz, **35** (1):11–13.

H[ORNADAY], W. T.

1918. Note. Bull. New York Zool. Soc., **21** (4):1635.

JONES, F. WOOD.

1924. The mammals of South Australia. Government Printer, Adelaide.

JONES, MARVIN L.

1958. Mammals in captivity. Mimeographed MSS (unpublished).

LE SOUEF, A. S., and HARRY BURRELL.

1926. The wild animals of Australasia. Geo. D. Harrap & Co., London. 388 pp.

LYDEKKER, RICHARD.

1893–96. The royal natural history. Frederick Warne & Co., New York and London. 6 vols.

MANN, WM. M.

1930. Wild animals in and out of the zoo. Smithsonian Sci. Ser., 6. 362 pp.

MATTHEWS, L. H.
1943.   Parturition in the kangaroo. Proc. Zool. Soc. London, Ser. A, 113:117–20.

MINCHIN, A. KEITH.
1937.   Notes on the weaning of a young koala (*Phascolarctos cinereus*). Records S. Australia Mus., 6 (1):1–3.

MITCHELL, P. CHALMERS.
1911.   On longevity and viability in mammals and birds; with a note on the theory of longevity. Proc. Zool. Soc. London, pp. 425–548.

MOHR, ERNA.
1942.   Einiges über Wombat-Formen und Marsupialia-Beutel. Zool. Garten, Leipzig (N.F.), 14 (1/2):55–68.

MOXLEY, ELLEN.
1958.   A rarity in the Children's Zoo. Zoonooz, 31 (4):3.

PATTEN, R. A.
1938.   Observations on the koala. Parks and Recreation, 22 (3):125–26.

POURNELLE, GEORGE H.
1961.   Notes on reproduction of the koala. Jour. Mammal., 42 (3):396.

RENSHAW, GRAHAM.
1914.   Rare beasts in continental zoos. Year book, Amateur Menagerie Club, England, pp. 141–59.

ROBERTS, MARY G.
1915.   The keeping and breeding of Tasmanian devils (*Sarcophilus harrisi*). Proc. Zool. Soc. London, pp. 575–81.

SADLEIR, R. M., and J. W. SHIELD.
1960.   Delayed birth in marsupial macropods—the euro, the tammar and the marloo. Nature, 185 (4709):335.

SCHNEIDER, KARL MAX.
1954.   Vom Baumkanguruh (*Dendrolagus leucogenys* Matschie). Zool. Garten, Leipzig (N.F.), 21 (1/2):63–106.

SCLATER, P. L.
1880.   Additions to the menagerie. Proc. Zool. Soc. London, pp. 355–56.
1882.   Additions to the menagerie. *Ibid.*, p. 547.

SHARLAND, M. S. R.
1941.   Tasmania's rare "tiger." Bull. New York Zool. Soc., 44 (3):83–88.

SHARMAN, G. B.
1955.   Studies on marsupial reproduction. 3. Normal and delayed pregnancy in *Setonix brachyurus*. Australian Jour. Zool., 3 (1):56–70.

TATE, G. H. H.
1947.   On the anatomy and classification of the Dasyuridae (Marsupialia). Results of the Archbold Expeditions. 56. Bull. Amer. Mus. Nat. Hist., 88 (3):101–55.

TROUGHTON, ELLIS.
1951.   Furred animals of Australia. Angus & Robertson, Ltd., Sydney. 376 pp.

UDALL, D. H.
    1943. The practice of veterinary medicine. By the Author, Ithaca, N.Y.
        723 pp.

ZUCKERMAN, S.
    1953. The breeding seasons of mammals in captivity. Proc. Zool. Soc.
        London, 122 (4):827–950.

ORDER INSECTIVORA

.

Solenodons, Tenrecs, Hedgehogs, Shrews, Etc.

The members of this order are small, inconspicuous creatures, mostly nocturnal in habit. For these reasons they are comparatively little known, yet the numerous species are widely distributed in most parts of the world, although they are absent from Australia and most of South America. Like other small nocturnal mammals, most are not particularly useful for exhibition purposes. However, all are of interest, some particularly so, and much still remains to be learned concerning their habits.

FAMILY SOLENODONTIDAE

Solenodons

These curious creatures, largest of the New World insectivores and second in size only to the common tenrec in the entire order, are confined to the islands of Cuba and Hispaniola. The Cuban species, *Solenodon cubanus*, is now thought to be extinct, but the Hispaniolan animal, *S. paradoxus*, better known in the literature as the Haitian solenodon, still exists. Living specimens are occasionally available at rather high prices.

The Haitian solenodon has been represented here by seven specimens, the first having been received on July 20, 1910. The species is nocturnal in habit and dislikes exposure to strong light. However, since it quickly becomes accustomed to handling and seldom or never bites, it is readily made available to small groups of viewers.

Since the animal climbs upward readily enough but, like many others, is less agile in retracing its steps, it has been kept here, at least in later years, in glass-fronted box cages furnished with a sleeping shelter. The feeding schedule includes a mixture of chopped raw horseflesh and fine bone meal with cod-liver oil added, hard-boiled egg (raw eggs are relished but result in looseness), American "chameleons" (*Anolis*), mealworms, milk, and banana. Other fruits and also lettuce may be sampled sparingly.

Our best longevity record for this species is 4 years, 2 days, established by a female received on December 9, 1935. Mohr (1951) reports 6½ years in Breslau.

No solenodon has been bred here, but on December 26, 1935, 17 days after arrival, the female referred to above gave birth to a single young in a deep nest of hay she had built in her sleeping box. The male was promptly removed and the mother was not disturbed, but the young animal died 2 days later, apparently never having nursed. It has been figured, after death, by Bridges (1936).

The first living Cuban solenodon to be exhibited was one collected by Gundlach in 1886 (Allen, 1942). After being shown at a meeting of the Biological Society of Washington, the animal was turned over to the Zoological Garden of Philadelphia, where it lived for the very creditable period of 5 years, 7 months (Bridges, 1936).

According to Allen (1942) two excellent photographs of a living specimen captured in 1909 and reproduced by Mohr (1937) are the only ones in existence.

FAMILY TENRICIDAE

TENRECS

The common tenrec (*Tenrec ecaudatus*) of Madagascar and the Comoro Islands is the largest of the insectivores, adults reaching a length of 16 inches. As the specific name indicates, it is tailless. It is nocturnal and fossorial in habit and is known to hibernate during the Madagascar dry season—May or June to December (Lydekker, 1893–96, 1:342), and May to October (Rand, 1935).

Even before the protective measures now in force in Madagascar became effective, the tenrec was seldom seen in collections, only four specimens having been kept here up to 1956, when one was received on December 17. This animal was in very poor condition but improved rapidly on a diet of dog meal mixed with chopped raw meat, milk with raw yolk of egg added, mice, and earthworms given in a shallow box of earth. From May to September, 1957, very little food was taken but good condition was maintained. Torpidity was not noted. Late in September, however, food intake began to increase. In 1958 the animal became torpid in July, occasionally changing position or even moving from its hollow log to another secluded spot. Normal activity was not resumed until late December, when the tenrec began to take its usual food allowance. It appeared to be in good condition but died on February 1, 1959, necropsy revealing a liver neoplasm. The span of 2 years, 1 month, 15 days approximates results reported elsewhere.

There appears to be no record of the breeding of the tenrec in captivity. Such an event could produce results of great interest because of the surprisingly large number of embryos recovered from collected females (Asdell, 1946). Rand (1935) gives one count of twenty-five and three of eighteen each.

FAMILY ERINACEIDAE

HEDGEHOGS

This numerous and widely distributed Old World family is typified by the common hedgehog (*Erinaceus europaeus*), which extends, in several forms, from Ireland to eastern Siberia. Largely but not exclusively nocturnal, the hedgehog is a voracious feeder, missing very little edible material that comes its way. It is partial to eggs and consequently destructive to ground-nesting birds. As an exhibition animal it has little value but quickly becomes tame and handleable. Its habit of rolling into a tight ball with defensive spines on end is thus readily demonstrable. Although the hedgehog is well known to hibernate in winter, at least in the colder parts of its range, specimens kept here in heated quarters have shown no tendency to do so.

With animals of such broad food requirements, a suitable diet is not difficult to devise. We have found here that either canned dog food or a mixture of raw horseflesh and fine bone meal with cod-liver oil and a small dish of whole milk will satisfy a hedgehog's needs. In addition, hard-boiled egg, mealworms, American "chameleons" (*Anolis*), mice, and diced vegetables are always welcome.

Hedgehogs do not breed readily in captivity. There are scattered records for the European, as given by Edwards (1957), who also outlines the procedure followed for breeding in the laboratory. A pregnant female received here on August 24, 1900, produced two young on September 10, but the soft-spined youngsters died 2 days later. Asdell (1946) gives the gestation period as 34–49 days and adds that "it is difficult to obtain accurate data as captivity is detrimental to breeding in this species."

Hedgehogs are notoriously short-lived in captivity. A specimen of *E. e. europaeus* lived for 3 years, 4 months in the National Zoological Park, Washington (Mann, 1930); another of the same race lived in our own collection for 3 years, 11 months, 8 days. A long-eared hedgehog (*Hemiechinus a. auritus*) from Cyprus lived here from June 8, 1946, to September 8, 1949, or 3 years, 3 months.

FAMILY MACROSCELIDIDAE

Elephant Shrews

The members of this African family are characterized by extended, mobile muzzles and strongly developed hind legs. The English name, of course, derives from the trunklike nose and not from the body size. While it was once thought that the long legs indicated a jerboa-like mode of progression, the animal walks in the normal four-footed manner, although it is capable of leaping when under pressure. The elephant shrews are small, secretive creatures, partially but not entirely nocturnal in habit. They are difficult to maintain in captivity, and their requirements are so little known that they are seldom seen in collections. Pocock (1912) has recorded notes on appearance and behavior and presented figures of two species of elephant shrew—the common or Shaw's (*Macroscelides proboscideus*) and the rock (*Elephantulus rupestris*), received at the Zoological Gardens of London in November, 1911.

In 1948 the Medical Division of the United States Navy deposited in the National Zoological Park, Washington, 104 specimens of one of the forms of the East African elephant shrew (*E. rufescens*) (Mann, 1949). Two of these animals were later transferred to the New York Zoological Park, where they were received on October 28, 1948. One survived until June 18, 1949, a span of 7 months, 21 days. Flower (1931) reports a specimen of *E. rozeti* as having lived in the Zoological Gardens of Frankfurt for 3 years, 4 months, 4 days.

On the return of the New York Zoological Society's Congo expedition on June 15, 1949, Charles Cordier, then our collector, brought us four specimens of the much larger Torday's elephant shrew (*Petrodromus tordayi*). One of this resistant but still very difficult group lived here until September 15, 1950, a period of 1 year, 3 months.

After trying various food items, we found that the diet preferred by both species consisted of chopped hard-boiled egg, whole milk, and a mixture of ground raw horse meat and fine bone meal, moistened with cod-liver oil. Amounts required of each item by the individual animals are easily determined, for elephant shrews are so quarrelsome and aggressive that even specimens of opposite sex cannot be kept together, at least in small areas.

FAMILY SORICIDAE

SHREWS

The tiny but widely distributed members of this family are seldom seen as zoological-garden subjects, and while much has been learned in recent years concerning their requirements in captivity, their extreme shyness, short lives, and diminutive size militate against them. Where conditions warrant and the necessary close supervision can be provided, a glass aquarium or other container with unclimbable sides is suitable as a home. Loose earth and dried leaves should cover the floor, and a small nest receptacle in a corner will complete a satisfactory environment. Because of their quarrelsome nature, two or more animals cannot usually be kept together in close confinement. However, with sufficient space and abundant food, serious fighting is less likely to result.

Shrews are ravenous eaters and when fed on a natural diet, consume immense quantities of earthworms and insects, mice when available, and limited amounts of berries, seeds, and greens. In captivity, a suitable diet could be found in the ground raw horseflesh, bone meal with cod-liver oil, and chopped hard-boiled egg recommended for other insectivores. In addition, earthworms, mealworms, mice, and bits of diced fruits and greens are suggested. Walker (1954) advises the use of cottage cheese, a valuable food item for any insectivore. A useful, if rather complicated, basic formula for the smaller forms is given by Walker (1951).

While experience with shrews in zoological gardens does not appear to be a matter of record, valuable contributions to methods of care and maintenance in captivity have come from other sources, notably Pearson (1950), Crowcroft (1951, 1953, 1957), Rudd (1953), Walker (1954), Rood (1958), and Conaway (1958). Walker furnishes illuminating data on the remarkable reproductive abilities of the lesser short-tailed or least shrew (*Cryptotis parva*). In just 8 days less than 1 year, a captive pair of these little creatures produced no less than sixty-six young, with births in almost every month of the year. The gestation period is given as between

12 and 16 days, and sexual maturity is achieved at 3 months or possibly less.

The greatest longevity listed by Flower (1931) for any species is 1 year, 3 months, 2 days for an Egyptian shrew (*Crocidura olivieri*) in the Giza Zoological Gardens. Probably the greatest recorded duration for any shrew in captivity is that of a short-tailed shrew (*Blarina brevicauda*) reported by Reed (1961) to have lived in the National Zoological Park, Washington, from December 27, 1957, to March 28, 1960, or 2 years, 3 months, 1 day.

FAMILY TALPIDAE

MOLES

In general, the moles are even less satisfactory exhibition animals than the shrews. While usually larger, hence more readily observed, their burrowing habits, limited eyesight, and sensitivity to light make them very difficult subjects. A star-nosed mole (*Condylura cristata cristata*) seen at the National Zoological Park, Washington, in 1948 is the only specimen I can recall noticing on public exhibition. This animal, kept in a small glass-fronted, darkened cage deeply floored with earth, was active and reasonably visible in spite of the dimness of the interior. It seemed quite content and had been living for some months.

Hisaw (1923) found that for the prairie mole (*Scalopus aquaticus machrinus*) a wooden box 3 feet wide, 5 feet long, and $2\frac{1}{2}$ feet deep with 8 inches of soil was the most satisfactory cage for experimental work. His investigations showed that preferred foods were earthworms and white grubs, other insect larvae, adult insects, corn (maize) soaked in water, ripe tomatoes, white potatoes, and apples, in the order named. Average daily intake for each of six animals tested was 26.28 grams, the average weight of the six individuals concerned being 84.33 grams. This works out to a daily intake of 32.08 [31.16] per cent, or nearly one-third, of body weight. Under these conditions, one animal lived for "over a year."

Henning (1952) presents sketches of much smaller boxes, with special conveniences for cleaning and for providing food and water. He found that an adequate diet was provided by ground raw horseflesh or liver and commercial dog food, fortified with vitamin supplements and a pinch of chopped grass blades. On this regimen, one specimen of the eastern mole (*S. a. aquaticus*) lived for $14\frac{1}{2}$ months, until destroyed for experimental purposes. Henning adds: "Breeding of Moles in captivity seems to be very improbable on the basis of observations made during this work." I find no record in refutation of this statement.

FAMILY TUPAIIDAE

TREE SHREWS

While members of this family are considered to be more properly assigned to the primates by many authorities (Simpson, 1945), for practical purposes, at least, it seems best to treat them here. There is even authoritative support for this position in the classifications adopted by Ellerman and Morrison-Scott (1951) and Hill (1953). The controversial point involved can wait, but a hungry tree shrew cannot.

Active, diurnal, and aboreal, the tree shrews are strikingly squirrel-like at first glance. The members of the genus *Tupaia* complete the resemblance by possessing well-haired tails. Sharp, elongated noses and differences in dentition quickly dispel the illusion. The group is confined to India, Burma, the Malay Peninsula, and nearby islands.

Tree shrews have always been scarce in the animal market, and of the typical genus, *Tupaia*, only three specimens of the Malayan form, *T. glis ferruginea*, have been kept here, the last being received in 1937. Of this animal, Claude W. Leister (1938), then curator of mammals, says: "Our specimen ate his food, consisting of bits of fruit, insects and the meat of small birds, while sitting upright like a squirrel and holding the food with his forefeet. . . . It died after being on exhibition for a week. There was no apparent cause of death but it is not too far-fetched to believe that its nervous temperament was incompatible with the ever-moving stream of visitors that passed its cage." This suggestion is certainly in accord with general experience with these animals.

Steinbacher (1940) reports better results with a specimen of one of the forms of *T. tana*, the Bornean tree shrew, received at the Frankfurt Zoological Gardens. This animal was fed on bananas, apples, carrots, crushed oats, and mealworms, with black tea to drink. It had lived for approximately a year on this diet at the time of writing and remained in excellent condition. Flower (1931) gives 2 years, 3 months, 28 days for this species in the Zoological Gardens of London, the best known to him for any tree shrew.

On July 9, 1947, Charles Wharton arrived in New York with a large collection of Philippine animals, including a number of Philippine tree shrews (*Urogale everetti*), obtained in Mindanao. Wharton (1950) gives an excellent account of habits and natural food, with a report of the history of specimens from this shipment in the zoological gardens of Philadelphia, Chicago, and New York. In all of these institutions young were born but none fully reared, although one lived for 3 months at Chicago. A report of this event is given by Snedigar (1949).

One pair from Wharton's collection was retained here. These were placed on exhibition in an inclosed cage about 3 feet in each dimension with glass front and wire top. The floor was kept covered with dried leaves, and branches for climbing and a small hollow log for retirement were included. Illumination was provided by blue fluorescent tubes in addition to some natural top light. Under these conditions, with a darkened public space, the animals were indifferent to the flow of visitors and remained in a presumably normal state of continuous high activity.

They appeared willing to eat almost anything available. They fed continuously throughout the day, taking only small bits at one time but consuming large amounts daily. Items provided included diced bananas, cherries and apples, ground raw horseflesh and fine bone meal with cod-liver oil, peanuts, American "chameleons" (*Anolis*), mealworms, hard-boiled egg, and whole milk.

Male and female lived well together with no quarreling. On October 7, 1947, two young were born, one of which lived for 2 days, the other for 8. The male was not removed. At death, the first measured 13 centimeters total length (tail $4\frac{1}{2}$ centimeters) and weighed 19.15 grams.

Copulation began soon after the young were born, and a single birth occurred on December 11, 1947. This confirms, in general, the estimate by Wharton (1950) of a gestation period of approximately 56 days. This young animal was removed directly after birth and was found to weigh 20.8 grams. It was kept in a small box, electrically warmed, and fed at frequent intervals with whole cow's milk at body temperature, administered with a glass medicine dropper and later with a doll's nursing bottle. It appeared to be thriving but died on December 22, following overexposure to the rays of an ultraviolet lamp.

Copulation by the parents continued, but there were no further births until August 29, 1948. Just prior to this time, the female gave evidence of pregnancy and was removed to a wire cage about 3 feet long with a retiring box attached. Two young were born in the box, in which the mother had constructed a well-formed nest of hay. Undisturbed, she took excellent care of them until their first emergence from the nesting box on October 1. One died on that day and the other followed 2 days later, no cause of death being determinable. The first measured $7\frac{1}{2}$ inches total length (tail 3 inches) and weighed 33 grams at death. The second, of which no measurements were made, weighed 35 grams. Both appeared to be in perfect condition.

The female was then returned to the male, and copulation was immediately resumed. However, the female retrogressed in condition and died on November 22, 1948, after living with us for 1 year, 4 months, 13 days. The male remained in good health until his death on June 13, 1953. This longevity of 5 years, 11 months, 4 days is an extremely long span for a member of this group.

Efforts to breed various tree shrews in captivity have so far met with indifferent success. Hendrickson (1954), in discussing a large colony of *T. glis* at the University of Malaya, Singapore, says that in thirteen pregnancies the young were aborted or eaten immediately by the mother, except in two births to the same female. In one of the latter instances the young were found dead after 4 days, and in the other were eaten by the mother at 3 days. As recorded in the minutes of the meeting of the International Union of Directors of Zoological Gardens held at Copenhagen in September, 1959, W. Windecker described a birth of *T. tana* at Cologne in 1956, thought to have been the first in Europe; the young died some days later. He also reported further births at both the Max-Planck Institute at Giessen and at Cologne in 1959, the young in one instance having survived to 4 weeks and still living. The Annual Report of the Zoological Society of London for 1958 lists a Malayan tree shrew as having been born at Regent's Park in that year, and the *International Zoo Year Book*, Volume 2, 1960, published by the Zoological Society of London, credits Cologne with the birth of a Bornean tree shrew (*T. tana*) and Stuttgart with one of the Malayan tree shrew (*T. glis*), both in 1960.

· REFERENCES

ALLEN, GLOVER M.
    1942.   Extinct and vanishing mammals of the Western Hemisphere. Amer. Comm. Internatl. Wild Life Protect. 620 pp.
ASDELL, S. A.
    1946.   Patterns of mammalian reproduction. Comstock Publishing Co. Ithaca, N.Y. 437 pp.
BRIDGES, WILLIAM.
    1936.   The Haitian solenodon. Bull. New York Zool. Soc., **39** (1):13–18.

CONAWAY, C. H.
   1958.   Maintenance, reproduction and growth of the least shrew in captivity.
           Jour. Mammal., **39** (4):507-12.

CROWCROFT, PETER.
   1951.   Keeping British shrews in captivity. Jour. Mammal., **32** (3):354-55.
   1953.   A study of wild and captive shrews. Zoo Life, **8** (1):14-17.
   1957.   The life of the shrew. Max Reinhardt, London. 166 pp.

EDWARDS, J. T. G.
   1957.   The European hedgehog. In: The UFAW handbook on the care and
           management of laboratory animals. The University Federation for
           Animal Welfare, London. 951 pp.

ELLERMAN, J. R., and T. C. S. MORRISON-SCOTT.
   1951.   Checklist of Palaearctic and Indian mammals. British Museum
           (Natural History), London. 810 pp.

FLOWER, S. S.
   1931.   Contribution to our knowledge of the duration of life in vertebrate
           animals. 5. Mammals. Proc. Zool. Soc. London, pp. 145-234.

HENDRICKSON, J. R.
   1954.   Breeding of the tree shrew. Nature, **174** (4434):794-95.

HENNING, WILLIAM L.
   1952.   Methods for keeping the eastern mole in captivity. Jour. Mammal.,
           33 (3):392-95.

HILL, W. C. OSMAN.
   1953.   Primates. 1. Strepsirhini. Interscience Publishers, New York, and
           University Press, Edinburgh. 798 pp.

HISAW, FREDERICK L.
   1923.   Feeding habits of moles. Jour. Mammal., **4** (1):9-20.

L[EISTER], C[LAUDE] W.
   1938.   The Malayan tree shrew. Bull. New York Zool. Soc., **41** (1):37-38.

LYDEKKER, RICHARD.
   1893-96. Royal natural history. Frederick Warne & Co., London and New
           York. 6 vols.

MANN, WM. M.
   1930.   Wild animals in and out of the zoo. Smithsonian Sci. Ser., 6. 362 pp.
   1949.   Report on the National Zoological Park for the year ended June 30,
           1948. Smithsonian Inst. Rept. for 1948, pp. 89-116.

MOHR, ERNA.
   1937.   Schlitzrüssler. Mitteil. Zool. Garten Stadt Halle, **32** (4):1-5.
   1951.   Lebensdauer einiger Tiere in zoologischen Garten. Zool. Garten,
           Leipzig (N.F.), **18** (1/2):60.

PEARSON, OLIVER P.
   1950.   Keeping shrews in captivity. Jour. Mammal., **31** (8):351-52.

POCOCK, R. I.
  1912. Exhibition of living specimens of the common elephant-shrew (*Macroscelides proboscideus*) and the rock elephant-shrew (*Elephantulus rupestris*). Proc. Zool. Soc. London, pp. 142–44.

RAND, A. L.
  1935. On the habits of some Madagascar mammals. Jour. Mammal., **16** (2):89–104.

REED, THEODORE H.
  1961. Report on the National Zoological Park for the year ended June 30, 1960. Smithsonian Inst. Rept. for 1960, pp. 131–71.

ROOD, JOHN P.
  1958. Habits of the short-tailed shrew in captivity. Jour. Mammal., **39** (4):499–507.

RUDD, R. L.
  1953. Shrews in captivity. Jour. Mammal., **34** (1):118–20.

SIMPSON, GEORGE GAYLORD.
  1945. The principles of classification and a classification of mammals. Bull. Amer. Mus. Nat. Hist., 85. 350 pp.

SNEDIGAR, ROBERT.
  1949. Breeding of the Philippine tree shrew, *Urogale everetti* Thomas. Jour. Mammal., **30** (2):190–95.

STEINBACHER, GEORG.
  1940. Beobachtungen am Spitzhörnchen und Panda. Zool. Garten, Leipzig (N.F.), **12** (1):48–53.

WALKER, ERNEST P.
  1951. In: Report on the National Zoological Park for the year ended June 30, 1950. Smithsonian Inst. Rept. for 1950, pp. 82–115.
  1954. Shrews is shrews. Nat. Mag., **47** (3):125–28.

WHARTON, CHARLES H.
  1950. Notes on the Philippine tree shrew, *Urogale everetti* Thomas. Jour. Mammal., **31** (3):352–54.

ORDER DERMOPTERA

·

FAMILY CYNOCEPHALIDAE

FLYING LEMURS

The curious and beautiful members of this group have been the center of long controversy about their proper position in the zoological scale. Present thought generally supports their assignment to a separate order containing a single family and genus. Confined to southeastern Asia and nearby islands, the flying lemurs are largely if not entirely nocturnal, inhabiting heavily forested areas. They fly only in the manner of flying squirrels, scaling downward for considerable distances with the aid of broad flaps of skin attached to the legs. The name "lemur" is based on general appearance, for there is no relationship with the group to which the name properly belongs. The heads of flying lemurs have been compared to those of ruminants, fruit bats, foxes, and various others but actually they seem very suggestive of those of true lemurs.

Principally because of specialized feeding habits, the flying lemur is one of the few mammals that have so far resisted all efforts to maintain them in captivity. Leaves of specific trees are the principal item of diet, the stomach and intestines being especially adapted to bulky food.

Perhaps the only living specimen to be seen alive outside its native habitat was a Philippine flying lemur (*Cynocephalus volans*) that arrived in New York on July 9, 1947, having been flown here from the Philippines by Charles Wharton. Partial success had been achieved in getting some specimens in the field to eat various fruits and vegetables (Wharton, 1950), but certain leaves were still preferred. A supply of these leaves accompanied the shipment as far as California, but there the small quantity remaining was confiscated according to law (Wharton, 1948). The animal was greatly weakened on arrival in New York and refused a wide variety of fruits and leaves, including the leaves of the Russian mulberry (*Morus*), which most leaf-eaters accept readily. Two or three days later the flying lemur succumbed, bringing to a dismal end what was probably the most determined attempt that has been made to keep this intriguing creature in captivity.

· REFERENCES

WHARTON, CHARLES H.
    1948.   Seeking Mindanao's strangest creatures. Natl. Geogr. Mag., **44** (3):388–408.
    1950.   Notes on the life history of the flying lemur. Jour. Mammal., **31** (3):269–73.

ORDER CHIROPTERA

·

BATS

Because of their nocturnal habits and highly specialized food requirements and adaptations for satisfying them, the great majority of the nearly two thousand known forms of bats are unsuitable, in our present state of knowledge, for the zoological garden. Notable exceptions are the fruit bats or flying foxes of the Old World tropics and, to a lesser degree, the vampires and some others of Central and South America.

Because of their seemingly mysterious ways, bats are generally regarded with apprehension, if not actual fear, as reflected in the voluminous and ancient folklore relating to them. However, much public interest was aroused by the discovery of the use of supersonic waves, by at least some species, in obstacle avoidance (Griffin and Galambos, 1941). The ability of both sexes of certain species to store living sperm for periods of several months has received the attention of numerous investigators (Hamilton, 1943; Asdell, 1946; Pearson, Koford, and Pearson, 1952).

It is obvious that if the techniques of bat-keeping could be advanced to the point where zoological gardens could maintain exhibits of the purely insectivorous species, much good might be accomplished. Encouragement may be found in the extensive experience that has been gained in the keeping of insectivorous bats, especially of the families Vespertilionidae, Molossidae, and Rhinolophidae, for comparatively short periods, under laboratory or home conditions.

Gates (1936) gives an excellent account of the treatment of numerous small North American forms, his recommended diet consisting of chopped hard-boiled egg with cream cheese, cream, or milk added, and occasional chopped raw meat, vegetables, banana, yeast, dry malted milk, Ovaltine, or finely chopped nuts. Cut-up honey bees were also used, but the ubiquitous mealworm, the usual standby for insect-eaters, is not mentioned. No exact longevities are given, but several specimens lived for some months before being destroyed for purposes of investigation.

Gates reports lack of success with the Florida free-tailed bat (*Tadarida brasiliensis cynocephala*), but Constantine (1952) had satisfactory results with the Mexican free-tail (*T. b. mexicana*). Mealworms were presented to each animal by forceps and taken without difficulty. Amounts and frequency were increased gradually until the bat learned to feed for itself from a dish on the cage floor. It was found that individuals that did not learn to feed from the dish within a week were unlikely ever to do so.

Maintenance of several species in the laboratory is described by Orr (1958). Here the preferred food was the mealworm, with a supplement of multiple-vitamin concentrate. Some excellent longevity records are given, including 4 years, 5 months, 8 days and still alive for a Mexican free-tailed bat and a maximum span of 8 years, 3 months, 7 days for the Pacific pallid bat (*Antrozous pallidus pacificus*). Novick (1960) reports successful breeding of the Jamaican fruit-eating bat (*Artibeus jamaicensis*) in the laboratory. Principal foods provided were banana, canteloupe, and honeydew melon. In a paper describing laboratory procedure in the study of hibernation in bats, Mohos (1961) discusses the apparently wide distribution of rabies in the group and adds an extensive bibliography containing many references to work in this somewhat controversial field.

Some success has likewise been achieved with insectivorous bats in Europe. The editor of *The Countryman* (37 [2]:288) quotes Michael Brickmore as stating that he has kept greater horseshoe bats alive for nearly 2 years, and there are numerous other instances of similar feats. Kummerlöhe (1929) gives an extended account of a long-eared bat (*Plecotus auritus*) which lived with him for more than 14 months. Flower (1931) gives 4 months, 8 days for a noctule bat (*Nyctalus noctula*) kept in the Zoological Gardens of London—certainly an exceptionally good record for a public institution.

Judging from these accounts, there appears to be hope that increasing knowledge and skill may yet bring these fascinating creatures into the purview of the zoological garden. It seems reasonable to suggest that if individual bats were taught to feed from dishes, as practiced by Constantine (1952), and then liberated together in larger cages they should thrive as well as insectivorous birds similarly treated. Perhaps we may yet see flight cages devoted entirely to insect-eating bats. The use of red light (Davis, 1961), where practicable, could be of great advantage with this group.

Following are notes on those groups of bats which experience has already shown can be maintained under zoological-garden conditions if sufficient attention is given them.

FAMILY PTEROPIDAE

Fruit Bats or Flying Foxes

Probably because of the ease with which their food requirements, consisting principally of fleshy fruits, can be met, the members of this tropical Old World family do well in captivity. The larger species, which may have a wingspread of nearly 5 feet, are particularly attractive as exhibits. While they usually spend the days suspended from whatever supports may be provided, they are continually active in small ways, shifting their wings, dressing their fur, or quarreling with their neighbors. Their large, bright eyes return the viewer's gaze with an apparent awareness not ordinarily expected in a bat.

Unfortunately for American zoological gardens, the importation of fruit bats into this country has been prohibited by law, on the basis that escaped specimens might become menaces to fruit crops in the warmer sections. For this reason, experience with fruit bats in America has been rather limited. In 1902 eleven specimens of the Indian fruit bat (*Pteropus giganteus*) were received here, one surviving for 2 years, 6 months. Amelioration of these restrictions, made effective in 1960 for approved institutions, will bring welcome relief.

Experience in Europe and elsewhere, of course, has been much more extended, and fruit bats are commonly kept and bred in collections. No less than fourteen forms kept in the Zoological Gardens of London are listed by Flower (1929). Zuckerman (1953) reports eighty-eight births in four species in London. Some remarkable longevities in captivity have been established by bats of this group, Flower (1931) recording 17 years, 1 month, 26 days for the Indian fruit bat (*Pteropus giganteus*) in the Zoological Gardens of London and 19 years, 9 months, 25 days for the African collared fruit bat (*Rousettus leachii*) in the Giza Zoological Gardens.

Sányál (1892), in recounting his experience with the Indian fruit bat (*Pteropus medius* = *giganteus*), reports that, in addition to fruits, "they readily eat bread and milk, biscuits and boiled rice, and drink often, especially during the summer."

FAMILY PHYLLOSTOMIDAE

Leaf-nosed Bats

Besides purely insectivorous species, this large neotropical family contains several bats which include either fruit or flesh or both in their diets

(Allen, 1939:49–50). Such animals, of course, are much more readily provided for than are the insect eaters.

Apparently the only experience with the giant bat or false vampire (*Vampyrum spectrum*) followed the arrival from Trinidad on October 15, 1935, of Raymond L. Ditmars, then curator of mammals and reptiles at the New York Zoological Park, with four living specimens. These bats, largest of the neotropical species, proved to be extensively carnivorous, and during the journey north were fed on freshly killed pigeons (Ditmars, 1935). After arrival here they were kept on a diet of cut-up raw meat and such small mammals and birds as could be provided. They were exhibited in a large cage of $\frac{1}{2}$-inch-mesh wire cloth, with a darkened roosting shelter at the back. All lived for approximately 18 months, the greatest span being 1 year, 6 months, 15 days. A single birth occurred on July 14, 1936, the young bat surviving until May 16, 1937.

In investigations of the feeding habits of the Panamanian spear-nosed bat (*Phyllostomus hastatus panamensis*), Dunn (1933) found that bats of other species, mice, and small birds were killed and eaten by a captive specimen, in addition to fruit and insects. Thirteen specimens of this form received here in 1933, as well as a further eleven received in 1947, proved reasonably viable, the longest survival being 9 months, 4 days. In 1934 Dr. Ditmars brought six representatives of the species from Trinidad. All six of these animals lived in excess of 10 months, the best record being 11 months, 12 days.

The basic food used here was raw beef or horseflesh and banana, both cut into small bits. The meat was usually consumed first, but the banana was taken well as a second choice.

FAMILY DESMODONTIDAE

True Vampires

While local beliefs have attributed "bloodsucking" habits to bats of many kinds in many lands, the only species known actually to feed on the blood of other creatures are the members of the present small neotropical family. The first experiments in the maintenance of vampires in captivity probably were those made at the Gorgas Memorial Laboratory in Panama by Herbert C. Clark, director, and Lawrence H. Dunn. It was found that if provided with fresh blood which had been defibrinated to prevent clotting, there was no difficulty in keeping the animals alive for the duration of various investigations.

In 1933 Dr. Ditmars, accompanied by Arthur M. Greenhall, visited Panama and brought back a single female specimen of the Panamanian vampire (*Desmodus rotundus murinus*). This animal arrived in New York on September 21, 1933, gave birth to a single young on December 1, and died on December 24, the orphaned infant soon following. However, in this short span Dr. Ditmars was able not only to confirm the previous observation of Dunn (1932) that the bat laps the blood with its tongue rather than sucking it but also to demonstrate the fact by means of moving pictures (Ditmars and Greenhall, 1935). Following these investigations, King and Saphir (1937) were able to show that the flow of blood following the bite of a vampire is maintained by the sharpness of the incision and by licking of the wound, rather than by the presence of an anticoagulant, as previously supposed.

After this first arrival, a considerable number of specimens of the Panamanian vampire and of *D. r. rotundus* from Trinidad were received here. The maximum longevity achieved by *murinus* was 5 years, 7 months, 27 days and by *rotundus* 6 years, 3 months, 17 days.

Our latest importation of vampires consisted of four specimens of *murinus* received from Panama on April 26, 1947. Three of these animals had badly damaged claws, caused by the attrition of the fine wire mosquito netting with which they had been inclosed—a point to be borne in mind when bats are to be housed—and did not survive long. The fourth, less severely injured, was exhibited in the Small Mammal House for nearly 3 years, when our inability to secure fresh blood brought about its loss.

This animal was kept under a blue fluorescent light in a glass-fronted case about 3 feet in each dimension. During the day it hid in the crevices of a section of log, but at 4:00 P.M., when a Petri dish containing 1 ounce of defibrinated blood was introduced, the bat came down promptly and was readily observed.

The action of the creature on the ground is most interesting, since its wings can be so folded that it walks swiftly in quadruped fashion or leaps with surprising speed and agility. When feeding, the lapping action of the tongue may be plainly seen.

The principal difficulty in keeping vampires lies in the establishment of a certain and continuous supply of fresh blood. This should be caught, as it flows, in a sterile vessel and may then be whipped with wooden applicators or agitated with roughened glass beads. The fibrin will adhere to either applicators or beads, and the blood, no longer in danger of coagulation, will remain usable, under refrigeration, for at least a week. In older times fresh blood was readily obtainable at local abattoirs, but such an arrangement has now become impossible, and without it successful maintenance of vampires can no longer be accomplished here.

In an account of the well-known vampire colony formerly maintained at the Gorgas Memorial Laboratory in Panama, Trapido (1946) mentions several captivity births, including five in 1943 and 1945. Records of 27 individuals living for more than 5 years in the Laboratory are given, the maximum longevity being 12 years, 9 months. Work with vampires has been carried on at Cornell University by Wimsatt and Guerriere (1961), who report successful breeding under laboratory conditions.

· REFERENCES

ALLEN, GLOVER M.
  1939. Bats. Harvard University Press, Cambridge, Mass. 368 pp.
ASDELL, S. A.
  1946. Patterns of mammalian reproduction. Comstock Publishing Co., Ithaca, N.Y. 437 pp.
CONSTANTINE, DENNY G.
  1952. A program for maintaining the freetail bat in captivity. Jour. Mammal., **33** (3):395–97.
DAVIS, JOSEPH A., JR.
  1961. Red means go! Animal Kingdom, **64** (4):114–18.
DITMARS, RAYMOND L.
  1935. Collecting bats in Trinidad. Bull. New York Zool. Soc., **38** (6):213–18.
DITMARS, RAYMOND L., and ARTHUR M. GREENHALL.
  1935. The vampire bat. Zoologica, **19** (2):53–76.
DUNN, LAWRENCE H.
  1932. Experiments in the transmission of *Trypanosoma hippicum* Darling with the vampire bat, *Desmodus rotundus murinus* Wagner, as a vector in Panama. Jour. Prevent. Med., **6** (5):515–24.
  1933. Observations on the carnivorous habits of the spear-nosed bat, *Phyllostomus hastatus panamensis* Allen, in Panama. Jour. Mammal., **14** (3):188–99.
FLOWER, S. S.
  1929. List of the vertebrated animals exhibited in the gardens of the Zoological Society of London, 1828–1927. 1. Mammals. Zoological Society of London. 419 pp.
  1931. Contributions to our knowledge of the duration of life in vertebrate animals. 5. Mammals. Proc. Zool. Soc. London, pp. 145–234.

GATES, WM. H.
　1936.　Keeping bats in captivity. Jour. Mammal., **17** (3):268–73.
GRIFFIN, D. R., and R. GALAMBOS.
　1941.　The sensory basis of obstacle avoidance by flying bats. Jour. Exptl. Zool., **86**:481–506.
HAMILTON, WILLIAM J., JR.
　1943.　The mammals of the eastern United States. Comstock Publishing Co., Ithaca, N.Y. 432 pp.
KING, BARRY G., and ROBERT SAPHIR.
　1937.　Some observations on the feeding methods of the vampire bat. Zoologica, **22** (18):281–87.
KUMMERLÖHE, H.
　1929.　*Plecotus auritus* L. in der Gefangenschaft. Zool. Garten, Leipzig (N.F.), **2** (4/6):106–13.
MOHOS, STEVEN C.
　1961.　Bats as laboratory animals. Anat. Record, **139** (3):369–77.
NOVICK, ALVIN.
　1960.　Successful breeding in captive *Artibeus*. Jour. Mammal., **41** (4):508–9.
ORR, ROBERT T.
　1958.　Keeping bats in captivity. Jour. Mammal., **39** (3):339–44.
PEARSON, OLIVER P., MARY R. KOFORD, and ANITA K. PEARSON.
　1952.　Reproduction of the lump-nosed bat (*Corynorhinus rafinesquei*) in California. Jour. Mammal., **33** (3):273–320.
SÁNYÁL, RAM BRAMHA.
　1892.　A hand-book of the management of animals in captivity in Lower Bengal. Bengal Secretariat Press, Calcutta. 351 pp.
TRAPIDO, HAROLD.
　1946.　Observations on the vampire bat with special reference to longevity in captivity. Jour. Mammal., **27** (3):217–19.
WIMSATT, WILLIAM A., and ANTHONY GUERRIERE.
　1961.　Care and maintenance of the common vampire in captivity. Jour. Mammal., **42** (4):449–54.
ZUCKERMAN, S.
　1953.　The breeding seasons of mammals in captivity. Proc. Zool. Soc. London, **122** (4):827–950.

ORDER PRIMATES

•

LEMURS, LORISES, GALAGOS, POTTOS, TARSIERS, NEW WORLD MONKEYS, MARMOSETS, OLD WORLD MONKEYS AND BABOONS, GREAT APES*

In order of visitor attraction in the zoological garden, it is certain that, at least among the mammals, the primates have first place. While it is true that reactions to exhibits of these animals find expression on varying levels, there is no doubt that the universal interest they arouse is based on the obvious human comparisons they so readily evoke. For this reason if no other, it is essential that primates be shown under the best possible conditions.

The species most adaptable to exhibition are those of the higher categories, the marmosets being a nearly neutral dividing point, for while they are lively and attractive by day, their requirements are not always easily satisfied. The lemurs, while largely diurnal and easily maintained when obtainable, are not readily accepted by the visiting public as primates. The nocturnal forms of this and other groups have the usual disadvantages associated with activity at night only. Most popular, then, are the monkeys, the baboons, and the great apes, and it is to them that most attention is usually devoted by both management and visitors.

Monkeys have been kept in captivity from antiquity to modern times, their progress in this capacity having been traced in detail by Loisel (1912). Through the years, housing arrangements have grown from primitive beginnings to the stately buildings erected in zoological gardens in the late years of the nineteenth century and up to the present day. Actually, the innovations of current practice are largely matters of detail.

The use of glass to insulate animals from visitors was introduced near the turn of the present century, but there was much objection on the basis

* In considering the zoological groups, I have followed the arrangement of Simpson (1945), with the exception that the tree shrews have already been treated under insectivores. It should be pointed out that Hill (1953a) places the lorises and the galagos below the lemurs and their close relatives.

that the animals pined when deprived of human contact (Loisel, 1912, 3:164–65). Also, it was felt that the glass prevented proper circulation of air, producing, according to Loisel (1912, 3:392), unfortunate results in both London and Dublin. Abandoned generally in favor of bars and wire netting, glass has returned to use in fairly recent years. The development of air-conditioning apparatus now insures control of ventilation, temperature, and humidity, the close attention of well-trained keepers insures sympathetic treatment, and the risk of transmission of infectious diseases from visitors to animals is eliminated.

Glass brings with it a variety of problems. One of the objections of Loisel (1912, 3:392) is to the effect that glass greatly increases the work of keepers, a complaint still so realistic that the result, in practice, is too likely to be a soiled and unsightly barrier. However, various solutions for this important housekeeping problem have been developed. Experience here has shown that shock-resistant glass, in itself, is quite capable of restraining a heavy ape. I have seen an angry male gorilla, weighing in excess of 400 pounds, drive against a sheet of laminated Herculite, $\frac{1}{2}$ inch thick and measuring $3\frac{1}{2}$ by 4 feet, and strike it with his shoulder at full force, with no result beyond the frustration of his ambition. But this is largely beside the point, for the cleaning difficulty still remains. The erection of a glass partition at guard-rail distance from barred cage fronts, as used in the Great Apes House constructed here in 1950, has proved to be a practical solution where heavy animals are concerned.

A more direct method, used here for the smaller species, has proved equally successful. The interior of our Monkey House, built in 1901, was completely remodeled in 1958–59, providing twenty compartments of varying sizes, all equipped with glass fronts (Bridges, 1959). Eight of these cages, intended for the more powerful animals, such as baboons, are fronted with electrified glass, the current being carried by a conductive coating on the inner surface, an innovation already in use at the zoological gardens of Chicago and Milwaukee. The charge is very light, but as few monkeys care to touch it more than once, it is seldom soiled. It does, however, gather dust and it is then that its weakness may be revealed, for vigorous scrubbing by an overambitious keeper may damage the inner coating or remove it altogether. When young are born, as has frequently happened, the current of the individual cage is turned off until the infant is old enough to learn its lesson. The remainder of the cages are fronted with plain plate glass, with which some cleaning difficulty was anticipated. However, it was found that the smearing bound to occur is not noticeable from the reduced light of the public space, so that once-a-day cleaning is adequate. These cages, sealed against visitor contact, are individually heated and ventilated by forced draft.

While the use of glass is important in the control of atmospheric conditions within the animals' quarters, in improved visibility, and in elimination of offensive odors, a major value is the reduction of exposure to tuberculosis and other contagious diseases of man. Losses from such causes are always likely to occur among unprotected animals. Here, as an added precaution, no specimen is added to the collection until it has been subjected to a prolonged period of quarantine, from which it is not released until it has twice been negative, at 30-day intervals, to the tuberculin test (Brown, 1909; Schroeder, 1938; van Wagenen, 1950). During this time its internal parasite population is reduced to the minimum, and finally, it must give evidence by general appearance and reactions of good health and condition.

When primates are permitted the use of outdoor inclosures and the public is kept at a reasonable distance, the risk of infection appears to be negligible. On the other hand, while exposure to the open air was once considered to be necessary to the maintenance of good health in primates, the practice now seems more sentimental than essential. Various primates living here in excellent condition have not been so exposed for ten years or more. It appears that the psychological effects of artificial lighting and the physical benefits of controlled vitamin intake are capable of compensating for the lack of direct sunshine.

The subject of the exhibition of primates should not be left without some reference to the ever popular "monkey island." This definite bow to the general necessity of attracting visitors has had a turbulent career and has assumed a variety of forms. In the earlier stages unfortunate results often followed the liberation on such "islands" of large groups of baboons or monkeys without regard to sex or age. This practice led inevitably to serious fighting, heavy losses from mass infections, and an unfavorable impression on the public. For these reasons, the idea was largely abandoned. However, it has now been shown that there are at least three methods by which such exhibits can be operated with complete success.

First, there is the baboon group, probably seen at its best in the Parc Zoologique du Bois de Vincennes, Paris. The exhibit area is long and rather shallow, with simulated rock base and background. Viewed from one side only, it is separated from the public by a deep, broad dry moat. Easily accessible winter quarters are concealed by the rockwork. More important than the details of design is the method of operation. In the summer of 1951, as on previous occasions, the group was seen to contain about fifty adult Guinea baboons (*Papio papio*) in the approximate proportion of one male to ten females. Young animals were numerous and ranged from jealously guarded babes in arms to those already weaned. The latter were constantly active, riding on the backs of adults of either sex, staging mock battles, or tumbling each other about in riotous play. Among the mature animals there was no noticeable quarreling beyond local squabbles. I was informed by the late Professor A. Urbain, then director, that he considered the success of this attractive exhibit to depend upon the proportion of sexes, which was rigidly maintained, and upon the removal of any male that became overaggressive. Another solution has been found at the Detroit Zoological Park, where approximately sixty female Guinea baboons are maintained with but a single male. This certainly reduces the risk of fighting, and Mr. Frank McInnis, the director, assures me that from fifteen to twenty young are born annually. These are removed when one year old, thus preserving the ratio.

Next is the family group, suitable for a fairly small area. An excellent example of this type is a colony of pig-tailed macaques (*Macaca nemestrina*) inhabiting a miniature stone mountain surrounded by a water moat, at Artis, the zoological gardens of Amsterdam. Headed by an especially large and fine male with perhaps a dozen females and young, this group makes an excellent exhibit. Actually, it also exemplifies the ideal method of showing and keeping monkeys, whether indoors or out.

Finally, there is the "renting" system, probably practiced only in America. Under it, troops of young rhesus (*M. mulatta*) or other macaques, imported in spring for eventual laboratory use, are farmed out by dealers with the agreement that allowances will be made when the survivors are returned in the autumn. For the smaller institution, lacking suitable winter accommodations, this plan assures a lively summer exhibit, with no risk of serious fighting and at reasonably small cost.

FAMILY LEMURIDAE

LEMURS

In spite of the general public reluctance to accept lemurs as primates, most of these lowest members of the group make lively and attractive exhibits. Most of the six recognized species of *Lemur* with their somewhat hazy forms (Hill, 1953*a*) are predominantly or entirely diurnal, the ruffed (*L. variegatus*) and the black (*L. macaco*) being more definitely nocturnal,

All are docile in nature and easily maintained. Under favorable conditions they breed freely and agree reasonably well in family groups.

During the early years of the present century, lemurs were exported from Madagascar in some numbers and were readily obtainable. However, the enforcement of local protective regulations has become so effective that members of the group have almost disappeared from the open market, and only odd individuals are now occasionally available.

The lemurs in general are practically omnivorous in feeding habits (Hoogstraal, 1950; Hill, 1953b), although many individuals reject flesh in all forms. The following diet, on which a single ring-tailed (L. catta) was kept here, would apply equally well to any. The animal was a male, weight 6 pounds, 8 ounces. Items supplied daily were:

> 1 banana
> 3 oz. whole milk with 3 drops of vitamin concentrate
> ½ apple
> ¼ orange
> 2 slices of bread
> 2 oz. raisins
> 6 cherries or 2 oz. blueberries, in season
> ¼ head of lettuce
> 6 peanuts
> ½ carrot

Meat and fish occasionally offered were always refused, as were live insects and small lizards.

While most of the members of this genus are essentially arboreal, the ring-tailed is a rock dweller and spends much of its time on the ground. The tree-dwelling species naturally require adequate climbing perches, and Hediger (1950:90) points out the necessity for these animals to be able to get well above the floor level. Progress through the branches is accomplished with great speed, usually in an upright position, under propulsion of the hind legs. These arboreal forms seem to dislike coming to earth, where they are ill at ease (Rand, 1935).

A number of small members of the group, including the mouse lemurs (Microcebus) and the dwarf lemurs (Cheirogaleus and Phaner), have been assigned to the subfamily Cheirogaleinae. These diminutive, largely nocturnal forms feed principally on insects and fruit and thrive well in captivity. They are now so seldom imported, however, that they are practically unobtainable. At least one species, the lesser mouse lemur (Microcebus murinus), is of special interest as the smallest of the primates, with a total length of 11 inches, including the tail (Hill, 1953a:330).*

*See Addenda, p. 731.

Zuckerman (1953) records 71 births in the genus *Lemur* in the Zoological Gardens of London and 85 in the Giza Zoological Gardens, the dates indicating a fairly well-fixed season from March to June. The London births included seven pairs of twins and those at Giza three pairs of twins and one set of triplets. In the New York Zoological Park, between 1904 and 1931, there were nineteen births, as follows: ring-tailed lemur (*Lemur catta*), five; black lemur (*L. macaco*), four; ruffed lemur (*L. variegatus*), one; mongoose lemur (*L. mongoz*), nine. One pair of twins was produced in *L. mongoz* and one set of triplets in *L. catta*. With the exception of one birth on the last day of February, these occurred from March to June, confirming previous findings. Asdell (1946) gives 146 days as the gestation period for the black lemur (*L. macaco*).

Lemurs are markedly long-lived in captivity, the best record reported by Flower (1931) being 25 years, 6 months and "left alive" for a red-fronted lemur (*L. fulvus rufus*) in the Giza Zoological Gardens. Mann (1930:61) gives 28 years for a lemur of unstated species in the Zoological Gardens of Cincinnati. The mongoose lemur (*L. mongoz*) has done better here than any other, many having lived in excess of 10 years and one just a day short of 18. The beautiful black and white ruffed lemur (*L. variegatus*) seems somewhat less enduring than the others, Flower's best longevity being 13 years, 3 months, 14 days in Rotterdam. The maximum for the species in New York is 9 years, 5 months. A black lemur (*L. macaco*) lived here for 16 years, 3 months, 10 days.

FAMILY INDRIDAE

Sifakas, Avahi or Woolly Lemur, and Indris

Although apparently not at all uncommon in Madagascar (Rand, 1935), none of these curious lemur-like creatures has more than a scattered history in captivity. In the course of years occasional specimens have reached European institutions, but definite records are not easily come by. As far as I have been able to learn, none has ever reached a zoological garden in this country.

All of the group are largely, probably even entirely, vegetarian in diet, feeding on leaves, fruits, and nuts. This probably accounts for their scarcity and reputed delicacy in captivity since, as in the colobus and proboscis monkeys and others, suitable leafy diets are not easily provided, particularly on long ocean voyages. They are almost entirely arboreal, leaping through the branches from upright to upright. On infrequent visits to the ground, they progress by bounding much after the fashion of kangaroos (Rand, 1935). The sifakas (*Propithecus*) and the indris (*Indri*) are diurnal, but the little woolly lemur (*Avahi*) is nocturnal.

A single specimen of the crowned sifaka (*Propithecus diadema*) was received at the Zoological Gardens of London in 1908 (Flower, 1929). Hill (1953a: 554) reports that Coquerel's sifaka (*P. verreauxi coquereli*) was represented in the Berlin Zoological Gardens in 1912. Webb (1946) gives an account of a tame sifaka (*P. diadema*) kept at semi-liberty in Madagascar. This animal showed a preference for the leaves, blooms, and bark of the introduced eucalyptus but later learned to eat fruit and groundnuts (peanuts). Webb presented this animal to the zoo at Tananarive in 1939, and Hill (1953a: 566) reports that it was still living there in August, 1946. The animal had by that time accommodated itself to a wide variety of leaves, fruits, and nuts. Rand (1935) describes three specimens of *P. v. deckeni*, kept at semi-liberty in Madagascar. They were fed principally bananas, cooked rice, and bread, but it seems probable that this diet was largely supplemented by the foliage of trees to which the animals had ready access.

The only record of the breeding of *Propithecus* in captivity known to me is that of Paulian (1955), who reports that a female *P. v. deckeni*, kept at the Parc de Tsimbazaza, in Madagascar, produced a viable offspring in 1954 when mated with a male *P. v. coronatus*.

I find no reference to the avahi or woolly lemur (*Avahi laniger*) in captivity. It is much smaller than its relatives and differs from them also in being nocturnal. Aside from this peculiarity, its general habits and diet appear to resemble those of the sifakas and the indris.

Readily distinguished from the avahi and the sifakas by the extreme shortness of its tail, the indris (*Indri indri*) is a large animal of great individual variation in color. Its habits in general are those of its relatives. The only reference I find to the species in captivity is that of Hill (1953a: 610), who reports that "eight or ten specimens were received at the Paris Ménagérie in 1939, all of which died within one month."

FAMILY DAUBENTONIIDAE

Aye-Aye

Last of the lemur-like primates of Madagascar to be considered here is the aye-aye (*Daubentonia madagascariensis*). In spite of its secretive, nocturnal habits and the awe in which it is held by many native tribes, the aye-aye has been exhibited occasionally by various European zoological gardens since a single specimen, presumably the first to reach Europe alive, was received at the Zoological Gardens of London in 1862. As far as I am aware, the species has not been seen in America, but I have had the good fortune to see it twice: once in the Zoological Gardens of Berlin, in 1912, and again at Amsterdam's Artis, in 1920. Renshaw (1914) reports having noted the Berlin specimen and another at Cologne, both in 1914. Brightwell (1950) mentions two that were brought to the Zoological Gardens of London in 1931 by Cecil Webb, the well-known collector.

The principal food of the aye-aye is believed to consist of wood-boring larvae of beetles, which it exposes by means of its rodent-like incisors and extracts with the elongated, slender third digit of the hand. Hill (1953a:696) gives the pith of bamboo shoots and probably other vegetable material as further items of diet in nature, and in captivity, sugar cane, bananas, dates, mangos, boiled rice, coconut, and milk. Bartlett (1900), in describing the food which the aye-aye received at London in 1862, says: "This creature exhibits no inclination to take any kind of insects but feeds freely on a mixture of milk, honey, eggs and any thick, sweet glutinous fluid, rejecting mealworms, grasshoppers, the larvae of wasps and all similar objects." Bartlett also describes the method of drinking, which is to dip the fingers into the fluid and pass them rapidly through the mouth. The occasional lapping he mentions does not appear to be typical. It seems quite probable that the more orthodox requirements of the aye-aye account for its arrival in Europe with greater frequency than the leaf-eating members of the Indridae.

Flower (1931) gives four examples of longevity in captivity: 6 years, 5 months, 6 days and 7 years, 9 months, 18 days in the Jardin des Plantes, Paris; 4 years, 8 months, 9 days and 8 years, 10 months, 24 days in the Zoological Gardens of London. I know of no record of the breeding of the aye-aye in captivity.*

FAMILY LORISIDAE

LORISES, POTTOS, AND GALAGOS

While we here follow Simpson (1945) in the inclusion of the galagos in this family, it should be pointed out that Hill (1953a) assigns the galagos to the family Galagidae.

*See Addenda, p. 731.

The lorises and pottos agree in being both arboreal and nocturnal, habits which account, at least in part, for the general impression that these animals are dull, sluggish, and uninteresting. But under cover of night or even in the dull light of late evening, the slow-moving lorises and pottos go about their affairs with alert persistence, lacking only the ability to leap. All are more or less omnivorous, although there is some generic variation of preference for fruits or animal foods (Hill, 1947–48).

The slender loris (*Loris tardigradus*) is the sole representative of the genus, with four subspecies in Ceylon and two in southern India (Ellerman and Morrison-Scott, 1951). In general, this small, long-limbed, sharp-faced species should be readily distinguished from the forms of the slow loris (*Nycticebus coucang*), although it must be said that these differences are not always recognized.

The slender loris has never been common in collections, probably as a result of its inclination to delicacy and also of its irascible temper, which makes it desirable, except at mating times, to keep each specimen singly (Hill, 1937a). However, once settled in suitable quarters and provided with a suitable diet, a solitary individual is not especially difficult to maintain.

In the New York Zoological Park, we have used a glass-fronted, wire-topped box cage about three feet in each dimension, lighted by a blue fluorescent tube. Stout branches were provided for climbing and sleeping, and the floor was covered with dry leaves. While it is true that even in the dull light provided the animal was usually to be found in sleeping position, I have seen it, on occasion, prowling about the floor and searching in the leaves for possible edibles.

The food used here for a single animal consisted of about 2 ounces of canned dog food, one quarter of a banana, diced, and 1 ounce of whole milk with 1 drop of multiple vitamin concentrate added. Small lizards or any edible insects, when available, were always relished but certainly are not essential. As in all members of this family, milk was taken by dipping the hands and licking them dry. Notes on the feeding of the slender loris in captivity are given by Hill (1937a) and Phillips (1931).

Fed on the diet outlined above, a male received July 3, 1947, lived until July 23, 1954, a period of 7 years, 20 days. This is the greatest longevity known to me for this species. Records of the breeding of the slender loris in captivity are few, and I know only of those reported by Hill (1935) and Nicholls (1939).

The slow loris (*N. coucang*), as already noted, is a much larger and stouter animal than its relative, with rounder head and shorter face. Hill (1953a) lists ten forms, all from areas well eastward of the range of the slender loris, extending from Bengal to Indochina and southward through the Malay Peninsula to the neighboring islands.

Less aggressive and far more social than the slender loris, the slow loris is a fairly frequent inhabitant of the zoological garden. As Hediger (1950:85) points out, it is extremely sensitive to bright light, perhaps even more so than its smaller relative. Even under the very low illumination used for our specimens here, they are invariably found, during the daytime, curled up together in a seemingly inextricable mass on a high branch, fast asleep. In fact, when slow lorises are seen on the move by daylight, however halting the action, the observer may be certain that conditions are not to the animals' liking.

The slow loris is somewhat more frugivorous than the slender, so that in addition to the preferred item, diced banana, our animals receive a mixture of cut apples, oranges, and grapes. They are also given a mixture of canned dog food, fine bone meal, and cod-liver oil, fortified by the addition of a small quantity of raw ground horseflesh. The slow loris will also take milk, licking it from its fingers in the usual style of the family. Lizards and insects, when available, are readily taken.

It seems curious that for an animal kept with such frequency (a total of twenty have been received here since 1900) a search of the literature should reveal so few captivity breeding instances. Hill (1937b) records two cases of births from captive mothers, both possibly pregnant when received. Two births to a pair kept privately in Washington, D.C., followed by a third, on November 26, 1954, after the animals had been received at the San Diego Zoological Garden, are recorded by Pournelle (1955). In the light of this paucity of material, the following events are offered in some detail.

Of an adult pair of slow lorises of the nominate race (*N. c. coucang*) received here on June 21, 1941, the female died in March, 1944, having produced no young during her short stay here. The male lived alone for more than 4 years until, on November 10, 1948, a female of the large, light-gray race (*N. c. bengalensis*) was received. The animals were introduced with some trepidation but accepted each other with no show of hostility. On August 31, 1949, a young loris was found clinging to the fur of its mother's back. It was strong and active, with eyes open. Its color was intermediate between the father's brown and the mother's gray. It continued to thrive, and as the parents slept close together, the infant might be found on either, a fact I do not recall as having previously been recorded. Hill (1937b:387) says the female slow loris may deliberately place her baby on the ground, later picking it up. In our experience with this and following births I have never seen a young loris so treated nor have I ever seen a mother touch an infant, beyond the usual cleaning treatment with the tongue.

On June 4, 1950, a second young was born. Lacking experience and fearing the new offspring might be jeopardized, we removed the older one, then about 9 months of age. This proved to be a mistake, as the separated animal died 3 months later.

Subsequent births occurred on April 9, 1951, February 27, 1952, and February 11, 1953. On these occasions, previous young were allowed to remain with the family group, and it was found that the most recent arrival was as likely to be found clinging to an older sibling as to either of the parents. The original male died on April 29, 1953, but a younger male took over and twins were born on September 6, 1954, a single young on March 22, 1955, and twins again on December 31, 1958. The single youngster was reared, but in both cases the twins were found dead within a day or two. It was presumed that the female *bengalensis* was the dam in each instance, but in any case there were no further births, and this female died on July 14, 1961. In 1963 the single survivor of the colony was a male born on March 22, 1955.

Because of the conditions under which the animals were kept, it was impossible to determine the gestation period. It is given by Asdell (1946) as 174–80 days. All births were of single young, with the exception of the two instances of twinning noted. The widely spread birth dates are in accord with the investigations of Zuckerman (1932b), as indicating the absence of a restricted breeding period. The young appeared to be dependent upon their mother for at least 9 months, perhaps even longer. I have seen a youngster nursing when it was so large that parent and offspring were almost of a size.

Our best longevity for the typical race is that of the male that was received here on June 21, 1942, and died on April 29, 1953, after 10 years, 10 months, 8 days. The female *N. c. bengalensis*, received here November 10, 1948, died July 14, 1961, having lived even longer than her mate—12 years, 8 months, 4 days. Sányál (1892: 40) says a slow loris "lived as many as ten years" in the Zoological Gardens of Calcutta.

Strictly arboreal and nocturnal, the pottos are inhabitants of the forested areas of tropical Africa. The golden potto or angwantibo (*Arctocebus calabarensis*) is a small, slender creature, very suggestive of the slender loris, as the common pottos (*Perodicticus*) are of the slow loris. Its apparent scarcity in nature, combined with paucity of knowledge concerning its habits and the romantic attraction of both English and native names, have given the golden potto a definite place in the list of zoo desiderata. No living specimen has ever reached America, as far as I am aware, and only occasional individuals have been seen in Europe. Schwarz (1932) describes and figures an example that had then been living in the Zoological Gardens of Berlin "for some time" and which, he says, was the first of its kind to be seen alive in Europe. One was brought to the Zoological Gardens of London from the British Cameroons, in 1948, by Durrell and Yealland (Cansdale, 1948; Durrell, 1949); another was received by the same institution in 1960.

Concerning feeding preferences in captivity, Schwarz (1932) says the food of the Berlin specimen consisted of various fruits, cooked rice, and insects; Cansdale (1948) reports of the first London animal that it took freshly killed mice, mealworms, locusts, and some fruit. In describing the food of golden pottos collected in Africa, Durrell (1949) lists wild fruits, banana, avocado, pawpaw, canned pears, soft-bodied grubs and caterpillars, and the bodies of small birds, with special fondness for the brains. In his much-quoted account, Sanderson (1940) gives mashed plantain, minced raw meat, bird meat, soft-bodied grubs and insects, and small earthworms as items favored by specimens kept in the field in Africa. From this fairly extensive information it is evident that the golden potto is a creature of catholic tastes and should not be too difficult to maintain when available.

Both Berlin and London specimens appear to have been representatives of the northern form (*A. c. calabarensis*), from southern Nigeria and the Cameroons, rather than of the southern subspecies (*A. c. aureus*), from Río Muni and the Cameroons.*

The pottos of the genus *Perodicticus* are considered to be members of a single species, *potto*, with a number of subspecies, not all firmly established. They are readily distinguished from the lorises by absence of the rather striking markings of the former and by the abbreviated but still fairly lengthy tail. The obvious tail again serves as a distinction from the golden potto, but an even better character is the marked projection of the spines of the cervical vertebrae, which can readily be felt if the animal is held in the hands. Sanderson (1940) suggests that these spines are useful in repelling enemies, but Cansdale (1947) does not agree.

Pottos are fairly frequently imported, but for some reason, perhaps inadequate feeding, seldom survive long—2 years would certainly represent the average span in captivity. Of a pair of the reddish Congo potto (*Perodicticus potto ibeanus*), found from the eastern Congo to Kenya, received here on June 15, 1949, the female lived until June 30, 1957 (8 years, 15 days) and the male until May 14, 1958 (8 years, 10 months, 29 days).

*See Addenda, p. 731.

Like other members of this family, the pottos are omnivorous but often erratic in food choice. Cansdale (1947) considers fruit to form the bulk of the natural diet, with insects and other animal food taken when available. The pair of Congo pottos mentioned above received daily, between them, one half of a banana, diced, the preferred item; 2 ounces of whole milk, with 2 drops of multiple vitamin concentrate added; 2 ounces of canned dog food, with a speck of ground raw horseflesh added. They were also given a small dish of diced fruits and vegetables which they picked over, presumably finding some bits to their liking.

Little information is available concerning the breeding of the potto in captivity. In fact, the only record I find, beyond our own, is that of Mann (1948) who records the birth of a single young in the National Zoological Park in 1947. Our experience here has been actually frustrating since, in spite of several births, we have been able to learn next to nothing concerning procedure. Births to the female of the pair of Congo pottos already mentioned occurred on the following dates: April 20, 1951; September 4, 1952; April 17, 1953; November 2, 1953; July 16, 1954; February 24, 1955; and October 3, 1956. These dates do not appear to support the suggestion of Hill (1953a:189–90) that there is a fixed breeding season. In each case there was a single young. Birth appeared to take place at night, for in two instances the infant was found dead on the cage floor in the morning, while in the five others it was seen clinging tightly to its mother's fur when the keeper made his early check-up. On each of the five latter occasions, however, the young potto was later found on the floor in weakened condition and unable to maintain its grip when returned to the mother, which accepted it and licked it. None survived while in the mother's care. The infant born on April 17, 1953, measured $5\frac{1}{8}$ inches from tip of nose to the end of the $\frac{1}{2}$-inch tail at birth. Its weight was one ounce. All were pale gray in color, contrasting strongly with the reddish-brown of the parents.[*]

The young potto born on February 24, 1955, found cold and weak on the cage floor later in the day, was picked up, warmed, and eventually fully reared by hand. Reconstituted evaporated milk, fortified after the first week with a multiple vitamin concentrate and heated and fed from a doll's nursing bottle, proved adequate. Tame and gentle through the first year of its life, this animal eventually became too irascible for safe handling. It lived until February 2, 1960.

It should be mentioned that pottos are not overly social and that strange animals should be introduced with caution. They are capable of administering a severe bite and even animals of opposite sexes may inflict serious injury on each other.

[*]See Addenda, p. 731.

The galagos or bush babies are readily distinguished from the lorises and pottos by their long, bushy tails, large ears capable of retraction by folding, and by their saltatory or leaping mode of progression, aided by the noticeably long hind legs. Tails, of course, are non-prehensile and doubtless function as balancing organs, as in squirrels, during the long leaps of which the animals are capable. Hill (1953a:208) gives "upward of ten feet in an oblique direction" as not unusual.

Although the galagos are essentially arboreal and nocturnal, they are less rigid than their relatives in their adherence to these habits. Galagos may become active in early evening, and since most of the forms inhabit open bush country rather than dense forest, excursions on the ground are frequent.

The galagos are usually considered in two genera: *Galago*, containing the majority of species, and *Euoticus*, the needle-clawed galagos, distinguished by the extended, pointed nails of certain digits as opposed to the flattened ones of *Galago*. Odd specimens of *Euoticus* have been received occasionally by European zoological gardens, but none appears to have reached this country. Nothing seems to have been recorded concerning behavior in captivity. Distribution of the group covers most of Africa in favorable areas from south of the Sahara to Natal.

While galagos spend most of the daylight hours engaged in sleep, they are extremely active at night. To permit some exercise of their leaping powers, cages of fair size are required, particularly for the larger forms. A pair of grand galagos (*Galago c. crassicaudatus*) living here occupied a glass-fronted compartment 5 feet long, 4 feet wide, and 6 feet high. Moholi galagos (*G. senegalensis moholi*) seem content in a similar cage, about 3 feet in each dimension. Blue fluorescent tubes were previously used here, but red light (Davis, 1961) has proved to be more satisfactory. Stout perches should be provided, and since most, if not all, of the forms are hole-nesters, there should be a sleeping box. For a particularly timid specimen of the lovely, pale gray and white Monteiro's galago (*G. c. monteiri*) we furnished a short section of hollow log, laid on its side. To this he resorted during the daytime, although, rather curiously, I cannot recall ever seeing him there with his eyes closed. Dried leaves make excellent cage-flooring material, as the animals enjoy prowling through them. Galagos are fairly social in habit and agree well, at least in family groups. However, adult males are likely to quarrel, which brings up the difficulty in hasty determination of sex. The clitoris of the female is long and pendulous, easily confused with the male organ. The presence of a scrotum, of course, will end any doubts.

In feeding habits the galagos are truly omnivorous, for they will take fruits, vegetables, insects, and small vertebrates. As pointed out by Mann (1930:64), individuals vary widely in food preference, often from day to day. Daily amounts furnished here to a Moholi galago are as follows: 2 ounces of orange juice, sweetened with sugar and fortified by 1 drop of multiple vitamin concentrate; one half of a small banana, diced and mixed with bits of other fruits and vegetables; 1 ounce of canned dog food with fine bone meal added; 1 ounce of whole milk. A speck of raw meat is eaten occasionally, and small lizards (*Anolis*) are taken with avidity. One individual has been known to take as many as six of these small creatures in a single night. In drinking, galagos usually lap with their tongues but may occasionally dip their hands and lick them after the fashion of the lorises. This rather appalling array of food will certainly not all be consumed in a single night but is furnished to provide the dietary choices the animal seems to require. Cansdale (1944), reporting his experiences with Demidoff's galago (*G. d. demidovii*) in captivity in Africa, mentions insects, fruits, fruit juices, and milk as principal food items. Specimens of the related spectral galago (*G. d. phasma*) received here in 1949 from the Congo lived only just under a year each. They were kept on our regimen outlined above, suggesting that the much lighter diet suggested by Cansdale might be more suitable for the very small members of this genus.

Galagos are fairly free breeders in captivity, and numerous instances have been reported. The Moholi galago was bred in the Zoological Gardens of London as early as 1855 (Flower, 1929). Lord Lilford (1892) reports the birth of a Demidoff's galago in 1891, perhaps the first of this species to be born in England. Zuckerman (1953) lists three births of Garnett's galago (*G. crassicaudatus garnettii*) in 1929 and 1930 and twelve of the Moholi between 1927 and 1937 in the Zoological Gardens of London. Twins are usual, but single young frequently appear.

Lowther (1940) has given a detailed account of the birth and development of twin Moholi galagos kept under close observation. The gestation period was definitely established as 4 months. The young were left in the nest box and were not carried about clinging to the mother's fur as in the lorises and pottos. In this respect Lowther's observations are in opposition to the statements of Haagner (1920:19) and Shortridge (1934:14), both of whom say, in effect, that the young are carried about clinging to the mother. When transportation of the young was necessary, Lowther reports that the mother took them by the scruff of the neck with her mouth and carried them cat-fashion. The young male became sexually mature at 20 months.

For some reason, the only birth that has occurred here in this group was

that of a grand galago (*G. c. crassicaudatus*), born May 13, 1944, and died
May 22, 1958, after 14 years, 9 days. Hill (1953*a*:209) reports a Pangani
galago (*G. c. panganiensis*) as having been 11 years in captivity and still
alive. A specimen of the Moholi galago, born in the Zoological Gardens of
London on May 5, 1938, is listed by Jones (1958) as having lived until
October 10, 1948, or 10 years, 5 months, 5 days.

FAMILY TARSIIDAE

Tarsiers

Until fairly recently, very little was known of the natural history of the
tarsier (*Tarsius*) and even less of its proper treatment in captivity. This tiny
primate is distributed in a number of forms in the islands of southeastern
Asia, from Sumatra, Borneo, and Celebes to the southern Philippines.
Its small size and nocturnal habits, coupled with the dread its bizarre
appearance has aroused in the native peoples of the area, have made even
the collection of museum specimens difficult. Because of this scarcity of
material, the systematics of *Tarsius* have not yet been fully clarified. We
have used *Tarsius syrichta carbonarius* for the Mindanao animal, to which
most of the following notes refer, in compliance with the designation of
Hill (1953*d*;1955).

On July 9, 1947, Charles Wharton arrived in New York by direct flight
from Manila with a large collection of mammals, birds, and reptiles
gathered on the island of Mindanao, southern Philippines. Included were
thirty tarsiers (*T. s. carbonarius*), of which only one pair was retained here,
the remainder being taken to the National Zoological Park in Washington.
Eventually, many were distributed to other institutions, including the
zoological gardens of St. Louis, Chicago, and Philadelphia, although the
majority remained in Washington as a pool, still the property of Wharton.
General experience of durability was not encouraging, but the satisfactory
longevities of a few individuals suggest that better techniques might have
resulted in a considerable improvement of the average span.

While in the field, Wharton (1948) found that captive tarsiers would eat
grasshoppers (locusts), mealworms, small crabs, lizards, bird flesh, beef,
liver, and mice. The previous experiences of Cook (1939) add only
lizard eggs, fresh-water shrimp, and small fish to this list. Eventually,
Wharton struck upon the idea of injecting egg yolk and vitamin compound
into the abdomens of geckos immediately before these creatures, thus

fortified, were fed to the tarsiers. This innovation was completely successful and served to land the animals in New York in excellent condition.

When first received, our tarsiers were assigned to the Animal Nursery until permanent housing and feeding methods could be developed. For this purpose the animals were transferred from the tiny cubicles in which they had arrived to separate, small wood-and-wire cages. While in Wharton's care, the tarsiers had been accustomed to receiving injected geckos offered by forceps through the open doors of the cubicles. In larger cages this method of presentation was obviously difficult, so a variety of food was placed in each cage, in the hope that the animals might feed by themselves. During that first night one tarsier ate three baby mice, one small frog, five large roaches, and six mealworms, while the other took one baby (hairless) mouse, six roaches, and two mealworms. There was thus no difficulty in getting the animals to feed themselves. By the process of trial and error we eventually found that while the animals rejected any sort of vegetable matter they would accept bits of chicken, raw horseflesh, heart and fish cut into strips $\frac{1}{2}$ inch wide by $2\frac{1}{2}$ inches long, small lizards (*Anolis*), and milk, which they drank by lapping, as they did water.

Having established an acceptable and obtainable diet, we next undertook to introduce the animals to each other in a cage about 3 feet in each dimension. Released in strange quarters and uncertain in the rather bright light, the tarsiers moved slowly over the floor, apparently unaware of each other, until their bodies happened to touch. They immediately fastened to each other with both hands and feet in what seemed to be a death grip and went into the stiffened, convulsive state described by Wharton (1950). After perhaps a minute of this frightening embrace we separated the animals with some difficulty and placed them on the floor at opposite ends of the cage. As soon as they found themselves free of encumbrance, both leaped agilely to the branches that had been provided. There was no repetition of convulsive behavior, and the little creatures soon became friendly, often sitting together closely wrapped in each other's arms.

The tarsiers now seemed ready for transfer to permanent quarters and were removed to a glass-fronted, wire mesh–topped cage about 3 by 3 by 4 feet, in our Small Mammal House. This was lighted by the blue fluorescent tube then used here for nocturnals, and as a further concession to the known sensitivity of the animals to bright light (Hill, Porter, and Southwick, 1952) the open wire top was partly shielded from the skylight above. Stout branches were set upright in the cage, and the floor was covered with dry leaves. During this exhibition period the following food items were supplied each evening for the two animals: four strips each of raw horseflesh, heart, and fish; eight lizards (*Anolis*); twenty mealworms (each dipped in cod-liver oil), and 2 ounces of whole milk. Most, if not all, of this food was taken nightly.

Both animals appeared to be in excellent condition until on June 22, 1948, both died suddenly, having lived just under 1 year. Weights after death were 93 and 92 grams respectively, as compared with the maximum of 145 grams for a male in good health recorded by Hill, Porter, and Southwick (1952), and 220 grams for a captive female at the Yale University School of Medicine (Catchpole and Fulton, 1943).

On July 8, 1948, two further specimens were purchased from the diminishing Washington pool. Subjected to identical housing and feeding schedules, one of these animals lived until July 1, 1949, the other until July 12 of the same year, a period of just over 12 months. Post mortem reports on these animals, furnished by Dr. L. J. Goss, then staff veterinarian, showed degenerative conditions of liver and kidneys in three specimens, with no definite determination in the fourth. Internal parasite content in all four cases was negligible.

One male and two female tarsiers from the Washington pool were received at the Zoological Gardens of London on March 19, 1948. These animals were kept in the laboratory of the Reptile House and apparently were publicly exhibited for only a day or two. They were frequently viewed, however, by privileged visitors, including the present writer, and seemingly showed no indication of undue disturbance. These animals became the subjects of intense study, as reported by Hill, Porter, and Southwick (1952). At first these tarsiers were induced to take a variety of food by hand-feeding, but when they finally learned to feed themselves it was found that they favored mealworms (*Tenebrio*) so strongly that these, together with such insects of other sorts as might be available, became the main diet. The maximum number taken in one night by a single animal was ninety-nine. The mealworms were irradiated with ultraviolet rays to increase the vitamin D content. Milk was taken only when water was not available. One of the females aborted a single fetus at the 11 weeks' stage. The male of this trio survived until January 25, 1951, a period less than 2 months short of 3 years, the best completed longevity recorded up to that time.

By far the best results with the Wharton tarsiers were obtained by the Zoological Garden of Philadelphia, for of a pair purchased on July 28, 1947, the female lived until June 20, 1959, a period of 11 years, 10 months, 23 days (Ulmer, 1960). This individual not only greatly exceeded the longevities previously recorded but also gave birth to two single young, both of which died on the same day through "accidental injury" (Anon.,

1952*a*). So remarkable was this animal's durability that the following excerpts from a letter dated April 26, 1952, from Frederick A. Ulmer, Jr., curator of mammals in the Philadelphia Zoological Garden, are of special interest:

> I feed dead skinned mice, lizards (*Anolis*) and Orthoptera in season. Lizards are the most important and most desired by the animals. I . . . freeze them in paper cups covered with water. I also freeze insects for them and still they eat them readily. I have never fed them mealworms . . . and I think this is significant, for most of the others did get mealworms . . . because *Tenebrio* is host to the horny-headed worm parasite.
>
> I think that the damp conditions that prevail in our Mammal House all contribute to the well-being of the Tarsiers . . . . The surviving Tarsier is kept in a cage measuring about three feet wide by three feet deep by five feet high—solid on three sides, wire on top and glass in front. I have a fluorescent light in the cage but do not always put it on. Normally, the cage is not brightly lighted. The eyes of Tarsiers are very sensitive to ultra-violet and these should be kept away.

Non-use of mealworms for the Philadelphia tarsier is a point to be considered. Mealworms with a supplement of salt mixture and cod-liver oil added to the dish two or three times weekly were the diet used at the Yale University School of Medicine for the two tarsiers that lived there for over 18 months (Catchpole and Fulton, 1943). Mealworms were fed almost exclusively to the tarsiers at the Zoological Gardens of London, one living for nearly 3 years (Hill, Porter, and Southwick, 1952), and they formed a substantial part of the diet used here, one of our specimens surviving for just over 1 year. Post mortem examinations of the London and New York animals, at least, revealed no parasites that might have been transmitted by mealworms. Nevertheless, the point that the one tarsier that far exceeded all others in longevity received no mealworms cannot be disregarded. Also, it is reasonable to assume that the almost entirely natural diet used at Philadelphia is most nearly correct, even though some of its components are not always readily available.

FAMILY CEBIDAE

Douroucoulis, Titis, Uakaris, Sakis, Howlers, Capuchins, Squirrel Monkeys, Spider Monkeys, and Woolly Monkeys

This large family contains all of the New World primates, excepting only the marmosets. Extending from southern Mexico to northern Argentina, there is wide variation in form and habit, but there are also points of agreement. No American primate has either cheek pouches or callosities on the buttocks, as seen in most of the Old World monkeys. The howlers, capuchins, woolly monkeys, and spider monkeys are further distinguished by having prehensile tails, but this special advantage is not possessed by the douroucoulis, titis, uakaris, sakis, or squirrel monkeys. With the exception of the douroucoulis, all are diurnal in habit.

While the Cebidae in general are less resistant to the conditions of captivity than most of the primates of the Old World, several of the groups are of great importance from the point of view of the zoological garden and all are of interest. The capuchins, of course, are most commonly kept and probably are the most enduring, although closely followed by the spider monkeys. Most difficult of the group are the titis, uakaris, sakis, and howlers, all of which present maintenance problems as yet only partially solved.

As already noted, the douroucoulis (*Aotus*), sometimes known as night monkeys or owl monkeys, are nocturnal in habit and, in fact, are unique among the New World primates in this respect. At a quick glance, the douroucoulis have a superficial resemblance to the equally nocturnal pottos (*Perodicticus*), the long tails of the former being an obvious distinction. Many kinds of douroucoulis have been described, and the status of the group is somewhat confused. However, it appears (Hershkovitz, 1949) that all are forms of a single species, *Aotus trivirgatus*, and that many assigned names are synonyms.

A douroucouli of the Ecuadorian subspecies (*Aotus t. vociferans*) received here in July, 1950, was housed in a box-type cage about 3 feet in each dimension, with glass front and wire-mesh top. It was illuminated by the usual blue fluorescent tube and furnished with branches for climbing and an upright section of log with a large cavity. The quaint little animal might often be seen peering from the recesses of this sleeping compartment, even during daylight hours. It should be noted here that douroucoulis have reacted particularly well under red light (Davis, 1961).

This douroucouli's daily ration consisted of one half of a banana cut into 1-inch pieces, 2 ounces of canned dog food, 1 slice of raisin bread, chopped cabbage, lettuce and raw carrot, a few cherries or grapes, 2 ounces of whole milk, and 1 teaspoonful of sweetened orange juice containing 1 drop of multiple vitamin supplement. Walker (1954) mentions cottage (or pot) cheese, cooked egg yolk, and shelled nuts as being especially liked by a pet animal. Mealworms and small lizards, of course, are readily taken.

Douroucoulis are not frequently bred in captivity but several instances have been recorded. English (1934) reports on the hand-rearing of a single young born in England, Hill (1960:167) gives 1939 for a douroucouli birth in the Zoological Gardens of London, Mann (1950) lists a single birth in the National Zoological Park, and Stott (1954) includes this species among mammals bred in the San Diego Zoological Garden. Later births are reported at the Zoological Gardens of London (1959) and Frankfurt (1957).

General experience in maintaining douroucoulis in captivity has not been fully satisfactory. Bourdelle and Mouquet (1930) give 2 years, 6 months as maximum longevity in the Jardin des Plantes, Paris, while Mitchell (1911) reports 3 years, 9 months as the best for the Zoological Gardens of London, up to that time. The greatest span for a douroucouli in the New York Zoological Park is 7 years, 1 month, 13 days. Hill (1960:168) quotes Krieg as reporting the duration of a specimen in the Zoological Gardens of Berlin as "approximately twelve years" and gives 141 months for a douroucouli in the Zoological Gardens of London.

The gentle, beautifully colored titi monkeys (*Callicebus*) are seldom seen in American zoological gardens, probably because their well-known delicacy in captivity discourages the dealers who might otherwise import them. On the other hand, the Zoological Gardens of London have exhibited at least seven of the numerous described forms (Flower, 1929), and European arrivals in general appear to exceed those in this country. Nevertheless, I am able to find little in the literature that is useful in determining methods of procedure and therefore can record only our own limited experience.

Scattered specimens seen in the hands of dealers have seldom been in condition good enough to justify purchase. This situation undoubtedly accounts for the fact that a female dusky titi (*Callicebus cupreus cupreus*) that was received here on July 25, 1952, and lived until October 2, 1956, or 4 years, 2 months, 7 days, was the first titi we ever had. Apparently fully adult on arrival, this animal was extremely shy and unresponsive. Her slow, deliberate movements and general immobility gave a definite impression of sluggishness, counteracted by the alert brightness of her eyes. Eventually she gained sufficient confidence to come forward and accept food from the hand or softly touch a finger held within easy reach. However, she still retreated if the finger moved, however slightly, in her direction and would not willingly allow herself to be touched.

All efforts to induce her to make friends with more active sakis and woolly monkeys having failed, this titi was shown alone in a large glass-fronted compartment, 5 feet wide and long and 7 feet high. In it she seemed quite content, her social needs apparently satisfied by the frequent visits of her keeper, to whom she appeared to be strongly attached.

Unlike most monkeys, this titi was noticeably neat in feeding habits, choosing favored morsels with care and refraining from the usual messy scattering of the rejected remainder. Each day she ate perhaps 1 ounce of canned dog food, one half of a banana, a few bits of orange, apple, celery, and raisin bread and drank, directly by mouth, 2 or 3 ounces of whole milk. She received, also, the usual teaspoonful of sweetened orange juice containing 1 drop of multiple vitamin concentrate. A second specimen of the same race, received here on March 17, 1959, remained in good condition in 1963 and was well adjusted to the companionship of a douroucouli. A similar association in the Zoological Gardens of London is noted by Hill (1960:166).

Among the more baffling members of the Cebidae in captivity are the uakaris (*Cacajao*). The short tails of these animals distinguish them readily enough but as pointed out by Bates (1863) these abbreviated appendages in no way hamper the activities inherent to life in the tree tops.

The uakaris are more frequently imported into the United States than the even more delicate titis, but in general appear to thrive little better in captivity. However, as noted below, more encouraging results have been obtained in recent years, and it is evident that once firmly established, uakaris may be expected to survive longer than those of the past.

Of a pair of red uakaris (*Cacajao rubicundus*) received here on May 15, 1958, the female lived only to November 27, 1959, but the male was maintaining excellent condition in 1963. This animal lives alone in a glass-fronted compartment approximately 8 by 8 feet in width and depth and 10 feet high, provided with high shelves and natural tree branches. Here he is almost constantly active, leaping from point to point with surprising agility. His food consists of a variety of greens and fruits, monkey pellets, a small allowance of milk, and hard-boiled egg. Nuts of all sorts, regardless of hardness, are cracked with the teeth and eaten. Some uakaris refuse meat, but this individual has learned to take small quantities. Chameleons (*Anolis*) and mealworms are always welcome. The longevity established by this animal up to 1963 is the best so far obtained for this species here. A specimen received at the National Zoological Park on June 19, 1956, is reported by Marvin Jones (*in litt.*) to have died on June 4, 1961, after 4 years, 11 months, 16 days. Frederick A. Ulmer, Jr. (*in litt.*) informs me that a female received at the Philadelphia Zoological Garden on August 19, 1952, died of hepatitis on June 8, 1961, after 8 years, 9 months, 20 days, apparently the greatest longevity so far recorded for this species in captivity.*

The bald or white uakari (*Cacajao calvus*) appears to have been kept less frequently by zoological gardens than has the red and has given even less satisfactory results. Only two specimens have been received here: one in 1936 that lived for just over 6 months and the second on November 28, 1958, still living in 1963. Kept with the pair of red uakaris noted above and later with the male only, the bald uakari, although playful and active, was unable to cope with his more powerful cagemates and eventually began pointedly to avoid them. Removed to the company of a quiet albino toque macaque, the uakari was accepted at once and was allowed to continue the incongruous but obviously favorable association. Its feeding habits are those of the red uakari already noted. The longevity so far established is the best known to me for the species in captivity.

The black-headed uakari (*Cacajao melanocephalus*) has not been received here, but Mann (1930) lists a specimen as having lived for 3 months in the National Zoological Park.

The saki monkeys have acquired a reputation for delicacy, at least in the colder latitudes, that is hardly more encouraging than that of the titis and the uakaris. They are commonly described as morose, even sullen, and certainly their recorded life spans have usually been short. Mitchell (1911) reports seven months as the maximum for sixteen members of the genus in the Zoological Gardens of London. Up to 1953, the best result obtained with any saki in the New York Zoological Park was just 4 days short of 1 year for a black (*Chiropotes s. satanas*).

À far more optimistic picture, however, develops from experience at the San Diego Zoological Garden, where, under the salubrious conditions of California, really remarkable results have been achieved. When this institution was visited in the autumn of 1947, the collection included three saki monkeys: a female black (*Chiropotes s. satanas*), a male golden-headed (*Pithecia p. chrysocephala*) and a female thought to be a Humboldt's or hairy (*P. monachus*) but later identified as *chrysocephala* (George H. Pournelle, *in litt.*). These animals were kept in outdoor cages of good size, provided with stout branches, shelves, and small shelters. They were in superb condition, their long coats in perfect array and their bushy tails almost as thick as those of foxes. The black saki had been received in November, 1938, in very poor condition, but soon recovered her health in the warm atmosphere of the Reptile House (Anon., 1953a). She died on November 28, 1953, "after establishing a longevity record for her simian species. She had lived in the Zoo exactly fifteen years" (Anon., 1954).

*See Addenda, p. 731.

The golden-headed sakis arrived at San Diego on November 29, 1946. Their complete adaptation to conditions there is demonstrated by the production of single young in October, 1951, on an unspecified date in 1952, and on July 27, 1953 (Bode, 1953a). The male of this pair lived until August 26, 1960, or 13 years, 8 months, 28 days (George H. Pournelle, *in litt.*).

These San Diego sakis, therefore, have not only established longevity records far in excess of any others known to me but also two of their number have been responsible for what are probably the only instances of captivity breeding for this group. As given by Bode (1953a), the food provided for these animals "includes not only various fruits but vegetables, bread and milk, hard-boiled eggs and grains."

Encouraged by these marked successes, we secured a young male white-headed saki (*P. p. pithecia*) on July 1, 1953, and a pair of red-backed sakis (*Chiropotes satanas chiropotes*) on July 22, 1953. All were quite tame and in excellent condition, having been hand-reared in the Guianas by Charles Cordier.

The white-headed saki was kept by himself in the Animal Nursery, occupying a cage 5 feet long by 3 feet wide and high. He was gentle but not timid, extremely active periodically but never boisterous. He appeared to be mildly interested in the marmosets and other animals about him, but all efforts to persuade him to accept companionship failed. He reached out and touched a tiger cub brought to his cage, but recoiled from the rough antics of the red-backed sakis. The daily ration consisted of one banana cut into 1-inch pieces, one slice of a head of cabbage or lettuce, one slice of raisin bread, one half of a carrot and one half of an orange, all diced, six or eight grapes, $\frac{1}{2}$ ounce of canned dog food, of which he ate only bits, and one half of a hard-boiled egg. Night and morning he received 2 ounces of whole milk containing 1 drop of multiple vitamin concentrate and $\frac{1}{2}$ teaspoonful of cod-liver oil, which he consumed by dipping his fingers and licking them. Mealworms and lizards were ignored. All food was examined with care, the animal selecting special items and leaving the remainder unscattered. This saki lived until May 6, 1958, or 4 years, 10 months, 5 days.

The red-backed sakis presented many radically different characteristics. In no sense dull or morose, they were active, rough, and boisterous, running and leaping in play with abandon. In spite of their apparently bold demeanor, they showed strong fear reactions when the tiger cub was presented to them. They were housed in a glass-fronted cage approximately 10 feet long, 5 feet wide, and 7 feet high in the Small Mammal House, well furnished with rock work and natural branches.

In contrast to the dainty feeding habits of the white-headed saki, the red-backs exhibited the voracious appetites and wasteful habits generally seen in more hardy species. Each day, for two animals, the following food was provided: 1 ounce canned dog food (all eaten), two oranges, three apples, four bananas, one half of a carrot, four stalks of celery (all diced), two hard-boiled eggs (halved), fifteen grapes, two slices of a head of cabbage or lettuce, and two slices of raisin bread, diced. Eight ounces of whole milk (or its equivalent in evaporated milk) with 2 drops of multiple vitamin concentrate and 2 teaspoonfuls of cod-liver oil added were given morning and night. This was taken directly by mouth. Not all of the solid food was eaten, of course, much of it being scattered and soiled in the course of selection. While the red-backed sakis took the dog food eagerly, they rejected raw meat, mealworms, and lizards.

The female lived until April 16, 1956, or 2 years, 8 months, 25 days, the male until November 18, 1956, or 3 years, 3 months, 27 days. Frederick A. Ulmer, Jr., has informed me (*in litt.*) that a female Humboldt's or hairy saki lived in the Philadelphia Zoological Garden from August 19, 1952, to October 10, 1959, or 7 years, 1 month, 21 days. Although it still seems unlikely that zoological gardens in northern latitudes can hope to duplicate the successes of San Diego, at least as far as longevity is concerned, there is reason for the expectation that proper care and diet will bring improvement over the rather dismal results of the past.

Largest of the American primates are the howling monkeys or howlers (*Alouatta*), Beebe (1910:325) reporting an adult male red howler, *Alouatta seniculus*, shot in British Guiana, as weighing 20 pounds. The howlers are widely distributed in tropical America, extending from southern Mexico to northern Argentina, and at least five species, with numerous subspecies, are known. The name, of course, originates from the booming voice of the male, amplified by an enlargement of the vocal apparatus produced by development of the hyoid bone (see Hershkovitz, 1949). This chamber is much smaller in the female, resulting in lessened volume. The overpowering sound made by a troop of howlers, audible for great distances through the tropical forest, has been described as terrifying, but actually it always sounded to me like a distant storm, echoing tremendous winds and crashing trees. Carpenter (1934) concludes that the roaring of howler monkeys has to do with "inter-group coordination," rather than with the frightening of enemies, as has sometimes been suggested.

In spite of their broad distribution and comparative abundance, few howlers are imported, and the group is seldom represented in zoological gardens. This appears to be due to the temperamental inability to adapt to captivity conditions, commonly known as "moroseness," as well as to the specialization of feeding habits. As observed in detail by Carpenter (1934), the food of howlers in nature consists largely of leaves, buds, and blossoms, supplemented by seed pods and certain nuts. It is obvious that unless any animal can accommodate to food substitutes readily obtainable, it cannot survive under artificial conditions. The howler is no exception to this rule.

It is because of these obstacles that howling monkeys have fared so poorly in captivity. Mitchell (1911) gives an average of $3\frac{1}{2}$ months and a maximum of 11 months for nine members of the genus in the Zoological Gardens of London. Up to that time and even after it, our own results were no better. However, there appeared to be hope for improvement when, in 1920, a young red howler (*Alouatta seniculus*) was brought to us by William Beebe and taken to the home of Raymond L. Ditmars, then curator of mammals and reptiles. There it was cared for by Miss Gladys Ditmars and lived until June, 1922, a period of approximately 18 months (Ditmars, 1922). This record was improved upon by a red howler received here on April 29, 1925, and kept in the Reptile House, where it survived until September 16, 1928, or 3 years, 4 months, 18 days. A male of this species received at the Lincoln Park Zoological Gardens, Chicago, on May 22, 1951, lived until October 16, 1956 (R. Marlin Perkins, *in litt.*). This longevity of 5 years, 4 months, 24 days is the best known to me for any captive howling monkey. Mr. Perkins adds that this animal was a well-grown pet when received and was unusually active for a howler. It eventually was found to have become anemic and was given a daily dosage of 4 drops of an iron product known as Mol-iron Liquid, to which he responded so well that Mr. Perkins now considers this supplement to be essential to good health in captive howling monkeys.

On July 20, 1950, Charles Cordier returned from Ecuador with an infant male mantled howling monkey (*Alouatta villosa aequatorialis*) bearing the fairly descriptive name of "Ugly." This tiny creature was still being bottle-fed, a system that was continued in our Animal Nursery. Within a few days Ugly began nibbling ripe banana, the amount increasing daily. He continued for some time to receive reconstituted evaporated milk with $\frac{1}{4}$ cup of Pablum and 2 drops of multiple vitamin concentrate added for each cup of milk. This was administered at frequent intervals with a small nursing bottle.

Ugly grew rapidly and at an early age was provided with a small rough towel, changed daily. Like most young primates he became deeply attached to this bit of cloth, using it not only as a cape but as a means of retirement, sometimes covering himself completely. Eventually it had to be removed, following a period of several days during which Ugly refused to leave his shelter even for food. Prompt return to normal followed, and the towel was never returned.

After the first year, when Ugly had abandoned the nursing bottle, he was kept on the following schedule:

Early morning: 8 oz. reconstituted evaporated milk, thickened with cooked rolled oats or Pablum, with 2 drops of multiple vitamin concentrate added. This he drank from a dish, directly by mouth.

Midmorning: ½ head of raw cabbage, sliced
3 slices of raisin bread, diced
1 carrot
3 stalks of celery

Afternoon: 1 hard-boiled egg
1 dozen grapes
1 sweet apple, diced
1 oz. canned dog food

Evening: 8 oz. milk gruel, prepared as in morning

Oranges or orange juice were given with caution, in very small quantities, as the least overdose resulted in severe diarrhea.

Up to the age of two years Ugly welcomed visitors by creeping forward in a crawling position, growling softly. He then sought the proffered finger or knuckle, upon which he chewed frantically but gently. After passing this age his temper became more uncertain, except toward his keeper. He had acquired the ability to roar, too, and did so on frequent occasions.

Between the ages of two and three Ugly shared his double cage, at intervals, with an adult female weeping woolly monkey (*Lagothrix cana lugens*), an animal of almost identical temperament. During these periods they ignored each other, never becoming friendly nor actively quarreling. When the cage was approached the first monkey to engage attention was allowed to enjoy it, while the other sulked at a distance.

By the time Ugly was three years old, he had become so irascible that he was considered unsafe even by his keeper, Mrs. Helen Martini, a woman of great sympathy and feeling. He was therefore removed to a cage in the Small Mammal House, similar to the one occupied by the red-backed sakis. Here he lived until May 18, 1954, establishing a record of 3 years, 9 months, 28 days. At the time of death Ugly was quite black throughout and weighed 11.44 pounds or 5.2 kilograms.

Regular checking by L. J. Goss, then our veterinarian-pathologist, during Ugly's lifetime showed him to be entirely free from blood and intestinal parasites, a situation confirmed at post mortem examination. The card on which the results were recorded gives the cause of death as acute pulmonary edema. An added line reads: "Spasmodic inappetence for three to four weeks prior to death."

Summing up, there appears to be at least one serious obstacle to keeping howlers for lengthy periods. Taken young enough, the animals' basic temperamental resistance can be overcome. Also, food requirements can then be reconciled to a diet that can readily be supplied, provided there is sufficient leafy bulk. But the psychological necessity for companionship, apparently especially strong in howlers, was no longer satisfied in the case of Ugly, when his changing nature blocked established human contacts and he would accept no other. It may be that the solution lies in rearing a pair of infants together. If so, this remains to be done.

Best known and hardiest of the Cebidae are the capuchins or sapajous, perhaps more commonly known as "ring-tails." Ranging through the heavily forested areas of the American tropics from Honduras to Paraguay are numerous forms the status of which has long been in dispute. However, the four species designated by Hershkovitz (1949) are now generally accepted, although Hill (1960) retains *griseus* for *nigrivittatus*. These specific names, as used here, are *Cebus capucinus*, the white-throated capuchin; *Cebus albifrons*, the white-fronted or cinnamon; *Cebus apella*, the hooded or horned; and *Cebus nigrivittatus*, the weeper. Numerous subspecies are recognized but are seldom determined in zoological-garden practice.

In general, the capuchins are robust animals of medium size. The prehensile tail lacks the hairless area of the underside, near the tip, as seen in spider, woolly, and howler monkeys. It is usually carried low, with a distinct forward curl, which gives rise to the common designation of "ring-tail." Temperamentally, the capuchins are usually active and alert, with less inclination toward aggression than most others. When brought into captivity at an early age they often remain gentle through life, a character once utilized to great advantage by itinerant organ-grinders.

In zoological gardens capuchins are often kept in mixed groups, and it must be said that this method is reasonably successful, if the occasional quarrelsome individual is removed and strangers are not introduced to established units. However, as with most monkeys, best results are obtained with animals kept in pairs or family groups.

While the capuchins are more resistant to adverse conditions than other American primates, they still are sensitive to low temperatures and must be carefully protected. Dampness, of course, is as much to be avoided as cold. The capuchins are not particularly specialized in feeding habits, but waste and soil as much as they eat. For this reason it is necessary to supply more food than the quantity that will actually be consumed, which is readily determined by practice. Bananas, oranges, mealy apples, carrots, sweet or white potatoes, raw or cooked, lettuce or cabbage, raisin bread, small amounts of raw chopped meat or canned dog food, peanuts, and a scattering of sunflower seeds with monkey pellets, provide a well-rounded diet. In addition, we furnish daily for each animal about 6 ounces of reconstituted evaporated milk with coddled egg, Pablum, and ½ teaspoonful of cod-liver oil added.

Under favorable conditions and especially when kept in pairs, capuchins quite frequently breed in captivity. Only one, a hooded (*Cebus apella*), has been born here. Mann (1930) records one birth each for *Cebus capucinus* and a mating of that species with *Cebus apella*, while Zuckerman (1953) gives four births of various forms in the Zoological Gardens of London. Stott (1954) lists *Cebus albifrons*, *Cebus capucinus*, and two forms of *Cebus fatuellus* (= *apella*) as having been bred in the Zoological Garden of San Diego. However, the mere fact of the breeding of a species becomes insignificant in the light of the report of Stott (1953a) that approximately twenty young have been sired by a male hooded capuchin known as "Irish" with two successive females at San Diego. Single young are usual in *Cebus*, but twins were produced by the San Diego pair in 1952. The gestation period is given by Asdell (1946) as 6 months.

The relative hardiness of capuchin monkeys in captivity is attested by established records. Mann (1930) gives 8 years for a white-throated (*Cebus capucinus*) in the National Zoological Park, while our best here is 11 years, 7 months, 12 days, for a hooded (*Cebus apella*). Flower (1931) reports 18½ years and still living in the Giza Zoological Gardens, and "about 25 years" in the Zoological Gardens of London, both figures for *Cebus fatuellus* (= *apella*). He adds the record of Brown (1925) for an animal of the same species which was "25 years old when received" at the Philadelphia Zoological Garden and which died 2 years and 18 days later. There appears to be nothing to equal the record of the male hooded, Irish, received at the San Diego Zoological Garden in 1927 and still living in 1963 (George H. Pournelle, *in litt.*). His age on arrival was estimated to have been four years (Anon., 1952b).*

The gay and spirited little squirrel or moss monkeys (*Saimiri*) have a special appeal because of their active habits and quaint appearance. Most frequently imported are the forms of *Saimiri sciureus* with black muzzles and grizzled crowns from northern South America, while the black-crowned

*See Addenda, p. 732.

golden or red-backed squirrel monkey (*S. örstedii*) is occasionally brought from Central America.

When first received, squirrel monkeys are almost invariably heavily parasitized and require careful checking and treatment. Once cleared, they should be given ample quarters that will provide adequate space for exercise and protection from drafts and dampness. A sleeping box containing hay or shredded paper should be provided, and the temperature should be maintained at not less than 72°–75° F.

Squirrel monkeys here are given diced fruit, especially banana, cut lettuce, raisin bread, hard-boiled egg, bits of canned dog food with a few drops of cod-liver oil added, and reconstituted evaporated milk in the ratio of 1 ounce per animal, with 1 drop of multiple vitamin concentrate added. Mealworms and small lizards (*Anolis*) are given in late afternoon and are eagerly awaited.

Unfortunately, while squirrel monkeys appear hardy and robust, experience does not seem to justify the expectation. Mitchell (1911) gives an average longevity of 9 months for forty-four specimens of *S. sciureus* in the Zoological Gardens of London, his maximum of 9 years being discredited by Flower (1931) as a clerical error. Mann (1930) records 1 year, 9 months for the same species in the National Zoological Park, while George H. Pournelle (*in litt.*) gives 4 years for a specimen in the Zoological Garden of San Diego. Our best here is 3 years, 9 months, 27 days; Jones (1958) reports 6 years, 4 months, 12 days in the Philadelphia Zoological Garden. All of these records are eclipsed by that of a female *S. sciureus* kept in London by Hume and Smith (1951); Hill (1960: 298) says this animal was "over twenty years old when she died."

Up to 1952 there appear to have been no births of squirrel monkeys in captivity. In that year the female of a pair of *S. sciureus* received at the Bristol Zoo, England, in 1950, produced a single youngster, Hill (1960:297) giving the date as September 24. Later single births in the United States include three at the San Diego Zoological Garden: April 14, 1958 (George H. Pournelle, *in litt.*), August 15 and September 20, 1959 (Anon., 1959*a*), and one at the National Zoological Park on April 12, 1959 (Theodore H. Reed, *in litt.*). The Annual Report of the Cheyenne Mountain Zoological Park, at Colorado Springs, Colorado, for 1959, lists squirrel monkeys as having been born there on August 9 and August 24 of that year. A second birth at Bristol occurred on September 2, 1961 (Sherborne, 1962).*

The spider monkeys (*Ateles*) are aptly named, for their comparatively

*See Addenda, p. 732.

slight bodies and disproportionately long and slender limbs are strongly suggestive of furry arachnids. Their delicate appearance, however, should not be taken as indicating lack of strength, for an adult male is a powerful and sometimes aggressive animal. I can recall the escape of such a specimen, pressed against the ground in a catching net, by raising the ring above his head without the least difficulty, in spite of my utmost effort to hold it down. The tail is probably more completely prehensile than in related groups, and the hands, either lacking thumbs or retaining only tiny tubercles to represent the missing digits, are well adapted for use in speedy movement through the trees.

Spider monkeys range from southern Mexico over most of tropical South America, and many names, often untenable, have been assigned. However, the confusion has been largely clarified by Kellogg and Goldman (1944), who recognize four species, each divisible into two or more subspecies. Most commonly imported are the red-faced black spider monkey (*Ateles p. paniscus*) from northeastern South America and the more or less black and buff forms of *Ateles geoffroyi* from northwestern Colombia, Central America, and Mexico.

Among the Cebidae, the spider monkeys are second only to the capuchins in point of hardiness. Even then they are not as commonly seen as might be expected, since their hardiness is only relative. They are sensitive to cold and dampness and seem to be especially susceptible to tuberculosis.

Spider monkeys require spacious quarters, and if these are provided do well in groups, especially if these are formed of one adult male and several females, a ratio conforming, in general, to organization in nature (Carpenter, 1935). In selecting animals for such exhibits it is important to note that the clitoris of the female is long and pendulous, while the penis of the male is comparatively short and inconspicuous (see Pocock, 1920).

The zoological gardens at Taronga Park, Sydney, and San Francisco, California, both have excellent examples of spider monkey groups. The Taronga animals are shown in a large, high wire inclosure, situated on a steep slope and provided with conveniently placed branches. When seen in 1928 the monkeys were in beautiful condition, a tribute to both climate and care. At San Francisco a dozen or more animals are shown in a modern, moated area where, again, their condition leaves nothing to be desired. In the zoo at Denver, Colorado, spider monkeys are confined to a small island by a water moat 12 feet wide and 4 feet deep at the outer wall. This barrier was completely effective, probably because inclosed shrubs and branches did not provide sufficient height for the "outward and downward" leaps of thirty or more feet ascribed to spider monkeys by Carpenter (1935).

Spider monkeys, in fact, seem reluctant to enter water but certainly will do so under some circumstances. We once placed a half-dozen on a small island in one of our lakes, separated from shore by perhaps 35 feet of water about 18 inches deep. All went well for a few days, after which one animal was found to have reached the mainland. It was captured and replaced and a careful watch kept. This resulted in my being able to witness a mass escape as the entire troop walked through the water one after another, each nearly upright and with one hand clutching the upraised tail near its tip.

Spider monkeys are fed here exactly as noted above for capuchins. The field studies of Carpenter (1935) resulted in an estimate that fruits and nuts form 90 per cent of the food of spider monkeys in nature, the balance being made up of buds and flowers and probably larvae and insects. No evidence was found that birds' eggs or young birds are eaten. Nevertheless, the small amounts of raw chopped meat or canned dog food furnished are readily taken and appear to be essential.

Spider monkeys occasionally breed in captivity, although they do not reproduce as freely as do the capuchins. No *Ateles* has been born here but Mann (1949, 1950) reports single births of *Ateles geoffroyi vellerosus* in 1948 and 1949, while Stott (1954) lists both the golden spider monkey (*Ateles g. geoffroyi*) and the red spider monkey (*Ateles g. panamensis*) as having been bred in the Zoological Garden of San Diego. Twin spider monkeys of an undesignated form, born at the Myrick Park Zoo, La Crosse, Wisconsin, on February 8, 1960, are figured in the *Newsletter* of the American Association of Zoological Parks and Aquariums for June, 1960. Asdell (1946) gives the gestation period in *Ateles ater* (=*p. paniscus*) as 139 days.

Records of the duration of spider monkeys in captivity seem to indicate a comparatively low viability. Mann (1930) gives 4 years, 1 month for *Ateles geoffroyi* in the National Zoological Park; our best here is 5 years, 1 month, 26 days for *Ateles p. paniscus*; and Flower (1931) reports 6 years, 4 months, 18 days for *Ateles ater* (=*p. paniscus*) in the Zoological Gardens of London. These established longevities make all the more remarkable a record of 18 years for *Ateles geoffroyi* in the Chicago Zoological Park reported by Rabb (1960) and that of a female red-faced black spider monkey (*Ateles p. paniscus*) in the Prospect Park Menagerie, Brooklyn, New York. I am informed by John Galm, supervisor of menageries, that this animal was received there on June 28, 1935, and died on July 15, 1955, after 20 years, 17 days. When seen in 1953 she was in superb condition, with an especially fine development of the broad tail-base typical of this race.

A specimen of the interesting and little-known woolly spider monkey (*Brachyteles arachnoides*), a native of eastern Brazil from the State of Bahía to São Paulo (Cabrera, 1957), was received here on April 24, 1959. Collected in the latter area as an infant, she was so completely tame and gentle as to be strongly suggestive of a woolly monkey (*Lagothrix*) of similar age, except that her pelage, while thick, lacked the plushlike quality found in the latter. Kept in the company of a young woolly of comparable temperament in a compartment of our Monkey House, she seemed to thrive at first but eventually succumbed, on May 27, 1960, to the last of a series of unaccountable and debilitating internal parasite invasions. Her food was the same as used here for woolly monkeys, and although she was more particular than most in the choice of items, she fed well during intermittent periods of good health. The species appears to have been received rarely in Europe, an arrival at the Zoological Gardens of Leipzig being noted by Schneider (1937). Our specimen is presumed to have been the first to reach America alive.

Most sought of the Cebidae as family pets are the woolly monkeys (*Lagothrix*). Imported specimens are usually young individuals that have been hand-reared by Indian women and are invariably as gentle and trusting as they are reputed to be. The short, dense coat is soft and velvety, and the bare, black face has an appeal of its own. At the early age at which they are usually received, young woolly monkeys seem to have a special need for companionship and sympathetic care, to which they respond with gratifying results. At the same time, they are sensitive to low temperatures and dampness and appear to have low resistance to infections. As pointed out by Walker (1954), "These monkeys do not reach maturity in captivity under the conditions usually provided." An average duration of 5.2 months, with a maximum of 16 months for fourteen specimens of Humboldt's woolly monkey (*L. humboldti* [= *lagotricha*]), in the Zoological Gardens of London, is reported by Mitchell (1911). Some improvement in results is shown by an average of 14.3 months, with a maximum of 42 months, for thirty-eight specimens of various forms received and deceased here between 1911 and 1953. However, woolly monkeys surviving for more than 2 or 3 years in captivity are still exceptional.

This short expectation is presumably responsible to a large extent for the continuing reputation of woolly monkeys for gentleness. The few really mature animals I have seen have generally been no longer fully trustworthy. Also, once the vicissitudes of youth have been safely passed and resistances established, woollies may become reasonably rugged and well able to hold their own in mixed groups. A large adult female weeping woolly (*L. cana lugens*), purchased from a small dealer in Trinidad because of her tameness, was received here on April 16, 1951. It soon developed that while this animal was still apparently gentle, she was not averse to an occasional nip. This tendency finally developed to a point where she was actually unsafe for handling. She was then introduced to a mixed group of female monkeys of comparable size, with which she lived on equal terms until her death on July 17, 1955.

While she was still segregated, the daily menu of this woolly was as follows:

Early morning:	4 oz. reconstituted evaporated milk
	1 drop multiple vitamin concentrate in 1 oz. sweetened orange juice
Midmorning:	Diced fresh vegetables and greens
	1 hard-boiled egg
	2 oz. canned dog food
Afternoon:	Diced fruits
Evening:	4 oz. reconstituted evaporated milk

The difficulties encountered in carrying woolly monkeys through to adulthood probably account for the paucity of breeding records. However, some details of such an event have been supplied to me by Arthur Watson, director of the zoo at Baltimore, Maryland. A female Humboldt's woolly monkey (*L. lagotricha*) was received on December 31, 1949, and a male of the same species was obtained on February 13, 1951. The animals quickly became attached to each other, and on January 2, 1954, the female gave birth to a male young. The reactions of the male to the infant were interpreted as dangerously aggressive and he was removed. The young animal was well cared for by the mother until September, when symptoms of rickets developed and it was removed to a private home. It appeared to make a good recovery but died of pneumonia on October 9, 1955, after return to the zoo. A second birth, this time of a female, to the same pair occurred on October 21, 1956. This infant was removed immediately and fully reared by hand. It lived until August 4, 1961, when it died of a heart ailment. No actual matings were observed, so that the gestation period was not obtained. Asdell (1946) gives 139 days for this species. The breeding female died on April 11, 1960, after 10 years, 3 months, 11 days. The male was still living in 1962, having then exceeded the remarkable longevity of the female.

To the longevities already noted the following should be added: 6 years, 5 months, 9 days for a brown woolly in the Zoological Garden of San Diego (George H. Pournelle, *in litt.*); 7 years, 4 months, 23 days in the

Zoological Gardens of London for Humboldt's (Jones, 1958); and 8 years, 3 days for the same species in the Philadelphia Zoological Garden (Jones, *loc. cit.*).

FAMILY CALLITHRICIDAE

Marmosets

With their bright, beady eyes, alert expressions, and fully diurnal, active habits, the marmosets of tropical America are obviously most desirable as zoological-garden inhabitants. However, it is only during fairly recent years that substantial progress has been made in the development of maintenance techniques. General and usually unhappy experience has convinced most zoo authorities that marmosets are too delicate to survive under ordinary conditions. The difficulties of providing more satisfactory treatment have usually seemed too great, a situation which largely accounts for the scarcity of these tiny primates, even in large collections. It is still true that unless suitable quarters can be provided and constant, sympathetic care assured, marmosets are best avoided. On the other hand, when these essentials are available, results very much worthwhile can be obtained.

Serious efforts to maintain marmosets were made at the Zoological Gardens of Frankfurt where, in March, 1939, twenty-one specimens of seven species were living in specially designed cages (Zukowsky, 1940). These cages had glass fronts with wire-mesh tops and sides and measured 2 meters high by 1 long and 80 centimeters wide. When furnished with branches and sleeping boxes, they were well suited for the purpose. Satisfactory longevities of up to 4 years were established, and several species were bred.

Marmosets were not really taken seriously here until January, 1932, when a pair of goldens (*Leontideus rosalia*) was installed in the Reptile House (Ditmars, 1933). The cage was about 4 feet in each dimension and glass-inclosed, except for the side toward the window, which was covered with wire mesh. This was to permit entrance into the cage of unfiltered sun rays through Vitaglass used in the window, in accordance with the then accepted view that direct sunlight was essential. On April 25, 1933, February 22, 1934, and July 7, 1934, the animals responded to this treatment by producing pairs of young, all of which were successfully reared. Unfortunately, all but the parents succumbed to an outbreak of tuberculosis late in 1934.

Early in the forties, with the installation of our Animal Nursery, the attempt to establish a marmoset collection was renewed. Here, in glass and wire cages 3 by 3 by 2 feet, with enlargement made possible by removable partitions, the little animals thrived so well that in December, 1951, there was a total of fourteen species (Crandall, 1951a). Each of these Nursery cages was provided with a sleeping box, essential for the well-being of marmosets. For floor covering we used shredded newspapers which, when changed daily, are clean, warm, and absorbent. Once established, specimens of the hardier sorts were removed to the Small Mammal House, where they were shown under fluorescent lights in the glass-fronted cages already described. Here, small hollow logs were substituted for wooden sleeping boxes, and floors were covered with dry leaves, both for the sake of better appearance. Space for larger branches permitted more extensive exercise, and results were little, if any, inferior. Temperatures averaging 75° F. were maintained.

In general, marmosets are best kept in pairs, not necessarily of the same species. Single, tame animals that have learned to depend for their social needs upon human associations require constant attention if they are to thrive. However, even the most dependent of these can be conditioned, under supervision, to transfer their demands to a mate or even to another of the same sex, so that less constant association with their keeper is required. It is often possible to keep together several specimens, even of mixed species and sexes, although in this case vigilance is required to make certain that bullies are promptly suppressed.

Much has been written concerning the diet of captive marmosets (Fitzgerald, 1935; Lucas, Hume, and Smith, 1937; Zukowsky, 1940; Walker, 1954), so that the essentials are readily available. The system followed here does not differ markedly. In the early morning each animal receives a teaspoonful of orange juice containing 1 drop of multiple vitamin concentrate and sweetened with sugar, without which many individuals will refuse it. In midmorning we provide diced banana, orange, apple, celery, lettuce, and raisin bread, with peanuts, shelled or whole, hard-boiled egg, and bits of canned dog food or a mixture of raw chopped meat, dog meal, bone meal, and cod-liver oil. Lucas, Hume, and Smith (1927) point out the difficulty of getting marmosets to take cod-liver oil. However, oil is readily accepted in the mixture just noted or on halved grapes when heavily sweetened with sugar. Late in the afternoon 1 ounce of whole or reconstituted evaporated milk is given each animal. Mealworms and lizards (*Anolis*) are freely taken when offered.

Marmosets are particularly subject to rickets or "cage paralysis," so that a constant supply of vitamin D, without which calcium and phosphorous cannot be utilized, is essential to good health. Here we depend chiefly on cod-liver oil and vitamin concentrate for the purpose, but to make certain that there is no shortage, ultraviolet lamps are used also. These lamps are located 2 feet above the cages, and new animals are exposed to their rays for 1 minute only at first, the period being increased gradually to 15 minutes, in order to minimize the risk of conjunctivitis. Safe length of exposure varies, of course, with the strength of the lamps, which decreases with continued use.

Unsightly loss of hair from the tail and even parts of the body is often seen in marmosets affected by rickets. This association led Lucas, Hume, and Smith (1927) to assume that exposure to ultraviolet light was directly responsible for the restoration of hair in an animal which previously had been deprived of vitamin D. Whether or not this assumption is warranted, it is certain that a marmoset free from rickets will keep its pelage drier, cleaner, and in better condition than one which is partially immobilized by this crippling condition. Rinehart and Greenberg (1949) have shown that in rhesus monkeys (*Macaca mulatta*) deprived of pyrodoxine hydrochloride (vitamin B_6) the hair becomes thin and its growth arrested. Since there is reason to presume that the effect of this deficiency is not confined to rhesus monkeys, it is important that vitamin B_6 as well as others of the B-complex concentrates are used, and that orange juice, a potent natural source for vitamin C, be included in the diet.

Properly housed and fed, marmosets breed readily in confinement, as reported by Lucas, Hume, and Smith (1927, 1937), Fitzgerald (1935), and Zukowsky (1940). Under ordinary conditions best results are obtained from isolated pairs, since in small quarters the presence of older young or odd adults will almost invariably result in disaster. Young have been produced here by five species: golden (*L. rosalia*), common (*Callithrix jacchus*), black-tailed (*Callithrix argentata*), cottonhead (*Saguinus oedipus*), and imperial (*S. imperator*). No exact observations of gestation periods were possible. Jennison (n.d.) gives 140 days for *L. rosalia*, and Lucas, Hume, and Smith (1937) estimate the period for *Hapale* (=*Callithrix*) *jacchus* as about 140 days. Rabb and Rowell (1960) give elapsed time between two births of *L. rosalia* in the Chicago Zoological Park as 134 days, pointing out that the gestation period could not exceed this figure. Births to a female of the same species here occurred at a confirming interval of 135 days. Based on similar spacing of births of golden marmosets in the Philadelphia Zoological Garden, Ulmer (1961) sets the gestation period as from 132 to 134 days. The seventeen births that have occurred here in the five species listed took place in every month of the year except January, June, and November, with only April and May having as many as three each. In 4 instances the number of young was one, in 12 there were two, and in 1, triplets. In the latter case (*Callithrix jacchus*) the parents seemed unable to cope with so many, and one was found dead on the floor the day after birth, the two survivors being successfully reared. Lucas, Hume, and Smith (1937) record several births of triplets in this species, no more than two having been reared in each instance.

In the golden, common, black-tailed, and cottonhead, care of the young is taken over by the male, and they are surrendered to the female only for the frequent feeding periods. Usually, they can be seen curled about the father's back or shoulders as he moves about. The pattern in the black-tailed showed some variation from that of the others. Following the birth of twins on December 29, 1953, the male seemed reluctant to take them over, although he occasionally did so. When the young were 3 days old the mother was seen to press them with her back against the wire of the cage top, to which they finally clung. During ensuing days they could frequently be seen in this position or buried under the paper strips on the floor, varied with intermittent carrying by the father. In spite of this apparently unconventional behavior, both young were successfully reared.

A quite different and less happy result followed the birth of twin imperial marmosets. The parents had been received here before their growth was completed, the male in June, 1952, the female in June of the following year. On the morning of May 24, 1954, investigation of movement under the paper strips on the floor disclosed two newborn young. When they were exposed both parents became violently excited, leaping wildly about the cage at each movement. During this activity one of the young managed to seize the father's hair and climb onto his back. It was only after frantic efforts by the parent that the infant was finally dislodged and dropped back to the cage floor. The two young were then removed and fed with a solution of two parts whole milk to one of water with a little sugar added. They survived for 3 days, finally succumbing to injuries that must have been inflicted during the parents' efforts to avoid them. Each weighed $1\frac{1}{2}$ ounces when removed, and the white hair of the lips showed the first indications of the long moustaches with which the adults were adorned. Incidentally, these moustaches sweep back and down, not upwards in a Bismarckian twirl, as sometimes described and figured. I cannot recall another instance of rejection of young by any marmosets.

At somewhere about five months of age young marmosets should be feeding well for themselves. Unless quarters are much larger than those usually provided, they should then be removed. At this age it is essential that they receive a full complement of vitamins and minerals, which cannot be assured if the young are allowed to remain longer. When the removal is accomplished, it should be a complete one, for if separated parents and young can see each other they will make frantic efforts toward reunion.

Authentic longevities for captive marmosets are not easily found or reconciled. Everyone has heard verbal reports of very long durations for animals in private hands, but verification is usually difficult. Mitchell (1911) gives 16 years for a "marmoset" privately kept in England, and Flower (1931) reports 11½ years for *H.* (= *Callithrix*) *jacchus* in Europe. Lucas, Hume, and Smith (1937) give a properly documented span of 9 years, 6 months, 15 days for a laboratory specimen of the common marmoset in England.

Because of the scarcity of records in the literature, it seems worth while to report our best results in Table 1, even though some undoubtedly have been exceeded elsewhere.

TABLE 1

LONGEVITY IN CALLITHRICIDAE

Species	Years	Months	Days
Golden, *Leontideus rosalia*	10	4	18
Common, *Callithrix jacchus*	6	4	7
Black-tailed, *Callithrix argentata*	8	9	9
Pygmy, *Cebuella pygmaea*	4	11	14
Cottonhead, *Saguinus oedipus*	7	2	13
Red-handed, *S. midas*	5	10	11
Golden-mantled, *S. tripartitus*	5	9	19
Río Napo, *S. graellsi*	5	8	1
Imperial, *S. imperator*	7	0	9
Martin's, *S. martinsi*	9	10	0
Pied, *S. bicolor*	8	2	10
White-handed, *S. leucopus*	5	8	8

When our first specimen of Goeldi's marmoset (*Callimico goeldii*) was received here on December 20, 1954, it was the center of great interest (McClung, 1955). This little-known species, thought to be confined to a restricted range in northern Bolivia, western Brazil, and contiguous parts of Peru, had previously been kept only at the small zoo attached to the Goeldi Museum at Para, Brazil, and at the Zoological Gardens of London, where a single specimen was received in 1915 (Flower, 1929). Ours, apparently, was the first representative to reach the United States. The proper systematic assignment of this little creature has long been the subject of controversy, since in many characters it has appeared to be intermediate between the Cebidae and the Callithricidae. Cabrera (1957) placed *Callimico* in a subfamily Callimiconinae of the family Cebidae, while Hill (1957) assigned it to a separate family, Callimiconidae. However, in the Introduction to the volume, Hill (*loc. cit.*), after examination of a specimen that died in our collection on January 21, 1955, reduced it to a subfamily, Callimiconinae, of the family Hapalidae (Callithricidae). This position is maintained by Hill (1959) in his monograph on the anatomy of the species.

The general coloration of *Callimico* is black, but there appears to be much individual variation, for there is often a scattering of white or reddish hairs, sometimes forming distinct patches. A male and a female received here on April 6, 1955, were black, with only a slight infusion of brown in the dorsal area. A year later the male had the hair of the face, the last third of the tail, and irregular spots on the body and limbs white, while the forehead and crown were brown mixed with white. At the same time the female had white on the face only, with faint brown areas on the back.

Kept in the marmoset section of our Animal Nursery, the six specimens received here up to 1963 were given the usual diet for marmosets but seemed to have a special predilection for small lizards and took *Anolis* ravenously (Bridges, 1955). In taking fluids they drank by lapping with their tongues in typical marmoset fashion. A male received here on September 1, 1959, was still living in 1963, having established the best result with this species obtained here up to that time.*

FAMILY CERCOPITHECIDAE

MACAQUES, MANGABEYS, BABOONS, GUENONS, LANGURS, PROBOSCIS AND COLOBUS MONKEYS

The members of this family are distinguished from the monkeys of the New World by numerous characters, the most evident of which are the narrowness of the separation between the nostrils, non-prehensile tails where these appendages are present, the possession of cheek pouches, except in the colobus and proboscis monkeys and the langurs, and callosities, often brightly colored, on the buttocks. In general, they are far hardier in captivity than their relatives of the New World, although the leaf-eating species present serious dietary problems. In point of numbers, at least, the Cercopithecidae predominate among the primates in most of the zoological gardens of the world.

*See Addenda, p. 732.

MACAQUES

Most commonly seen, of course, are the macaques (*Macaca*), some species of which will be found in even the smallest collections. Probably because of the extensive use of certain members of this group for laboratory purposes, much work has been done on the reproductive biology, particularly in the rhesus monkey (*Macaca mulatta*), as summarized by Asdell (1946). Maintenance, feeding, and breeding under laboratory conditions have been treated in detail by van Wagenen (1950), while behavior at semi-liberty has been studied by Carpenter (1942) and Eckstein and Zuckerman (1957).

For the zoological garden, the macaques present some interesting problems. With few exceptions, they are dull in color and to the initiated are probably the least attractive of the primates. On the other hand, they are relatively easy to maintain and are always in good favor with the public, which finds their antics and grimaces in accord with the popular conception of monkey behavior.

As stated earlier in this section, the "renting" system which provides groups of young animals, usually either rhesus monkeys or the common or crab-eating macaque (*M. irus*), returnable at the end of the summer season, provides the smaller institution with a workable solution. Where a more serious exhibit is feasible or when a series of species is to be maintained permanently, an effort to establish family groups is in order. In this category the pig-tailed macaques (*M. nemestrina*) at Amsterdam have already been mentioned.

Such family groups can be set up on an indoor-outdoor basis as well as on "islands." Rhesus and some of the more northerly forms can be kept out of doors the year round, with unheated shelters, where winter conditions are not too severe. In New York, where extreme low temperatures may reach 0° F. or even lower, we have tried only the Japanese macaque (*M. fuscata*) which, with an open shelter, has proved quite indifferent to cold.

When macaques—or most other monkeys, for that matter—are kept in adjacent cages, it is essential that partitions be of solid materials, preferably opaque. The use of wire netting, however strong and fine in mesh, will inevitably result in serious fighting and eventual damage, the least of which will be severed digits and tail tips. Where bar fronts are used, they must be impervious for at least 12 or 15 inches at either side of the partition, to prevent injury to the exploring hands of aggressive or inquisitive animals.

At one time we had here a rhesus family, consisting of a very large male, a female, and a three-year-old daughter. Like most adult male macaques, this animal was powerful and aggressive, so that only steel plate, almost hermetically sealed, prevented him from finding means for attacking the baboons and gibbons in adjoining cages. For such animals and even for those somewhat less savage, a shifting cage or other means of confinement during servicing periods is essential for the safety of the keepers.

In maintaining family groups it is necessary to check carefully on the sex of maturing young animals. In close quarters the mature male will not tolerate the presence of a potential rival, although young females are usually treated with moderation.

In planning the "island" exhibit, the over-all arrangement may be varied practically at will, as long as the basic essentials are observed. For macaques it is customary to provide a surrounding water space some 18–20 feet across, the thought being not how far the animal can jump but rather how far he cannot! Water depth should be graduated so that a shallow area is provided, with a depth of perhaps 3 feet at the outer perimeter. Here, a smooth concrete wall should rise to a height of at least 5–6 feet above water level. This requirement results from the fact that certainly most, probably all, of the macaques swim like beavers and will escape from a water moat if it is at all possible. I recall an instance of rhesus monkeys frequently escaping from an "island" where the outer wall rose three feet above water level. Careful observation revealed that this was accomplished by one swimming animal climbing upon the back of another, then leaping quickly to the wall top from this flimsy support. In the following season the rhesus were replaced by green monkeys (*Cercopithecus aethiops sabaeus*), ending the escape problem.

Various methods of feeding macaques and other monkeys have been devised, the system usually being adapted to the purpose for which the animals are used but all making certain that the necessary elements, as far as known, are provided. For laboratory monkeys kept in comparatively close quarters, van Wagenen (1950) suggests cod-liver oil or vitamin D concentrate on a lump of sugar, followed by bread and milk and half an orange as the morning meal, with egg, potatoes, cooked rice, greens, vegetables, and fruits given in the afternoon.

For use in partial conjunction with the general formula above, various commercial baked foods are now available, at least in America. The basis for these biscuits is furnished by Yerkes (1943), the resulting "Chim-crackers" containing various grain meals, powdered milk, bone meal, salt, wheat germ, and irradiated yeast. At the Philadelphia Zoological Garden a somewhat more complicated mixture devised by Dr. Herbert L. Ratcliffe, pathologist of that institution, is used with excellent results. This "monkey cake," prepared in the afternoon for use on the following day, has been described in its progressive stages by Ratcliffe (1940, 1947, 1953).

It now becomes obvious that the basic purpose of these varying diets is to make certain that the animals receive the essential components, as far as these are known, and that the method by which they are provided is of secondary importance. For very large operations, the over-all system of prepared foods, which all must eat, serves the purpose well. We have not fully adopted this method here because we have felt that supplemented natural diets, under close supervision, permit adjustment to the needs and vagaries of individual animals. Following is the feeding system used here for macaques, the daily amounts of each item being those allotted to a single adult rhesus. These are varied, of course, for related species, considering size, age, sex, and individual needs.

Morning: ½ pint reconstituted evaporated or powdered milk, to which are added 1 coddled egg, 1 tbs. Pablum, Cerevim, or similar cereal food, and 1 drop of multiple vitamin concentrate.

Afternoon: 2 slices raisin bread
2 bananas
2 apples
2 carrots (raw)
1 orange
1 raw potato (white or sweet)
⅓ head of lettuce or equivalent amount of cabbage
1 stalk of celery
5 or 6 peanuts
2 oz. of a mixture of raw or steamed chopped meat, dog meal, and bone meal, with ½ tsp. of cod-liver oil. Commercial "monkey pellets" may also be given.

In general, the macaques breed freely in captivity when properly kept. Most zoological gardens have bred at least some of the numerous species, Stott (1954) listing eight forms that had produced young in the Zoological Garden of San Diego up to that time. Most interesting of these is the black or Moor macaque (*M. maurus*) of Celebes. San Diego has also bred the impressive Celebes crested "ape" (*Cynopithecus niger*). The Barbary "ape" or magot (*M. sylvana*) of North Africa and Gibraltar has been bred in America, at least in the National Zoological Park (Reed, 1961), and there are numerous European records (Zuckerman, 1953; Nouvel, 1952).

When kept in pairs or in family groups in sufficiently roomy quarters, most female macaques will bear and rear their young without difficulty. Following a birth, the male usually becomes fiercely protective and later, when the youngster's mother allows it increasing periods of freedom, generally is tolerant of its playful advances. The occasional troublesome male and the unreliable female should be isolated before the birth, a precaution that is routine in laboratory breeding procedure (van Wagenen, 1950). The gestation period in the rhesus is given as approximately 164 days (Asdell, 1946). The reddened, corrugated skin which may cover almost the entire body of the sexually mature female rhesus monkey (Zuckerman, van Wagenen, and Gardiner, 1938) often causes needless alarm when first observed. Its first appearance coincides with the onset of puberty, usually at the age of about 2 years. Maturity in males does not occur until a year later (van Wagenen, 1950).

Occasionally a female macaque will refuse to accept the newborn infant. Usually such rejected babies cannot be rescued before they have been fatally injured, perhaps by being dropped to the cage floor, but when one is retrieved undamaged, it is fairly easily reared by hand.

On June 17, 1954, the female of a pair of lion-tailed macaques or wanderoos (*M. silenus*) gave birth to a male infant which, apparently, she immediately dropped. The youngster, cold and hungry, was eventually retrieved uninjured by the keeper. It was carried at once to the Animal Hospital where, after it had been warmed to activity, it was placed on the formula suggested by van Wagenen (1950: 31), consisting of 4 ounces of whole milk, 2 ounces of water, and 1 teaspoonful of sucrose, heated to body temperature and administered in small quantities at 2-hour intervals through a small rubber nipple. This procedure proved completely successful, so that only a few notes furnished by Dr. L. J. Goss, then our veterinarian, are needed to complete the story. At the age of 3 weeks 1 drop of multiple vitamin concentrate was added to the formula daily; at 4 weeks the infant first took solid food, in the form of mashed banana; at 5 weeks 1 drop of cod-liver oil was given, the amount being gradually increased; at $7\frac{1}{2}$ weeks the young animal first drank milk from a dish. At birth the baby's weight was 348.8 grams, on July 30 it was 479.4 grams, and on November 26 it had increased to 1098.7 grams. By this time the young wanderoo had become fully independent.

As a group, the macaques are relatively long-lived in captivity. Three individuals, each of a different species, have lived here in excess of 15 years: pig-tailed (*M. nemestrina*), 15 years, 15 days; common (*M. irus*), 15 years, 5 months, 1 day; Japanese (*M. fuscata*), 15 years, 9 months,

18 days. George H. Pournelle (*in litt.*) reports 18 years for the Moor macaque (*M. maurus*) at the San Diego Zoological Garden, while Mann (1930) gives 21 for a rhesus in the National Zoological Park in Washington. Flower (1931) lists 16 years, 11 months, 16 days for a wanderoo (*M. silenus*) at Rotterdam, 19 years, 6 months, 12 days for a Japanese macaque in the Zoological Gardens of London, 27 years for a common macaque (*M. irus*) at Capetown, and, quoting Pocock (1906), "probably 29 years old at the time of its death" for a rhesus. Pocock's statement is to the effect that this animal had been in the possession of Colonel S. M. Benson for 28 years. A Moor macaque is listed in the centennial celebration brochure of the Philadelphia Zoological Society, 1859–1959, as having lived in that organization's Garden for 28 years, 1 month, and is referred to also in *America's First Zoo* (Anon., 1955b). The two latter longevities would seem to represent maxima for *Macaca* in captivity.

George H. Pournelle (*in litt.*) reports 17 years, 8 months, 2 days for the related Celebes crested "ape" (*Cynopithecus niger*) at San Diego, Flower (1931) gives 18 years and still living for the same species in the Mysore Zoological Gardens, and Simon (1943) records 21 years in the Trivandrum Zoo.

MANGABEYS

Found throughout the tropical forests of equatorial Africa with a preponderance of distribution in the west, the mangabeys (*Cercocebus*) are essentially arboreal in habit, although they may sometimes descend to the ground in search of food. With long limbs and slender bodies, they give an impression of lightness, although adult males reach a comparatively large size. At least in the gray-cheeked (*C. a. albigena*) and Johnston's (*C. a. johnstoni*), the lengthy tail is usually carried erect with a forward curl at the tip.

While all of the mangabeys lack the brilliant coloration found among the guenons, some, such as the male gray-cheeked with its flowing mane and head tufts, are impressive while others, such as the black mangabey (*C. aterrimus*) with its erect, pointed crest, are both curious and attractive. Most young animals are gentle in disposition, but adult males may react savagely if their inclosures are invaded.

Mangabeys are agile leapers and require ample quarters with branches, shelves, and ledges conveniently spaced. They are sensitive to cold and do best when temperatures do not fall below 70° F. The food provided for mangabeys here is that already outlined for macaques, with age, sex, and condition governing the amounts of each item to be given.

For some reason not readily discerned, results in the maintenance of mangabeys in captivity have been rather indifferent, so that, as in similar cases, breeding successes have not been frequent. Zuckerman (1953) reports five births in two species—the sooty (*C. fuliginosus = torquatus atys*) and the white-crowned (*C. torquatus = t. lunulatus*)—and two of hybrids born in the Zoological Gardens of London between 1844 and 1937. However, since construction of the Zoological Garden of San Diego, begun in 1922, no less than four forms have been bred there (Stott, 1954): the sooty, the white-crowned, the white-collared or cherry-headed (*C. t. torquatus*), and the gray-cheeked (*C. a. albigena*). The latter especially has become so firmly established that specimens have been furnished to many other institutions in this country, including the New York Zoological Park, a male and two females having been received here on April 16, 1945.

One of these females produced single young here on May 25, 1946, September 23, 1947, September 5, 1949, and December 18, 1950, all of which were safely reared. The second female gave birth to a single young on July 5, 1949. This event precipitated a violent struggle between the two females for possession of the baby, resulting in its death a week later and necessitating the removal of the second female in the interests of peace.

As already suggested, available longevity records indicate comparatively short average spans for mangabeys in captivity, although some more satisfactory records have been established. The male gray-cheeked referred to above had been here approximately 18 years and was still living in 1963. George H. Pournelle (*in litt.*) reports a white-collared or cherry-headed mangabey as having lived 12 years in the San Diego Zoological Garden, "then given away." The best noted by Flower (1931) is fourteen years in the Lisbon Zoological Gardens for a mangabey of unstated species. Jones (1958) reports 20 years, 9 months, 13 days for a sooty mangabey in the National Zoological Park and 20 years, 4 months, 8 days for a cherry-headed in the Zoological Gardens of London.

BABOONS

Largest and most powerful of the primates, excepting only the anthropoids, are the baboons. While Lydekker (1893–96, **1**: 138) uses "hideous" twice in a single sentence describing the mandrill, "bizarre" now seems more appropriate, with "handsome" for the hamadryas and "fearsome" for the chacma. But adjectives, after all, record only individual impressions of animals whose size, strength, and obvious defensive abilities are certain to arouse strong reactions in all who see them at close range.

Apart from a form of the hamadryas (*Comopithecus hamadryas arabicus*) which occurs in southern Arabia, the baboons are African in distribution, the eight currently recognized species, several extensively subdivided, covering most of that continent except the northern and northeastern areas. The great chacma (*Papio ursinus*), largest of the group, is found in South Africa, the yellow (*P. cynocephalus*) occupies eastern districts from Mozambique to Kenya, the olive (*P. anubis*) extends across tropical Africa from Nigeria to the Sudan, Kenya, and Tanganyika, while the Guinea (*P. papio*), smallest but not least attractive of the baboons, is found in the forests of West Africa. The brilliantly colored mandrill (*Mandrillus sphinx*) and the smaller and duller drill (*Mandrillus leucophaeus*) are likewise West African, while the typical hamadryas (*Comopithecus h. hamadryas*) inhabits lowland areas from Somaliland to eastern Sudan. The aberrant gelada (*Theropithecus gelada*), readily known by the fact that its nostrils are set back from the end of the muzzle rather than lying at the extended tip, lives at high altitudes in Ethiopia.

Up to 1939 all of these baboons were imported freely, only the drill perhaps being seen less frequently than the others. Since that time importations have been scattered and infrequent, the Guinea baboon being the only generally available species, at least in this country. An exception might be made in the case of very young drills and mandrills which have been appearing fairly often with shipments of African monkeys. Unfortunately, these youngsters are delicate and timid in mixed company, usually being younger than the monkeys with which they must compete, and few succeed in establishing themselves. On the other hand, those that do manage to progress beyond the stage of infancy are likely to advance to maturity. After the declaration of peace in 1945, an important source of supply for gelada baboons was a small but successful breeding stock in the Rotterdam Zoological Gardens. Later, however, both the gelada and the hamadryas began to arrive sparingly from Africa.

Methods used in maintaining and exhibiting baboons do not differ in principle from those already suggested for other members of this family. The moated area plan for large groups, such as the successful operation at Vincennes, has already been discussed. The unfortunate results that follow the inclusion of an excessive number of males in such colonies may be read between the lines of Zuckerman's (1932a) classic investigations of baboon behavior.

Where a series of baboon species is desired and proper accommodation can be provided, the animals will do well in pairs or in family groups. Solitary males can seldom be shown, as they almost invariably develop undesirable sex habits. In preparing cage space it must be remembered that powerful, often savage, animals are to be dealt with, so that bars or wire mesh must be strong enough to resist any attack. Glass fronts, both electrified and heavy plate, have been successful here under suitable conditions. A space 15–20 feet long, 8–10 feet deep, and 8–10 feet high will nicely accommodate a pair of baboons, even with several immature offspring. While baboons are essentially terrestrial, living principally on the ground or on the rocky ledges usually frequented, they are excellent climbers and should have heavy branches and strong elevated shelves to provide variety. A shift cage to which the animals may be confined during service operations is essential. In roomy quarters of this type even the most truculent male will usually make no trouble following births and will tolerate with gentleness the playful attentions of the infant as it begins to move about. This is not always the case if cage space is restricted and the harassed father is unable to seek seclusion on a high shelf.

While baboons are largely vegetarian in feeding habits, some animal protein is required to replace the insects, reptiles, young birds, and small mammals that are eaten under natural conditions. A pair of Guinea baboons, with a yearling youngster and an infant still carried by the mother, were fed here daily as follows:

Morning: 1½ pints of reconstituted evaporated or powdered milk, to which were added 2 coddled eggs, 3 tsp. Pablum, Cerevim, or similar cereal food, and 3 drops of multiple vitamin concentrate

Afternoon: 1½ heads lettuce
10 bananas
6 apples
4 oranges
½ loaf raisin bread, sliced
3 dozen peanuts
4 or 5 carrots, raw
3 white potatoes, raw
1 sweet potato, raw
6–8 oz. of a mixture of equal parts chopped raw horse meat and dog meal, with 1 tsp. fine bone meal and ½ tsp. cod-liver oil added. A small allowance of monkey feeding pellets was also given.

With the exception of the drill and the mandrill, the baboons breed so freely in captivity that records for most species are too numerous to require detailed citation. The Zoological Garden of San Diego alone has bred the Guinea, the olive, the yellow, the hamadryas, and the drill (Stott, 1954). As already stated, the gelada has bred well at Rotterdam and doubtless elsewhere. Until recent years the mandrill was seldom bred. Hill (1953c) reports a birth in the Zoological Gardens of London on October 10, 1953, the first to occur there, and refers to a previous breeding in England, at the Chester Zoo, in 1937. Perhaps because of the greater prevalence of adult females, births in this country, at least, have now become almost commonplace. The female of the first potential breeding pair to be kept in our own collection produced a single youngster on August 5, 1960, rearing it successfully with the full acquiescence of the male. Births on April 19, 1962, and May 9, 1963, added two more members to this thriving group. The birth of twin mandrills at the Zoological Gardens of Baltimore, on August 13, 1961, is reported by the director, Arthur Watson (*in litt.*). The great chacma baboon (*P. ursinus*) seems to breed reluctantly in zoological gardens, although at least two births have occurred at Philadelphia (Anon., 1951). However, in the course of studies carried on at the University of the Witwatersrand, Johannesburg, a series of fourteen single births with an average gestation period of 187 days is reported by Gilbert and Gillman (1951). Zuckerman (1931) gives the gestation period of the hamadryas baboon as 154–85 days, with a definite record of 183 days.

The hardiness of baboons in captivity is attested by longevity records for most species approximating those established by the macaques. Flower (1931) reports two male hamadryas still living after 24 years in the Cologne Zoological Gardens and a female mandrill that lived in the Belle Vue Zoological Gardens, Manchester, England, for 26 years, 5 months. He also records reports of 45 years for a chacma and 46 for a mandrill, both spans, if authentic, far exceeding all others known to me. A Guinea baboon lived 16 years, 6 months, 9 days, a drill 21 years, 10 months, 16 days and still living, and an olive 25 years, 3 months, 21 days, all in the San Diego Zoological Garden (George H. Pournelle, *in litt.*). A chacma is recorded as having lived in the Philadelphia Zoological Garden for 27 years, 7 months (*Rept. Penrose Res. Lab.*, 1938:32) while a female yellow baboon was exhibited in the New York Zoological Park for 27 years, 8 months, 15 days, producing four healthy youngsters during her earlier years.

GUENONS AND PATAS OR HUSSAR MONKEYS

Most attractive of the Old World monkeys, both for the handsome coloration of many forms and for the sprightly manners of all, are the guenons (*Cercopithecus*). Since there is no English name for the group, "guenon" has been taken from the French, and in this country, at least, is commonly used in the collective sense. The guenons are exclusively African, Allen (1939) recognizing a total of ten species and seventy-two subspecies, ranging through forested areas from the Sudan and Ethiopia to Cape Province. They are essentially arboreal in habit, seldom coming to the ground.

The one most commonly seen in this country is the green monkey (*C. aethiops sabeus*), with the vervet (*C. a. pygerythrus*) a close second and the grivet (*C. a. aethiops*) among the rarities. These three are among the most dully colored of the guenons, distinguished from each other by small differences. Next come the spot-nosed monkeys, forms of *C. nictitans*, and the moustached monkeys (*C. cephus*). The pretty little mona (*C. m. mona*) and Campbell's monkeys (*C. m. campbelli*) and the beautiful Diana (*C. d. diana*) with the long-bearded roloway (*C. d. roloway*) appear less often, although sometimes available. Beyond these, almost any member of the genus is a rarity here, obtainable only by fortunate chance. The guenons are usually thought of as small and gentle creatures, perhaps because imported specimens are usually immature. Actually, there is great variation in size within the group, for fully adult males of some forms, such as the Diana and the moustached, may really be very large. The range extends downward through the smaller mona to the tiny talapoin (*C. talapoin*), smallest of the group. There is more truth in the designation "gentle," since even the largest males, if not entirely trustworthy, are seldom savage and most females are inclined to be friendly and docile.

Young animals of different species are readily induced to live peaceably together, and most interesting groups can be organized on this basis. However, as soon as the males begin to mature, quarreling follows and removals become necessary. The residual results of such reductions are sometimes curious. We have found ourselves with a superb male Hamlyn's monkey (*C. hamlyni*) living with a female L'Hoest's (*C. l'h. l'hoesti*) and a hybrid youngster, and a male Wolf's monkey (*C. mona wolfi*) with a female Congo spot-nose (*C. nictitans ascanius*) and a female Brazza's (*C. neglectus*), the latter having produced several hybrid young which she failed to rear. Both of these groups were relics of much larger ones organized in 1949, while the animals were still immature.

While in theory guenons, like most other monkeys, are best kept in family groups, we never have been fully successful in maintaining such arrangements nor can I recall having seen this accomplished elsewhere. In two instances, involving Campbell's and Diana monkeys living in pairs, the males behaved well while the young were being carried by the mother, but in each case attacked and injured the female as soon as the youngster began to move about. All efforts to return these males to the females at later periods failed, so that separate establishments had to be maintained.

The feeding system used here for guenons does not differ from that adopted for macaques, as already described.

When kept in pairs or in family groups under favorable conditions, the guenons breed readily, although perhaps not quite so well as do the macaques. Three forms—Diana, Campbell's, and green—have reared young here, while Stott (1954) lists no less than seven kinds as having bred successfully in the Zoological Garden of San Diego. Births are usually of single young, but twins have been born to a green monkey in San Diego (Anon., 1952b). Asdell (1946) gives the gestation period for *C. (aethiops) cynosurus* as 7 months, while Mann (1930) gives the same figure for the mona.

Maximum longevities recorded for guenons in captivity compare well with those for macaques. Among those best known to me for this country are 16 years for a mona in the National Zoological Park (Flower, 1931), 16 years, 10 months, 29 days for a grivet in the San Diego Zoological Garden (George H. Pournelle, *in litt.*), 18 years for a mona in the St. Louis Zoological Park, and 19 years for a Diana in the Chicago Zoological Park (Rabb, 1960). Old World records, as given by Flower (1931), include 19 years and left alive for a talapoin at Amsterdam, 22 years, 5 months, 22 days for a mona at Rotterdam, and 24 years for a grivet at Giza.

Pairs of a small, obscurely colored monkey known as *Allenopithecus nigroviridis*, obviously closely related to the guenons if not actually congeneric with them, were received in 1953 at the National Zoological Park and the San Diego Zoological Garden. There were simultaneous European arrivals but the two pairs noted were presumably the first to be seen in this country. A single female was added to our own collection in 1959. Single young were born in San Diego on June 10, 1959, July 15, 1960, and July 27, 1961 (Anon., 1961a). Described by Pocock (1907) from a specimen which had died in the Zoological Gardens of London in 1894, the species has remained rare in collections and little has been learned of its habits. Schouteden (1947) gives its range as central Belgian Congo and Ubangi (French Equatorial Africa).

Much larger than the typical guenons are the monkeys of the genus *Erythrocebus*. Bright reddish-bay in coloration and active in deportment, they are among the most attractive of the family. Two forms are usually seen in captivity: the black-nosed patas or hussar monkey (*Erythrocebus p. patas*), found from Senegal to Lake Chad, and the white-nosed nisnas or dancing red monkey (*E. patas pyrrhonotus*), which ranges from the Sudan to Uganda).

Noticeably long in leg and slender in body, the members of this group are dwellers in open country, avoiding forested areas. In conformance with this habit, fairly extensive floor space is required to provide for proper exercise, with shelves and ledges for variation. As a further divergence from the guenons, males are likely to become savage and dangerous as they advance in age. Food requirements do not differ from those suggested for macaques.

Neither form of *Erythrocebus* has been bred here, and few successes have been recorded elsewhere. The only definite records I have come across are a reference by Walker (1954) to a birth in the National Zoological Park, a photograph of a youngster born in the Ueno Zoo, Tokyo (Anon., 1959*b*), and one in the Cheyenne Mountain Zoological Park, Colorado Springs, Colorado, on May 17, 1961 (Davis, 1962), all for *E. p. patas*.

As pointed out by Flower (1931), the patas does not seem to do as well in captivity as does the nisnas. Flower gives no records for the former, and 10 years, 5 months, 16 days is our best here for the form. Jones (1958) reports 20 years, 2 months, 9 days for a patas in the Zoological Garden of Philadelphia. A nisnas lived for 16 years in the Zoological Garden of San Diego (George Pournelle, *in litt.*), and Flower (1931) gives 19 years, 1 month, 9 days, and still living for a female at Giza.

Langurs, Proboscis Monkeys, and Colobus or Guereza Monkeys

While the monkeys of this group are considered by some authorities to form a separate family (Colobidae) it is more convenient here to follow Simpson (1945) and Ellerman and Morrison-Scott (1951) and consider them as a subfamily (Colobinae) of the family Cercopithecidae. As already noted, they differ from the other members of this family in the absence of cheek pouches. However, this lack is amply compensated by the sacculated stomach, an adaptation to the leaf-eating habits common to the group.

In four genera and numerous races (Ellerman and Morrison-Scott, 1951; Chasen, 1940), the langurs are found from the lower Himalayas and western China southward through peninsular India and the Malay Peninsula to the larger islands, including Sumatra, Java, and Borneo. Probably a dozen forms have been kept in zoological gardens, but nomenclatural usage is so thoroughly confused that an exact check would take us beyond the bounds of our present field.

While ordinarily quiet, almost phlegmatic, in general behavior, langurs at times are extremely active. On such occasions they are capable of leaps of some length, Beddard (1905) stating these may be as long as 20–30 feet. For this reason ample cage space is required, with the usual branches and elevated shelves supplied for other arboreal monkeys. Great strength of restraining barriers is not essential, for while members of some of the forms are both large and heavy, they lack the aggression of many others. This characteristic has been used to advantage by some zoological gardens, notably that of San Diego, in developing fairly large family groups with a minimum of quarreling.

Because their diet in nature consists largely of leaves, there is always difficulty in getting them over the gap to the food materials usually available in colder latitudes (see Mitchell, 1931). In summer we have found that the leaves of the Russian mulberry (*Morus*) and young shoots of bamboo are taken eagerly, in addition to abundant supplies of lettuce and kale, with such raw vegetables, fruits, and bread as individual animals will take. Most will drink milk with cereal, providing a vehicle for the administration of essential cod-liver oil or multiple vitamin concentrate. No langur, as far as I know, will take flesh in any form. During the winter months, when leafy materials are difficult to obtain, increased supplies of lettuce and kale with the leaves of hardy bamboos, when available, will usually carry over well-acclimatized specimens. At San Diego, where great success has been achieved with langurs, sweet potato vines, growing profusely in the borders fronting the cages, are an important food item. The complete diet used for langurs at San Diego is given by Benchley (1941) as follows: in addition to various green leaves, lettuce, cabbage, celery, green beans and peas, corn on the cob (maize), bamboo, carrots, sweet potatoes, and fruits.

In spite of the almost universal difficulty in keeping langurs in captivity, there are breeding records for a number of kinds. The common entellus, hanuman monkey, or Indian langur (*Presbytis entellus*) is reported by Sányál (1892) to have bred frequently in the Zoological Gardens of Calcutta, producing single young at each birth. The Zoological Garden of San Diego, the Chicago Zoological Park, and doubtless others have also bred at least one of the many forms of this species, while Zuckerman (1953) reports four births of the capped langur (*Presbytis aygula*) in the Zoological Gardens of London. The best result in this field has been accomplished by the Zoological Garden of San Diego, where, in addition to the Indian langur, the silvered leaf monkey or lutong (*Presbytis cristatus*), the pileated langur (*Presbytis pileatus*), and the Siamese spectacled langur (*Presbytis obscurus flavicauda*) have also been bred (Stott, 1954; Bode, 1953b). The silvered leaf monkey represents a special achievement, for the red-coated babies of both the black and the red color phases have been produced. One pair of each was received at San Diego from Java on August 20, 1940, and with the support of a second pair of blacks obtained in the following year, both groups have been continuously maintained (Benchley, 1941).

Of special interest is a photograph on the cover of *Zoonooz*, the publication of the San Diego Zoological Society, for November, 1941. This shows a male of the red phase of the silvered leaf monkey holding in his arms an infant. The caption of this photograph reads: "Red Luton, born in the San Diego Zoo, August 20, 1941, in the arms of its father, who seizes it and rushes onto a high shelf or into the back room the second anyone approaches his child." Whether or not this behavior is normal for male langurs of all species I do not know.

Flower (1931) says that langurs "seldom live to more than 7 or 8 years in Europe," probably an overoptimistic view. Our best here is 2 days short of 7 years for a male Indian langur (*Presbytis entellus*), but Rabb (1960) gives 22 years for this species in the Chicago Zoological Park. While Sányál (1892) gives the maximum for *Presbytis entellus* in the Zoological Gardens of Calcutta as 6 years, he reports both Phayre's leaf monkey (*Presbytis phayrei*) and the crested monkey (*Presbytis cristatus*) as having been kept there for 10 years and still living. Flower (1931) reports 15 years for a Nilgiri langur in the Trivandrum Zoological Gardens.

The douc langur (*Pygathrix nemaeus*) was kept for a few months in 1936 at the Zoological Gardens of London, and the golden or snub-nosed langur (*Rhinopithecus roxellanae*) was also represented at that institution for a short time, in 1939. Pang-Chieh (1957) describes and figures one of a pair of golden langurs kept at the Peking Zoological Park, adding that it is "very difficult to keep them healthy." There appears to be no captivity record for the pig-tailed langur (*Simias*), known only from small islands off the western coast of Sumatra.

The proboscis monkey (*Nasalis larvatus*) is a native of Borneo, two forms (*l. larvatus* and *l. orientalis*) being listed by Chasen (1940). As far as the zoological garden is concerned, the species still remains a problem only partially solved. That the solution is not entirely beyond reach is shown by the fact that the animal has frequently been kept as a pet in its own country, and that specimens were available in the market many years ago. Hornaday (1910:298) reports seeing in the market at Singapore, about 1880, "a fine pair of Proboscis Monkeys at $100." It is difficult to believe that such animals should not have reached Europe or America with some frequency, even though I have been able to find only a single definite early record. That relates to a young specimen which was received at the Zoological Gardens of London on June 30, 1902, and died "suddenly" on September 6 of the same year (Sclater, 1902:225). The colored plate accompanying this report shows the upturned nose typical of the immature proboscis.

Useful notes on the proboscis monkey in captivity are furnished by Sányál (1892:17–18). These have to do with specimens kept in the Zoological Gardens of Calcutta, where one lived for 2 years, 6 months. Sányál says that the animal showed a "liking for the green stocks [stalks] of paddy and young wheat and young shoots of Kalmi (*Convolvus repens*)." He further suggests that in addition to leaves and grass, the diet should include fruits, vegetables, bread, and biscuits. He describes the proboscis monkey as slow and phlegmatic, abandoning its lethargy only on introduction of the food dish. No animosity was displayed when a young female was placed in a cage with an older male.

The previously dim prospect for the maintenance of the proboscis monkey in captivity brightened perceptibly following the arrival of a young pair at the San Diego Zoological Garden on January 8, 1956 (Pournelle, 1956). Not only were these the first arrivals in the New World, but so well did they accommodate themselves to new conditions that the male lived until January 18, 1960, establishing the remarkable record of 4 years, 10 days, the female having died on November 14, 1956, through an intestinal volvulus. In a résumé of the history of these animals, Pournelle (1960a) gives the daily menu, which included boiled white potatoes and yams, peaches, bananas, apples, oranges, grapes, green corn (maize), peanuts, bread carrying a multiple vitamin supplement, celery, Romaine lettuce, stems and leaves of cup of gold (cupflower), and leaves and berries of *Eugenia*. A second young pair, brought to San Diego from Borneo by K. C. Lint on September 13, 1961, figures in *Zoonooz* for October, 1961.*

Among the world's most strikingly colored primates are the colobus or guereza monkeys, which range through the tropical rain forests of Africa from east to west. Allen (1939) assigns the superb black and white races to a single species (*Colobus polykomos*) and the largely bay, reddish, or olive forms to a second (*C. badius*). In all, the thumb is missing or represented by a mere tubercle. The colobus monkeys are strongly arboreal in habit, climbing and leaping with an agility surprising for animals of their size (a male of *C. p. angolensis* kept here weighed 23 pounds

*See Addenda, p. 732.

when in fine condition). On the rare occasions when a colobus finds itself
on the ground it is curiously slow and awkward. A perfectly healthy
specimen that once escaped here was easily run down and recaptured on an
open lawn by a single keeper, himself none too fleet. This inability may
account for the fact that groups are sometimes isolated in small "islands"
of forest to which they are practically confined.

Up to recent years the colobus monkeys have proved very difficult subjects in the zoological garden. Flower (1931:153) says simply that
"African Colobus or Guereza Monkeys appear to be even more difficult than
the Langurs to keep alive in captivity." Mitchell (1911) gives a maximum
of 13 months for ten specimens, mostly *C. (p.) vellerosus* in the Zoological
Gardens of London. When a single specimen lived in the New York
Zoological Park for 3 years, 24 days (1924–27) the record was considered
noteworthy.

On October 1, 1940, a male Kikuyu colobus (*C. p. kikuyensis*) was
received at the Zoological Garden of San Diego. Stott (1952) gives
the history of this animal, destined to set new standards for colobus
monkeys in captivity. Captured in the Kenya forests while still an
infant, "Solemn John" was evidently well looked after, for he
had matured at the time of his purchase by a representative of the San
Diego Zoological Society. Once settled at San Diego, he thrived on a
diet of fruits, vegetables, and leaves, developing a special fancy for the
foliage of the blackwood acacia, an Australian import established in
the Garden. So complete was the adaptation of this animal to
new conditions that he was still living in 1963 (George H. Pournelle, *in litt.*),
having established a longevity record far in excess of any previously
known.*

In New York our own first really successful experience with colobus
monkeys began on June 15, 1949, when Charles Cordier, then our collector,
arrived from the then Belgian Congo with a large consignment. This included
four Angola (*C. p. angolensis*) and three Uele colobus (*C. p. uellensis*).
The former group consisted of a mature female and three subadult males
of which she had taken charge. The Ueles were a male and two females,
also living peaceably together. When acquired by Cordier, the animals had
already been kept in captivity and had been fed largely on sweet potato
vines, a diet that was continued by him. Before arrival of the shipment in
New York, we secured from the South a quantity of fresh vines which,
kept in cold storage, carried the animals until they became accustomed to
food more readily obtainable. When the change had finally been accomplished, the diet, still continued, was as follows:

*See Addenda, p. 732.

Angola colobus, per animal, daily:

1 head lettuce
8 white potatoes, raw
1 sweet potato, raw
4 carrots, raw
2 bananas
25 peanuts, whole
4 slices rye or raisin bread
½ pt. reconstituted evaporated milk with coddled egg, Cerevim or similar cereal, and ½ tsp. cod-liver oil
celery, leaves of bamboo, and Russian mulberry, when available

Uele colobus, per animal, daily:

Same regimen, with the exception that these animals will not drink milk and cod-liver oil is given on bread or peanuts

Grapes are taken sparingly by both races, but oranges are refused. Neither will eat apples but will pick out the seeds and sometimes chew the skin. Meat in any form is refused.

In reference to the food requirements of colobus monkeys, Urbain and Nouvel (1954) advance the opinion that *C. abyssinicus (polykomos) occidentalis* cannot survive in captivity without an abundant supply of the leaves of the vine *Vitis vinifera*, mulberry (*Morus alba*) or Aucuba (*Aucuba japonica*). They suggest that these leaves supply an essential element not present in garden vegetables, fruits, or greens. The opinions of such authorities cannot be disregarded, and since there seems to be no reason why the requirements of the many races should vary widely, there is the possibility that the comparatively small supplies of mulberry leaves available here during the summer and the blackwood acacias of San Diego may be of more importance than the mere supplying of bulk.

Up to 1959 our colobus groups were kept in summer in outdoor cages about 15 feet square and 13 feet high, with open shelters. Protection from strong sunshine was provided by split bamboo shades attached above the cage tops. Heavy branches were arranged for maximum leaping distances, of which the animals made full use. Late in October the monkeys were removed to heated indoor cages of slightly smaller dimensions. In 1959, with the completion of alterations of the interior of our Monkey House, the colobus families were installed there. While they no longer had access to the open air, they had shown no loss of condition or vigor up to 1963.

These apparently successful solutions of the problem of the maintenance of colobus monkeys have resulted in several instances of breeding. The first birth of a colobus monkey in captivity, as far as I know, was that of an Angola born here on February 15, 1952 (McClung, 1952). It was typically pale buffy-white in color, with the skin of face, ears, hands, and feet pinkish. By the next day these parts had all become dark gray. At the time of birth the mother was still in the company of the three males, and we were faced with the necessity of deciding whether or not to remove them. Unfortunately, we made the wrong decision and allowed the males to remain, with the result that constant disturbance caused the loss of the infant on February 26. Its weight, at the age of eleven days, was .924 pounds. Following this disaster, one of the males was selected at random as a mate for the female and the two others were removed.

On September 25, 1952, an infant was born to one of the Uele colobus females. This birth was followed by a struggle between the two females for possession of the youngster, amicably settled by removal of the mother's rival (McClung, 1952). The weight of this youngster, which was picked up by the keeper during the disturbance, on the day of birth, was 1.18 pounds. It proved to be a male and was fully reared.

The third colobus birth of which I have knowledge occurred when the female of a pair of the Kikuyu race received at San Diego in April, 1950, produced a youngster on December 25, 1952. This animal was safely reared, and notes on its color changes have been recorded by Stott (1953b) and an anonymous author (1953b). Several further births have occurred in the San Diego colony, including one on July 15, 1961 (Anon., 1961a).

Births to our Angola female occurred on January 30, 1953, and December 23, 1954, and births of Uele colobus occurred on June 5, 1959, June 24, 1960, and July 20, 1961. In each case rearing progressed normally and without difficulty. Twin fetuses were aborted by a Uele female on March 27, 1963. The birth of a Kikuyu colobus at the Zoological Gardens of Frankfurt on July 9, 1959, appears to have been the first in Europe (Kirchshafer, 1959).

In all instances of colobus births here, except only the first, the father, ordinarily docile, became extremely defensive and aggressive. I have been informed by Ken Stott, Jr., that the same reaction was noted following the San Diego birth. The absence of this behavior in the three males present when the first Angola was born made identification of the father impossible. All showed curiosity concerning the baby, but when the cage was approached, none came forward in defense.

In 1963, our Uele colobus colony consisted of a male obtained from the Lincoln Park Zoological Gardens, Chicago, in 1956, two females from the 1949 importation, and two youngsters born in 1960 and 1961, respectively.

Of the Angolas, only the original female of 1949 and her daughters of 1953 and 1954 remained, the last male having died in 1956.

For some reason, the beautiful races of *C. badius*, in various combinations of red, bay, olive, and black, are even more rare in captivity than the black and white forms of *C. polykomos*, and I have found few references. A bay colobus (*C. badius* ?subsp.) is listed by Flower (1929:10) as having been shown in the Zoological Gardens of London, with the note, "A female purchased 16 October 1890, lived for a few days only." Hayman (1950) says a young female of Temminck's red colobus (*C. b. temminckii*) was received at the Zoological Gardens of London in 1949 but "unfortunately lived only a short time."

A pair of bay colobus (*C. b. ellioti*) sent to us from the western Belgian Congo by Charles Cordier arrived here on October 2, 1959. The female was in moribund condition and died almost at once, but the male lived until October 4, 1961—not an encouraging record but apparently the best so far recorded for the species. When first received, this animal was given raw white and sweet potatoes, bread, lettuce, kale, mulberry leaves, carrots, peanuts, bananas, grapes, monkey pellets, raw chopped meat, bits of fish, and milk. From this array he fed sparingly, taking bits of all of the items without showing particular liking for any. This practice continued during his short stay here.

FAMILY PONGIDAE

GREAT OR ANTHROPOID APES: GIBBONS, ORANG-UTAN, CHIMPANZEES, AND GORILLAS

In this family the general interest in primates as zoological-garden exhibits reaches its climax. Fortunately, members of all of the groups can be maintained in captivity under proper conditions, even the gorillas, once thought impossible, having yielded at last. All of the great apes lack tails and cheek pouches, but the gibbons, at least, possess callosities on the buttocks as do members of the Cercopithecidae. Distribution is confined to the forests of the Old World, the gibbons being found in southeastern Asia and some nearby islands, the orang-utans in Borneo and Sumatra, the chimpanzees and gorillas in the tropics of central and western Africa.

GIBBONS

Smallest of the manlike apes, the gibbons are considered by some authorities to form a family of their own, Hylobatidae, rather than a subfamily

Hylobatinae of the Pongidae, as treated here. The gibbons are usually thought to include seven species, with numerous races, of a single genus, *Hylobates*. These extend from Assam and western Yunnan south through Burma, Indochina and the island of Hainan, Thailand and the Malay Peninsula to Sumatra, Java, Borneo, and some smaller islands.

Because of variations in body color, some of the gibbons present difficulties of identification in life. There is no trouble with the siamang (*Hylobates syndactylus*), which, in addition to large size and inflatable throat pouch, is always black in both sexes, as is the dwarf gibbon (*H. klossii*). But the matter is less simple with the white-handed (*H. lar*), in which hands, feet, and facial ring are white, the agile (*H. agilis*), with only a white facial ring, and the hoolock (*H. hoolock*), in which the white is usually reduced to a band on the forehead. All of these species occur in two color phases, black or shades of brown, independently of sex. Even more confusing is the Indochinese or crested gibbon (*H. concolor*), in which the adult male is black with white or buffy cheeks in some races and the female pale buff with dark cap. The young of both sexes are buff at birth, later turning black, the females eventually reverting to their natal coloration (Pocock, 1905; Delacour, 1942). In this species the clitoris of the female is very long (Pocock, 1905, 1925), as it is in female spider monkeys, often resulting in the same errors in sexing. The several forms of the gray or silver gibbon (*H. moloch*), of Java and Borneo, are readily known by the gray coloration set off by a black cap.

More completely adapted for an arboreal life than are the other anthropoids, the gibbons move through the trees with great facility, swinging by their elongated arms and getting tremendous momentum by releasing their holds at the most advantageous instant. Leaps of 30 and 40 feet from branch to branch are easily accomplished in this way. On rare visits to the ground they walk upright and even run, sometimes at surprisingly good speed. The same method is used in walking along lofty branches. Ability to maintain balance in the upright position is highly developed, and I have often watched gibbons walking a tightly stretched wire, used as a tree support, sometimes with food held in their hands.

The loud, musical voices of gibbons, intensified in the siamang, are well known to zoo visitors. Carpenter (1940) found that the calls of white-handed gibbons in the forests of Thailand were heard most frequently in the morning, less often in the afternoon, and seldom during the middle of the day. This timing appears to be maintained by captive animals.

Over-all experience with gibbons in captivity has brought them a reputation for delicacy. Poor results have followed the acquisition of groups of young animals, among which serious fighting develops as they mature. Restricted cage area that does not allow sufficient space for proper exercise and lack of an effective source of vitamin D are further causes of failure. When these basic requirements are satisfied, gibbons will give results as satisfactory as those to be expected with other anthropoids.

The most natural method for grouping gibbons is plainly indicated by the field researches of Carpenter (1940). It was found that the white-handed gibbon lives in small parties consisting of an adult male and female, such offspring, perhaps as many as four, as have not yet reached maturity, and occasionally a senescent male. Such families are strongly territorial and resist invasion of their areas by others. Carpenter considers that maturity is reached between the ages of 6 and 8 years, at which time, whether voluntarily or by expulsion, the animal leaves the group and presumably seeks a mate of its own. These observations confirm the empirical practice of keeping adult gibbons in pairs and the obvious fact that adult males are natural enemies. The same rule does not always apply to females, which may sometimes become friendly with each other. An instance is found in two animals of this sex, a white-handed and a gray (*H. moloch*), which have lived peacefully together here since 1941.

Cage space for gibbons should not be less than 20 feet in length, longer if possible, with width and height proportionately ample. Branches or other perch devices should be so arranged as to allow as much space as possible for brachiation. In such an inclosure, whether indoors or out, healthy gibbons will be almost constantly in movement during daylight hours, making a most attractive exhibit.

When gibbons are kept indoors, there is some difficulty in supplying vitamin D. The common practice of adding cod-liver oil or drops of vitamin concentrate to milk will not serve, for most adults will not drink milk or, at best, very little. This may be related to the almost invariable habit of drinking water by dipping the hands, elevating them, and allowing the fluid to drip into the mouth. It has always seemed to me that they dislike putting their hands into milk—at any rate, they usually will not do so. Incidentally, where constantly running "bubble" fountains are provided, our gibbons drink from them by placing their mouths directly over the small outflow. This refusal of milk makes it necessary to administer cod-liver oil in some part of the food, as suggested below. Because of the uncertainty of this method, we have resorted to brief exposure daily to the rays of ultraviolet lamps, thus insuring a sufficient supply of vitamin D.

In planning a cage for gibbons, a shift cage should always be included.

Young gibbons which have been hand-reared invariably are tame and most engaging. However, as they mature they become unreliable, some actually savage. Since females as well as males possess very long, slender canine teeth, the sexes may be equally dangerous. Consequently there should always be means for secluding the animals before a gibbon cage is entered.

During the winter months we keep our gibbons behind glass at temperatures between 70° and 75° F., with humidity maintained at about 50 per cent. Some of the species, at least, can endure very much lower temperatures. Delacour (1933) says that Indochinese gibbons (*H. concolor*) kept at semi-liberty on his estate at Clères, in northern France, endured temperatures as low as −11° C. (12.2° F.) without difficulty.

While gibbons may be accommodated in the usual wire-covered outdoor cages during the summer months, the island method described by Delacour (1933) and used by him at Clères provides an approximation of natural conditions that is possible for few captive animals. The point is that while it appears to be true that no anthropoid is able to swim naturally, gibbons have a particular aversion to water and will not willingly cross or enter it (Carpenter, 1940; Delacour, 1933). The small islands at Clères, each usually inhabited by a single gibbon, are separated from the mainland by narrow strips of water hardly more than 10 feet across, yet they form impassable barriers. On one of my visits, I noticed that the branches of a tall tree growing on the mainland were so close to those of one on an island that they could be easily reached by a gibbon. Yet Mr. Delacour assured me that even at such a height above the water the island inhabitant had never ventured the crossing.

In 1942 we placed two white-handed gibbons, along with a small troop of spider monkeys, on an island approximately 150 feet long by 75 feet wide in one of our lakes. As already related, the spider monkeys soon found means to cross the 35 feet of water, 18 inches deep, that separated the island from the mainland. Gibbons, however, have never attempted to do so, although they have had opportunity in each summer but one, following the original experiment. It is of interest to note that visitors, who are provided with a viewing area on the mainland, frequently attempt to throw food to the gibbons. This usually lands in the water and if it floats close enough, the animals will gingerly retrieve it. Never, however, have they been seen to enter the water nor will they reach beyond safe distances.

Since leafy trees of various sizes grow on the island, the gibbons are completely at home and their remarkable brachiated leaps, musical voices, and upright walking habits combine to form an exhibit surpassingly attractive. During these more than 20 years of island operation only two tragedies occurred. In the absence of keepers a young white-handed gibbon just over a year old was seen by a visitor to miss his grip on an overhanging branch and fall into water not more than 2 feet deep, 3 or 4 feet from the island. While it floundered helplessly, its mother watched from the shore but made no effort to assist it. By the time keepers could arrive, the young gibbon had drowned. The second instance concerned another young animal, killed when a tree crashed during a summer hurricane.

Carpenter (1940) gives a detailed account of the food materials eaten by wild white-handed gibbons. The principal item is fruits, with leaves, buds, flowers, birds' eggs and young, insects, and possibly honey. A typical daily feeding for an adult gibbon here is as follows:

2 apples
2 oranges
2 bananas
2 slices rye, whole-wheat, or raisin bread
2 hard-boiled eggs
½ head lettuce or equivalent amount of cabbage
2 oz. steamed chopped horseflesh, with ½ tsp. fine bone meal and
    1 tsp. cod-liver oil added
a handful of monkey pellets

Gibbons have not bred too frequently in captivity, perhaps because potential breeders have not often been kept together until maturity. Sányál (1892) says, "Nothing is known about their breeding in captivity," although it might be supposed that the Calcutta Zoo would have afforded favorable conditions. The first captivity breeding record appears to be that of a white-handed gibbon born in 1920 to a mother kept at semi-liberty in a compound in Thailand (Ogilvie, 1923). This was followed by two births of the same species in 1923 and 1924, in the Zoological Gardens of Rangoon (Robinson, 1925). Robinson concluded in the first instance that the gestation period was 9 months, but closer observation prior to the second birth caused him to reduce the estimate to 7 months.

Since these early records were established, births of gibbons in captivity have become much more frequent. The first in this country appears to have been that of a gray or silver gibbon (*H. moloch*) in the San Diego Zoological Garden on May 10, 1938 (Benchley, 1938, 1940*a*). This was quickly followed by a white-handed gibbon, born in the Zoological Garden of Philadelphia on August 14, 1940 (Ulmer, 1955). A hybrid between a male black-capped (*H. lar pileatus*) and a female agile (*H. agilis*) was born and reared in the National Zoological Park, Washington (Walker, 1954). The birth of a siamang at the Milwaukee County Zoological Park on July 10, 1962, seems to be the first recorded instance of the breeding of this species in captivity (Speidel, 1963).*

In Europe an Indochinese gibbon (*H. concolor*) was born at Clères, France, on Christmas Day, 1941 (Delacour, 1942). Hill (1949) reports the birth of a white-cheeked gibbon (*H. c. leucogenys*) in the Zoological Gardens of London.

Very remarkable results appear to have been achieved in the Zoological Gardens of Adelaide, Australia. In *Zoo News*, a report sheet of the Royal Zoological Society of South Australia, for July–August, 1954, it is stated that no less than ten gibbons (species not given) have been bred and that a female born in October, 1944, gave birth to her first young in August, 1954. This probably is the first instance of reproduction by a captivity-bred gibbon.

Our own experience in the breeding of gibbons is limited to the offspring of a single pair of white-handed received here on September 11, 1942, and still living in 1963. These animals are both of the buff phase, and the seven viable single young so far born to them have been of this color. During recent winters they have been kept behind glass in a large cage in our Great Apes House, but previously in whatever quarters were available. All summers but one have been spent on the island already described. On September 10, 1945, while the animals were still on the island, the mother was seen to be carrying an infant transversely across her lower abdomen. Later in the same day it climbed upward and nursing was observed.

Notes on the progress and development of this first infant have been recorded (Crandall, 1945*a*, 1945*b*, 1946). The principal points were as follows: At birth the body was naked or nearly so, with crown patch and thin mantle of buffy hair, the exposed skin being dark in color. On October 6, when the gibbons were removed to a large wire-inclosed indoor cage separated from the public by a barrier of glass, hair covered the back and the outer surfaces of the limbs as far as knees and elbows. Its interest in its surroundings had progressed to the point of picking up bits of food as its mother was feeding. These she invariably took away before the infant could convey the food to its mouth. Soon after the family had been brought indoors, the father began to show increased interest in the baby, which culminated in a squabble between the parents. The male was then removed to an adjoining cage and when he was returned, several weeks later, he made no further trouble. The young gibbon was seen off its

*See Addenda, p. 732.

mother's body for the first time on October 22, but not until another month had passed did she allow it to crawl as much as a foot away. On December 14 the infant was seen clinging to the wire netting; two months later it was climbing freely and the first efforts at brachiation were noted. At this time, too, it was observed walking upright, holding tightly to one of its mother's hands; up until then it had progressed on flat surfaces by creeping on all fours. Not until it was 15 months old and had passed a summer on the island with its parents was it seen to walk upright, alone. The young gibbon's first solid food, a few bread crumbs, was taken at the age of 4 months, and even at 7 months its intake was carefully limited by the mother.

This young gibbon, which proved to be a female, continued to live amicably with her parents until early in January, 1952, when she was approximately 6 years, 4 months old. Persecution by both parents, beginning a few weeks earlier, had then become so serious that it was necessary to remove her. Shortly afterward she was introduced to a cage containing a young male and the two animals quickly became companionable. Unfortunately, the female soon afterward developed an irreducible rectal prolapse and euthanasia was required.

During the period when this young female was living with her parents there were two further births, one on June 10, 1948, the other on March 29, 1951, followed by a stillbirth on November 7, 1952. The older sister caused no difficulty at these times. She played freely but gently with the first youngster when it began to get about, until its death by drowning on July 31, 1949, as already related. The infant born on March 29, 1951, may have been somewhat premature, for it was less vigorous than its siblings, exposed skin was pinkish instead of being dark, and its development failed to progress normally. It lived for 14 months and at death was found to have been afflicted with advanced rickets.

The fifth birth to this pair was that of a male, on August 13, 1953. This infant made normal progress but was killed by a falling tree, as already recounted. This date of birth is of particular interest, since copulation by the parents was observed by the keeper on January 10, 1953. This indicates a gestation period of 215 days, which is as nearly accurate as single observations can be and closely approximates the estimate of Robinson, already noted. Copulation by the parents for the first time following this birth was seen by their keeper in January, 1955, but no birth resulted. Normal births followed on December 29, 1955, December 3, 1958, and May 23, 1961, with an intervening stillbirth on March 5, 1960. It is of interest to note that when the gibbons were brought indoors in October, 1961, persecution of the young male born December 29, 1955, was so serious that his removal was necessary. His age at that time was just under 6 years.

As family life progressed, the behavior of the male changed markedly. After the first birth he no longer interfered with mother and young. Instead, he developed strong defense reactions. Indoors there was no difficulty because a shift cage was always available. However, when the family was on the island during the summer, his aggression was another matter. His fierce, incredibly swift bite-and-run tactics, typical of gibbons, resulted in damage to the clothing and sometimes to the persons of visiting keepers. For this reason it became necessary for two men to make the trip by boat, one to defend the other.

Recorded durations of gibbons in captivity would seem to indicate a comparatively low viability for the group. Mitchell (1911) gives an average of 9 months and a maximum of 51 months for thirty-nine specimens of *Hylobates* received at the Zoological Gardens of London up to then. Flower (1931) says, "Instances of their living in captivity to 9 years are rare." However, he quotes the report of Robinson (1925) that a specimen of the white-handed lived for 18 years in the Zoological Gardens of Rangoon and also mentions the remarkable animal of the same species in the Philadelphia Zoological Garden as still living after more than 23 years.

Our best records here have been established by a white-handed gibbon received June 27, 1940, and a gray received June 13, 1941, both still living in 1963. A noteworthy longevity for a siamang is that of a superb male that lived in the National Zoological Park for "about 14 years" (Walker, 1954). Most remarkable of gibbon records is that of the white-handed referred to by Flower, which finally died in the Philadelphia Zoological Garden in 1938, after 31 years, 7 months (*Rept. Penrose Res. Lab.*, 1938:10). I well remember seeing this animal for the first time in 1909. It was a male of the black phase and spent its life alone in a long, narrow, and rather dark cage in the old Mammal House, famous for the excellent condition in which its inhabitants were kept. The unique accomplishment of this gibbon goes beyond the mere establishment of a record. It makes obvious the point that maximum longevity potentials in this group have not previously been realized, and that better results may be in store.

ORANG-UTAN

The orang-utan (*Pongo pygmaeus*), "man of the woods," is found only in heavily forested lowland areas of Borneo and northwestern Sumatra.

Early accounts of its habits in nature have been furnished by Wallace (1869) and Hornaday (1880, 1910), while Yerkes and Yerkes (1929) and Hooton (1942) have fully summarized information more recently available.

Progressive physical changes from birth to maturity are extreme in the orang-utan, particularly in males, and it is possible that these have caused the long continued confusion in speciation and the many names that have been assigned to supposed species and races. While at the present time it is usually thought that there is a single species, with no races, it is possible that the Bornean and Sumatran populations may yet prove to be separable (Chasen, 1940).

Adult male orang-utans are very much larger than females, but there are wide differences in the few actual weights that have been recorded. Hornaday (1880:447) gives the average for males as from 120 to 160 pounds, but the same authority (1904:10) later revised the maximum to 250 pounds for "a large, full-grown male," an estimate which Yerkes and Yerkes (1929:104) call "surprising." Schultz (1940a) reports the average weight of thirteen adult males as 74.89 kilograms, or approximately 165 pounds, and for eight adult females 36.85 kilograms, or approximately 81 pounds.

Animals that have died in captivity do not always give a true picture, since an ailing orang-utan loses weight rapidly. A very large male with cheek callosities fully developed, deposited here in 1936 by the late Martin Johnson (Anon., 1936), was estimated to weigh 200–300 pounds. However, at necropsy, 4 months after arrival, he was found to weigh $127\frac{1}{2}$ pounds.

Recent weights of living animals indicate that Dr. Hornaday's revision is closer to the truth, at least as far as captive specimens are concerned. The late Axel Reventlow, former director of the Zoological Gardens of Copenhagen, told me in 1954 that a male kept in his institution had reached a maximum weight of 120 kilograms (264 pounds). Robert Bean, director of the Chicago Zoological Park, has informed me (*in litt.*) that a male obtained by his institution in 1940 weighed 265 pounds on the day of arrival. In a résumé of the past year's events, *Zoonooz*, February, 1953, reports that "the Orang-utan 'Kokok,' received from Soerabaya in August, 1940, died today [March 18, 1952]. At autopsy he weighed 335 pounds." Mrs. Belle J. Benchley, former director of the Zoological Garden of San Diego, has confirmed this weight (*in litt.*). A male known as "Andy," received here in 1947, weighed 450 pounds in 1959, at an estimated age of just over 13 years. The suggestion that animals in nature would be unlikely to acquire such bulk seems to be in order.

Accurate weights of females have been recorded even less frequently than those of males. As already noted, Schultz (1940a) gives the average for eight adult females as 36.85 kilograms or approximately 81 pounds. The greatest weight for a female that I can find in our older records is 85 pounds for an animal of unrecorded age that had been here for 5 years and was still living. A young female called "Sandra," received here in 1948 when her age was estimated to be 2 years, weighed 168 pounds in 1959 at the approximate age of 13 years.

In contrast with the other anthropoids, the orang-utan is slow and deliberate in its movements. It is almost entirely arboreal in habit, drawing itself from limb to limb with unfailing caution by means of its long and immensely powerful arms. The building of sleeping platforms or nests in trees has been described by many authors, as summarized by Yerkes and Yerkes (1929:119–22).

On the ground the orang-utan usually progresses on all fours. However, it is perfectly capable of walking upright, waddling slowly on its short and bowed hind legs, usually with arms extended above the head. This ability may be the result of captivity conditioning, for the method is not practiced by all individuals.

Early experience with the orang-utan in captivity was scattered and certainly not encouraging. Loisel (1912, 2:31) says that the first living specimen seen in Europe probably was one kept in Holland in 1640 by Frédéric-Henri of Nassau, one of the princes of Orange. The Zoological Society of London received its first orang-utan in 1830, but it survived for only two days (Flower, 1929). A sensation was created by the arrival in America in 1825 of an orang-utan credited with looking after its own cage-cleaning details (Jeffries, 1825). Later importations became increasingly more successful as far as longevity is concerned, but most of the real advances are fairly recent. Best results have probably been obtained with animals imported while still young. Although such specimens once were maintained only with great difficulty and considerable loss, it is probable that the majority are now safely reared or at least carried beyond the stage of infancy. A survey of orang-utans living in captivity in this country in 1960 showed a total of seventy-nine individuals as of December of that year.

Between 1925 and 1930, many "families" of orang-utans were imported into this country and elsewhere. These groups usually consisted of a large adult male (separately caged), a female, and a youngster, all presumably wild-caught. For the most part, these "families" gave unsatisfactory results, and the unpleasant traffic was soon abandoned.

For any lack of activity and alertness in captivity the orang-utan compensates with persistence. In constructing quarters, therefore, it is essential to make certain that there are no parts that may yield to the constant attention of strong, untiring fingers or to more direct force. Sufficient space for necessary exercise and varying levels for the sake of interest should be provided, for while the orang-utan becomes less active as he gains in age and weight, he still requires living room. A shift cage, of course, must be provided where adult animals are involved.

Young orang-utans are especially keen on swings and soon acquire great skill in operating them. In constructing these we have found even the heaviest rope to be useless, as it is too quickly unbraided by the animals. Chains may be dangerous, as a young orang-utan easily becomes entangled and is then likely to hang helplessly until rescued. The only safe and successful swings we have been able to devise are made of rigid metal piping, hung at the top from stout eyes just large enough to permit free movement but with insufficient clearance for the insertion of an exploratory finger. As the animals become older and heavier they lose interest in swings, which then serve only as encumbrances and therefore have been omitted from our indoor arrangements.

Andy and Sandra, referred to above as having been received here in 1947 and 1948, respectively, were still living together in 1963 in a cage measuring 16 feet, 9 inches long by 15 feet, 6 inches deep and 16 feet, 8 inches high in our Great Apes House. It is provided at the back with ledges at broken levels. Imbedded in the surface of the upper one is a large section of pressed wood which serves as a sleeping bench and offers variation from the finely troweled concrete with which the cage is floored. A simulated tree form with a small elevated platform gives opportunity for climbing exercise.

Cage fronts are of $\frac{5}{8}$-inch bars of cold-rolled steel, set on 3-inch centers. The sections are 6 feet high with two cross-members of $1\frac{3}{4}$ by $\frac{7}{16}$-inch steel, set 2 feet apart. These bars, painted dark green, do not interfere unduly with visibility and have so far proved fully efficient in restraint. A glass barrier erected at guardrail distance seals the animals from visitors.

Hediger (1950:59) gives an account of the unsuccessful use of electric barriers for confining orang-utans and chimpanzees in the Zoological Gardens at Düsseldorf. I have only once seen this method of restraint tried for an orang-utan and in that instance it was completely successful. The animal in question was a very large and powerful male though still subadult, kept at the small but well-operated Hershey Zoo at Hershey, Pennsylvania. His outside inclosure was of heavy wire mesh but his constant attentions had resulted in the loosening of one section. An electrified wire, about 12 inches from the floor and the same distance from the damaged side, had so completely baffled the animal during the entire summer that he no longer approached it.

Open outdoor quarters for orang-utans may be simple in design and offer many advantages over the barred or wire-inclosed cage. The water moat does not make a practical barrier, because while this animal seems to lack the inherent fear of water seen in the gibbons and may readily learn to wade in shallows, it appears to be helpless beyond wading depth. But a 10-foot wall at the outer perimeter of the moat and the same height of side walls is sufficient restraint, since the leaping ability of the orang-utan is practically nil. As for all of the great apes, which are essentially forest animals, protection from the direct rays of the summer sun must be available in at least some part of the outdoor inclosure.

Five of the seven indoor cages of our Great Apes House connect with large moated outdoor areas (Crandall, 1950). These yards are separated from each other by brick walls 10 feet high and from the public by strips of water 14 feet across, surmounted by an outer wall of concrete, also 10 feet high. As originally constructed, the water depths ranged from 3 to 6 feet but later, to avoid risk of accidental drowning of animals, the depths were reduced to stand at from 6 to 18 inches.

It was in one of the smaller of these inclosures, in the autumn of 1950, that our only experience with an orang-utan in water beyond wading depth occurred. The new building was not quite complete, but to test the animal's reactions, Sandra, the young female referred to above, then approximately 4 years old, was placed in the outdoor yard. A keeper was assigned to remain with her until the experiment had been completed, but an emergency called him away for perhaps 5 minutes. On his return, Sandra was missing, but a slight rippling of the surface of the moat explained the mystery. Leaping into 3 feet of water, the man quickly found the young orang-utan weakly fumbling about on the bottom, making no proper effort to extricate herself. First-aid treatment brought complete recovery, but until the water depth had been reduced beyond the danger point the orang-utans were never again allowed outside unattended. Yerkes and Yerkes (1929:117–18) have summarized published accounts of the swimming ability of this species, most of which support the supposition that any skill in this direction is nonexistent.

Feeding schedules followed here for orang-utans, from infancy to adulthood, contain most of the basic items of human consumption, with the exception that these animals do not ordinarily eat meat. Goss

(1947*a*) gives the following regimen used for the young Andy, received here on June 27, 1947, at the estimated age of 18 months, weight 10 pounds 13 ounces:

8:30 A.M.: 5 heaping tsp. of precooked baby cereal, plus 3 drops multiple vitamin concentrate, in 2 cups whole milk
11:00 A.M.: 1 cup tomato or orange juice
1:00 P.M.: strained vegetable or baked potato, 1 apple, orange, or banana; 1 slice of bread
4:30 P.M.: 3 tsp. precooked cereal baby food in 1 cup whole milk, with 1 fresh egg (poached, soft-boiled, or raw), on Mondays, Wednesdays, and Fridays

It was soon found that Andy was having difficulty in assimilating whole milk, and reconstituted evaporated milk was substituted with better results. He had not been accustomed to taking liquids from a bottle but drank freely from a cup.

About one year later, when Andy's weight had increased to 30 pounds, his diet was as follows:

8:30 A.M.: 1 pt. reconstituted evaporated milk, to which were added 10 drops multiple vitamin concentrate, 1 tsp. cod-liver oil, $\frac{1}{2}$ tsp. dicalcium phosphate, 1 poached egg, 1 tbs. honey, and $\frac{3}{4}$ cup precooked cereal baby food
11:00 A.M.: 2 carrots, $\frac{1}{2}$ stalk celery, $\frac{1}{4}$ head cabbage, 2 raw white potatoes, 3 beets
3:00 P.M.: 3 bananas, 2 apples, 2 oranges, $\frac{1}{4}$ lb. grapes, 3 slices raisin bread
5:00 P.M.: same as 8:30 A.M.

This extensive menu brings up an important point. While it is possible that an orang-utan of Andy's size and weight might occasionally consume the greater part of the solid food provided, ordinarily it picks and chooses, wasting far more than it eats. However, it seems safer to supply food in abundance and variety, to make certain that even a finicky appetite will be satisfied. If the allowance is restricted, consumption will certainly be reduced and malnutrition may result.

When Andy had reached the weight of 225 pounds and the estimated age of just over 9 years, his schedule was:

8:30 A.M.: 3 qts. milk mixture made by stirring into a small quantity of water 4 level tsp. powdered milk, 3 poached eggs, 1 tsp. cod-liver oil, 1 tbs. Karo corn syrup, 1 tsp. salt, 4 oz. precooked cereal baby food, $\frac{1}{2}$ tsp. dicalcium phosphate, and 10 drops multiple vitamin concentrate. Water was then added to make up the three quarts.

3:00 P.M.: 6 apples   ¼ head cabbage
            3 oranges   ½ stalk celery
            10 bananas   2 raw white potatoes
            3 carrots   1 raw sweet potato
            ½ head lettuce   2 slices raisin bread
            Also scattered green beans, spinach, grapes, pears, and
                melons as available, and two handfuls of monkey
                pellets.
5:00 P.M.: 3 qts. milk mixture, as above, but minus vitamin drops.

Sandra, the female orang-utan received on October 18, 1948, was fed
in the same manner but in lesser quantity. There was also the important
difference that while Andy, at 225 pounds, drank 6 quarts of milk mixture
daily, Sandra, at 110 pounds, took only 1 pint at a sitting or 1 quart daily.
The milk mixture was fed to the orang-utans, as to chimpanzees and gorillas,
by means of a metal pitcher, the lip of which was narrow enough to be
inserted between the cage bars from the front. It was held in position by
the keeper until each animal had its fill. Neither of these orang-utans
ever accepted meat in any form.

Difficulties periodically encountered in getting these orang-utans to the
scales prevented the recording of complete progress on weights. However,
the figures in Table 2, at intervals of roughly 1 year, offer a general
record in spite of unavoidable gaps.

TABLE 2
WEIGHTS OF ORANG-UTANS

Andy, Male			
June 27, 1947	10 lbs. 13 oz.	Mar. 16, 1955	225 lbs.
June 8, 1948	30 lbs.	Mar. 21, 1956	280 lbs.
July 1, 1949	56 lbs.	Mar. 8, 1957	340 lbs.
June 20, 1950	70 lbs.	Mar. 19, 1958	395 lbs.
July 13, 1951	90 lbs.	Apr. 24, 1959	450 lbs.
1952	No record	Mar. 1, 1960	444 lbs.
July 19, 1953	141 lbs.	Mar. 13, 1961	405 lbs.
Aug. 3, 1954	186 lbs.	Mar. 13, 1962	380 lbs.

Sandra, Female			
Oct. 18, 1948	9 lbs. 14 oz.	Mar. 21, 1956	136 lbs.
Oct. 3, 1949	28 lbs.	Mar. 8, 1957	148 lbs.
Sept. 21, 1950	40 lbs.	Mar. 19, 1958	140 lbs.
1951	No record	Apr. 24, 1959	168 lbs.
1952	No record	Mar. 1, 1960	162 lbs.
Nov. 17, 1953	69 lbs.	Mar. 13, 1961	160 lbs.
Oct. 25, 1954	92 lbs.	Mar. 13, 1962	150 lbs.
Mar. 16, 1955	110 lbs.		

As will be noted, both Andy and Sandra reached maximum weights in
1959. At that time Andy was noticeably obese, Sandra less obviously so,

and food allowances, particularly of milk mixture, were drastically reduced, with fairly satisfactory results in weight reduction, as listed.

When first received, at the estimated age of 18 months, a tiny fold of skin at each side of Andy's face forecast the great pads that might one day develop there. These folds appeared to enlarge only proportionately as Andy grew, but on March 16, 1955, when his weight had increased to 225 pounds, it was noted that the folds had acquired a width of about 1 inch and that there was a slight but definite filling out of the face, suggesting the curious disklike flattening seen in fully adult males. The change was fully completed within a year, the disk measuring $12\frac{1}{2}$ inches across. The laryngeal sac had reached really tremendous proportions, extending from armpit to armpit and falling in great folds over his massive chest.

Presence or absence of cheek pads has caused much confusion in the past, since very large males often lack them. Ulmer (1946) says the pads appear when the animal is about 10 years of age, growing to full size in approximately 6 months, but later (1958) gives an instance in which 17 years were required. He states, also, that "Guas," the large male still living in the Philadelphia Zoological Garden in 1963, did not develop pads until after his arrival in Philadelphia in 1931, although he had already sired an infant in Cuba before his transfer. From the scanty evidence available, it appears that male orang-utans may reach large size and even become sexually mature before the facial pads develop. Perhaps there are still insufficient grounds for presuming that all normal males eventually produce them, but the supposition is difficult to avoid.

Although field observations, as summarized by Yerkes and Yerkes (1929), seem to indicate that in nature adult males do not consort regularly with females and young in family groups, more work is necessary to clarify the point. In any case, male and female ordinarily will live amicably together in captivity, although some provision may be required at feeding times to make certain that the female is not deprived of her due share. Groups of females usually get on well, once the animals have become acquainted, but males beyond the stage of infancy cannot, of course, be kept together.

While it is generally assumed that the orang-utan achieves sexual maturity at somewhere between 8 and 10 years (Yerkes and Yerkes, 1929:141) the facts have not yet been fully determined. The only exact report of the gestation period is that of Aulmann (1932:84), who found it to be 275 days. This uncertainty concerning the sex life of the orang-utan is undoubtedly due to the fact that until fairly recently pairs were seldom maintained to maturity, a situation paralleling that of the gorilla today.

The first orang-utan actually bred in captivity was probably one born on January 12, 1928, in the Zoological Gardens of Berlin, followed in the same year by others at Nuremburg and Philadelphia. Since that time births have been fairly numerous and have occurred in this country, particularly, in the zoological gardens of San Diego, St. Louis, and Philadelphia. Guas and Guarina, received at Philadelphia from the collection of Mme Abreu of Cuba in 1931, produced their ninth offspring in 1955 (Anon., 1955a). A complete account of the breeding successes of this pair and their descendants is given by Ulmer (1957). A successful breeding colony, consisting of an adult male and several females, some with young, was observed in the Rotterdam Zoological Gardens in 1951 (van Bemmel, 1959).

When a birth is anticipated, it is customary to isolate the expectant female. In Philadelphia it has become the practice to remove the youngster at about 6 months and complete the rearing by hand, in order to avoid possible development of rickets (Ulmer, 1946, 1955).

While it is probably true that average longevities of orang-utans in captivity are still rather low (Flower [1931:152] says they "rarely live over 8 years in captivity"), the maxima compare well with those established for other anthropoids. Our best here was accomplished by a female called "Gabong" who was purchased from the Zoological Gardens of London on June 28, 1916, and lived until November 20, 1936, or 20 years, 4 months, 23 days. Flower (1931) gives the record of "Sandy," who lived 8 years in Singapore and 18 years, 6 months in London, making a total of 26 years, 6 months, while Rabb (1960) lists 28 years for an orang-utan in the Chicago Zoological Park. Both Guas and Guarina, received at Philadelphia on May 1, 1931, after having been kept for some time in Cuba, were still living in 1963 (Frederick A. Ulmer, Jr., *in litt.*) and had already surpassed all previously known records.

CHIMPANZEES

Hardy, adaptable, and amenable, the chimpanzees are the best known and the most studied of the great apes. The extensive literature has been fully summarized by Yerkes and Yerkes (1929), Hooton (1942), and Yerkes (1943). While much work has been done with chimpanzees in captivity, very little has been learned concerning their lives in nature. That they are highly social in habit is well established, but as yet there is little definite knowledge of the composition of the groups in which they live. Nissen (1931:16–18) reports that numerous bands observed in French Guinea consisted of an adult male (or sometimes two), several adult females, and varying numbers of infants and immature animals. The question of whether or not polygamy is the rule among chimpanzees remains unanswered.

Groups observed by Nissen spent most of the daylight searching for food, either in the trees of the forest or on the ground. As night approached, the building of nests or sleeping platforms high in the trees was observed on several occasions. Nissen concluded that each animal built its own platform and slept alone, with the exception that infants usually shared the nests of their mothers or other adults. From the review of the literature provided by Yerkes and Yerkes (1929:220–28), it is evident that nest-building is practiced by chimpanzees throughout most, if not all, of their range.

The chimpanzees are found nearly across equatorial Africa in forested areas, from Gambia and the lower Congo River in the west almost to the shores of Lake Victoria in the east. They are considered by Allen (1939) to comprise two species: *Pan troglodytes*, the larger chimpanzees, and *P. paniscus*, the pygmy chimpanzee. Three forms of *P. troglodytes* are recognized: *P. t. verus*, ranging from Gambia to the Niger River, *P. t. troglodytes*, found from the Niger to the Congo River, and *P. t. schwein-furthii*, which occurs north and east of the Congo River, from the Ubangi to just west of Lake Victoria. *P. paniscus*, the pygmy chimpanzee, inhabits the (former) Belgian Congo, south of the great bend of the Congo River.

The first two forms of *P. troglodytes* illustrate perfectly one of the greatest difficulties experienced by zoological gardens: correct identification of living specimens, with only external characters to serve as unstable guides. Two readily distinguishable sets of characters are found in commonly imported chimpanzees. In one the skull rises in a high, narrow dome, between large, light-colored, protruding ears. In young animals the facial skin is pale flesh in tone, but with age, pigmented patches appear and gradually cover the area, so that in adults the face may become entirely black. Here we know this as *P. t. verus*, the white-faced chimpanzee. We distinguish *P. t. troglodytes*, the black-faced chimpanzee, as having a low, broad skull and smaller, darker, less protruding ears. In young animals a black mask crosses the eyes and slowly expands as growth progresses, so that the face becomes black, with the hair of the muzzle and sometimes the brows white. These views have already been expressed (Crandall, 1956), with illustrations of the four forms of chimpanzee as we recognize them here. Because of the difficulties in identification of these two forms, it seems best, at least for the present, to follow the lead of other baffled students of living animals (Yerkes and Yerkes, 1929:206; Hooton, 1942:4) and refer to the group simply as chimpanzees, allowing our vernacular to expand as suggested above where we are certain that our usage will be understood.

In Schweinfurth's or the long-haired chimpanzee (*P. t. schweinfurthii*), indicated characters are more readily discernible. The coat is long and full and the face is narrow, coal-black, and almost baboon-like in the adult, usually with only a few white hairs on the chin. The brain case is low but narrow when viewed from the front, while the ears are relatively small, dark, and rather closely set. Schweinfurth's chimpanzee is not common in collections, and I believe the only specimen ever received here is a female purchased in 1951, still living in 1963.

The pygmy chimpanzee (*P. paniscus*) is a small, slender animal with long, thin arms and legs, strongly suggestive of a tailless spider monkey. A young chimpanzee left here by its owner in 1923 was purchased a few days later by Professor Robert M. Yerkes, as recounted and figured by him (1925). Both description and illustration are suggestive of *P. paniscus*, described by Dr. Ernst Schwarz in 1929. I can recall having seen only two examples, an adult female and a younger male, living in the Zoological Gardens of Antwerp in 1951. My notes made at that time read: "Pelage black, rather long. Ears very black, small, partly hidden (by hair). Head noticeably small, face long and narrow. Top of head flat. . . . Skin of face black, including nose. Area about both lips, also chin, pinkish white."

A brief account of *P. paniscus*, well illustrated with photographs of a living specimen in the Zoological Gardens of Antwerp, is given by Palmans (1956). A young chimpanzee of this species was received by the San Diego Zoological Garden in 1960 (Pournelle, 1960b). The first birth of a pygmy chimpanzee in captivity is reported to have occurred at the Zoological Gardens of Frankfurt on January 20, 1962 (Anon., 1962).

Living chimpanzees must have reached Europe during the eighteenth century, perhaps even earlier—Yerkes and Yerkes (1929:199) believe that the animal received in Holland by Frédéric-Henri, prince of Orange, in 1640 was a chimpanzee and not an orang-utan as maintained by Loisel (1912, 2:31). The records are obscure and difficult to unravel. There is no doubt that the first chimpanzee owned by the Zoological Society of London arrived on March 25, 1836, but lived only a little over 5 months. Not until 1845 was another purchased, for £300, a very large sum for those days, so chimpanzees obviously were still great rarities. This second specimen survived for only just above 7 months (Flower, 1929:3). These early experiences must have been discouraging, but they laid the foundation for the improved results of the present day, when chimpanzees are kept and bred without great difficulty.

True weights of living adults of the forms of *P. troglodytes* are not easily come by since, as with others of the larger anthropoids, they are not readily conveyed to the scales. A young male, known as "Buff," born at the Yerkes Laboratories of Primate Biology at Orange Park, Florida, on March 19, 1945, and received here in October, 1950, weighed 140 pounds on March 16, 1955, when almost exactly 10 years old and certainly not at maximum size. A female called "Beti," born at the same institution on May 5, 1947, and received here with Buff, weighed 127 pounds on May 3, 1957, when just short of 10 years of age. The weights of both these animals are considerably in excess of the means indicated by the growth scale given by Grether and Yerkes (1940) and reproduced by Yerkes (1943:57).

Schultz (1940b) gives the maximum of nineteen living adult females as 121.3 pounds and of nine males as 132.3 pounds, with respective averages of 87.78 and 100.1 pounds. Hooton (1942:4) mentions the well-known obese female at Orange Park which weighed 176.4 pounds, probably the highest for the sex that has been recorded. We have here a huge male known as "Jimmy" which we had long been confident would well exceed the average weight. He was received here on May 25, 1945, from the St. Louis Zoological Park at the estimated age of 12 years. His weight on arrival was 147 pounds. Later, as it became obvious that Jimmy was still growing although his figure remained trim, we made continued efforts to check his weight. However, while there was no difficulty in moving him to a neighboring gorilla cage containing a built-in weighing device— when the rightful occupant was out of doors—nothing would induce Jimmy to trust himself on the platform. It was not until June 3, 1955, that a well-directed stream of water confined him to a small area and he took the risk. He was recorded at 190 pounds, the greatest weight then known to me for a chimpanzee of either sex. However, on June 14, 1956, Jimmy reached exactly 200 pounds.

Comparative pulling strengths of chimpanzees and men have been tested by Finch (1943), who found that the ability of male chimpanzees was comparable to that of large men. On the basis of pound for pound of body weight, however, the power of the chimpanzees was superior.

In ordinary locomotion the chimpanzee walks on all fours, resting on the knuckles of the hands and with the feet applied flatly to the ground. In this position it can move with surprising speed when it wishes. The upright or bipedal position is perfectly possible but seldom assumed, except by specially conditioned animals and then for short periods only. Chimpanzees are able brachiators, swinging freely from branch to branch. They are also capable of considerable leaps by means of leg propulsion, an ability that must be considered when outdoor quarters are planned.

Here our chimpanzees are kept in the Great Apes House, in cages similar to that already described for orang-utans. With temperature, humidity, and fresh air intake under complete control, efficient restraint furnished by light but strong bars, isolation from the public by means of glass barriers, and internal arrangements suitable for the animals' needs, we have found this sort of housing completely satisfactory for chimpanzees of all ages. No bedding is provided for these animals nor for any of our anthropoids, beyond the bits of cloth to which very young specimens become so strongly attached.

In the case of chimpanzees, especially, the glass barrier serves a reverse secondary purpose in actually protecting the public from the animals. Chimpanzees often develop an unpleasant habit of spitting saliva which, when reinforced with a mouthful of drinking water, can be projected with force and accuracy. Frustrated by the intervention of glass, the practice is soon abandoned. Many individuals acquire a fair amount of skill, also, in the throwing of food, feces, or other objects with the hands. I well remember being struck by a small stone thrown a considerable distance by a chimpanzee on a moated island at Whipsnade. Only fairly soft materials are—or should be—available to indoor animals, and here again, the glass barrier defeats them.

Our great apes' cages are lined with glazed tiles with the interstices narrow and smoothly finished. Young and medium-sized chimpanzees are able to perform the surprising feat of climbing these walls, in the corners, to the very top by clinging to the almost imperceptible joints while facing either inward or outward. This ability, too, must be borne in mind when the arrangement of light fixtures, etc., is being considered.

Because of the climbing and leaping accomplishments of the chimpanzee, outdoor quarters need careful planning. Our moated great apes' yards, as already described for the orang-utans, present two wall corners of brick. When first used for chimpanzees, we expected that animals so skilful at corner-climbing would undertake to negotiate them and provided electric barriers at some height from the ground to discourage any effort. Rather curiously, no chimpanzee has ever been seen to attempt this feat, and the wires are now in disuse. It seems probable that the greater diversions available out of doors do not make slow and laborious effort worthwhile.

Perpendicular walls ten feet high and fourteen feet horizontally across the shallow moat evoked no escape attempts by either Beti or Buff, the two chimpanzees whose weights are given above. However, we have never dared liberate the big male, Jimmy, for this animal is actually a highly trained acrobat, and we have feared his advanced conditioning might reveal abilities beyond our expectation. Before coming to us, Jimmy had been the star of a remarkable troupe of performing chimpanzees maintained at the St. Louis Zoological Park under the expert supervision of director George P. Vierheller. Jimmy's principal act had been to leap high into the air from the back of one of a circling line of cantering ponies, turn a complete somersault, and alight on the back of the following pony. A chimpanzee of such size and prowess certainly would not easily be contained.

For chimpanzees, the water moat is a safer and more useful barrier than it is for orang-utans. Chimpanzees may learn to enjoy wading in shallows but are more cautious than orang-utans as depths increase. We have had no experience here bearing on the swimming ability of chimpanzees, and I have found no useful references in the literature. Chimpanzees were successfully confined for some time at Whipsnade by a water moat 15–20 feet across and about 2 feet deep in the middle. The animals eventually discovered, however, that they could escape by wading and did so with such persistence that the experiment was abandoned. At the Zoological Park at Vincennes, Paris, in the summer of 1948, a group of five young chimpanzees occupied a large outdoor inclosure of simulated rock fronted by a water moat. There was a drop of about 3 feet from the moat's edge to water level, with a similar depth of water directly below. After viewing this arrangement on several occasions with some concern, I finally was able to make inquiries. "What," I said, "happens when one falls in?" The terse reply was, "They don't!" I was further informed that experience at Vincennes has shown that while chimpanzees may wade into water to chest level, they will not venture farther.

Like young orang-utans, young chimpanzees are greatly attracted by swinging devices of almost any type and are far less likely to become dangerously entangled. Indoor devices that do not mar the appearance of the exhibit are difficult to devise, but in larger outdoor areas there is more latitude. Ingenuity may have a fairly loose rein here, and even the ubiquitous suspended automobile tire, greatest attraction of all, may well produce amusement value to compensate for unsightly appearance.

Shade, of course, is as essential for the chimpanzee as for other anthropoids during the summer months. Where this must be furnished by artificial means it is often difficult to do so without providing obstructions which may hide the animals from the view of spectators. We have found a thick slab of carefully shaped and finished concrete, resting on three or four slender pillars of the same material 4–5 feet high a satisfactory solution. The structure fits well into general decor and will provide temperatures several degrees lower than those registered in the direct rays of the sun. Animals seeking their shelter are never completely hidden. In use in our great apes' inclosures for some years, these slabs were later replaced by more decorative shades of wood that are attractive if somewhat less effective.

Feeding methods in use for captive chimpanzees are now so varied that it is not possible even to summarize them here. The carefully developed schedules of Yerkes (1943), Ratcliffe (1940, 1947, 1953), and numerous other authors are well known and readily available.

Known food preferences closely approximate those of man, so that wide variations in the choice of items may still produce satisfactory results as long as the basic requirements are met. The most complete notes on the feeding habits of chimpanzees in nature are those of Nissen (1931), made in western French Guinea. He lists a total of thirty-four fruits, leaves, and blossoms, many of astringent nature, which are included in the diet. Although it is commonly presumed that chimpanzees eat a considerable amount of animal food, Nissen (*op. cit.*, p. 64) says, "My observations provided no evidence that chimpanzees catch and eat large animals, such as birds, rodents and fish, or that they eat birds' eggs. I consider it entirely possible, however, that they do use any or all of these organic foods without my having seen them do so." *

These notes fit well with the fact that there is great variation among individual chimpanzees regarding animal products. Some will take meat freely, others will not touch it. Results of feeding experiments conducted by Benson, Young, and Fremming (1955) indicate that meat and eggs may be omitted from the diet without adverse results. It was found that mixed groups of adult chimpanzees given fruits, vegetables, and cereal, the latter prepared to include powdered milk, salt, and mineral and vitamin supplements, were adequately nourished, while diets composed exclusively of either fruits and vegetables or cereal alone did not produce satisfactory results.

The feeding schedules followed here for chimpanzees are those already described for the orang-utan, with allowances for weight and age variations. There is the important difference that most chimpanzees will take meat in some form, although occasional individuals will refuse it altogether

*See Addenda, p. 732.

(see Yerkes and Yerkes, 1929:231–34). When it is taken, we provide an adult animal daily with about 4 ounces of steamed chopped horse meat, with 1 teaspoonful of fine bone meal and 2 teaspoonfuls of cod-liver oil added.

A typical day's feeding of the very large male, Jimmy, mentioned above, is as follows:

8:30 A.M.: 1 or 1½ qts. milk mixture, made as described for orang-utan, Andy

3:00 P.M.: 3 oranges (sometimes refused)
6 apples
6 bananas
¼–½ loaf raisin bread
¼ head cabbage
1 head lettuce
5 medium-sized carrots
3 pieces celery
½ lb. grapes
1 sweet or 2 white potatoes
Meat mixture, as described above (this is sometimes refused)
2 handfuls monkey pellets

5:00 P.M.: 1 or 1½ qts. milk mixture less vitamin drops

This regimen approximates that of Andy, the orang-utan, a much heavier animal, except that the intake of milk mixture is greatly reduced. Also, Jimmy usually takes meat mixture, which Andy never does.

We have had no experience here in the feeding of newborn chimpanzees but should expect satisfactory results from the formula of van Wagenen (1950), already described under lion-tailed macaque (p. 110). Early care of a chimpanzee born in the Philadelphia Zoological Garden and neglected by its mother has been fully described by Fox (1929). A detailed account of the care and development of four chimpanzees born in the Zoological Gardens of London is furnished by Budd, Smith, and Shelley (1943), and a study of a single infant is reported by Jacobson, Jacobson, and Yoshioka (1932).

Drinking water, of course, should be available at all times. In the early days of transport by slow and tortuous means, difficulties in providing unpolluted drinking water led to the common practice of providing tea for chimpanzees. This served the twofold purpose of giving assurance that the water from which it was made had been boiled and acting as a mild curb on the diarrhea to which the animals were notoriously subject. This suspicion of drinking water, no doubt well founded, has never been completely eliminated from the word-of-mouth lore of animal diet, and water is still sometimes withheld from chimpanzees in the belief that it is harmful. Chimpanzee quarters here are provided with constantly running bubble-type fountains set at floor level, from which the animals drink by applying their mouths directly over the flow.

Writing as late as 1929, Yerkes and Yerkes (p. 263) were able to list only ten births of chimpanzees in captivity: five in the Cuban collection of Mme Abreu, three in the New York Zoological Park, one in the Philadelphia Zoological Garden, and one in Berlin. The first Cuban birth occurred on April 27, 1915 (Montané, 1916), the first in New York on July 14, 1920 (Blair, 1920), the Berlin event on April 1, 1921 (Von Allesch, 1921), and the first Philadelphia success on October 1, 1928 (Fox, 1929).

Following the opening of the Yerkes Laboratory for Primate Biology at Orange Park, Florida, in 1930 (Yerkes, 1943:289–301), captivity breeding of chimpanzees became fairly frequent. A pregnant female brought down from Yale University provided the first birth at Orange Park on September 11 of the opening year. Incidentally, this infant, known as "Alpha," was still living at Orange Park in 1955 (Gray, 1955). She was the first of a long and continuing series; Gray says more than fifty chimpanzees have been born at Orange Park "in the last 10 years."

At Philadelphia, "Sultan" and "Marianne," who produced their first infant in 1928, followed with six more in successive years (Ulmer, 1955). At least two generations of young have been bred at the San Diego Zoological Garden (Stott, 1954) as well as at Orange Park, and there have been numerous other instances in this country.

The first birth of a chimpanzee in England occurred at the Clifton Zoological Gardens, Bristol, in 1934 (Clarke, 1934), the second at the Zoological Gardens of London in 1935, the same male having functioned as father in each instance (Wyatt, 1935).

It has been customary to isolate the expectant mother in the supposition that the male might damage the infant. However, Yerkes (1936) describes an instance of a well-mated pair left together during gestation, parturition, and rearing with completely successful results. Ulmer (1955) reports an opposite and unfavorable result with orang-utans in the Philadelphia Zoological Garden.

Yerkes (1943:56) gives the mean age at first menstruation as 8 years, 11 months, and the average gestation period as 231 days. Single births are usual, but Peacock and Rogers (1959) have reported several occurrences of twins at the Yerkes Laboratory for Primate Biology.

The best longevity recorded here was achieved by a female named "Fanny," received April 1, 1916, died October 3, 1941—25 years, 6 months,

2 days, most of it in pre-glass days. Flower (1931) reports 26½ years for a chimpanzee in the Zoological Gardens of London as the longest span known to him at that time. There are chimpanzees at Orange Park with estimated longevities in excess of this figure (Gray, 1955). At least four animals are known to have lived in zoological gardens in this country for well over 30 years: Sultan and Marianne, the famous breeding pair of the Philadelphia Zoological Garden, arrived there on May 29, 1924. Marianne died on August 8, 1957, after 33 years, 2 months, 10 days, and Sultan on March 16, 1962, after 37 years, 9 months, 17 days (Frederick A. Ulmer, Jr., *in litt.*).

Bondo, a male, was received at the San Diego Zoological Garden on March 13, 1924, was transferred to the San Francisco Zoological Gardens on September 25, 1934, and died there on February 6, 1962, after 37 years, 10 months, 24 days (George H. Pournelle and Carey Baldwin, *in litt.*).

The survivor of this remarkable group, "Heinie," a male received at the Lincoln Park Zoological Gardens, Chicago, on June 10, 1924, and still living, apparently in excellent health, in 1963, exceeded the records of his rivals in that year (R. Marlin Perkins, *in litt.*). None of these animals was born in captivity, so far as known, so that their actual ages were greater than stated spans in captivity.

GORILLAS

As late as 1915 William T. Hornaday, director of the New York Zoological Park from 1896 to 1926, in writing a review of the history of the gorilla in captivity, took a dim view of the possibilities of the future. He said, "There is not the slightest reason to hope that an adult Gorilla, either male or female, ever will be seen living in a zoological park or garden. . . . It is unfortunate that the ape that, in some respects, stands nearest to man, never can be seen in adult state in zoological gardens; but we may as well accept that fact—because we cannot do otherwise."

These are not the negative words of a confirmed pessimist but rather those of a rugged and determined realist, whose unhappy experiences with captive gorillas had convinced him of the soundness of his position. Although he mentions the fact that a gorilla (the well-known "Pussi") had lived in Breslau for just over 7 years (1897–1904), he evidently considered this achievement to have little bearing on the problem. How could he have known that Pussi's record was actually only the beginning, to be followed by the advances in knowledge reflected in the list presented by

Grzimek (1953) showing a total of fifty-six gorillas living in captivity at that time, at least three having been kept for more than 20 years ? Or that the sturdy, active younger captive animals, many approaching maturity, could be as vigorous and full of life as any chimpanzee ? For it is true, at least as far as maintenance is concerned, that the gorilla, last of the anthropoids to yield, is no longer an enigma.

It is not strange that early efforts to keep gorillas in captivity were carried on so persistently, in spite of many disappointments. Although properly described and named by Savage and Wyman in 1847, the gorilla still remains, in popular conception, a fearsome, almost mythical creature. This impression, largely fostered by the lectures and writings of Du Chaillu (1861), perhaps will never be completely eradicated. No one can view a superb adult male gorilla, such as those that have been seen in various zoological gardens since Dr. Hornaday's declaration of frustration, without feeings of awe. It is only too easy to transmute him, in imagination, into the storied terror of the jungle, abductor of native women. That he is ordinarily quiet, even inclined to lethargy, unless disturbed or annoyed is not easily accepted.

While encouraging progress has been made in the maintenance of the gorilla in captivity, it is only recently that extended field studies have revealed some of the details of its life in nature. Most earlier writers have agreed, as summarized by Yerkes and Yerkes (1929), that the gorilla lives in groups but that the composition of such bands and the relationship of their members to each other were difficult to determine. That parties of gorillas may include more than one adult male has frequently been reported. Akeley (1923:447), in describing the tracking of an old male, says, "When we finally came up with him there were, in addition to a number of females and youngsters, at least two and I believe three, other old gray-backed males in the troup." Whether such bands are normal or fortuitous, whether the family group is dominated by a single adult male, as reported to Hooton (1942:82–84) by the missionary George Schwab, or even whether the gorilla is actually monogamous or polygamous were long unknown. The necessity for intensive study of all phases of the biology of the gorilla before it is too late has been strongly emphasized by Yerkes (1951).

Such studies, at least relating to the mountain gorilla (*Gorilla g. beringei*), have since been undertaken. The first really detailed investigation was carried on in the Uganda Gorilla Sanctuary by Miss R. Osborn from October, 1956, to January, 1957, and continued from that date to the end of September, 1957, by Miss J. H. Donisthorpe, altogether completing a year of intensive observation. Many notes on habitat, group territories, movements, and behavior were made, and a detailed list of food plants is given (Donisthorpe, 1958). Between March, 1959, and October, 1960, under the sponsorship of the New York Zoological Society, John T. Emlen, Jr., and George B. Schaller worked intensively in both the Uganda Sanctuary and the mountains of the eastern Congo, the former for the first six months, the latter for the entire period. Intimate contact was established with gorilla bands, and much information concerning family organization and behavior was obtained (Emlen and Schaller, 1960a). A thorough study of distribution was also made, and it was estimated that the total population of the mountain gorilla ranges between 3,000 and 15,000 individuals (Emlen and Schaller, 1960b). An illustrated account of the expedition has been given by O'Reilly (1960). Detailed results of these studies of the mountain gorilla have been published in monographic form by Schaller (1963).

There seems to be no doubt that gorillas are accustomed to spending the night in nests grouped closely together on the ground, but there is less agreement about whether or not these nests are sometimes built in low trees or vines. Raven (1931:233) presents a photograph of nests in both situations, which probably represents a fair summary of this habit. Fletcher Reynolds, late director of the Cleveland Zoological Park, informed me that two young animals in his collection carried automobile tires each night to their sleeping shelves and lined them with empty sacks, forming serviceable nests. "Oka," our adult female, laboriously gathers dry leaves in autumn as they fall into her inclosure and forms them into a flimsy circle in which she sprawls. Benchley (1940a:123) reports that each of the two huge male mountain gorillas then living in the San Diego Zoological Garden built a nest of straw at night.

Even the distribution of the gorilla was long in doubt, and presumably because of the great variation in skeletal characters that exists in these huge anthropoids, numerous species and races, many of which are now considered to be untenable, have been described. Based largely on the studies of Coolidge (1929), it is now generally agreed (Allen, 1939) that there are two recognizable races: the lowland or coast gorilla (*Gorilla g. gorilla*), found in southeastern Nigeria, the Cameroons, and the Congo Republic (formerly French Equatorial Africa), east to the Sanga River, entirely north and northwest of the Congo River; and the mountain gorilla (*Gorilla g. beringei*), which inhabits the highlands of the eastern Republic of the Congo (formerly Belgian Congo), extending from just north of the equator southward to the western side of Lake Tanganyika and spilling down into Uganda on the eastern slopes of the mountains. While it seems probable that the range of the gorilla may at one time have been continuous, there is no evidence that it now exists in the vast jungle area, several hundreds of miles across, that separates the two present populations, and the few existing records from the past are of doubtful value (Coolidge, 1929).

Characters distinguishing the two subspecies have been summarized by Coolidge (1929) and Schultz (1934), the most obvious points being the short arms, long black hair, and the narrow lengthened face of the mountain gorilla. Fleshy pads at the back of the head are found in both races, as pointed out by Strauss (1942). There is the further distinction that the adult mountain gorilla appears to attain greater weight than does the lowland. Willoughby (1950) gives the average weights of adult animals taken in nature as follows:

> Mountain gorilla, male, 458 pounds
> Mountain gorilla, female, 240 pounds
> Lowland gorilla, male, 344 pounds
> Lowland gorilla, female, 188 pounds

As might be expected, weights of some captive specimens have greatly exceeded those reported for wild animals. The weight of "Ngagi," one of the huge male mountain gorillas kept at the San Diego Zoological Garden, is given as 639 pounds just before his death on January 12, 1944 (Anon., 1944). Willoughby (1950) gives the weight of "Mbongo," the second of San Diego's male mountain gorillas, as 660 pounds. However, Benchley (1942) says the last definite weight recorded for this animal was 618 pounds, and that in later efforts to determine it, the scales "fluctuated from 645 pounds to nearly 670" because of the inability of the platform of the scales to accommodate the huge bulk of his body. Consequently, there seems to be no definite weight maximum for Mbongo.

The greatest recorded weights for captive male lowland gorillas appear to be those of "Bobby," who lived in the Zoological Gardens of Berlin from March 30, 1928, to August 1, 1935, and weighed $262\frac{1}{2}$ kilograms (577.5 pounds) at death (Heck, 1936), and the superb "Bushman," who lived in Lincoln Park Zoo, Chicago, from August 18, 1930, to January 1, 1951, and achieved a maximum weight of 550 pounds in November, 1949 (Steiner, Rasmussen, and Fisher, 1955). The large male "Phil," received at the St. Louis Zoological Park in September, 1941, was estimated to weigh 236 kilograms (519.2 pounds) in 1953 (Grzimek, 1953). Unfortunately, no apparatus was available for weighing this fine animal in life.

The greatest weight attributed to a captive female is that of "Susie," who lived in the Cincinnati Zoological Gardens from June 20, 1931, to October 29, 1947. In 1940 her weight was given as 305 pounds (Stephan, 1940), but Gordon (1947) says, "Susie's weight, before her [final] illness was 458 pounds." The female, "Toto," received by Mrs. E. Kenneth Hoyt in 1932 and transferred to Ringling Brothers Circus in 1941, is reported by Grzimek (1953) to have weighed 197 kilograms (433.4 pounds) at that time. Grzimek also raises a question concerning the true sex of this animal. "Oka," received at the New York Zoological Park in September, 1941, achieved her greatest weight, 350 pounds, in August, 1956. "Solange," received at the Jardin des Plantes, Paris, in 1931 and who died December 20, 1954, is reported by Grzimek (1953) to have weighed 120 kilograms (264 pounds). Solange was a noticeably small and slender animal, so that Grzimek's statement seems more appropriate than the estimate of 150 kilograms (330 pounds) given me verbally by her supervisor in 1951.

Locomotion in the gorilla closely parallels that in the chimpanzee, the weight being carried on the flat of the feet or sometimes on their outer edges and on the knuckles of the hands. An adult gorilla is perfectly capable of standing upright, but seldom attempts locomotion in that position except for short distances when hand supports are available. However, I have frequently seen our large female, Oka, take three or four running steps bipedally before dropping her hands to the ground. In nature the gorilla seeks most of its food on or near the ground, although younger animals, at least, are quite capable of climbing trees when occasion demands (Yerkes and Yerkes, 1929:408). In captivity the same general pattern is followed, young or at least immature specimens climbing freely but with none of the agility of the chimpanzee, while the heavier adults are far less venturesome. Our female Oka appears to enjoy drawing herself up to solidly supported heights, but her bulk makes such adventures look risky. Young animals in play may often launch themselves in flat or downward leaps for distances of a few feet, but I have never seen an adult attempt such feats. Certainly, leaping plays but a small part in gorilla activities.

Breast-thumping is a common practice in gorillas. It usually consists of rapid blows of the open hands struck against chest or abdomen. The performance is generally of short duration, for the animal must stand nearly upright, a position it cannot maintain for long without support. This gesture has often been interpreted as one of rage or defiance, but actually it appears rather to be an expression of well-being and is usually followed by activity of inoffensive nature. Breast-thumping is frequently practiced by very young animals and may be seen in adult females. I believe it is less common in adult males, although they certainly perform this action on occasion.

Experience with the gorilla in captivity, outside Africa, extends over only a century, so that the record is fairly clear. Early arrivals in Europe and America have been listed in detail by Yerkes and Yerkes (1929) and by Tratz (1953). It appears that the first gorilla to be seen alive in Europe was an animal kept in England in 1855 by Wombwell's traveling menagerie. Shown as a chimpanzee, it was not until after its death that it was identified as a gorilla (Sclater, 1877). Young living specimens were received in Berlin in 1876, 1881, and 1883 (Lydekker, 1893–96, 1:45–46) but none lived for more than a few months. The Zoological Gardens of London's first gorilla was a young animal purchased in 1887 (Bartlett, 1899:146). As already mentioned, the first longevity of consequence was established by "Pussi," who lived in the Breslau Zoological Gardens from September, 1897, to October, 1904 (Yerkes and Yerkes, 1929:384). Since those early days, of course, there have been many gorilla arrivals in Europe. Most famous of these are "Bobby," Berlin, 1928–35; "Alfred," Bristol, 1930–48; and the gentle "Solange," who arrived in Paris in 1931 and died December 20, 1954.

The first living gorilla to reach the United States is said by Hornaday (1897) to have been an infant animal which arrived at Boston on May 2, 1897, where it lived for only 5 days in the possession of the Edwards brothers, who had imported it.

The second arrival in this country was that of a young female brought to the New York Zoological Park by R. L. Garner on September 23, 1911. Due to long transportation delays, the animal was in weak condition when received and died twelve days later on October 5. The only food taken during her brief stay here was the hearts of two small banana trees, sacrificed by the New York Botanical Garden, and the inner linings of banana peels (Hornaday, 1915).

The third living gorilla to arrive in America and the first to be exhibited was "Dinah," collected in what was then French Equatorial Africa by R. L. Garner for the New York Zoological Park and received here on August 24, 1914. Dinah appeared to be in excellent condition and throve, at first, on a varied diet (Hornaday, 1915) which included fruits, cooked beef, chicken, or lamb, milk, and raw eggs. However, she began eventually to fail and died 11 months and 7 days later, on July 31, 1915. The cause of death is given on her record card as "malnutrition, rickets." The impending loss of Dinah was directly responsible for Dr. Hornaday's unhappy forecast of the future of the gorilla in captivity, quoted earlier in this section.

The first really viable gorilla to come to America was "John Daniel," a lowland male whose sojourn here was short indeed. John Daniel was obtained in London in 1918 by Miss Alyse Cunningham and carefully reared in her home there. A fine, robust animal, he was taken to the Zoological Gardens of London on summer afternoons and shown there in an outside cage of the Lion House, where I well remember seeing him in 1920. Miss Cunningham (1921) has furnished a full account of the history of John Daniel. Sold to an American circus in the spring of 1921, he died soon after his arrival in this country. Following the unfortunate death of John Daniel, a new era for gorillas in America began. On August 5, 1927, the infant "Bamboo," weighing 11 pounds, arrived at the Philadelphia Zoological Garden. Bamboo lived at Philadelphia until January 21, 1961, establishing at his death the so far unequalled longevity of 33 years, 5 months, 16 days. An account of Bamboo's life at Philadelphia is given in *America's First Zoo* (Anon., 1961b). Conant (1939) gives the general diet of the young Bamboo and a companion chimpanzee as including fruit, lettuce, zwieback, milk, honey, and cod-liver oil.

On October 31, 1928, a female lowland gorilla known as "Janet Penserosa" was received at the New York Zoological Park, her weight on arrival being 17¼ pounds. As is too often the case, both Janet and a companion chimpanzee suffered from a severe dermatitis and were heavily parasitized, conditions which soon yielded to treatment. Noback (1931) gives the principal items of the diet of these two young animals as milk, raw eggs, bananas, oranges, boiled rice with raisins, cod-liver oil, and bone and blood meal. He notes particularly a fondness for the inner lining of banana peel or for the peel entire. Janet continued to develop well on this diet, even after the removal of her chimpanzee companion, which finally became unmanageable. Noback (*loc. cit.*) gives a chart of her weight increases from 7.84 kilograms (17.25 pounds) at the estimated age of 19 months on arrival to 26.36 kilograms (approximately 58 pounds) at the estimated age of 49 months. Janet later contracted a partial paralysis of the legs, resulting in a permanent deficiency. She was transferred to Dr. J. F. Fulton of the Yale School of Medicine on July 29, 1940, having been kept here for 11 years, 8 months, 29 days. Her weight then was 74.89 kilograms (approximately 165 pounds).

Less than 2 years after the arrival of Janet Penserosa, the famous "Bushman" was received at the Lincoln Park Zoo, Chicago, on August 18, 1930. His weight was then 38 pounds; in November, 1949, he had reached approximately 550 pounds (249.4 kilograms), as already noted. Bushman's early history at Lincoln Park has been recorded by Young (1940), who emphasizes the point that the animal was a vegetarian. Bushman's diet, presumably at the time of writing, is given as totaling about 20 pounds of food daily, including 2 quarts of milk and cream with eggs, honey, chocolate, and a small amount of beef extract, vegetables, fruits, and cereals. He also occasionally was given bread spread with fruit jelly. Later, according to Steiner, Rasmussen, and Fisher (1955), the milk-mixture allowance was increased to 3 quarts, the cream was eliminated to control threatened obesity, and multiple vitamins were added. Abstention from meat is confirmed by these authors.

"Susie," the well-known lowland gorilla female, was received at the Cincinnati Zoological Gardens on June 20, 1931, after several years of traveling exhibition in both Europe and America. Her weight on arrival was 85 pounds and in 1940, 305 pounds (Stephan, 1940). As already stated, Gordon (1947) gives her weight as 458 pounds just before her death in 1947. Stephan makes the point that Susie, like Bushman, was a vegetarian: "Fish, fowl or meat have no place upon her menu." Her daily food regimen, at the weight of 305 pounds, is given as follows:

Breakfast: 12 oz. cream of wheat
                3 raw eggs in 1 qt. milk
                3 pieces of zwieback with currant jelly
                1 orange
11:30 A.M.: 1 pt. Jello
                8 oz. sliced peaches with pineapple and strawberries
                1 qt. malted milk
                3 stalks celery
                1 head lettuce
                1 handful grapes
                sliced plums or apricots
4:30 P.M.: sliced apple
                2 bananas
                1 qt. weak tea with 3 raw eggs
                wafers
6:00 P.M.: 6 bananas
                3 stalks celery

Susie was immensely popular with Cincinnati Zoo visitors, and her death on October 29, 1947, after 16 years, 4 months, 9 days brought genuine grief to many.

These accounts of successes in the maintenance of gorillas in captivity in this country, after the death of John Daniel in 1921, would be incomplete without further mention of Ngagi and Mbongo, the magnificent mountain gorillas of San Diego. Captured in the Belgian Congo in 1930 by Martin and Osa Johnson, these animals finally arrived at the San Diego Zoological Garden on October 5, 1931. Benchley (1940b) gives the weight of Ngagi as 147 pounds and of Mbongo as 122 pounds on arrival. She also estimates the age of the larger animal as 5 years and of the smaller 4½ years at that time. On this basis of weight and age, it seems probable that Ngagi and Mbongo were the largest gorillas of either race successfully taken into captivity up to that time. Both animals were males and lived together peacefully, although Ngagi appeared to dominate the more sluggish Mbongo (Benchley, 1940b). The food of these animals is given as between 30 and 35 pounds of fruits and vegetables, each, in five feedings daily. This included carrots, potatoes, apples, and citrus fruits. They were particularly fond of green corn (maize), often eating the husks and cobs, as well as of green bananas. Whole milk was also given, but they refused meat in any form, including small birds, mammals, and reptiles. As already stated, Ngagi weighed 639 pounds prior to his death on January 12, 1944, and Mbongo between 645 and 670 pounds before his death on March 15, 1942.

In the 10 years from 1931 to 1941 several now well-known gorillas reached this country. These included Gargantua and Toto of the Ringling Brothers Circus, Massa of Philadelphia, Phil of St. Louis, and Makoko and Oka of New York.

Improved understanding of the requirements of the gorilla in captivity, coupled with the great advantage of air transportation, has resulted in gradual increase of its numbers in collections. Riess, Ross, Lyerly, and Birch (1949) were able to list twenty-five specimens then living in the United States, Yerkes (1951) found the number to have increased to forty at that time, and Grzimek (1953) gives details of fifty-six individuals, forty-four in this country, twelve in Europe. An unpublished census made by Marvin L. Jones in September, 1961, showed a total of one hundred and nineteen lowland and seven mountain gorillas living in the world, outside Africa, of which seventy-three lowland and one mountain were in the United States.

In the preceding brief account of the history of gorillas in captivity, remarkable improvement in results is obvious, although the means are perhaps less clear. Two points of paramount importance have been advanced by Yerkes and Yerkes (1929:428–29). These are the necessity that the animal be taken at an early age and that it should attach at once to a person, male or female, who will give it the care and security it would have received from its mother. The further need to accustom it to a variety of suitable foods is then readily satisfied. This attachment of the young gorilla is usually transferable to another sympathetic person without a time lapse sufficient to cause loss of condition.

Once the stage of dependent infancy has been passed, the psychological needs of the young animal naturally change. Two successive young gorillas passed their dependent periods here in the care of a particularly sympathetic woman keeper, Mrs. Helen Martini. At the respective weights of 45 and 62 pounds, these animals were moved to exhibition areas in our Great Apes House, where they quickly transferred to a skilful male keeper. It certainly is desirable that contacts of this sort continue throughout the animal's lifetime, even though, at least in males, the attachment may seem to become more tenuous as age increases. Adult females seem to retain a stronger feeling of dependence. This was certainly true of both Susie and Solange, while Oka remains friendly, gentle, and even handleable to a degree.

It has sometimes been considered that an animal companion, usually a young chimpanzee, should be provided for an infant gorilla. However, it has always seemed to me that such a companion reduces the strength of the essential human attachment, and that if the latter is properly maintained, no other companionship is necessary or even desirable.

A variation of this suggested treatment occurs when two or more young gorillas of approximately the same age arrive together. The natural procedure in such cases is to attempt to rear them together, in the hope that any resulting complications can be dealt with as they occur. A case in point is that of the lowland gorillas Makoko and Oka, received here on September 7, 1941. Makoko, a male, then weighed 28.16 pounds and was judged to be about 2 years old. Oka, a female, weighed 20.46 pounds and was considered to be about 18 months old. Both were timid and easily frightened at first, but once a sympathetic male keeper had secured their confidence, their assurance soon improved. However, whenever the more susceptible Oka was startled by unexpected sounds or movements she sought refuge in the arms of the somewhat larger Makoko, who rapidly developed a strongly protective attitude. This situation, of course, blocked complete transfer of either animal to the keeper, and it is to his credit that excellent relations with both were maintained until the death of Makoko by drowning on May 13, 1951 (Crandall, 1951b). Following this tragedy, Oka became more strongly attached to her keepers, as might be expected.

The advancing stages by which present-day feeding systems for gorillas were reached are plainly indicated in the accounts given above of successive animals. Progress seems normal enough except for differences in the use of meat and meat products. Observations made in nature, as summarized by Yerkes and Yerkes (1929:416–19) and Hooton (1942:80–82), indicate that the gorilla is normally a vegetarian. Its raids on the gardens of native villages are largely responsible for the warfare constantly waged against it. Based on these findings, earlier diets of captives, even including Susie and Bushman, usually were meat-free. A notable exception is seen in the case of Dinah, received here in 1914, although the use of "beef, chicken, or lamb" did not prevent her demise in less than one year. Solange arrived in Paris at about the same time (1931) that Susie and Bushman reached America and lived until December, 1954. Her daily diet, as given by Urbain and Nouvel (1954) was as follows:

Cooked meat	250 gms.
Carrots	300 gms.
Cabbage or lettuce	2,000 gms.
Cooked potatoes	150 gms.
Peanuts	100 gms.
Bananas	250 gms.
Dates, figs, oranges, or apples	300 gms.
Bread	250 gms.
Milk	0.5 l.
Eggs	2

Ratcliffe (1940:465), in discussing the diet of Bamboo and Massa in the Philadelphia Zoological Garden, says that in addition to the mixed ration already referred to plus fruits, vegetables, and whole milk, they "are also fed about 200 grams of uncooked horsemeat each day and an equal quantity of boiled horse liver three or four times each week."

The long lives of these three animals indicate the efficiency of the meat-inclusive diet. Reconciliation of this divergence from what is known of the gorilla's feeding habits in nature may be found in the theory of Reichenow, as discussed by Yerkes and Yerkes (1929:417–18) and Grzimek (1953:181–82), to the effect that because of changes in the intestinal fauna of captive gorillas their ability to digest cellulose is reduced and that meat offers a more readily assimilable substitute. Steiner, Rasmussen, and Fisher (1955) suggest that B-avitaminosis may have been responsible for at least some of the pathological conditions disclosed when the necropsy of the meatless Bushman was completed. In any case, the use of meat is now practically universal, and Grzimek goes to some trouble to list the kinds of meat and meat products included by various institutions in the diets of gorillas.

Besides the satisfaction of the psychological needs of infant gorillas and the addition of meat to the diet, other factors have favorably affected the maintenance of captive gorillas. Among these, the use of vitamin supplements, the antibiotics, and the immense advantage of fast transportation by air must be given full credit.

Diets now used for gorillas here appear to be satisfactory and probably approximate generally prevalent treatment. A female mountain gorilla named "Sumaili," the only specimen of this race known to be in captivity in this country up to 1963, was brought to us by Charles Cordier from the Belgian Congo on June 15, 1949. Sumaili then weighed 16½ pounds and was estimated to be between 12 and 18 months old. She was still taking milk from the bottle but also ate some solid food. Her regimen at that time was essentially the same as that used for the orang-utan Andy, as itemized in the section devoted to that species (p. 137). Since Sumaili was a bottle baby, her milk formula was mixed in a Waring Blendor and sometimes thinned, if necessary, by the addition of a little milk. Also, Sumaili was accustomed from the first to take small bits of raw chopped meat, which she accepted readily.

As Sumaili grew, amounts of solid food were gradually increased until, at the weight of 45 pounds, her menu was as follows:

8:00 A.M.: 1 pt. reconstituted evaporated milk to which were added 10 drops multiple vitamin concentrate, 1 tsp. cod-liver oil, 1 raw egg, 1 tbs. honey, and ¾ cup precooked baby food. Mixed in Waring Blendor but drunk from receptacle held by keeper.

10:00 A.M.: 2 carrots
¼ head cabbage
2 raw white potatoes
3 raw beets
2 oz. raw chopped meat with 1 tsp. fine bone meal and 1 tsp. cod-liver oil added.

2:00 P.M.: 3 bananas
2 apples
2 oranges
¼ lb. grapes
3 slices raisin bread

5:00 P.M.: Milk mixture as given in the morning.

As in the case of Andy, not all the solid food was always eaten nor all of the milk mixture drunk, although little of the meat was ever left. Since she was thoroughly familiar with all of the items listed and had developed no dislike for any of them, there was no difficulty in making appropriate increases as required. Sumaili never developed the habit of regurgitating food, especially milk, and swallowing it again, so often seen in young gorillas.

Sumaili's progressive growth, recorded at intervals of approximately one year, was as shown in Table 3.

TABLE 3

WEIGHTS OF FEMALE MOUNTAIN GORILLA, SUMAILI

Date	Weight (Pounds)	Date	Weight (Pounds)
June 15, 1949	16½	June 14, 1956	230
June 7, 1950	41	July 12, 1957	250
July 13, 1951	59	July 30, 1958	270
July 19, 1952	86	Sept. 8, 1959	270
July 9, 1953	117	Oct. 11, 1960	270
May 3, 1954	146	Mar. 13, 1961	255
June 3, 1955	180	Mar. 13, 1962	230

"Mambo," a male lowland gorilla, was received here on May 22, 1951. His weight then was 16 pounds, 5 ounces, and his presumed age between 12 and 18 months. Since both weight and age approximated those of Sumaili on arrival, his diet and treatment were identical with hers. Recorded progressive weights of Mambo are shown in Table 4.

TABLE 4

WEIGHTS OF MALE LOWLAND GORILLA, MAMBO

Date	Weight (Pounds)	Date	Weight (Pounds)
May 22, 1951	16 lbs. 5 oz.	May 3, 1957	236
May 23, 1952	43	July 30, 1958	322
April 29, 1953	66	April 2, 1959	390
May 3, 1954	80	March 1, 1960	398
May 2, 1955	130	March 13, 1961	392
June 14, 1956	180	March 13, 1962	385

Weight drops in both animals after 1960 resulted from reduction of food allowances, to avoid risk of obesity.

Our most extended experience here with gorillas of really large size relates to the lowland pair, Makoko and Oka. As already stated, these animals were received on September 7, 1941, at the respective weights of 28.16 and 20.46 pounds and estimated ages of 2 and 1½ years. The reactions of these animals to each other and to their keeper have been mentioned. Their feeding schedule approximated that used for Sumaili and Mambo, although, since greater weights were reached, volume of food consumed increased.

In March, 1955, the food supplied to Oka, at the weight of 325 pounds, was as follows:

8:00 A.M.: 4 tbs. powdered milk, 2 tbs. Karo corn syrup, 6 tbs. precooked baby food, 3 raw eggs, 1 tsp. dicalcium phosphate, 1 tsp. salt, 1 tbs. cod-liver oil, and 15 drops multiple vitamin concentrate, carefully blended and brought to 3 qts. by the addition of water

2:00 P.M.: 1 lb. chopped horse meat, scalded
8–12 bananas
4 oranges
6 apples
1 bunch celery
6 carrots
1 head lettuce
¼ head cabbage
2 raw or cooked sweet potatoes
4 raw white potatoes
½ lb. string beans
3 stalks scallions
4 slices whole-wheat or raisin bread
Melons, peaches, and grapes in season

5:00 P.M.: 3 qts. milk formula, as above, but without cod-liver oil and vitamin drops

As with younger and smaller animals, Oka's appetite and fancies vary, so that while she may sometimes spoil more food than she eats, at others she obviously would take more. At his maximum weight of 448 pounds at the time of his death by drowning in 1951, Makoko's food requirements were about 25 per cent greater than Oka's. Both animals continued to take milk mixture from the narrow lip of a pitcher inserted between the bars by the keeper, as they had learned to do while still young.

Selections from Makoko's weight records at intervals of roughly one year, are as shown in Table 5.

TABLE 5
WEIGHTS OF MALE LOWLAND GORILLA, MAKOKO

Date	Weight (Pounds)	Date	Weight (Pounds)
Sept. 7, 1941	28.16	1946, 1947	No record
Nov. 9, 1942	64	Oct. 1, 1948	356
Sept. 4, 1943	88	Oct. 4, 1949	418
Sept. 11, 1944	122	Sept. 21, 1950	430
Mar. 8, 1945	138	May 13, 1951	448

Gaps in the records of Makoko were caused by lack of suitable weighing apparatus. Oka's figures (Table 6) are more complete, since they were made, before a proper device was installed, by the keeper stepping upon a small foot-scale with Oka upon his back (Bridges, 1946).

TABLE 6
WEIGHTS OF FEMALE LOWLAND GORILLA, OKA

Date	Weight (Pounds)	Date	Weight (Pounds)
Sept. 7, 1941	20.46	Sept. 9, 1952	270
Sept. 2, 1942	42.9	Nov. 17, 1953	290
Sept. 4, 1943	70.5	Oct. 25, 1954	300
Sept. 11, 1944	102	Sept. 9, 1955	326
Oct. 8, 1945	134	Sept. 7, 1956	330
Sept. 11, 1946	168	Sept. 10, 1957	347
Aug. 24, 1947	208	Oct. 9, 1958	345
Oct. 1, 1948	236	Sept. 8, 1959	350
Oct. 4, 1949	284	Oct. 11, 1960	330
Sept. 21, 1950	306	Dec. 12, 1961	265
Aug. 21, 1951	286	Mar. 13, 1962	250

It will be noted that while Oka progressed fairly steadily until 1950, she showed a sharp drop during the following year, a period marked by the death of Makoko on May 13. Perhaps because of the sudden cessation of the violent exercise to which she had been accustomed during her daily playtimes with Makoko, Oka showed widely fluctuating interest in food, which perhaps accounts for her weight loss. There appeared to be no marked psychological upset beyond increased attachment to her keeper. Drops in 1961 and 1962 followed diet reductions.

Housing and exhibition areas here for orang-utans, as already described, have proved entirely suitable for gorillas, including animals of large size, the only difference being that the principal gorilla cage measures 17 feet, 6 inches in length, slightly longer than that used for orang-utans. Bars of cold-rolled steel, $\frac{5}{8}$-inch in diameter, set on 3-inch centers, have been fully efficient in restraint. They have the further advantage of preventing the extension of a huge hand which might otherwise menace an unwary keeper. A shift cage, of course, with doors operated by remote control, is essential in the management of adult gorillas.

While both young and adult gorillas of both sexes seem to enjoy moving from one floor or shelf level to another, actual tree- or perch-climbing activities become reduced as the animals increase in size and bulk. Oka still ventures, cautiously, on high perches, but Makoko, in his later years, would not risk it.

Installed weighing devices are most important for checking bodily changes in anthropoids. The huge mountain gorillas in San Diego were weighed by extending the platform of the scales into their inclosure at intervals and training the animals to sit upon it (Benchley, 1940a:22). Bushman sat in a great steel chair, suspended from chains attached to a balance (Young, 1940:308). Our method here was to construct a balanced platform, set in a steel coping with clearance too small for the insertion of prying fingers. This platform activates an eye-level register set in the keepers' space outside the center cage, where it is easily read by visitors and thus serves a double purpose. The floor of the platform was originally made of oak planking, but the animals were able to gouge the smooth surface by using their lower teeth as chisels. We then substituted a solid sheet of very hard dye-stock pressed wood, which has proved to be impervious. Since any animal in the building can readily be moved to the cage containing the platform by means of sliding doors, it is usually a simple matter to make regular recordings of weights.

Outdoor installations for gorillas may be of bar construction, but if these are sufficiently large to provide room for proper exercise, they are likely to be not only unsightly but very costly. Limited leaping and climbing abilities in large gorillas make moated inclosures particularly suitable, as long as safe reaching distances are maintained. With sight lines and visibility unimpaired, a large gorilla in an open inclosure gives an impression not likely to be forgotten. The yards of our Great Apes House, as described under "orang-utans" (p. 136), with minimum reaching distances of 10 feet perpendicularly and 14 feet horizontally, have proved entirely satisfactory for gorillas, at least since the water depth in the fronting moats was reduced from 6 feet to 18 inches.

This point brings up the question of swimming ability in the gorilla. The literature contains little evidence, and the scattered references are conflicting. However, such as there are lead Yerkes and Yerkes (1929:409–11) to conclude that the gorilla fears and avoids deep water and cannot swim "without tuition or practice." In a footnote Emlen and Schaller (1960b) say: "In driving animals into capture nets, C. Cordier could not force gorillas to cross streams more than 15 or 20 feet wide and more than 2 or 3 feet deep."

That the gorilla may become conditioned to water of shallow depth is shown by fairly recent experience. Kelly (1952) gives a lively account of water-play in depths up to 2 feet by young gorillas in the San Diego Zoological Garden. The fine male Phil, received at the St. Louis Zoological Park in 1941, became accustomed to water-play at an early age. George P. Vierheller, the former director, informed me that Phil learned to leap freely into water 4 feet deep which rose to his neck when he sat quietly on the bottom. However, he had not been seen to make any effort to swim. Our large female, Oka, who came to this country in the same shipment as Phil, and our two younger animals, Mambo and Sumaili, wade freely in shallow water when it serves their purpose, although they appear to derive no particular pleasure from it.

The tragic loss of Makoko by drowning, on May 13, 1951, has been reported in detail (Crandall, 1951b). Briefly, the animal lost his balance while moving along the moat edge and tumbled into the water, then 6 feet deep. Two keepers saw the accident from the visitors' rail but could not enter the inclosure from that position. Within minutes others entered the yard from the building, and one, himself barely able to swim, dived into the water and found one of Makoko's hands, by means of which the 448-pound animal was hauled out. It was judged that immersion had lasted from 5 to 10 minutes, and all efforts at resuscitation failed.

This fatal result of a trivial accident brings up several points of particular interest. Makoko had had no opportunity to become conditioned to water, so that the element encountered in his plunge was entirely strange to him. His reactions approximated those of the small orang-utan, Sandra, already noted. He sank from sight almost immediately, apparently making only futile efforts to extricate himself, and was completely submerged when found by the swimming keeper. Certainly he made no effective attempt to swim nor did he seize the steel cables set along the moat side, under water, against such an emergency. While this unfortunate incident would seem to establish the fact that the gorilla, like other anthropoids, does not swim naturally, it does not rule out the possibility that an animal like Phil of St. Louis might eventually learn to do so.

In the matter of swings, hanging ropes, and similar devices, gorillas show wide variation in reactions. As in so many other aspects of behavior, early conditioning undoubtedly plays an important part. At one period Makoko and Oka spent much time in hammocks made of stout chains. Later they seemed to lose interest, and the chains were removed as obstructive. When first received, Sumaili learned to make some use of a swing of chains with a metal crossbar. Eventually, however, she was saved, at the last moment, from death by strangling, when she hung suspended by one of the chains which she had managed to twist around her neck. After that experience nothing could induce her to go near a hanging rope or chain. On the other hand, the young male "Guy," when seen at the Zoological Gardens of London in 1948, showed unusual ability in swinging from a rope suspended from the top of his cage. Guy would seize this at its free end and, pushing with his feet against the walls, twist it until he had been drawn nearly to the ceiling. He then would release the tension and hang on firmly as he was spun swiftly to the floor. These sketchy and conflicting accounts, of course, furnish insufficient evidence for a definite statement. Nevertheless, my own feeling is to the effect that swings and similar devices are not essential for gorilla development and that the risk of entanglement outweighs any possible benefit.

Until very recently, reproductive processes in the gorilla were practically unknown, for up to 1956 there had been no captivity birth. The normal explanation of this situation is that in all of the years of experience with captive gorillas no mature male and female, with the possible exception of Makoko and Oka, had ever lived together. Moreover, a generally pessimistic feeling had arisen, based on the fact that in most large males brought to necropsy the sexual organs had been found to be undeveloped or atrophied, a condition usually attributed to food deficiencies (McKenny, Traum, and Bonestell, 1944; Hediger, 1952; Grzimek, 1953; Steiner, Rasmussen, and Fisher, 1955). The only exception followed the death of Makoko at the probable age of 11 years, 8 months, when scrapings of the testicles revealed motile sperm (L. J. Goss, pers. comm.).

The female cycle was unknown, except for the reports of C. V. Noback (1936) and C. R. Noback (1939). These relate to observations on the lowland gorilla, Janet Penserosa, who lived in the New York Zoological Park from October 31, 1928, to July 29, 1940. Menstruation was first detected on March 29, 1936, although this may not have represented the actual menarche. At that time Janet was presumed to be approximately 9 years old and at the beginning of the tenth year. Observation continued for just over a year, and the menstrual cycle was considered to average 43 days. The gestation period of the gorilla was unknown, and the only recorded birth weight was the report of Reichenow (1921) of 2 kilograms (4.4 pounds) for an infant captured at the estimated age of two weeks.

Makoko and Oka, the first captive pair of promise, might have achieved the goal but for Makoko's untimely end. The animals were strongly attached to each other, but because of the fear that their great weight and boisterous play might result in accidental injury, they were allowed to be together for only a few hours daily. When the separating doors were opened, they would rush together, embrace, and then engage in a period of wild chasing, wrestling, thumping, and mock biting in which the initiative might be taken by either. This might continue for as much as an hour and be resumed after a short period of rest. Despite the indicated maturity of Makoko and the fact that at the time of his death Oka was approximately 2 years older than Janet at menarche, the only sexual manifestation noted was casual and occasional digital exploration on the part of Makoko (Riess, Ross, Lyerly, and Birch, 1949).

Because of the difficulty of making observations without the indicated conditioning, undesirable in an animal constantly under the view of the public, we had no knowledge of Oka's developmental state. Menarche, of course, could not have been far off, although lack of sexual activity seems to indicate that it had not yet occurred. The problem of obtaining data on the progress of sexual development in the gorilla or, for that matter, the ready determination of sex in a given individual is complicated by the relatively small size of the genitalia and the density of the hair of the area. Useful guides for sexing living animals, especially when some handling is possible, are furnished by Goss (1947b).

The great increase in the numbers of gorillas in captivity, from the late forties on, much improved the possibility of breeding, for many potentially compatible pairs were included. This expectation was justified, on December 22, 1956, by the first birth of a lowland gorilla in captivity, at the Zoological Garden of Columbus, Ohio (Thomas, 1958). The parents were received on January 8, 1951, when the male was estimated to be aged a little over 4 years, the female 1½ years. As they developed, their play became so boisterous that time together was limited. However, contact was maintained through intervening bars, and eventually, during a period when they were together, first coitus was observed on January 9, 1955. Many further observations of coitus were made, in either dorso-ventral or ventro-ventral positions. Conception was believed to have occurred between April 6 and April 8, 1956, giving a gestation period of 257–59 days. The infant was abandoned by the mother but fortunately was discovered and revived, with some difficulty, within minutes. Its weight is given as approximately 4 pounds, 2 ounces. Placed in an incubator and fed on Olac, a commercial baby food, it made excellent progress and was a well-developed youngster in 1963. It had yielded, of course, biological facts of the greatest importance. A study of the development of this infant gorilla was made by Knobloch and Pasamanick (1959).

On March 29, 1958, a female at the Zoological Gardens of Basel aborted a fetus (Lang, 1958), but on the night of September 22–23, 1959, she gave birth to a normal baby (Lang, 1959). The mother refused to nurse her offspring, to which she clung so tightly that it could be removed only after she had been tranquilized. It was then reared by hand without difficulty (Lang, 1960). On April 17, 1961, a third birth occurred to the same female, after a gestation period of 252 days. This time the mother cared well for the infant, as described and figured by Lang (1961).*

On September 9, 1961, the female of a pair of lowland gorillas that had been received at the National Zoological Park on February 24, 1955, gave birth to a normal baby. The mother refused to care for it, and it was removed for hand-rearing. Late in 1963, it was progressing well (Theodore H. Reed, *in litt.*).*

Births of the mountain gorilla in captivity appear to have occurred only at the Belgian Institute of Scientific Research (IRSAC) at Lwiro, Bukavu, in the western Belgian Congo. Here, several specimens of the mountain gorilla captured by Charles Cordier in 1957 were kept in a large, secluded inclosure. On October 26, 1959, a single infant was born, but unfortunately it was killed, apparently by accident, by the mother. Its weight is given as 1 kilogram, 965 grams, or just over 4 pounds (van den Berghe, 1959). Mrs. Emy Cordier (*in litt.*) has reported a second birth to the same female on June 1, 1961, this young animal, although apparently well cared for by the mother, dying on June 24, 1961.

The potential age maximum of the gorilla in nature is, of course, unknown. At least six individuals, all of the lowland form, are known to have lived in captivity for 20 years or more. These are:

Bushman, received at the Lincoln Park Zoological Garden, Chicago, on August 18, 1930, died January 1, 1951, after 20 years, 4 months, 14 days.

Oka, received at the New York Zoological Park on September 7, 1941, still living, 1963.

Solange, received at the Ménagérie of the Jardin des Plantes, Paris, on September 20, 1931, died December 20, 1954, after 23 years, 3 months.

Massa, received at the Philadelphia Zoological Garden on December 30, 1935, still alive in 1963.

Toto, obtained in French Equatorial Africa by Mrs. E. Kenneth Hoyt in 1932, at the estimated age of 3 months (Hoyt, 1941). Kept in Cuba until 1941, Toto was then sold to Ringling Brothers Circus. Repurchased by Mrs. Hoyt in 1956, Toto has rejoined the Circus each year for its New York engagement. During this appearance in April, 1962, Mrs. Hoyt (*in. litt.*) confirmed this brief account and assured me that Toto remained in good health at that time.

Bamboo, received at the Philadelphia Zoological Garden on August 5, 1927, died January 21, 1961, after 33 years, 5 months, 16 days.

• *REFERENCES*

AKELEY, CARL E.
   1923. Gorillas—real and mythical. Nat. Hist., **23** (5): 29–47.

*See Addenda, p. 733.

ALLEN, GLOVER M.
 1939. A checklist of African mammals. Bull. Mus. Comp. Zool. Harvard
        University, 83.
ANON.
 1936. A big orang "on deposit." Bull. New York Zool. Soc., **39** (6):244–45.
 1944. Note. Zoonooz, **17** (1):5.
 1951. Note. America's First Zoo, **3** (4):3.
 1952a. The next time you visit the zoo: see the tarsier. America's First Zoo,
        4 (4):8.
 1952b. Two's a (record-breaking) crowd. Zoonooz, **25** (10):5–6.
 1953a. The bearded lady. Zoonooz, **26** (8):6–7.
 1953b. Whitey's new suit. Zoonooz, **26** (5):5.
 1954. 1953 the year 'round. Zoonooz, **27** (2):7.
 1955a. Note. America's First Zoo, **7** (1):2.
 1955b. Note. America's First Zoo, **7** (3):2.
 1959a. Zoo briefs. Zoonooz, **32** (10):15.
 1959b. Caption. Animals and Zoo, Tokyo Zool. Park Soc., **11** (8):4.
 1961a. Zoo briefs. Zoonooz, **34** (9):10.
 1961b. The death of Bamboo. America's First Zoo, **13** (1):3–6.
 1962. First bonobo born. Internatl. Zoo News, **9** (1):3.
ASDELL, S. A.
 1946. Patterns of mammalian reproduction. Comstock Publishing Co.,
        Ithaca, N. Y. 437 pp.
AULMANN, G.
 1932. Geglückte Nachzucht eines orang-utan in Düsseldorfer Zoo. Zool.
        Garten, Leipzig (N.F.), **5** (4/6):81–90.
BARTLETT, A. D.
 1899. Wild animals in captivity. Ed. EDWARD BARTLETT. Chapman and Hall,
        Ltd., London. 373 pp.
 1900. Life among the wild beasts in the "zoo." Ed. EDWARD BARTLETT.
        Chapman and Hall, Ltd., London. 375 pp.
BATES, H. W.
 1863. The naturalist on the River Amazons. John Murray, London. 2 vols.
BEDDARD, FRANK E.
 1905. Natural history in zoological gardens. Archibald Constable & Co., Ltd.,
        London. 310 pp.
BEEBE, MARY BLAIR, and C. WILLIAM BEEBE.
 1910. Our search for a wilderness. Henry Holt & Co., N.Y. 408 pp.
BENCHLEY, BELLE J.
 1938. Notes on the birth and infancy of a gibbon. Parks and Recreation,
        22 (2):67–72.
 1940a. My life in a man-made jungle. Little, Brown & Co., Boston. 294 pp.
 1940b. Mountain gorillas in San Diego Zoo. Parks and Recreation, **24**
        (1):19–27.
 1941. Rare monkeys. Parks and Recreation, **25** (2):77–78.
 1942. Mbongo—1926–1942. Parks and Recreation, **25** (9):377–80.

BENSON, RICHARD E., ROBERT J. YOUNG, and BENJAMIN D. FREMMING.
　1955.　Notes on diets for the chimpanzee. USAF School of Aviation Medicine, Randolph Field, Tex.

BLAIR, W. REID.
　1920.　Notes on the birth of a chimpanzee. Bull. New York Zool. Soc., 23 (5):105–11.

B[ODE], N[ANCY] C.
　1953a.　Saki, junior. Zoonooz, 26 (12):5.

BODE, NANCY C.
　1953b.　Too young for "specs." Zoonooz, 26 (12):3.

BOURDELLE, E., and A. MOUQUET.
　1930.　La longévité des mammifères à la ménagerie du Muséum National d'Histoire Naturelle. Bull. Mus. Hist. Nat. Paris, 2d ser., 2 (5):488–97.

BR[IDGES], W[ILLIAM].
　1955.　How to tempt the appetite of a callimico. Animal Kingdom, 58 (3):91–92.

BRIDGES, WILLIAM.
　1946.　How to weigh a gorilla. Animal Kingdom, 49 (6):200–203.
　1959.　The Monkey House. Animal Kingdom, 62 (3):77–81.

BRIGHTWELL, L. R.
　1950.　House to house at the zoo: the small mammals. Zoo Life, 5 (4):128–31.

BROWN, ARTHUR IRWIN.
　1909.　The tuberculin test in monkeys. Proc. Zool. Soc. London, pp. 81–90.

BROWN, C. EMERSON.
　1925.　Longevity of mammals in the Philadelphia Zoological Garden. Jour. Mammal., 6 (4):264–67.

BUDD, ARTHUR, L. G. SMITH, and F. W. SHELLEY.
　1943.　On the birth and upbringing of the female chimpanzee "Jacqueline." Proc. Zool. Soc. London, 113:1–20.

CABRERA, ANGEL.
　1957.　Catalogo de los mamiferos de America del Sur. 1. Rev. Mus. Argentina Cienc. Nat. Bernardino Rivadavia, Zool., 4 (1):1–307.

CABRERA, ANGEL, and JOSÉ YEPES.
　1940.　Historia natural ediar. Mamiferos Sud-Americanos. Compañia Argentina de Editores, Buenos Aires. 370 pp.

CANSDALE, G. S.
　1944.　The lesser bush baby. Jour. Soc. Preserv. Fauna Emp., N.S., 50:7–12.
　1947.　Bosman's potto. Zoo Life, 2 (2):41–43.
　1948.　The Calabar potto or angwantibo. Zoo Life, 3 (4):121–22.

CARPENTER, C. R.
　1934.　A field study of the behavior and social relations of howling monkeys (Alouatta palliata). Comp. Psychol. Monogr., 10 (2):1–168.
　1935.　Behavior of red spider monkeys in Panama. Jour. Mammal., 16 (3):171–80.

1940. A field study in Siam of the behavior and social relations of the gibbon (*Hylobates lar*). Comp. Psychol. Monogr., **16** (5):1–212.

1942. Sexual behavior of free-ranging rhesus monkeys (*Macaca mulatta*). Jour. Comp. Psychol., **33**:113–62.

CATCHPOLE, H. R., and J. F. FULTON.

1943. The oestrus cycle in *Tarsius*: observations on a captive pair. Jour. Mammal., **24** (1):90–93.

CHASEN, FREDERICK NUTTER.

1940. A handlist of Malaysian mammals. Bull. Raffles Mus., **15**:1–209.

CLARKE, R. C.

1934. Notes on the birth of a chimpanzee in the Clifton Zoological Gardens, Bristol. Proc. Zool. Soc. London, pp. 731–32.

CONANT, ROGER.

1939. Bamboo. Parks and Recreation, **22** (9):481–84.

COOK, NORMAN.

1939. Notes on captive *Tarsius carbonarius*. Jour. Mammal., **20** (2):173–78.

COOLIDGE, H. J.

1929. A revision of the genus *Gorilla*. Mem. Mus. Comp. Zool., **50** (4):295–381.

CRANDALL, LEE S.

1945a. Our first baby gibbon is born and seems to be doing well. Animal Kingdom, **48** (5):158–59.

1945b. Family affairs on gibbon island. *Ibid.*, No. 6, pp. 165–67.

1946. The carefree life of a baby gibbon. *Ibid.*, **49** (2):70–72.

1950. A new home for our great apes. *Ibid.*, **53** (6):185–93.

1951a. Those "forest sprites" called marmosets. *Ibid.*, **54** (6):178–84.

1951b. The loss of Makoko. *Ibid.*, No. 4, pp. 115–18.

1956. Chimpanzees as we see them—a guide to identification. *Ibid.*, **59** (1):30–31.

CUNNINGHAM, ALYSE.

1921. A gorilla's life in civilization. Bull. New York Zool. Soc., **24** (5):118–24.

DAVIS, DON G.

1962. Annual Report, The Cheyenne Mountain Zoological Park, 1961.

DAVIS, JOSEPH A., JR.

1961. Red means go! Animal Kingdom, **64** (4):114–18.

DELACOUR, J.

1933. On the Indochinese gibbons (*Hylobates concolor*). Jour. Mammal., **14** (1):71–73.

1942. Gibbons—the smallest apes. Animal Kingdom, **45** (2):35–39.

DITMARS, GLADYS.

1922. Rearing a red howler monkey. Bull. New York Zool. Soc., **25** (2):33–39.

DITMARS, RAYMOND L.

1933. Development of the silky marmoset. Bull. New York Zool. Soc., **36** (6):175–76.

DONISTHORPE, J. H.
  1958. A pilot study of the mountain gorilla (*Gorilla gorilla beringei*) in
         south west Uganda, February to September, 1957. S. African Jour.
         Sci., **54** (8):195–217.
DU CHAILLU, PAUL P.
  1861. Exploration and adventures in Equatorial Africa. John Murray,
         London. 479 pp.
DURRELL, GERALD M.
  1949. The angwantibo. Zoo Life, **4** (1):29.
ECKSTEIN, P., and S. ZUCKERMAN.
  1957. Monkeys. In: The UFAW handbook on the care and management of
         laboratory animals. Universities Federation for Animal Welfare,
         London. 951 pp.
ELLERMAN, J. R., and T. C. S. MORRISON-SCOTT.
  1951. Checklist of Palaearctic and Indian mammals. British Museum
         (Natural History), London. 810 pp.
EMLEN, JOHN T., JR., and GEORGE B. SCHALLER.
  1960a. In the home of the mountain gorilla. Animal Kingdom, **63** (3):98–108.
  1960b. Distribution and status of the mountain gorilla (*Gorilla gorilla
         beringei*)—1959. Zoologica, **45** (5):41–52.
ENGLISH, W. L.
  1934. Notes on the breeding of a douroucouli (*Aotus trivirgatus*) in captivity.
         Proc. Zool. Soc. London, pp. 143–44.
FINCH, GLEN.
  1943. The bodily strength of chimpanzees. Jour. Mammal., **24** (2):224–28.
FITZGERALD, ALICE.
  1935. Rearing marmosets in captivity. Jour. Mammal., **16** (3):181–88.
FLOWER, S. S.
  1929. List of the vertebrated animals exhibited in the gardens of the Zoo-
         logical Society of London, 1828–1927. 1. Mammals. Zoological
         Society of London. 419 pp.
  1931. Contributions to our knowledge of the duration of life in vertebrate
         animals. 5. Mammals. Proc. Zool. Soc. London, pp. 145–234.
FOX, HERBERT.
  1929. The birth of two anthropoid apes. Jour. Mammal., **10** (1):37–51.
GILBERT, CHRISTINE, and JOSEPH GILLMAN.
  1951. Pregnancy in the baboon (*Papio ursinus*). S. African Jour. Med. Sci.,
         16:115–24.
GORDON, CLYDE.
  1947. The queen is dead—long live the queen! Parks and Recreation,
         30 (12):591–92.
GOSS, LEONARD J.
  1947a. Yes sir, that's our baby! Animal Kingdom, **50** (6):179–87.
  1947b. The external genitalia of the gorilla, *Gorilla gorilla gorilla* (Savage
         and Wyman). Zoologica, **32** (10):97–99.

GRAY, GEORGE W.
1955.   The Yerkes laboratories. Sci. Amer., **192** (2):67–77.
GRETHER, W. F., and R. M. YERKES.
1940.   Weight norms and relations for chimpanzee. Amer. Jour. Phys. Anthropol., **27**:181–97.
GRZIMEK, BERNHARD.
1953.   Die Gorillas Ausserhalb Afrikas. Zool. Garten, Leipzig (N.F.), **20** (2/3):173–85.
HAAGNER, ALVIN.
1920.   South African mammals. H. F. & G. Witherby, London. 248 pp.
HAYMAN, R. W.
1950.   Guerezas or colobus monkeys. Zoo Life, **5** (3):92–95.
HECK, LUTZ.
1936.   Jahresber. Zool. Garten, Leipzig (N.F.), **8** (7/9):240–41.
HEDIGER, H.
1950.   Wild animals in captivity. Butterworths Scientific Publications, London. 207 pp.
1952.   Reproduction in zoo animals. In: CIBA Foundation colloquia on endocrinology. 3. Hormones, psychology and behaviour and steroid hormone administration. J. & A. Churchill, Ltd., London. 380 pp.
HERSHKOVITZ, PHILIP.
1949.   Mammals of northern Colombia. Preliminary report 4. Monkeys (Primates), with taxonomic revisions of some forms. Proc. U.S. Nat. Mus., **98** (3232):323–427.
HILL, W. C. OSMAN.
1935.   Communication. Nature, **536**:107.
1937*a*.   Treatment of the slender loris in captivity. Loris, **1** (2):85–88.
1937*b*.   On the breeding and rearing of certain species of primates in captivity. Spolia Zeylanica, **20** (3):369–89.
1947–   Paper read at meeting of Zoological Society of London. Proc. Zool.
48.   Soc. London, 117–278.
1949.   Gibbons. Zoo Life, **4** (2):40–42.
1953*a*.   Primates. 1. Strepsirhini. Interscience Publishers, Inc., New York, and University Press, Edinburgh. 798 pp.
1953*b*.   Lemurs and their allies in captivity. Zoo Life, **8** (4):136–44.
1953*c*.   Mandrills. Zoo Life, **8** (4):151–53.
1953*d*.   Notes on the taxonomy of the genus *Tarsius*. Proc. Zool. Soc. London, **123**:13–16.
1955.   Primates. 2. Haplorhini: Tarsioidea. Interscience Publishers, Inc., New York, and University Press, Edinburgh. 347 pp.
1957.   Primates. 3. Pithecoidea, Platyrrhini. Interscience Publishers, Inc., New York, and University Press, Edinburgh. 354 pp.
1959.   The anatomy of *Callimico goeldii* (Thomas). Trans. Amer. Phil. Soc., N.S., **59** (5):1–116.
1960.   Primates. 4. Cebidae, Part A. Interscience Publishers, Inc., New York, and University Press, Edinburgh. 523 pp.

HILL, W. C. OSMAN, ANNIE PORTER, and MARGARET D. SOUTHWICK.
  1952. The natural history, endoparasites and pseudo-parasites of the
         tarsiers (*Tarsius carbonarius*) recently living in the Society's menagerie.
         Proc. Zool. Soc. London, **122** (1):79–119.

HOOGSTRAAL, HARRY.
  1950. Deamer the lemur. Animal Kingdom, **53** (4):103–9.

HOOTON, EARNEST.
  1942. Man's poor relations. Doubleday, Doran & Co., Garden City, N.Y.
         412 pp.

HORNADAY, W. T.
  1880. On the species of Bornean orangs, with notes on their habits. Proc.
         Amer. Assoc. Advanc. Sci., **28**:438–55.
  1897. Two little apes. News Bull. Zool. Soc. (New York), No. 2, p. 6.
  1904. The American natural history. Chas. Scribner's Sons, New York.
         449 pp.
  1910. Two years in the jungle. Chas. Scribner's Sons, New York. 512 pp.
  1915. Gorillas, past and present. Bull. New York Zool. Soc., **18** (1):1181–85.

HOYT, A. MARIA.
  1941. Toto and I. J. B. Lippincott Co., New York. 238 pp.

HUME, MARGARET, and HANNAH HENDERSON SMITH.
  1951. Monkeys and sunshine. Zoo Life, **6** (1):3–5.

JACOBSON, CARLYLE F., MARION M. JACOBSON, and JOSEPH G. YOSHIOKA.
  1932. Development of an infant chimpanzee during her first year. Comp.
         Psychol. Monogr., Ser. 41, **9** (1).

JEFFRIES, JOHN.
  1825. Some account of a dissection of a *Simia satyrus*, ourang outang or
         wild man of the woods. Boston Jour. Phil. Arts, **2**:570–80.

JENNISON, GEORGE.
  N.d.   Table of gestation periods and number of young. A. & C. Black, Ltd.,
         London. 8 pp.
  1927. Natural history animals. The Macmillan Co., New York. 344 pp.

JONES, MARVIN L.
  1958. Mammals in captivity. Mimeographed MSS (unpublished).

KELLOGG, REMINGTON, and E. A. GOLDMAN.
  1944. Review of the spider monkeys. Proc. U.S. Nat. Mus., **96** (3186):1–45.

KELLY, JOAN M.
  1952. Bathing beauties. Zoonooz, **25** (11):2–3.

KIRCHSHAFER, VON ROSL.
  1959. Einige Verhaltensbeobachtungen an einem Guereza-Jungen *Colobus
         polykomus kikuyuensis* unter besonderer Berücksichtigung des Spiels.
         Zeit. Tierpsychol., **17** (4):506–14.

KNOBLOCH, HILDA, and BENJAMIN PASAMANICK.
  1959. Gross motor behavior in an infant gorilla. Jour. Comp. and Phys.
         Psychol., **52** (5):559–63.

LANG, E. M.
  1958. Einige seltenere Zuchterfolge im Basler Zoo. Zool. Garten, Leipzig (N.F.), **24** (3/4):282–83.
  1959. The birth of a gorilla at Basle Zoo. Internatl. Zoo Yearbook, **1**:3–7, Zoological Society of London.
  1960. Goma, das Basler Gorillakind, ein Jahr alt. Zolli, **5**:8–13.
  1961. Jambo—unser zweites Gorillakind. *Ibid.*, **7**:3–9.
LILFORD, LORD.
  1892. Communication to the secretary. Proc. Zool. Soc. London, p. 542.
LIMA, E. DA C.
  1945. Mammals of Amazonia. 1. Contribution from the Museu Paraense Emilio Goeldi de Historia Natural y Etnografia. Belim and Rio de Janeiro. 274 pp.
LOISEL, GUSTAVE.
  1912. Histoire des ménagéries de l'antiquité à nos jours. Octave Doin et Fils, Henri Laurens, Paris. 3 vols.
LOWTHER, FLORENCE DE L.
  1940. A study of the activities of a pair of *Galago senegalensis moholi* in captivity, including the birth and postnatal development of twins. Zoologica, **25** (27):433–62.
LUCAS, N. S., E. MARGARET HUME, and H. HENDERSON SMITH.
  1927. On the breeding of the common marmoset (*Hapale jacchus* Linn.) in captivity when irradiated with ultra-violet rays. Proc. Zool. Soc. London, pp. 447–51.
  1937. On the breeding of the common marmoset (*Hapale jacchus* Linn.) in captivity when irradiated with ultra-violet rays. 2. A ten years' family history. Proc. Zool. Soc. London, **107**:205–11.
LYDEKKER, RICHARD.
  1893– The royal natural history. Frederick Warne & Co., New York and
  96.   London. 6 vols.
McCLUNG, ROBERT M.
  1952. The case of the kidnapped colobus. Animal Kingdom, **55** (6):191–94.
  1955. We have a callimico, but is it a marmoset or a monkey? Animal Kingdom, **58** (1):29–30.
McKENNY, FRANK, J. TRAUM, and AILEEN E. BONESTELL.
  1944. Acute coccidiomycosis in a mountain gorilla (*Gorilla beringei*) with anatomical notes. Jour. Amer. Vet. Med. Assoc., **104** (804):136–41.
MANN, WM. M.
  1930. Wild animals in and out of the zoo. Smithsonian Sci. Ser., Vol. **6**. 362 pp.
  1948. Report on the National Zoological Park for the year ended June 30, 1947. Smithsonian Inst. Report for 1947, pp. 90–117.
  1949. Report on the National Zoological Park for the year ended June 30, 1948. Smithsonian Inst. Report for 1948, pp. 89–116.
  1950. Report on the National Zoological Park for the year ended June 30, 1949. Smithsonian Inst. Report for 1949, pp. 97–108.

MITCHELL, P. CHALMERS.
    1911.   On longevity and relative viability in mammals and birds; with a note
            on the theory of longevity. Proc. Zool. Soc. London, pp. 425–548.
MITCHELL, SIR PETER.
    1931.   Über die Haltung von *Semnopithecus* in europäischer Gefangenschaft.
            Zool. Garten, Leipzig (N.F.), **4** (8/9):298.
MONTANÉ, LOUIS.
    1916.   A Cuban chimpanzee. English translation by C. S. ROSSY. Jour.
            Animal Behavior, **6** (4):330–33.
NICHOLLS, L.
    1939.   Note. Nature, **543**:246.
NISSEN, H. W.
    1931.   A field study of the chimpanzee. Comp. Psychol. Monogr., **8** (1): 1–122.
NOBACK, C. R.
    1939.   The changes in the vaginal smears and associated cyclic phenomena
            in the lowland gorilla (*Gorilla gorilla*). Anat. Rec., **73** (2):209–25.
NOBACK, C. V.
    1931.   The Zoological Park's young female gorilla, Janet Penserosa. Bull. New
            York Zool. Soc., **34** (3):75–104.
    1936.   Note on menstruation in the gorilla (*Gorilla gorilla*). Amer. Jour.
            Phys. Anthropol., **21,** Suppl.
NOUVEL, J.
    1952.   La réproduction des mammifères au Parc Zoologique du Bois de
            Vincennes dans ses rapports avec l'alimentation. Mammalia, **16**
            (3):160–75.
OGILVIE, A. W.
    1923.   Breeding of the gibbon in captivity. Jour. Nat. Hist. Soc. Siam,
            6 (1):137.
O'REILLY, JOHN.
    1960.   The amiable gorilla. Sports Illustrated, **12** (25):69–76.
PALMANS, M.
    1956.   Le *Pan paniscus*. Zoo (Anvers), **21** (3):80–84.
PANG-CHIEH, T'AN.
    1957.   Rare catches by Chinese animal collectors. Zoo Life, **12** (2):61–63.
PAULIAN, R.
    1955.   Une naissance de Propithèque en captivité. Le Naturaliste Malgache,
            7 (1):104.
PEACOCK, L. J., and C. M. ROGERS.
    1959.   Gestation period and twinning in chimpanzees. Science, **129** (3354):
            959.
PHILLIPS, W. W. A.
    1931.   The food of the Ceylon slender loris (*Loris tardigradus*) in captivity.
            Spolia Zeylanica, **16** (2):205–8.
POCOCK, R. I.
    1905.   Observations upon a female of the Hainan gibbon (*Hylobates hainanus*)

now living in the Society's gardens. Proc. Zool. Soc. London, No. 2, pp. 169–80.

1906. Notes upon menstruation, gestation and parturition of some monkeys that have lived in the Society's gardens. Proc. Zool. Soc. London, pp. 558–70.

1907. A monographic revision of the monkeys of the genus *Cercopithecus*. Proc. Zool. Soc. London, pp. 677–746.

1920. On the external characters of the South American monkeys. Proc. Zool. Soc. London, pp. 91–113.

1925. On the external characters of the Catarrhine monkeys and apes. Proc. Zool. Soc. London, pp. 1479–1579.

POURNELLE, GEORGE H.
1955. The bashful clown. Zoonooz, **28** (2):23–25.
1956. Monkey noses make news! *Ibid.*, **29** (3):3–4.
1960a. Observations on captive proboscis monkeys. Sarawak Mus. Jour., **9** (15–16 N.S.):458–60.
1960b. The bonobo. Zoonooz, **33** (12):2–6.

RABB, GEORGE B.
1960. Longevity records for mammals at the Chicago Zoological Park. Jour. Mammal., **41** (1):113–14.

RABB, GEORGE B., and JAMES E. ROWELL.
1960. Notes on reproduction in captive marmosets. Jour. Mammal., **41** (3):401.

RAND, A. L.
1935. On the habits of some Madagascar mammals. Jour. Mammal., **16** (2):89–104.

RATCLIFFE, HERBERT L.
1940. Diets for a zoological garden: some results during a test period of five years. Zoologica, **25** (28):463–72.
1947. Scientific diets for the zoo. Fauna, **9** (1):26–28.
1953. Diets for captive wild animals as developed and used at the Philadelphia Zoological Garden. Minutes of the meeting of the International Union of Directors of Zoological Gardens, Antwerp, 1953.

RAVEN, H. C.
1931. Gorilla: the greatest of all apes. Nat. Hist., **31** (3):231–42.

REED, THEODORE H.
1961. Births and hatchings. Report on the National Zoological Park for the year ended June 30, 1960. Smithsonian Inst. Report for 1960, pp. 131–171.

REICHENOW, EDOUARD.
1921. Contribución a la biología de los antropomorfos africanos. Real Soc. Espan. Hist. Nat., tomo extraordinario: 50th Anniversary. Madrid.

RENSHAW, GRAHAM.
1914. Rare beasts in continental zoos. Year Book, Menagerie Club (England), 1914:141–59.

RIESS, B. F., SHERMAN ROSS, S. B. LYERLY, and H. G. BIRCH.
  1949.   The behavior of two captive specimens of the lowland gorilla, *Gorilla gorilla gorilla* (Savage and Wyman). Zoologica, **34** (13):111–17.

RINEHART, JAMES F., and LOUIS D. GREENBERG.
  1949.   Arteriosclerotic lesions in pyridoxine-deficient monkeys. Amer. Jour. Pathol., **25** (3):481–86.

ROBINSON, S. M.
  1925.   Birth of a white-handed gibbon (*Hylobates lar*) in captivity. Jour. Bombay Nat. Hist. Soc., **30**:456–58.

SANDERSON, IVAN T.
  1940.   The mammals of the North Cameroons forest area. Trans. Zool. Soc. London, **24** (7):623–725.

SÁNYÁL, RAM BRAMHA.
  1892.   A hand-book of the management of animals in captivity in Lower Bengal. Bengal Secretariat Press, Calcutta. 350 pp.

SCHALLER, GEORGE B.
  1963.   The mountain gorilla. University of Chicago Press. 431 pp.

SCHNEIDER, KARL MAX.
  1937.   Nachrichten aus Zoologischen Garten, Leipzig. Zool. Garten, Leipzig (N.F.), **9** (5):235–43.

SCHOUTEDEN, H.
  1947.   De zoogdieren van Belgisch Congo en van Ruanda-Urundi. Ann. Mus. Congo Belge, Ser. 2, **3** (1/3):1–576.

SCHROEDER, CHARLES R.
  1938.   A diagnostic test for the recognition of tuberculosis in primates; a preliminary report. Zoologica, **23** (21):397–400.

SCHULTZ, ADOLPH H.
  1934.   Some distinguishing characters of the mountain gorilla. Jour. Mammal., **15** (1):51–61.
  1940a. Growth and development of the orang-utan. Carnegie Inst. Washington, Contr. Embryol., p. 182.
  1940b. Growth and development of the chimpanzee. *Ibid.*, p. 170.

SCHWARZ, ERNST.
  1932.   Der Barenmaki (*Arctocebus calabarensis calabarensis* Smith) in Gefangenschaft. Zool. Garten, Leipzig (N.F.), **5** (2/3):1–3.

SCLATER, P. L.
  1877.   Quoting A. D. Bartlett. Proc. Zool. Soc. London, p. 304.
  1902.   Report of the secretary. Proc. Zool. Soc. London, p. 225.

SHERBORNE, JUNE.
  1962.   News from the Bristol Zoo. Internatl. Zoo News, **9** (1):6.

SHORTRIDGE, G. C.
  1934.   The mammals of South West Africa. Wm. Heinemann, Ltd., London. 2 vols. 779 pp.

SIMON, E. S.
  1943.   Life span of some wild animals in captivity. Jour. Bombay Nat. Hist. Soc., **44** (1):117–18.

SIMPSON, GEORGE GAYLORD.
  1945. The principles of classification and a classification of mammals. Bull.
         Amer. Mus. Nat. Hist., 85. 350 pp.
SPEIDEL, GEORGE.
  1963. Siamang born at Milwaukee County Zoo. Parks and Recreation, 46
         (1):56.
STEINER, P. E., T. B. RASMUSSEN, and L. E. FISHER.
  1955. Neuropathy, cardiopathy, hemosiderosis and testicular atrophy in a
         Gorilla gorilla. Amer. Med. Assoc. Arch. Pathol., 59:5–25.
STEPHAN, JOSEPH A.
  1940. "Susie," world's largest and oldest of her sex in captivity. Parks and
         Recreation, 23 (8):368–71.
STOTT, KEN, JR.
  1952. Solemn John and his neighbors. Zoonooz, 25 (10):8.
  1953a. Twinning in hooded sapajou. Jour. Mammal., 34 (3):385.
  1953b. Whitey places third. Zoonooz, 26 (3):2–3.
  1954. Baby food for thought. *Ibid.,* 27 (6):5.
STRAUSS, WILLIAM L., JR.
  1942. The structure of the crown-pad of the gorilla and of the cheek-pad
         of the orang-utan. Jour. Mammal., 23 (3):276–81.
TATE, G. H. H.
  1939. The mammals of the Guiana region. Bull. Amer. Mus. Nat. Hist.,
         76, 151–229.
  1954. On *Cebus apella* (Linnaeus), with a note on *Cebus capucinus* (Linnaeus).
         Jour. Mammal., 35 (3):415–18.
THOMAS, WARREN D.
  1958. Observations on the breeding in captivity of a pair of lowland gorillas.
         Zoologica, 43 (8):95–104.
TRATZ, EDUARD PAUL.
  1953. Chronologie der Erforschung und Gefangenhaltung des Gorillas.
         Zool. Garten, Leipzig (N.F.), 20 (2/3):163–70.
ULMER, FREDERICK A., JR.
  1946. Man of the woods. Fauna, 8 (4):98–103.
  1955. Breeding of orangutans. Parks and Recreation, 38 (5):21–23.
  1957. Breeding of orang-utans. Zool. Garten, Leipzig (N.F.), 23 (1/3):57–65.
  1958. Rusty becomes a backenwulster! America's First Zoo, 10 (2):7.
  1960. A longevity record for the Mindanao tarsier. Jour. Mammal., 41
         (4):512.
  1961. Gestation period of the lion marmoset. *Ibid.,* 42 (2):253–54.
URBAIN, A., and J. C. G. NOUVEL.
  1954. On keeping wild animals in zoos. Endeavour, 13 (52):184–89.
VAN BEMMEL, A. C. V.
  1959. Keeping apes at Rotterdam Zoo. Internatl. Zoo Yearbook, 1:16–18.
         Zoological Society of London.

VAN DEN BERGHE, LOUIS.
  1959.   Naissance d'un gorille de montagne à la Station de Zoologie Expéri-
          mentale de Tshibati. Folia Sci. Africae Centralis, **4**:81–83.

VAN WAGENEN, G.
  1950.   The monkey. In: The care and breeding of laboratory animals. Ed.
          EDMOND J. FARRIS. John Wiley & Sons, Inc., New York, Chapman &
          Hall, Ltd., London. 515 pp.

VON ALLESCH, G. J.
  1921.   Geburt und erste Lebensmonate eines Schimpanzen. Naturwiss.,
          39:774–76.

WALLACE, ALFRED R.
  1869.   The Malay Archipelago. Harper & Bros., New York. 638 pp.

WALKER, ERNEST P.
  1954.   The monkey book. Macmillan Co., New York. 153 pp.

WEBB, C. S.
  1946.   Some Madagascan animals. Zoo Life, **1** (2):57–58.

WHARTON, CHARLES H.
  1948.   Seeking Mindanao's strangest creatures. Natl. Geogr. Mag., **94**
          (3):389–408.
  1950.   The tarsier in captivity. Jour. Mammal., **31** (3):260–68.

WILLOUGHBY, DAVID P.
  1950.   The gorilla: largest living primate. Sci. Monthly, **70**:48–57.

WYATT, J. M.
  1935.   On the birth of a chimpanzee recently born in the Society's Gardens.
          Proc. Zool. Soc. London, pp. 195–97.

YERKES, R. M.
  1925.   Almost human. The Century Co., New York and London. 278 pp.
  1936.   A chimpanzee family. Jour. Genet. Psychol., **48**:362–70.
  1943.   Chimpanzees. A laboratory colony. Yale University Press, New
          Haven, Conn. 321 pp.
  1951.   Gorilla census and study. Jour. Mammal., **32** (4):429–36.

YERKES, R. M., and ADA W. YERKES.
  1929.   The great apes. Yale University Press, New Haven, Conn. 652 pp.

YOUNG, FLOYD S.
  1940.   "Bushman," the gorilla at Lincoln Park Zoo. Parks and Recreation,
          23 (7):305–08.

ZUCKERMAN, S.
  1931.   The menstrual cycle of the primates. 3. The alleged breeding season
          of primates with special reference to the chacma baboon (*Papio
          porcarius*). Proc. Zool. Soc. London, pp. 325–43.
  1932*a*. The social life of monkeys and apes. Kegan Paul, Trench, Trubner &
          Co., Ltd., London. 357 pp.
  1932*b*. The menstrual cycle of the primates. 6. Further observations on the
          breeding of primates, with special reference to the suborders Lemuroi-
          dea and Tarsioidea. Proc. Zool. Soc. London, pp. 1059–75.

1953. The breeding seasons of mammals in captivity. Proc. Zool. Soc. London, **122** (4):827–950.

ZUCKERMAN, S., G. VAN WAGENEN, and R. H. GARDINER.

1938. The sexual skin of the rhesus monkey. Proc. Zool. Soc. London, **108**:385–401.

ZUKOWSKY, LUDWIG.

1940. Zur Haltung und Pflege einiger Neuweltaffenarten. Zool. Garten, Leipzig (N.F.), **12** (2/3):92–110.

ORDER EDENTATA

.

Anteaters, Sloths, and Armadillos

While none of the animals in this order can be considered as basically important zoological-garden exhibits, all possess bizarre appearance or curious habits, so that members of some or all of the groups are usually maintained. All are inhabitants of the western hemisphere, where representatives of the order are found from Texas to Patagonia. While physical form as well as general habits are widely divergent, all have one point in common, the absence of incisor and canine teeth. Cheek or grinding teeth are present in both sloths and armadillos, and only anteaters are entirely toothless.

FAMILY MYRMECOPHAGIDAE

Anteaters

While the three existing members of this family—the giant anteater (*Myrmecophaga*), the tamandua or prehensile-tailed anteater (*Tamandua*), and the silky anteater (*Cyclopes*)—have little external resemblance to each other, they do have some similarities. Beyond the total absence of teeth, all have the long, slender, extensile tongue, and in the giant anteater and the tamandua the nose is greatly extended, with the tiny mouth at its tip. The muzzle is proportionately shorter and broader in the tiny silky. The giant, of course, is terrestrial; the prehensile-tailed tamandua may divide its time between earth and trees; while the little-known silky, also prehensile-tailed, appears to be almost entirely arboreal. All are chiefly but not strictly nocturnal, and all feed principally on ants, termites, and presumably such stray insects of other groups as may adhere to the viscous coating of the probing tongue.

The typical giant anteater (*Myrmecophaga t. tridactyla*) is found in tropical and subtropical regions of South America from Venezuela and the Guianas to northern Argentina. Farther north it is replaced by *M. t. artata* of western Venezuela and Colombia and by the Central American sub-species (*M. t. centralis*). Seen in captivity more frequently than either of its smaller relatives, the great size, strange appearance, and comparatively good viability of the giant anteater make its maintenance well worthwhile. Its habit of sleeping through much of the daytime is partially compensated by the curious practice of almost entirely covering itself with the long hair of the tail. In locomotion the long claws of the forefeet are turned inward, the animal supporting its weight on the outer surface of the toes. Ordinarily slow and deliberate in its movements, the giant anteater is capable of making fair speed at an awkward gallop. When need for defense occurs, it assumes an upright position and is then able to slash dangerously with the powerful claws. The giant anteater swims well, but as noted by Hess (1954), seems to regard water as merely incidental in its constant search for food.

Because of the digging ability of the forefeet, so useful for breaking down the hard walls of termite nests, we keep the giant anteater here on floors of smooth concrete. Stout wire netting offers sufficient restraint, for I have never known one to attack it. The floor is kept clean, save for a bed of straw in a darkened corner. When housing space permits, we like to have an adjoining shift cage available, so that the animal can be kept dry while its own quarters receive their daily hosing. The cages currently in use here measure about 10 feet in each dimension and appear to be sufficiently spacious. During the summer months our giant anteaters have the run of a large wired outdoor inclosure, again smoothly paved except for a small central area in which they are able to reach open earth.

The conventional diet for giant anteaters consists of milk, eggs, and chopped raw meat. Of late years it has become customary to add a small quantity of cooked cereal, such as oatmeal. Here we add to a quart of reconstituted whole milk about ½ pound of ground raw horse flesh from which all tendons and other hard tissues have been removed, three coddled or poached eggs, 2 tablespoonsful of prepared baby cereal, and ½ teaspoonful of cod-liver oil or a few drops of multiple vitamin concen-trate. This mixture, given once daily, in the evening, provides sufficient nourishment for an adult animal. We have never been successful in getting a giant anteater to take dried ant's "eggs" (pupae), dried locusts, or meal-worms, for when these have been added to the mixture the sensitive tongue has always left them carefully at the bottom of the dish.

Two records of the breeding of the giant anteater in captivity have come to my attention. Mr. Raymond F. Gray, director of the Overton Park Zoo,

Memphis, Tennessee, has provided me (*in litt.*) with the following information: An adult pair of giant anteaters, in excellent condition, was received on May 1, 1952. On November 12, 1955, the female gave birth to a single baby. Since such an event had not been anticipated, the parents had not been separated, and the young animal was killed immediately by the male. Weight at birth is given as 3 pounds, 6 ounces. A female received at the Columbus (Ohio) Zoo on May 11, 1961, was followed by a male on July 7 of the same year. On October 8, 1962, the female gave birth to a single youngster which, as in the Memphis experience, was killed at once by the male (Anon., 1962).

The only birth that has occurred here was that of a premature infant born in May, 2 weeks after the arrival of the mother. Females carrying young on their backs in the typical fashion are not infrequently received by importers. Asdell (1946) gives the number of young as one, following a gestation period of 190 days.

While the giant anteater is commonly considered to be a hardy and long-lived species, it is probable that the number of individuals able to accommodate to the radical change in diet they must undergo is comparatively small. Once established, however, many have continued to thrive for considerable periods. Our best records here are 6 years, 5 months, 25 days and 7 years, 4 months, 18 days. George H. Pournelle (*in litt.*) gives 10 years, 4 months, 11 days in the San Diego Zoological Garden, while Flower (1931) records 14 years, 4 months, 1 day in the Zoological Gardens of London. Mr. John F. Heusser, late executive director of the Zoological Gardens of Cincinnati, Ohio, has informed me (*in litt.*) that while the female of a pair of giant anteaters received at Cincinnati on November 10, 1928, died within a year, the male lived until April 11, 1948, or 19 years, 5 months, 1 day. Mr. Heusser added that this animal was kept in a cage 4 by 4 feet, that the food pan, placed outside, was reached through an opening 4 inches square, and that new born mice were devoured with apparent relish, all points at variance with usual practice.

The tamandua or prehensile-tailed anteater (*Tamandua tetradactyla*), in numerous races, ranges from southern Mexico to Argentina. It is intermediate in habits as well as in size, for it is equally at home on the ground or in the trees. In walking it turns the claws of the forefeet inward, as does the giant anteater, and adopts the same upright position in defense.

The handsome coloration of the tamandua is most attractive, but unfortunately it appears to be one of the most difficult of mammals to maintain in captivity. While it is frequently imported into this country, it is doubtful that the majority survive for more than a few months at most.

The tamandua is ordinarily gentler and more tractable than the giant anteater and with the exception that it requires a climbing perch, its treatment and feeding are the same as those usually followed for its larger relative. It appears, however, that further elements, at present not understood, are required in the feeding formula for captive animals. Goldman (1920:63) says that at least a pound of ants, representing five genera, were found in the stomach of a single specimen, so it would seem that the natural feeding habits do not differ greatly from those of the giant.

I find no records of breeding in captivity. Webb (1954:319) reports that an infant born to a female collected in British Guiana and apparently impregnated before capture was carried on the mother's back from birth.

The longest period for which we have been able to maintain a tamandua here is just over 1 year. However, Flower (1931) gives 4 years, 11 months, 1 day in the Zoological Gardens of London, which leads to the possibility that there may be even better records that I have failed to find.

Smallest and least known of the anteaters is the tiny silky or two-toed (*Cyclopes didactylus*), found from southern Mexico to northern Brazil. A number of races have been described. It is almost entirely arboreal, although Beebe (1918) says it walks readily on the ground, with the two claws of the forefeet turned inward in typical anteater fashion. In the trees it moves with slothlike deliberation, though not in the suspended position sometimes figured, using the prehensile tail to insure safety. The silky appears to be more completely nocturnal than either of the larger species.

When alarmed, the little creature secures a firm hold on a branch with tail and hind feet and draws itself upright, with the sharp claws of the forefeet held at either side of the face. In this position the animal presents a quaint and appealing appearance. However, close approach will bring a quick downward stroke, delivered with surprising force and power. Both Beebe (1918) and Webb (1954) record experiences with this effective means of defense.

Few examples of this attractive species have been kept in captivity. Specimens received here in 1917 and 1936 lived only 3 and 2 days, respectively, and Webb (1948) mentions similar experiences with two silky anteaters received at the Zoological Gardens of London in 1854 and 1858. Webb found that an animal maintained in British Guiana for a month did not take the usual liquid mixture well, though this was preferred when sweetened with honey. It also had a liking for wasp grubs.

A more recent experience with this species here had to do with a specimen of *C. didactylus dorsalis*, received from Costa Rica by air on June 27, 1949. Placed in a cage 2 feet wide and deep by 3 feet high and provided with small branches conveniently horizontal, it settled down well and after the first day or two would assume the defensive attitude only if seriously disturbed. Contrary to expectation, it fed almost at once on a mixture of whole milk, minced raw meat, and coddled egg, thoroughly combined in a Waring Blendor. When feeding, it kept a firm grip on a low branch with tail and hind feet, leaning downward to place its front feet on the rim of the dish while the extensile tongue drew the food into its mouth. For two months the little animal progressed without incident, when it began to give indications of failing health, leading up to its death on September 7. The cause of this disappointing result was revealed at necropsy, when the abdominal cavity was found to contain a large tumor. This brief experience suggests that with the aid of the airplane and prompt provision of suitable food and housing, the maintenance of the silky anteater for reasonable periods may not be as impossible as it has seemed. In fact, a silky anteater representing one of the South American races (which one being so far undetermined), received here on September 19, 1961, and similarly treated, remained in excellent condition until its death on March 4, 1963, after 1 year, 5 months, 13 days here. It had thus exceeded previous longevity records for the species.

FAMILY BRADYPODIDAE

SLOTHS

Although firmly established in popular thought as symbols of laziness, the sloths actually are extremely well adapted to their particular mode of life. Food consists of leaves, buds, and twigs of tall forest trees, so that speed and agility are not required for security. Apparently defenseless, the sloths are protected by dense coats of hair, highly resistant skin, and the ability to curl themselves into almost impenetrable balls. The green algae which grow on the hair, particularly during the wet season, serve as useful camouflage. Languid, hooking blows with the long claws of the front feet may inflict painful injuries, and principally because in *Choloepus* the front cheek tooth in each jaw is advanced and separated from the others, a serious bite may be administered by members of that genus.

So completely are the sloths adapted to an upside-down life in the tree-tops that on the ground they are almost helpless. However, they are able to progress on all fours, sprawling awkwardly and drawing themselves slowly forward, largely by the use of the forelimbs. Strangely enough, they swim with some facility, and Beebe (1926) reports considerable distances covered in this manner.

The habits of defecation in the sloths are somewhat peculiar. Enders (1940) reports that a young Hoffmann's sloth (*Choloepus h. hoffmanni*), kept in captivity in Panama, evacuated normally at 6-day intervals but was induced to defecate every 5 days by dipping her hindquarters in cold water! An adult of the same species, now living in our collection, clears her colon at periods varying from 2 to 5 days. The same spot is always chosen as a latrine, as noted by Hediger (1950:89) for animals in nature.

A point of special interest is the variation in the number of cervical vertebrae. In contrast to the usual mammalian count of seven, the three-toed sloth (*Bradypus*) is credited with nine, and Hoffmann's sloth (*C. hoffmanni*) with but six (Lydekker, 1893–96, 3:206, 207; Beddard, 1902).

A comparatively small space is sufficient for a single captive sloth, provided necessary simple requirements are met. In a wired inclosure the animal is likely to be found, too often, hanging from it. For this reason, sloths are shown here in smooth-walled, glass-fronted compartments 5 feet long, 4 feet deep, and 6 feet high, with gentle forced-draft ventilation.

The arrangement of perches is of paramount importance. In sleeping, sloths rest on the base of the spine, with head bent forward and the claws of one or both forefeet grasping the upright trunk or a branch immediately above the one on which they sit. Parallel perches on the same level are therefore entirely unsuitable. When a satisfactory sleeping spot has been found, the animal will devote itself wholeheartedly to making use of it. Beebe (1926) found that a sloth kept at semi-liberty in British Guiana averaged 18½ hours of each 24 curled up in sleep. Fortunately, artificial light, whether blue or white, appears not to disturb a sleeping sloth, so that even in slumber it is always visible to the public.

The sloths fall into two natural groups, sometimes considered to form separate families: those with three toes all around (*Bradypus*) and those with the toes of the front feet reduced to two (*Choloepus*). The three-toed sloths (*Bradypus*) are found in several forms, from Honduras to northern Argentina. Unfortunately, the members of this group have so far defied all efforts to maintain them in captivity for more than a few months at most. They are obviously somewhat specialized in feeding habits, the large, thick leaves of the Cecropia tree apparently being the preferred item of diet (Cabrera and Yepes, 1940:244). However, even in British Guiana, where fresh Cecropia leaves were supplied in abundance and eaten freely by captive specimens, Beebe (1926) reports a maximum longevity of only 8 months. After transportation to more northerly latitudes, where Cecropia is not ordinarily available, many three-toed sloths will refuse all food, although they may live for weeks without it. On the other hand, some will take such items as spinach, kale, celery, and bananas, ripe or green. But none of these seems to provide the elements necessary for continued maintenance.

The two-toed sloths (*Choloepus*) range from Nicaragua to central Brazil, numerous forms having been described. Obviously much more generalized in food requirements than the three-toed sloths, the two-toed forms are easily maintained in captivity. Greens, fruits, vegetables, and bread are taken readily, with no apparent evidence of deficiency. A specimen of Hoffmann's sloth (*C. h. hoffmanni*), received from Panama on April 26, 1947, and still living in late 1963, is fed largely on lettuce, bread, and bananas, with a small piece each of mealy apple and orange daily. The bread is moistened with water, which seems to provide sufficient moisture, since sloths appear seldom, if ever, to drink (Beebe, 1926:39). This individual will take spinach, kale, and escarole but refuses celery. It also shows no liking for the leaves of the Russian mulberry, although most sloths eat them freely.

No sloth has ever been born here, but Zuckerman (1953) records one birth of *C. hoffmanni* in the Zoological Gardens of London, and Mann (1954, 1955) reports three of *C. didactylus* in the National Zoological Park in Washington. Hediger (1952:79), following K. M. Schneider, suggests possible superfetation in the two-toed sloth. Dr. A. L. J. Sunier, former director of the Zoological Gardens of Amsterdam, reported at the meeting of the International Union of Directors of Zoological Gardens (Paris, 1948) the birth of a second infant to a two-toed mother already nursing a large young one, without having been in the company of a male since before the first birth. Five births of *C. didactylus* in the National Zoological Park from 1953 to 1956 are reported by Wm. M. Mann and seven from 1957 to 1961 by Theodore H. Reed, in the *Reports* on the National Zoological Park for those years. Stone (1957), in reporting a birth of this species in the Detroit Zoological Park on February 22, 1956, gives a minimal gestation period of 263 days. The female of a pair of two-toed sloths in the Philadelphia Zoological Garden produced a single young in July, 1959, after having lived for several years in the collection (Anon., 1959).

As already stated, there appear to be no recorded instances of a three-toed sloth having survived in captivity for more than a few months. With two-toed sloths, results have been very much better. Flower (1931) gives 9 years, 10 months, 1 day for *C. didactylus* in the Zoological Gardens of Amsterdam and 11 years, 3 months, 25 days for *C. hoffmanni* in the

Zoological Gardens of London. Our best record here for a South American two-toed (*C. didactylus*) is for one received August 18, 1925, which died June 10, 1941, after 15 years, 9 months, 23 days in our collection. An animal of the same species received at the Philadelphia Zoological Garden on May 14, 1932, died on July 18, 1955 (Frederick A. Ulmer, Jr. *in litt.*). This record of 23 years, 2 months, 4 days seems to be the maximum so far attained by a captive sloth.

FAMILY DASYPODIDAE

ARMADILLOS

Because of the nocturnal or at least crepuscular habits of most of the species, the armadillos probably are even less useful as zoological-garden exhibits than either the anteaters or the sloths. Even less capable of defensive action than the members of the related families, they rely for protection on the plates of armor and the surprising agility with which they reach the safety of their burrows or dig their way into soft soil. Some, although not all, are able to roll themselves into balls so tightly as to be practically impregnable. In fact, Sanborn (1930) says that the three-banded armadillo (*Tolypeutes tricinctus*) closes its shell "like a steel trap" and apparently with comparable result, for it seems to be seldom attacked by predators.

The armadillos are found, in numerous species, from southern Kansas and Florida (*Dasypus novemcinctus mexicanus*) to Patagonia (*Zaedyus pichiy*), with the greatest concentration in northern South America. In size they range from the giant (*Priodontes giganteus*), sparsely distributed from Argentina to Venezuela, which may measure more than 5 feet over-all, to the tiny fairy armadillo or pichiciego (*Chlamyphorus truncatus*) of Argentina, with a total length of only 5 inches. The protective armor, consisting of small bony plates set in the skin, is usually comparatively immovable except across the back, where narrow bands break the general rigidity. These bands are of taxonomic value, as reflected in the names of many species.

In reasonably warm climates, where armadillos may be kept out of doors, there is no housing problem, since the animals do best on an earth floor. In more northerly latitudes indoor quarters must be provided, for armadillos are unable to endure low temperatures (Buchanan, 1955). On bare concrete floors there is danger of injury to feet and claws through constant efforts to dig, which can be avoided by a covering of 6 inches or a foot of sand or soil. This, of course, must be cleaned daily and completely changed frequently. A sleeping box, if provided, will be much used—so much so that the animals will seldom be seen. Usually, however, they will be satisfied if half-buried in the floor covering, so that at least their backs may be visible.

Rather surprisingly for an animal of confirmed terrestrial habits, armadillos are excellent climbers of wire netting—at least, they have no difficulty in getting up, although getting down again is a different matter. Two nine-banded armadillos (*D. novemcinctus*) kept here in a large wire-inclosed cage were found to be missing one morning and were later found sleeping soundly on a high ledge. They had climbed 8 feet up the netting and squeezed through a narrow gap at the top. Smooth metal plates 2 feet high, set at the bottom of the partitions, ended their wanderings. Our first giant armadillo (*P. giganteus*), received in 1935, died from injuries received when it fell from high on a wire cage front up which it had climbed. A barrier of widely spaced perpendicular bars ended this danger for the next example, as side walls and back were already unscalable.

Armadillos swim well and are even said to be able to walk on the bottom of bodies of water. While accommodations for such activities are certainly not essential for captive animals, they will make use of such bathing facilities as may be provided. In any case, drinking water must be supplied.

While most of the armadillos are basically insectivorous or at least feed largely on invertebrates, many are actually omnivorous and at times may eat almost anything edible, from carrion, mice, young birds and birds' eggs, ants, termites, and earthworms to soft fruits and vegetables (Cabrera and Yepes, 1940; Taber, 1945).

In captivity the traditional diet is milk, eggs, and finely chopped raw meat. I am reminded that this was the regimen in use here in earlier days by a notebook entry made by myself in 1908. Armadillos did reasonably well on it, too, for a six-banded (*Euphractus sexcinctus*) that lived here from August 28, 1914, to August 1, 1924, or 9 years 11 months, 4 days, had nothing else. A giant armadillo kept here received "three pounds of raw chopped beef, five raw hen eggs, one quart of evaporated milk, one quart of tepid water and one pint of tomato juice" (Cully, 1939). Nowadays a more solid diet is in general use in this country. This consists of canned dog food with the addition of a small quantity of raw chopped meat and cod-liver oil and has given good results, at least with the larger species. A combination of these systems, with a few drops of multiple vitamin concentrate, is suitable for the more delicate forms.

Armadillos are not infrequently born in captivity, although under

zoological-garden conditions few are reared. Where more natural surroundings can be maintained, better results may be anticipated, as the
nine-banded (*D. novemcinctus*) is bred in some numbers at such establishments as the Apelt Armadillo Farm at Comfort, Texas. Division of the
fertilized ovum (polyembryony), resulting in the production of from
four (*D. novemcinctus*) to twelve (*D. hybridus*) young, all of the same sex,
occurs in at least these two species. Delayed implantation obscures the
actual gestation period in some cases (Asdell, 1946; Cabrera and Yepes,
1940; Talmadge and Buchanan, 1954).

Nine-banded armadillos have been born here at various times, but none
has ever been reared. Mann (1930) reports the births of four young of the
hairy armadillo (*E.* [=*Chaetophractus*] *villosus*) in the National Zoological
Park, and Zuckerman (1953) lists the same species as having produced single
or twin young in the Zoological Gardens of London on nine occasions.
Zuckerman also records births of the mulita armadillo (*D. hybridus*) and
the six-banded (*E. sexcinctus*) in London.

The armadillo most frequently seen in this country, of course, is the
nine-banded (*D. novemcinctus*). For some reason, this species appears to
be less viable than some, at least, of the South American forms, nowadays
seldom seen here. Our best record for the nine-banded is 4 years, 11
months, 22 days, and the 6 years, 6 months recorded by Mann (1930) in
the National Zoological Park is the longest I have found for the species.
Sanborn (1930) gives 11 years for the three-banded (*T. tricinctus*) in the
Berlin Zoological Gardens, and Flower (1931) reports 15 years, 7 months,
1 day for a hairy armadillo (*Chaetophractus villosus*) in Rotterdam. A giant
armadillo (*P. giganteus*) lived here from May 29, 1937, to November 14,
1941, or 4 years, 5 months, 16 days, and Jones (1958) gives approximately
7 years for a specimen in the Zoological Gardens of Berlin. Our best
result with the six-banded (*E. sexcinctus*), 9 years, 11 months, 4 days, has
been noted above. Jones (1958) reports 10 years, 4 months, 23 days for
a specimen of this species in the Philadelphia Zoological Garden.

· REFERENCES

ANON.
  1955. Note. America's First Zoo, **7** (3):2.
  1959. Summer review. America's First Zoo, **11** (3):34–35.
  1962. Greater anteater bred at Colombus Zoo. News Bull., A.A.Z.P.A.,
         3 (11): 4.

ASDELL, S. A.
  1946. Patterns of mammalian reproduction. Comstock Publishing Co.,
         Ithaca, N.Y. 437 pp.
BEDDARD, FRANK E.
  1902. Mammalia. Cambridge Natural History, Vol. 10. Macmillan & Co.,
         Ltd., New York and London. 605 pp.
BEEBE, WILLIAM.
  1918. A silky eater of ants. Bull. New York Zool. Soc., 21 (1):1561–66.
  1926. The three-toed sloth. Zoologica, 7 (1):1–67.
BUCHANAN, G. DALE.
  1955. Invader from the south. Animal Kingdom, 58 (3):82–88.
CABRERA, ANGEL, and JOSÉ YEPES.
  1940. Historia natural ediar. Mamiferos Sud-Americanos. Compañia
         Argentina de Editores, Buenos Aires. 370 pp.
CULLY, WILLIAM.
  1939. Day and night in the life of an armadillo. Bull. New York Zool. Soc.,
         42 (6):180–82.
ENDERS, ROBERT K.
  1940. Observations on sloths in captivity at higher altitudes in the tropics
         and in Pennsylvania. Jour. Mammal., 21 (1):5–7.
FLOWER, S. S.
  1931. Contributions to our knowledge of the duration of life in vertebrate
         animals. 5. Mammals. Proc. Zool. Soc. Lond., pp. 145–234.
GOLDMAN, EDWARD A.
  1920. Mammals of Panama. Smithsonian Misc. Coll., 69 (5):1–309.
HEDIGER, H.
  1950. Wild animals in captivity. Butterworths Scientific Publications,
         London. 207 pp.
  1952. Reproduction in zoo animals. In: CIBA Foundation colloquia on
         endocrinology. 3. Hormones, psychology and behaviour and steroid
         hormone administration. J. & A. Churchill, Ltd., London. 380 pp.
HESS, LILO.
  1954. An anteater named Teddy. Nat. Hist., 53 (1):8–15.
JONES, MARVIN L.
  1958. Mammals in captivity. Mimeographed MSS (unpublished).
LYDEKKER, RICHARD.
  1893–96. The royal natural history. Frederick Warne & Co., New York and
         London. 6 vols.
MANN, WM. M.
  1930. Wild animals in and out of the Zoo. Smithsonian Sci. Ser., 6. 362 pp.
  1954. Report on the National Zoological Park for the year ended June 30,
         1953. Smithsonian Inst. Report for 1953, p. 95.
  1955. Report on the National Zoological Park for the year ended June 30,
         1954. Smithsonian Inst. Report for 1954, p. 114.

SANBORN, COLIN CAMPBELL.
  1930. Distribution and habits of the three-banded armadillo (*Tolypeutes*).
         Jour. Mammal., 11 (1):61–68.
STONE, WALTER D.
  1957. The gestation period of the two-toed sloth. Jour. Mammal., 38
         (3):419.
TABER, F. WALLACE.
  1945. Contribution on the life history and ecology of the nine-banded
         armadillo. Jour. Mammal., 26 (3):211–26.
TALMADGE, ROY V., and G. DALE BUCHANAN.
  1954. The armadillo (*Dasypus novemcinctus*). A review of its natural history,
         ecology, anatomy and reproductive physiology. Rice Inst. Pamphlet,
         41 (2):1–135.
WEBB, C. S.
  1948. The pygmy anteater. Zoo Life, 3 (2):62–63.
  1954. The odyssey of an animal collector. Longmans, Green & Co., New
         York, London, and Toronto. 368 pp.
ZUCKERMAN, S.
  1953. The breeding seasons of mammals in captivity. Proc. Zool. Soc.
         London, 122:827–950.

ORDER PHOLIDOTA

·

FAMILY MANIDAE

Pangolins

The pangolins occupy a position in Africa and Asia comparable to that of the anteaters in the New World. Toothless, their bodies, except the underparts, covered with hard, sharp-edged scales, and their mouths equipped with slender, extensile tongues, they are perfectly adapted for securing the ants and termites on which they feed. Once included with the American edentates and the aardvark in a single order (Edentata), the pangolins are currently considered as forming an order and family of their own (Simpson, 1945:194–95). Three species are found in Asia and four in Africa. Assigned to six genera by Pocock (1924), most recent authorities follow Simpson (1945) in the use of a common generic term, *Manis*, to include all the species.

In spite of their obviously interesting characters, there has been comparatively little experience with pangolins in captivity and even that has been generally unsatisfactory. Sányál (1892), writing of various Asiatic pangolins kept in the Calcutta Zoological Gardens, says: "The garden has not yet succeeded in keeping these animals alive for any length of time, owing to the difficulty of procuring regularly and in sufficient quantity their natural diet, the termites. . . . Various other things have from time to time been tried but without avail." He adds the interesting observations that "A Manis has been found to swim across a tank 110 feet wide and burrow under the foundation of a wall six feet deep."

Bigalke (1932) says that after examination of the records of the National Zoological Gardens of South Africa at Pretoria showed that specimens of the Cape pangolin (*Manis temmincki*) had invariably died, apparently from starvation, after 2 or 3 weeks, an effort was made to devise a suitable feeding formula. Animals under close observation were offered a mixture of cow's milk, finely ground dog biscuit, and eggs, on which they fed well. However, the best duration obtained was one of just over 6 weeks.

More recently, in writing of the prehensile-tailed tree pangolins of West Africa, Cansdale (1947) says: "It is unfortunate that these interesting animals are almost impossible to keep in captivity. In the usual way old ones absolutely refuse to feed, even on their natural food. . . . Younger ones often take to condensed milk but even when they are taking this freely and also get unlimited amounts of insect food, they seldom thrive and I have not yet managed to keep one for more than about two months. . . ." Regarding pangolins in general, Flower (1931) says, "there appears to be no record of one living to even two years in captivity."

Our own experience with pangolins is in much the same vein as those quoted above. We had long wished to try our hands, of course, without opportunity. I well remember eagerly awaiting the arrival of a ship from Calcutta bringing an animal shipment said to include a pangolin. This, however, proved to be an armadillo, which somehow had strayed far from home. Perhaps the confusion resulted from the practice of English-speaking people living in pangolin country of referring to the animals as armadillos, just as sunbirds are often called hummingbirds.

Our first opportunity to gain firsthand knowledge of captive pangolins came with the arrival of our collector, Charles Cordier, on June 15, 1949, with a fabulous shipment of Belgian Congo mammals and birds. Included were one giant pangolin (*M. gigantea*), one long-tailed tree pangolin (*M. longicaudata*), and three white-bellied tree pangolins (*M. tricuspis*), all taken in the area to the northeast of Stanleyville. The huge, terrestrial giant pangolin, measuring well over 4 feet in length, was practically moribund on arrival, refused all food, and expired 6 days later. The post mortem report recorded profuse intestinal congestion and parasitism. This animal probably was the first of its species to be seen alive outside Africa.

Better results, though still certainly not satisfactory ones, were obtained with the slender, prehensile-tailed tree pangolins. All were quiet, slow-moving, and inoffensive. If any area of the body scales was lightly touched, the razor-sharp scales closed instantly, and further urging caused the animals to curl into tight balls which could not be opened. Gentle handling could induce a demonstration of the powerful gripping ability of the tail-tip, so that the animal would hang suspended from one finger of its handler. All were strongly nocturnal, sleeping loosely curled during the day and becoming more active at evening.

Food for these animals consisted of reconstituted evaporated milk, precooked baby food (Pablum), finely ground raw meat, and coddled egg, with a few drops of multiple vitamin concentrate. All had been conditioned to this diet, of course, before arrival, and all were feeding freely. Cordier reported some difficulty in the field with newly captured specimens, some that refused food for several days having to be released. In spite of general docility and willingness to feed, the four specimens all succumbed, after the following short periods: long-tailed, 19 days; white-bellied, 1 month, 16 days; 2 months, 29 days, and 3 months, 3 days. At necropsy all were found to be heavily parasitized. In an account of experience with the long-tailed tree pangolin in the Cameroons, Webb (1954) suggests that the absorption through the skin of formic acid acquired from the bites of ants may in some way be essential to the animal's survival. In any case, the present outlook for the maintenance of tree pangolins in captivity is not encouraging, although Miss Hattie Ettinger (*in litt.*) reports 10 months, 26 days, for a specimen of *tricuspis* in the St. Louis Zoological Park.

For the giant pangolin, with which there has been comparatively little experience, the outlook is brighter. On February 3, 1954, a young female giant (figured in *Life*, August 9, 1955), together with two tree pangolins, was received at the Fort Worth (Texas) Zoo and Aquarium (Curtis, 1956). These animals had been collected in Liberia by Dr. Thomas A. Burch, of the United States Public Health Service, and Mrs. Burch. One of the tree pangolins survived for 1 month, the other for about 3. At least the latter, again, was found to be heavily parasitized. For information concerning these animals I am indebted to Mr. Lawrence Curtis, curator of the Fort Worth Zoo, and the following notes concerning the surviving giant have been furnished by him:

The animal was brought to Dr. and Mrs. Burch by natives while it was quite young. It readily learned to feed on a prepared mixture and was kept by them in Liberia for about 6 months before it was brought by air to this country. On arrival at Fort Worth it was in excellent condition and quite tame. At that time it weighed just over 40 pounds and was 38 inches in length, over-all. By September, 1954, it had reached a weight of 58 pounds, and in May, 1955, its weight was 72 pounds and its length 50 inches.

The dietary items used were the same throughout, only the amounts of each having been increased as required. In May, 1955, its regimen was as follows:

> 2 cups finely ground raw beef heart
> 2 cups precooked cereal (Pablum)
> 4 cups reconstituted evaporated milk
> 1 cup warm water
> $\frac{1}{2}$ cup ants' "eggs"

This made up as a thick, viscid mixture, which the pangolin seemed to prefer to the more liquid preparation usually offered animals requiring similar diets. Wheat germ was sometimes added as well as an occasional raw egg, and both were accepted, but if cod-liver oil or vitamin concentrates were used, the food was rejected. The container, 2 feet long, 1 foot wide, and 3 inches deep, was made of concrete, its weight preventing tipping by the feeding animal. Food was offered in late afternoon, since the pangolin slept through the day and became active at about 4:00 in the afternoon. It appeared to enjoy soaking in a shallow bath and being sprayed with water from a hose. This animal lived until March 12, 1958, establishing a longevity of 4 years, 1 month, 9 days.

The salient points in this encouraging experience appear to be that this giant pangolin came into captivity while still young enough to be adaptable, was carefully and sympathetically handled from the beginning, and received recognition of its apparently definite food preferences. Transportation by air, an immense advantage, was certainly an important factor. The animal appears not to have been greatly troubled by the internal parasites so commonly found at necropsy, suggesting the possibility of an abnormal increase of parasites in debilitated specimens.

A young pair of giant pangolins received at the Zoological Gardens of Antwerp from the Zoological Gardens of Barcelona early in 1957 was kept on an approximation of the Fort Worth diet, with the addition of a spoonful of wheat-germ oil and a drop of formic acid (Anon., 1957). On this regimen they thrived until spring, 1959.

Of three Indian pangolins (*M. crassicaudata*) received here on April 28, 1961, one lived for only 4 months, another for 7, but the third remained in good condition in late 1963. Its diet was again based on the Fort Worth formula, with the addition of the raw yolks only of two eggs and a multiple vitamin supplement. This animal reacted well to day-and-night reversal under red light (Davis, 1961).

· REFERENCES

ANON.
    1957. Un couple de jeunes pangolins géants. Zoo, Anvers, **23** (1):29–30.
BIGALKE, R.
    1932. Beobachtungen an *Smutsia temminckii* (Smuts) in der Gefangenschaft. Zool. Garten, Leipzig (N.F.), **5** (7/9):173–78.
CANSDALE, G. S.
    1947. West African tree pangolins. Zoo Life, **2** (4):102–5.

CURTIS, LAWRENCE.
  1956. Pansy the pangolin. Parks and Recreation, **40** (4):39–40.
DAVIS, JOSEPH A., JR.
  1961. Red means go! Animal Kingdom, **64** (4):114–18.
FLOWER, S. S.
  1931. Contributions to our knowledge of the duration of life in vertebrate
         animals. 5. Mammals. Proc. Zool. Soc. London, pp. 145–234.
POCOCK, R. I.
  1924. The external characters of the pangolins (Manidae). Proc. Zool. Soc.
         London, pp. 707–23.
SÁNYÁL, RAM BRAMHA.
  1892. A hand-book of the management of animals in captivity in Lower
         Bengal. Bengal Secretariat Press, Calcutta. 351 pp.
SIMPSON, GEORGE GAYLORD.
  1945. The principles of classification and a classification of mammals.
         Bull. Amer. Mus. Nat. Hist., 85. 350 pp.
WEBB, CECIL S.
  1954. The odyssey of an animal collector. Longmans, Green & Co., New
         York, London, and Toronto. 368 pp.

ORDER LAGOMORPHA

.

Pikas, Hares, and Rabbits

The members of this order, once included with the rodents, are distinguished by, among other characters, the possession of four incisors in the upper jaw, a small pair lying behind the larger, chisel-like anterior pair. All are shy, timid creatures, depending on flight or sheltering holes for safety from their numerous enemies. They are terrestrial in habit and vegetarian in their food preferences.

FAMILY OCHOTONIDAE

Pikas

Usually described as being of the size of a guinea pig, the round-eared, nearly tailless pikas (*Ochotona*) are found in rock areas or "slides," generally at high altitudes. Two species, *Ochotona collaris* and *O. princeps*, the latter with many races (Hall and Kelson, 1959), are found in western North America, while twelve, some with several races, inhabit mountainous areas of northern Asia (Ellerman and Morrison-Scott, 1951).

Little attention seems to have been given pikas by zoological gardens, although their diurnal habits and apparent hardiness would seem to make them suitable. The practice of making "hay" and storing it for winter—pikas do not hibernate—adds greatly to their interest. These hay piles may amount to as much as a bushel of dried plant material, and Loukashkin (1940) says that in Mongolia sheepherders drive their animals in winter to large pika colonies to feed on the stored provisions.

While pikas may have been kept by American zoological gardens, I have been able to find no confirming records. Certainly, we have had none here, and Flower (1929) lists only the Himalayan pika or mouse-hare (*O. roylei*) as having been kept in the Zoological Gardens of London.

Although zoological-garden experience with pikas appears to have been slight, zoological workers in other fields have reported experiments with living animals that suggest the possibility of satisfactory results.

Dice (1927) says that of three specimens collected in July, 1926, one lived until the following March and two until July, the latter dying at a time when the temperature reached 96° F., suggesting inability to endure great heat. Efforts to induce breeding were frustrated by the quarrelsomeness of the animals. The principal foods eaten were timothy, clover or alfalfa hay, and greens, such as lettuce. Whole oats were taken sparingly.

Lettuce, cabbage, raw potatoes, dandelions, grass, oatmeal, bread, and "Wheaties," a commercial cereal, were provided for Colorado pikas (*O. princeps saxatilis*) kept by Martin (1943). Water did not appear to be taken. The animals thrived during one summer and were then released. For two animals collected in Oregon in October, 1950, Roest (1953) used rolled oats, rabbit pellets, carrots, apples, celery, grass, and cedar twigs. His pikas drank freely by lapping.

Severaid (1950) achieved success in breeding *O. princeps muiri* in captivity by introducing a male to a newly captured female on the day after she had produced a litter of four. Mating occurred almost at once, and parturition followed $31\frac{1}{2}$ days later, plus a few hours.

FAMILY LEPORIDAE

HARES AND RABBITS

Long hind legs and ears and short, fluffy tails characterize the members of this group. In fact, the over-all resemblances are so easily recognized that in this country all the many species, including the hares, are known colloquially as "rabbits." This confusion of names is natural enough, since distinctions are based largely on habits of reproduction. The hares (*Lepus*), in general, do not dig or enter burrows, and the females give birth to fully furred young with eyes opened. The European rabbit (*Oryctolagus cuniculus*) lives in communities, sometimes very large, and digs and uses burrows in the earth; in them are born the nearly naked, sightless, and helpless young. The American cottontail and its relatives (*Sylvilagus*) are intermediate in these respects, for while they do not dig burrows, they frequently make use of those abandoned by other animals. Their young, naked and sightless at birth, are born in shallow nests on the surface.

Members of this family are almost worldwide in distribution, although they are absent from the Australian region and Madagascar. The Cape hare

(*Lepus capensis*), in many races, is found from Mongolia to the Cape Province of Africa (Ellerman and Morrison-Scott, 1951). The European rabbit has been widely introduced, usually with disastrous results. Its establishment in Australia, early in the nineteenth century, is a classic example of good intentions gone awry. The European fox, brought in to check the rabbits, has seriously decimated the native fauna, including the lyre bird. Infection with a specifically lethal virus disease, myxomatosis, has now proved most effective in reducing the rabbit horde in Australia (Fenner, 1954), but serious ecological damage is feared as a result of the intentional infection of rabbits in France with this rapidly spreading virus (Andrews, 1954).

Wild hares and rabbits have never been kept commonly by zoological gardens, probably because the violence of their flight reactions is likely to lead to escape or injury and also because of their susceptibility to coccidiosis. Hediger (1950:138–42) describes and figures caging apparatus used at the Basel Zoological Gardens for keeping and breeding the very difficult European hare (*L. europaeus*). The basic principle was the use of large box cages, arranged in pairs, so that the animals could be induced to move quietly from one to the other without handling, every day or two, for cleaning purposes. Breeding was successfully accomplished to the third generation, and the previously unknown gestation period was determined as 42 days. Superfetation was also observed (Hediger, 1952:79). Matthews (1956) reports successful breeding of this species, on a simpler basis, in the Zoological Gardens of London.

Extensive experimental work has been done in this country with the American varying hare or snowshoe "rabbit" (*L. americanus*) to determine satisfactory methods for propagation in captivity as a supplement to natural game supplies. Excellent results have been obtained by penning the animals on wire cloth, as a precaution against coccidiosis. Severaid (1945) gives comparative results of keeping hares on the ground or on wire, showing 68.3 per cent survival of young born on wire as against 11.6 per cent born on the ground. The recommended mesh is $\frac{1}{2}$ inch, as it was found that newborn leverets fell through 1-inch netting and perished. The gestation period for thirty-seven females averaged 37.2 days, and females were usually receptive on the day of parturition.

The caging used by both Hediger and Severaid is perhaps either too cumbersome or too unsightly to fit well into present-day zoo planning. However, both types have been shown to be essentially successful and with some modifications for the sake of appearance might well prove adaptable. Even a small exhibit of captivity-bred varying hares, by means of which the semiannual change of coat color might be demonstrated, would be well worthwhile.

In the early days of the operation of the New York Zoological Park, the great jack rabbits of the western plains were frequently received, but none survived for more than a few months. Ditmars (1916) records a somewhat better experience with two black-tailed jack rabbits (*L. californicus*) received here during the previous year. Given a large box shelter in which they could find security, the animals gradually became accustomed to their outdoor run and refrained from mad dashes at the wire netting. Ditmars anticipated the establishment of a colony of jack rabbits, but this did not materialize, as the survivor of this pair lived only just under a year. As I recall these animals, they were wild-caught adults, with reflexes firmly established and difficult to suppress. There seems to be no reason to suppose that hand-reared jack rabbits, properly kept, should not do very much better.

The eastern cottontail (*Sylvilagus floridanus*), in its many races, is more likely than any other member of this order to be seen in American zoological gardens. Wild-caught adults do not readily become reconciled to the conditions of captivity, but in areas where the cottontail is abundant, youngsters of various ages are frequently found. If still nursing, these babies are easily reared on whole cow's milk, heated to body temperature and administered with a medicine dropper or a small rubber nipple, the only other requirement being that they be kept warm and sheltered. The eyes open at about 7 days, the body hairs rapidly, and by the time they are 2 weeks old the little animals will begin to nibble. Fresh clover and bread and milk are excellent starters, and commercial rabbit pellets, raw vegetables, greens, hay, and oats can soon be substituted. Little water is taken when greens are abundant, but it should always be available. Coprophagy or re-ingestion of excreted pellets by at least some forms of this group has been discussed by Hamilton (1955), Kirkpatrick (1956), Hall and Kelson (1959), and others. It has been suggested that these pellets, usually greenish in color, may contain large amounts of vitamin B, produced in the intestine (Bourlière, 1954).

Such animals, if constantly handled and not frightened, will remain quite tame. Varying numbers are reared here annually by our Children's Zoo personnel, serve as most attractive exhibits during the summer months, and are liberated in the grounds in autumn or carried through the winter and liberated in the following spring. Tame cottontails live well in comparatively small quarters if these are cleaned daily and kept dry. Palmer (1954) says captive eastern cottontails have lived for 5 years.

A varying hare (*L. a. bairdii*) has lived 3 years, 7 months in the National Zoological Park (Mann, 1930), and Palmer (1954) says animals of this species have lived 8 or more years in captivity. Flower (1931) gives 11 years, 11 months as maximum duration for the European hare (*L. europaeus*) in captivity in England.

· REFERENCES

ANDREWS, C. H.
   1954.   Myxomatosis in Britain. Nature, **174** (4429):529–30.
BOURLIÈRE, FRANÇOIS.
   1954.   The natural history of mammals. Alfred A. Knopf, New York, 363 pp.
DICE, L. R.
   1927.   The Colorado pika in captivity. Jour. Mammal., **8** (3):228–31.
DITMARS, R. L.
   1916.   Pacifying the jack rabbit. Bull. New York Zool. Soc., **19** (3):1365.
ELLERMAN, J. R., and T. C. S. MORRISON-SCOTT.
   1951.   Checklist of Palaearctic and Indian mammals. British Museum (Natural History), London. 810 pp.
FENNER, FRANK.
   1954.   The rabbit plague. Sci. Amer., **190** (2): 30–35.
FLOWER, S. S.
   1929.   List of the vertebrated animals exhibited in the gardens of the Zoological Society of London, 1828–1927. 1. Mammals. Zoological Society of London. 419 pp.
   1931.   Contributions to our knowledge of the duration of life in vertebrate animals. 5. Mammals. Proc. Zool. Soc. London, pp. 145–234.
HALL, E. RAYMOND, and KEITH R. KELSON.
   1959.   The mammals of North America. The Ronald Press Co., New York. 2 vols.
HAMILTON, W. J., JR.
   1955.   Coprophagy in the swamp rabbit. Jour. Mammal., **36** (2):303–05.
HEDIGER, H.
   1950.   Wild animals in captivity. Butterworths Scientific Publications, London. 207 pp.
   1952.   Reproduction in zoo animals. In: CIBA Foundation colloquia on endocrinology. 3. Hormones, psychology and behaviour and steroid hormone administration. J. & A. Churchill, Ltd., London. 380 pp.
KIRKPATRICK, CHARLES M.
   1956.   Coprophagy in the cottontail. Jour. Mammal., **37** (2):300.

LOUKASHKIN, A. S.
  1940. On the pikas of North Manchuria. Jour. Mammal., 21 (4):402–5.

MANN, WM. M.
  1930. Wild animals in and out of the zoo. Smithsonian Sci. Ser., Vol. 6. 362 pp.

MARTIN, KEN.
  1943. The Colorado pika. Jour. Mammal., 24 (3):394–96.

MATTHEWS, L. HARRISON.
  1956. Breeding hares in captivity. Proc. Zool. Soc. London, 126:161–63.

PALMER, RALPH S.
  1954. The mammal guide. Doubleday & Co., Inc., Garden City, N.Y. 384 pp.

ROEST, ARYAN I.
  1953. Notes on pikas from the Oregon Cascades. Jour. Mammal., 34 (1):132–33.

SEVERAID, J. H.
  1945. Breeding potential and artificial propagation of the snowshoe hare. Jour. Wildlife Management, 9 (4):290–95.

  1950. The gestation period of the pika (*Ochotona princeps*). Jour. Mammal., 31 (3):356–57.

ORDER RODENTIA

•

RODENTS

Successful and widely distributed, the rodents are known in more forms than those of any other order of mammals, Ellerman (1940) setting their number at 6,400. In their search for suitable biotic niches some have become largely aquatic, while others have taken to the trees or tunneled beneath the surface of the ground upon which the majority still live. Few land areas, from the Arctic region to the borders of Antarctica, have proved entirely inhospitable. Even Australia has its quota of rodents which, with the bats, are the only placental mammals indigenous to that continent.

Widely though they may vary in appearance and habits, all rodents possess a common character—a single pair of opposing chisel teeth (incisors) in each jaw. These teeth are essential, of course, to the gnawing practices for which the group is well known. Their growth continues throughout life, and upper and lower pairs bear upon each other to insure sharp edges and proper lengths. Occasionally their alignment is disturbed by injury or malformation, resulting in continued growth of one or more teeth, which may result in the death of the animal.

Plant life in some form composes the food of the great majority, although many will eat flesh if it is available, and a few are more directly carnivorous. Practically all depend upon flight for safety but usually will defend themselves fiercely if cornered. The larger species are able to inflict severe damage with their sharp incisors. While some, such as most of the squirrels and the agoutis, are chiefly diurnal in habit, many, particularly among the smaller forms, are nocturnal.

This diversity of habit has particular bearing on usefulness as zoological-garden exhibits. Such animals as the Patagonian cavy, the capybara, the coypu, the squirrels, and the agoutis, which are active during daylight hours, serve our purpose well. Others, such as the beaver and the porcupines, that are predominantly nocturnal, are adaptable under suitable conditions. The great host of entirely nocturnal forms, mostly of small size, present special problems. Many are so beautiful or so interesting that the wish to attempt their exhibition is hard to resist. Most institutions, from time to time, will have such species, even though they may not readily be available, but few undertake to maintain collections on the extensive scale of those in Washington and London. A fleeting glimpse of an African pygmy mouse flashing from one nest box to another at the urging of an indulgent keeper is not to be forgotten by those privileged to see it, but only a fraction of the visiting public can be so favored.

A means for exhibiting small nocturnal species in such a way that their normal activities, usually undertaken only in darkness, would be visible in daylight hours has long been sought by zoological gardens. Walker (1942) describes a method introduced at the National Zoological Park in that period by which some species were caused to sleep at night by subjecting them to bright artificial light and induced to become active by day under natural light filtered through blue-black or blue cellophane. The project was fairly successful, but the light was too dim for the animals to be seen well and still too bright to permit full activity. Reversal under blue light was carried another step forward at the Chicago Zoological Park, as reported by Snedigar (1949).

Probably the best results by the blue-light method have been those obtained at the English zoological gardens of Bristol and Chester (Mottershead, 1958) by accomplishing the same reversal but showing the animals by day under blue fluorescent tubes. This was reasonably successful for some species. Lawrence Curtis informs me (*in litt.*) that at Bristol, in 1956, he saw kinkajous, armadillos, genets, palm civets, jerboas, owl monkeys, and several other species so treated and found most of them active and visible at the noon hour. R. E. Greed, the director, reported satisfaction with his exhibit and planned to enlarge it.

As these experiments progressed, the use of red light for the study of nocturnal animals was advancing. Southern, Watson, and Chitty (1946) used an instrument known as a "sniperscope" which made use of a beam of infrared light to throw on a screen an image of the observed animal. Finley (1959) found that the rays of a flashlight, its lens shielded with a red acetate disk, allowed full nocturnal observation without disturbing the activities of the subject. This was the final key to the solution of the problem.

Reversal had never been attempted here, our only efforts having been directed toward the protection of nocturnal species from glare by the use of blue fluorescent tubes. A series of experiments conducted here by our curator of mammals, Joseph A. Davis, Jr. (1961), soon convinced him that red light instead of blue gives the desired result. The rods that predominate in the retinas of the eyes of nocturnal animals are insensitive to color, so that red light is not perceived as such. Under it animals conduct themselves as though they were in almost complete darkness.

Acting on this principal, a large section of our Small Mammal House was re-equipped as a "Red Light Room." Red fluorescent tubes of 15- to 40-watt capacity were installed and cage walls were painted red. There is no light in the public space except for the red reflections from the cages and scattered tubes overhead, but once the visitors' eyes have become accustomed to the change, visibility is excellent. Under these conditions the animals are active, indifferent to the public, and plainly visible. Mr. Davis assures me that so far he has encountered no small mammal resistant to reversal and that he has been successful with members of twenty families of nine orders. The exhibit was opened to the public in September, 1961, and became an immediate success, a progress report having been made by Davis (1962). Further development of this major breakthrough is planned here, as a "World of Darkness" building.

For purposes other than those of the zoological garden, many members of the order Rodentia have been subjected to intensive study in captivity. In addition to the guinea pig, domesticated rats and mice and the recently domesticated golden hamster (*Mesocricetus auratus*), many wild species have received the attention of medical research laboratories, animal supply houses, behavior investigators, and fanciers. The fur-bearers, especially the beaver, the muskrat, and the coypu, have been studied extensively with a view to finding profitable means of propagation. The zoological gardens themselves have been far from remiss in this field, for London and Washington, especially, have scored successes with many otherwise little-known species. Much detailed information is available, therefore, concerning care, breeding, and maintenance, when suitable exhibition means can be devised. Of the thirty-two families of the order Rodentia designated by Simpson (1945), only the more important from the viewpoint of the zoological garden can be considered here.

FAMILY APLODONTIDAE

Mountain Beaver or Sewellel

The mountain beaver (*Aplodontia rufa*) is a rather large and lethargic rodent ranging, in several forms, down a narrow strip in western North America, from British Columbia to California and western Nevada. It is not a close relative of the true beaver (*Castor*)—its tail, instead of being broad and flattened, as in the latter animal, is barely an inch in length.

In habits the mountain beaver is crepuscular or nocturnal, spending much of its time in a complicated series of underground tunnels from which it emerges in the evening or even on overcast days to seek its food. This consists of vegetable material, including bark, and it will sometimes ascend small trees to cut the branches and tops.

The scanty history of the mountain beaver in captivity is largely a record of disappointments. Walker (1942) says, "almost all of the numerous efforts to keep it in captivity have resulted in prompt failure." The species was first received here in 1905, when each of several arrivals survived for only a few days.

An animal of sturdy appearance such as the mountain beaver, which may measure as much as 18 inches in total length, would appear to have potentialities of viability which have not been fully realized. A note by Pfeiffer (1953) indicates that this may very well be the case. This author, who has had extensive experience with living mammals and birds, reports that he found no difficulty in keeping the mountain beaver alive for periods of "six months or more" in ordinary laboratory cages. Lettuce, carrots, apples, and whole-wheat bread were found to form an adequate diet, and large amounts of water were consumed. Breeding was not accomplished because the males invariably killed cage mates of either sex.

An even more encouraging experience followed the arrival here on September 28, 1960, of two animals of this species. Each was placed in one of the abandoned concrete bins once used for breeding and storing earthworms for our platypuses. Earth 9 or 10 inches deep provided means for burrowing, and wire-mesh covers prevented escape by climbing. Food provided included lettuce, carrots, apples, and sweet potatoes, with feeding pellets, as described under "Deer" (p. 559), and an assortment of grains and seeds, especially sunflower. Various kinds of hay were refused, but well-weathered tanbark, scattered over the floor, was sometimes eaten. Drinking water was always available. The animals appeared to be thriving until both were found dead, each in its own bin, on November 12, 1961, after 1 year, 1 month, 15 days. Death was thought to have been caused by the emission of gases from a nearby furnace.

These notes seem to indicate that the case of the mountain beaver in captivity is not as hopeless as it has appeared to be. With real or simulated provision for burrowing, protection from bright light, more space for movement, and adequately bulky food, better results are certainly to be anticipated.

FAMILY SCIURIDAE

Squirrels, Marmots, and Prairie Dogs

Many species of particular value to the zoological garden are included in this family. Most, with the exception of the flying squirrels, are diurnal, and many are active throughout the year, although both hibernation and estivation occur in some. Both colonial and solitary living habits are found in the group, so that, in spite of close relationships, there is wide variation in patterns of behavior.

The tree squirrels of the large genus *Sciurus*, members of which are found in Europe, Asia, and North and South America, are probably best known and are familiar to a very large segment of the world's population. Beautiful, active, and graceful, the tree squirrels are ideal zoo inhabitants.

The principal European and Asiatic representative of *Sciurus* is the European red squirrel (*Sciurus vulgaris* and races), which extends across Europe and Asia from Great Britain to Japan. For some reason, results with this attractive animal in this country have not been good. The longest span achieved in the New York Zoological Park is 1 year, 9 months, 16 days, and I do not know of a better one. Mitchell (1911) gives an average of 6 months' duration, with a maximum of 20 months, for seventy-seven specimens in the Zoological Gardens of London. Most European zoological gardens exhibit the species, but the general appearance of specimens seen and the difficulty of finding definite longevity records suggest that results in its native lands have not been much more satisfactory.

New World members of the genus *Sciurus* are more numerous than those of Europe and Asia, and a great number are known. Most likely to be seen in zoological gardens are the eastern gray squirrel (*Sciurus carolinensis* and races), the western gray (*S. griseus* and races), both from the indicated areas of North America, and the superb fox squirrel (*S. niger* and races), found in the eastern United States west to Colorado, Texas, and northeastern Mexico. All these are hardy and easily maintained. The beautiful, tufted-eared, white-tailed Kaibab squirrel (*S. kaibabensis*) and the closely related Abert's (*S. aberti* and races), both from the southwestern United States, have seldom been kept, although the latter has been exhibited at the National Zoological Park in Washington and in our own collection.

A great number of beautifully colored tropical squirrels are found from Mexico over much of northern South America. Of these, most often available are the variegated (*S. variegatoides* and races), found from Mexico to the Canal Zone, and the many forms of *S. granatensis*, the tropical red squirrel, ranging from Costa Rica to Colombia, Ecuador, and Venezuela. All the neotropical species, of course, require heated quarters in winter.

The eastern gray squirrel has lived here for 8 years, 5 months; the 181 months or 15 years, 1 month, reported by Mitchell (1911) for a specimen in the Zoological Gardens of London is a longer duration than any other known to me. The western gray has never been kept here, but Ross (1930) gives 11 years and still living for a male and two females privately kept in California. Our best span for a fox squirrel is 9 years, 1 month, 17 days; Flower (1931) lists 9 years, 11 months, 19 days in the Zoological Gardens of London. A white-bellied squirrel (*S. granatensis splendidus*) lived here for 7 years, 9 months, 3 days, and Hoffmann's squirrel (*S. g. hoffmanni*), 5 years, 1 month, 4 days.

The active, lively little American red squirrel or chickaree (*Tamiasciurus hudsonicus*) is widely distributed in the forested areas of northern North America, preferring growths of conifers. Twenty-five races of this almost ubiquitous species are listed by Hall and Kelson (1959). Wild-caught adults are intractable and difficult, but specimens taken while very young often become delightfully tame. Unfortunately, such animals may take advantage of familiarity and turn actually savage as they grow older, so that they must be approached with caution. The American red squirrel has lived here for 5 years, 8 months, 21 days, but Klugh (1927) reports a privately kept specimen as having lived to its ninth year.

The Old World tree squirrels, in addition to the red squirrel, are very numerous and are found in Asia, the East Indian islands, and Africa. All cannot be covered here, but the members of at least three genera, *Ratufa*, *Callosciurus*, and *Protoxerus*, are of special importance.

Among the largest and most spectacular of all the squirrels is the Malabar (*Ratufa indica maxima*), the only race of this fine species that has been commonly imported into this country. Others, of course, have been seen in European collections as well as at Calcutta. This handsome squirrel, as large as a small cat, has a somewhat coarse appearance but balances this with its glossy black, buff, and chestnut coloration. Most specimens imported are steady or quite tame, implying at least a degree of hand-rearing. Malabars thrive in captivity but are especially subject to unsightly loss of hair from the tail. We have attributed this difficulty to the too free use of water in cage cleaning and have managed to avoid it by resorting to dry cleaning.

Most beautiful of the Old World tree squirrels commonly imported is the one known collectively as Prevost's (*Callosciurus prevosti*), so many races having been named from the Malay Peninsula and nearby islands that subspecific determinations are difficult. Perhaps a little smaller than the eastern gray squirrel, Prevost's is slender and graceful and handsomely marked in black, white, and chestnut.

Stanger's squirrel (*Protoxerus stangeri*) extends, in several races, across equatorial Africa from Nigeria and Angola eastward to Kenya. While certainly not to be included among the commonly imported squirrels, it is so different in appearance and habits from other tree squirrels that it should be mentioned here. A single specimen was brought to us in 1949 from the Belgian Congo by Charles Cordier. Dull brown in general coloration, the body was noticeably long and slender and the head almost weasel-like, so that as it crept about the branches of its cage it had the appearance of a small arboreal carnivore. This impression proved to be more than superficial, for it was not until we added to its diet a small daily quantity of chopped raw meat that it began really to thrive. It lived here for 5 years, 1 month, 15 days.

A Malabar squirrel has lived here for 7 years, 11 months, 4 days. Sányál (1892) gives the length of life in the Calcutta Zoological Gardens as "upwards of 9 years," while Flower (1931) reports one said to have lived for over 16 years in the possession of the Bombay Natural History Society. Pournelle (1960) reports that a specimen of the Malayan giant squirrel (*R. bicolor*), received at the San Diego Zoological Garden in 1941, lived until June 20, 1958, or approximately 17 years, 6 months. We have been able to maintain Prevost's squirrel for only 2 years, 7 months, 16 days. Sányál (1892) says it has lived "nearly 5 years" in Calcutta.

Unless kept in very spacious quarters, the tree squirrels do best in pairs or at least in small groups including a single male, since animals of this sex will fight fiercely during mating seasons. Cage construction, of course, should be of tooth-resistant materials, since squirrels are inveterate chewers of wood. Most species will make use of a sleeping chamber, either a cavity in a section of natural log which we furnish here or a wooden box. In the latter case the entrance hole, at least, should be tinned around to prevent enlargement by the animals. It is often necessary to provide individual sleeping apartments, since many squirrels will not share these. Branches for climbing are essential. Nest boxes, logs, and branches will usually have to be replaced at intervals because of damage by chewing. This is a necessary evil, for not even the hardest nuts will always provide the constant attrition required to keep the animals' incisor teeth from overgrowing. The floors of our indoor squirrel cages are provided with a covering of dry leaves, collected and stored in bags in the autumn. These not only improve the appearance of the exhibit but serve a functional use in insuring protection from the dampness so inimical to captive squirrels.

The tree squirrels, as a group, are omnivorous, with some variation in specific needs and preferences. Hard-shelled nuts, such as pecans, filberts, and walnuts, grains and seeds, including whole corn, oats, and canary, raw vegetables, greens, fruits, and berries are the staples. The tropical species, from both the Old World and the New, show a preference for fruit, such as bananas and mealy apples. Many, as already noted for Stanger's squirrel, are at least partly carnivorous, and new arrivals should be tested for willingness to take animal protein. Hard-boiled egg will satisfy some. The needs of others can be met with a small portion of a mixture of dog biscuit and raw or cooked chopped meat, which gives opportunity for the introduction of finely ground bone meal and cod-liver oil. Many squirrels will gnaw dry bones, which not only provide needed calcium but serve to keep incisors in order. Most, if not all, squirrels are excellent swimmers, but I cannot recall ever having seen one bathe. However, clean drinking water should always be available.

Young eastern gray squirrels are easily reared on whole cow's milk given with a medicine dropper or very small rubber nipple. Vitamin concentrate drops and precooked baby food, such as Pablum, can be added. When ready to feed themselves, the youngsters can be started on bread and milk followed by soft fruits and vegetables, and soon can be brought gradually onto the adult diet. Such animals usually retain at least a degree of tameness and make very satisfactory zoo specimens. It is presumable that young squirrels of most species will give similar results.

Perhaps because space is usually lacking for the pursuit courtship of many species, the tree squirrels do not breed freely in captivity. As far as records and recollection go, no tree squirrel has ever been born in our collection. Zuckerman (1953) reports six births of eastern gray squirrels in the Zoological Gardens of London between 1907 and 1934, while Shorten (1951–52) describes successful rearing by two females that had been kept in captivity at Oxford, England, for approximately $3\frac{1}{2}$ years before breeding. Baumgras (1944) mentions two fox squirrels that had been born and reared in outdoor exhibition pens at the Swan Creek Wildlife Experiment Station at Allegan, Michigan. This species is also stated by Stott (1954) to have been bred for at least two generations in the San Diego Zoological Garden. Hill (1942) recounts the breeding of the Malabar squirrel in captivity in Ceylon and gives further details in a later report (1949). Palmer (1954) gives the following data for North American tree squirrels: eastern gray, gestation period about 44 days, eyes of young open in about

37 days; eastern fox, gestation period about 45 days, eyes of young open in 40–44 days; American red, gestation period about 40 days, eyes of young open in about 27 days.

The Cape ground squirrel (*Xerus inauris*) is a South African representative of a rather small group of African squirrels that parallel the ground squirrels of the genus *Spermophilus* in appearance and habits. It is dull brown in color, with lateral stripe, face, and underparts white. The rather bushy tail is mixed black and white, and the body hairs are thickened, almost spiny. It is colonial in habit, digging grouped burrows that resemble the "towns" of the prairie dog (*Cynomys*). The species is imported into the United States on occasion and is fed here as outlined for tree squirrels, with the inclusion of protein. Shortridge (1934) says that in addition to the usual vegetable foods, insects, eggs and young of birds, and small reptiles are taken. Haagner (1920) states that "numbers of these squirrels have been bred in the National Zoological Gardens" (Pretoria) and adds that litter size varies from two to six. The Cape ground squirrel has not survived here for more than 18 months, but Flower (1931) gives 6 years, 1 month, 26 days for a closely related species (*X. rutilus*) in the Giza Zoological Gardens.

The marmots (*Marmota*) are holarctic in distribution, occurring in North America and northern areas of Europe and Asia. All are essentially terrestrial, making their homes in colonial or solitary burrows. The woodchuck (*Marmota monax*) is found in several races from the eastern United States and Canada northwestward to Alaska. Unlike most of its congeners, the woodchuck is essentially solitary in habit, individuals seldom wandering far from their complicated burrows. An exception occurs in spring, when the males may travel for considerable distances in search of temporary mates. The young are born after a gestation period of 31 or 32 days, and their eyes open in 26–28 days (Palmer, 1954).

The many races of the yellow-bellied marmot (*M. flaviventris*) of the western United States and British Columbia and the hoary marmot (*M. caligata*) of northwestern North America live in colonies, usually at high elevations. The yellow-bellied has not been kept here and the hoary was first received in 1962. George H. Pournelle (*in litt.*) reports a specimen of the Montana hoary marmot (*M. c. nivaria*) as having lived for 4 years in the San Diego Zoological Garden, and Mann (1930) lists 7 years, 10 months for a dusky marmot (*M. c. obscura*) in the National Zoological Park in Washington.

The alpine marmot (*M. marmota*) is found, in several races, from mountain areas of central Europe to eastern Siberia, living in colonies. The alpine marmot has been received here on only one occasion and survived for but a few months. Mann (1930) reports 3 years for a specimen in the National Zoological Park. Much greater experience with this species has been had in Europe, and Flower (1931) gives a long list of creditable longevities, the greatest of which is 13 years, 6 months, 21 days in the Zoological Gardens of London.

Winter hibernation is a general phenomenon among the marmots, and representatives in the extreme northerly limits of their range may have a very short annual season of activity. In addition to the winter sleep, the yellow-bellied marmot in some areas may also estivate during periods of great summer heat.

Experience here with the woodchuck presumably would apply to other marmots in captivity. Young specimens, taken before they have left their mother's care, are easily reared on whole cow's milk and may be introduced gradually to solid food, as suggested for squirrels. Such animals, if kept under control, usually remain tractable, if not entirely trustworthy, and accept the conditions of captivity well. The woodchuck, a comparatively large and powerful animal, is capable of biting severely when inclined to be savage, so that wild-caught adults are not desirable as zoo exhibits.

Unlike many members of this family, the woodchuck is almost entirely vegetarian in feeding habits. Greens, such as lettuce and cabbage, raw vegetables, including carrots, turnips, and potatoes, apples, hard grains, and dry whole-wheat or rye bread provide an adequate diet as well as keeping the teeth in proper alignment.

Woodchucks are not particularly given to gnawing and will seldom damage a wooden nest box or hollow log. However, since they are able to dig with great power, metal and concrete cages are advisable. In spite of solitary habits in nature, woodchucks will share living and sleeping quarters, so that two or three may usually be kept together. In outdoor cages the animals will retire together to their sleeping box in late autumn and remain there in hibernation until early spring. The hibernating box should be well supplied with hay, and the animals must remain undisturbed until they emerge. Woodchucks kept indoors here usually retire to their sleeping box or rock crevice, sometimes closing the entrance with bedding, in the normal hibernating period. However, this retirement is likely to last for only a few days, when the animals may resume activity, only to retire again very shortly. These alternating periods often continue throughout the season of hibernation.

An albino woodchuck has lived here for 7 years, 4 months, and a normally colored specimen 7 years, 11 months, 25 days. Mann (1930) records 9 years, 3 months for a woodchuck in the National Zoological Park, while

Flower (1931) gives 9 years, 8 months for a specimen in the Zoological Gardens of London. No marmot has ever been born here. Zuckerman (1953) records the birth of two woodchucks (*M. monax*) in the Zoological Gardens of London.

The prairie dogs (*Cynomys*) extend, in several species and races, from northern Mexico across the great mountain and plains areas of the western United States to Saskatchewan, Canada. There are two principal species: the white-tailed (*Cynomys leucurus*), which is pale in color with white-tipped tail, and an inhabitant of the Rocky Mountain region, and the larger, darker black-tailed (*C. ludovicianus*). The latter, most commonly seen in zoological gardens, once spread its immense "towns" of burrows over the prairies from Montana to Texas and from Kansas to New Mexico. Now, however, it has become so greatly reduced in numbers, largely through the activities of rodent control forces, that special attention is being given to preserving it in suitable areas (Koford, 1958).

The black-tailed prairie dog is mainly herbivorous in feeding habits, its damage to grazing areas having contributed largely to its undoing. However, the diet may also include not only insects but the flesh of its dead fellows (Shadle, 1940). While the white-tailed apparently hibernates in winter, dormancy for short periods during cold weather is more usual for the black-tailed (Koford, 1958).

Provided with nesting boxes in lieu of burrows, prairie dogs, particularly those taken young, will thrive well enough indoors. One specimen each of the Zuni prairie dog (*C. gunnisoni zuniensis*) and the black-tailed were maintained for $8\frac{1}{2}$ years as house pets under conditions of fairly close confinement (Young, 1944).

Common practice in zoological gardens provides a large outdoor inclosure on open ground where prairie dogs can live under nearly natural conditions. The inclosure used here for many years was circular, with a diameter of about 80 feet. It was surrounded by a fence of $\frac{1}{4}$-inch bars set on 1-inch centers, 4 feet high and with an inturned overhang at the top. This rested on a wall of concrete which extended into the earth to an average depth of 6 feet, where it reached bedrock. The installation sat at the summit of a knoll, so that it was assured of drainage. It was presumed to be escape proof, but on one occasion a few animals did manage to make their way out underground, through a crevice that had developed in the concrete wall.

Present-day construction plans usually substitute a raised wall and graded, shallow moat for a fence of bars, as a concession to appearance, 3 or 4 feet of perpendicular clearance being sufficient to restrain the animals. Where bedrock cannot be reached conveniently by the outer wall, the area should be excavated to a depth of from 6 to 9 feet, so that the burrows can be extended well below frost line, floored over with carefully laid stone or copper wire netting, and refilled with earth. In at least one instance in which the soil proved too shallow for the safety of the dormant animals during the winter months, a thick layer of straw spread over the area was found fully efficient.

In our inclosure prairie dogs did well for considerable periods, producing numerous young. However, the colony was not completely self-perpetuating, for a search of the records discloses that following the first introduction, in 1899, it was found necessary to add new specimens at intervals of 15, 17, and 6 years, the last in 1937. This final colony was disposed of in 1942 and the inclosure adapted for Patagonian cavies (*Dolichotis*).

Food provided consisted of raw vegetables, greens, crushed oats, and canned dog food or dog biscuits, with grass cuttings, fresh clover, and alfalfa, as available. When greens are abundant prairie dogs drink sparingly, but water should always be available.

In an inclosure such as that described above, the black-tailed prairie dog breeds well but under conditions of close control seldom does so. However, Johnson (1927) has reported a birth in a laboratory cage about 3 feet square, the parents having been in captivity for approximately 6 months. The young animals' eyes opened in 33–37 days, and the minimum weaning age was considered to be 7 weeks. The gestation period for the white-tailed prairie dog is estimated by Stockard (1929) as 27–33 days. This author suggests that the period for the black-tailed may be the same, although this appears not to have been definitely established.

The ground squirrels (*Ammospermophilus* and *Spermophilus*) are found in both Europe and Asia but reach their greatest abundance and variation in western North America. Most of the many species are more or less colonial, excavating their burrows in close conjunction. They are diurnal in habit and search on the ground for their food, which consists mostly of plant material but may also include not only insects but the flesh of dead or injured fellows, as well as that of other creatures (Alcorn, 1940; Musacchia, 1954). Hibernation is common to most although not all forms, and estivation as well occurs in many. A study of these phenomena in several species has been made by Wade (1930).

While many of the ground squirrels are beautifully colored and some are of comparatively large size (the rock squirrel [*Spermophilus variegatus*] may reach a length of 21 inches), they are not entirely well suited for zoological-garden requirements. Although generally diurnal, they are inclined to remain in the concealment of such shelter as may be provided during the day, emerging late in the afternoon to feed. On the other hand, all species with which we have had experience have proved to be easily maintained and, except for some possible disturbance during the spring breeding season, well disposed toward each other. Hibernation and estivation are usually manifested by our animals, perhaps because of uniformity of temperature and food supply, only by occasional periods of dormancy, seldom enduring for more than 2 or 3 days.

Ground squirrels are shown here in indoor glass and metal boxes, with floor space about 2 feet in each dimension. Tops of adjustable fine wire mesh insure sufficient ventilation. We use dead leaves for floor covering, with a small section of hollow log or branch laid on its side across one corner. Most ground squirrels will make use of a pan of dry earth or sand, set out of sight behind the log, as an aid in keeping the pelage in order. Cages constructed of wood are unsuitable, since they are soon cut through or damaged by the animals.

Suitable food consists of grain and seeds, especially sunflower, greens and raw vegetables, in as great variety as may be available. In addition, we provide a small portion daily of either dry or canned dog food or a mixture of chopped raw meat, finely ground bone meal, and cod-liver oil. These flesh-containing foods are usually taken greedily. Drinking water is always available, although little is used when greens are abundant.

Like most of the members of this family, ground squirrels do not breed well in close confinement and none has ever been born here. However, the San Diego Zoological Garden has bred the golden-mantled or Say's ground squirrel (*Spermophilus lateralis*) (Stott, 1954) and there have been a number of successes by laboratory and field workers. Among these are the Columbian (*S. columbianus*), by Shaw (1925), the thirteen-lined (*S. tridecemlineatus*), by Wade (1927a), and the golden-mantled, bred to the third generation by Selle (1939). For the Columbian the gestation period was found to be 24 days, with eyes of young opening in 19–23 days; for the thirteen-lined the corresponding periods were 27–28 days and 28 days, respectively.

Our best longevities for ground squirrels here are:

Species	Years	Months	Days
White-tailed antelope (*Ammospermophilus leucurus*)	6	10	6
Richardson's (*Spermophilus richardsonii*)	4	0	15
Franklin's (*S. franklinii*)	7	2	10
Thirteen-lined (*S. tridecemlineatus*)	7	11	12

Flower (1931) gives 9 years, 10 months, 17 days for *S.* (*variegatus*) *grammurus*, the rock ground squirrel, in the Zoological Gardens of London.

The chipmunks (*Tamias* and *Eutamias*) are intermediate, in general habits, between the tree and ground squirrels. While their homes are made in deep burrows in the earth, rock outcrops, timber slashes, and even shrubs and low trees seem to be as attractive to them as the surface of the ground itself.

The eastern chipmunk (*Tamias striatus*) occurs in numerous races in eastern North America. The many species and forms of western chipmunks (*Eutamias*) range over western North America, from northern Mexico to the Yukon, sometimes at high altitudes. There are representatives, too (races of *Eutamias sibiricus*), in the Old World, from Russia across Siberia and from northern China to Japan. Ellerman and Morrison-Scott (1951) unite the two genera under *Tamias*.

The chipmunks are less social than the ground squirrels, and each usually guards its small territory jealously. Their diet consists of nuts, seeds, grains, berries, and such animal food as they can come by, including insects, birds and their eggs, and mice. Like the ground squirrels, the chipmunks are diurnal, but unlike their close relatives, they do not truly hibernate, passing the cold months in a state of dormancy from which they readily emerge during mild periods.

In captivity wild-caught adults do not accommodate well to close confinement. However, young specimens are easily reared, as recommended for tree squirrels. Such animals not only appear to be completely reconciled to cage life but are likely to become bold to the point of biting the proffered hand. Members of litters hand-reared here have become so antagonistic toward each other when about 3 months old that they have had to be separated.

Chipmunks are kept here in the glass and metal boxes described for ground squirrels. The furnishings are the same, except that small branches are provided for chipmunks. These animals have the disadvantage of being so much less social than ground squirrels that ordinarily they cannot be kept together in small quarters. However, since chipmunks are more inclined to be active throughout the day than ground squirrels, even a single animal may make an attractive exhibit. Food provided here consists of canary and sunflower seed, cut carrots, greens, fruit, nuts, and a small portion of either dry or canned dog food or raw chopped meat, with fine bone meal and cod-liver oil.

Because of the antagonism of individuals and the difficulty of determining the proper time to give the sexes access to each other, chipmunks are not readily bred in captivity. However, the long-eared chipmunk

(*E. quadrimaculatus*) bred freely when kept in a large screened porch in California (Ross, 1930). The coulee chipmunk (*E. minimus grisescens*) is reported as having been bred in the San Diego Zoological Garden (Stott, 1954). The gestation period for the eastern chipmunk (*T. striatus*) has been determined by Allen (1938) as 31 days, with the eyes of the young requiring an equal time to open.

A normally colored eastern chipmunk (*T. striatus*) has lived here for 4 years, 11 months, and an albino for 3 years, 9 months. Flower (1931) gives 7 years, 5 days for an eastern chipmunk in the Zoological Gardens of London, and Ross (1930) says that chipmunks, presumably *E. quadrimaculatus*, lived for 8 years in captivity in California, until destroyed by accident.

The flying squirrels are distinguished by nocturnal habits and the ability to glide diagonally downward for considerable distances by means of folds of skin which are attached at ankles and wrists and are drawn taut when the legs are extended. Essentially tree-dwellers, the flying squirrels make their homes in hollows well above the ground or, in those species familiar about human dwellings, in roofs or rafters of buildings to which they can gain entrance. When this occurs they are so secretive in habit that their presence is often unsuspected.

Flying squirrels occur in North and Central America, Europe, and Asia but are absent from South America, Africa, and Australia. Two species are found in North America: the southern (*Glaucomys volans*), the races of which are distributed from southeastern Canada across the eastern United States to Mexico and Honduras, and the larger northern (*G. sabrinus*) which, in many forms, spreads from Labrador across the forested areas of Canada and the northern United States to Alaska, with southern extensions where suitable conditions exist. These squirrels do not hibernate but remain more or less active during the winter months.

In the Old World, flying squirrels are known from Scandinavia across northern Asia to Japan and in the Indo-Malayan region, twelve genera with many species and subspecies being currently recognized (Ellerman and Morrison-Scott, 1951; Chasen, 1940). These squirrels vary widely in size and appearance, from the tiny pygmy flying squirrels (*Petaurillus*) of Borneo and the Malay Peninsula, with head and body 4 inches or even less in length, to the superb giants (*Petaurista*), widely spread over the Asiatic area, which may have the head and body as long as 18 inches or even more.

The giant flying squirrels have seldom been exhibited in this country, and Blanford (1888–91) comments on the difficulty of maintaining them in captivity. A specimen of the beautiful Formosan giant flying squirrel (*Petaurista alborufus lena*) received here on December 21, 1959, lived for only 1 year, 2 months. However, Mitchell (1911) gives 8 years, 5 months for the red-bellied flying squirrel (*Pteromys* [= *Petaurista*] *alborufus*) and 13 years, 7 months for the white-cheeked flying squirrel (*P. leucogenys*), both in the Zoological Gardens of London. Sányál (1892) reports a specimen of Hodgson's giant flying squirrel (*P. magnificus*) as having lived for over 11 years in the Zoological Gardens of Calcutta, Sányál makes no mention of animal protein in the diet of "fruits, nuts, biscuits, grain, Indian-corn and other grains and vegetables" listed for squirrels in general.

Experience with New World flying squirrels in captivity appears to have been much more extensive, at least as far as the races of the southern (*G. volans*) are concerned. While it appears that the northern (*G. sabrinus*) must have been kept, it has not been shown here and I have found no record of it elsewhere.

The southern flying squirrel must have been kept as a pet from the time of the earliest settlers, its soft fur, large eyes, and gentle disposition being most appealing. Even wild-caught adults settle down well, though seldom permitting familiarity. On the other hand, specimens taken young enough to require hand-rearing, as already described for other squirrels, become entirely confiding.

Flying squirrels respond remarkably well to reversal under red light (Davis, 1961), and a large glass-fronted compartment containing twelve animals, established here in 1961, makes a charming exhibit. Upright tree trunks and branches, with numerous cavities, provide sleeping places, and there is ample room for leaping and gliding. Like most other squirrels, flying squirrels are practically omnivorous, and the diet suggested for chipmunks seems to suit flying squirrels equally well.

The southern flying squirrel breeds readily in captivity under favorable conditions, as described by Walker (1948). Svihla (1930) gives 30 days as the age at which the eyes open, but Palmer (1954) says this is 26–28 days, with a gestation period of 40 days. A specimen of the typical race (*G. v. volans*) lived here for 7 years.

FAMILY GEOMYIDAE

POCKET GOPHERS

The pocket gophers are stout-bodied, weak-eyed creatures of nocturnal habits, strongly specialized for the digging of their extensive underground tunnels. Much of their food consists of roots and bulbs of plants drawn into their tunnels from below, so that ventures to the surface may be both brief and infrequent. They are named for the cheek pouches, used for the transportation of food and nest-building materials. The pocket gophers, in several species and almost innumerable races, are found from south-western Canada across the western, central, and Gulf areas of the United States and Mexico to Panama. According to Hall and Kelson (1959), more than three hundred forms in this family have been described.

Largely because of their fossorial habits, the pocket gophers are not usually considered as desirable zoo animals. Probably this explains, at least in part, the early demise of specimens received in the early days of this institution and the fact that no attempt to replace them has been made since 1915. Yet Mann (1953) reports that a digger pine pocket gopher (*Thomomys umbrinus mewa*) lived for just over 3 years in the National Zoological Park, Washington, adding the comment that "Pocket Gophers do not ordinarily live so long in captivity."

Successful attempts to keep pocket gophers in captivity under laboratory conditions have been described by Wade (1927*b*) and Criddle (1930). In both cases greens, vegetables, grain, and raw or cooked meat were taken freely. Hanley (1944) advises against the use of earth as cage-floor covering because it was soon fouled by urine. He found that cages of $\frac{1}{2}$-inch mesh wire gauze, only 12 inches in each dimension, with a pad of folded newspapers underneath, were so satisfactory that his specimens lived up to 6 months without loss, with the exception of one considered to have died from overexposure to the sun. Hanley made no attempt to keep more than one animal in a cage, a wise precaution in view of the known antagonism of individuals toward each other. Two instances of successful breeding of *T. bottae* in captivity are recorded by Schramm (1961), the gestation period being noted, in each instance, as a few hours short of 19 days.

In the light of available information there appears to be no reason why pocket gophers should not be expected to give satisfactory results if separately caged in boxes of the type described for ground squirrels.

FAMILY HETEROMYIDAE

KANGAROO RATS AND POCKET MICE

As indicated by the family name, the members of this group are diverse in size and appearance. There are, however, many points in common, such as external, fur-lined cheek pouches and nocturnal habits. Included are the kangaroo rats (*Dipodomys*), the pygmy kangaroo rats (*Microdipodops*), the pocket mice (*Perognathus*), and the spiny pocket mice (*Liomys* and

Heteromys). Distribution of the numerous forms includes southwestern Canada, the western United States, and Central America, extending into northern South America. For the most part dwellers in desert or at best arid regions, they pass the days in underground retreats, emerging at dusk to gather the seeds, roots, and other vegetable materials that form their food. They are not known to hibernate. The true desert dwellers appear to drink no water, except possibly drops of dew, and presumably obtain needed moisture from plants and roots and by synthesizing water from the carbohydrate intake. Orr (1939) records an instance of a pocket mouse (*Perognathus longimembris*) which lived in captivity for more than 7 years on a diet consisting wholly of mixed seeds, without either greens or water. We have kept here various kangaroo rats: banner-tailed (*Dipodomys spectabilis*), Merriam's (*D. merriami*), and Ord's (*D. ordii*). A specimen of the banner-tailed received in 1955 will serve as an example of general treatment. This little animal lived in one of the glass-fronted metal boxes, about 2 feet square by 3 feet high, already described. The floor was covered with dried leaves, and a small branch laid across one corner provided a shelter which seemed a satisfactory substitute for a burrow. Here the kangaroo rat spent most of the day in sleep, resting in a small depression in the leaves. A pan of dry earth and sand hidden in one corner was often visited and presumably aided in keeping the coat clean and dry. This was especially useful when the animal was accidentally dampened, a condition to which kangaroo rats seem particularly averse.

Food provided consisted of canary and sunflower seed, lettuce and raw carrot, all of which were taken. Sweet corn, when in season, was a preferred item. A small portion of a mixture of dog biscuit, chopped raw meat, bone meal, and cod-liver oil was added daily but was sparingly eaten only now and then. A small dish of water was kept in the cage at all times, but its only function seems to have been to cause an occasional unwelcome ducking, for the animal was never seen to drink.

Typically gentle and confiding, our banner-tail accepted the attentions of its keeper calmly and overcame its nocturnal habits to the point of feeding freely by daylight when fresh food was provided. At the end of its visit to the container, it usually made a trip or two to its sleeping quarters with filled pouches. Little was gained, of course, by these storage activities, for the cage was meticulously cleaned daily.

Usual experience has been to the effect that kangaroo rats are too antagonistic toward each other to be kept together. However, both Culbertson (1946) and Howes (1954) give instances in which, after preliminary skirmishes of some severity, groups were successfully established. After prolonged experimentation, Day, Egoscue, and Woodbury (1956), at the University of Utah, found that when a receptive female Ord's kangaroo rat was placed with a male in a cage new to both, successful mating often occurred. By this means thirty young in ten litters were produced by six females, after a gestation period of 29–30 days. By the same method, in twelve attempts, a single female Merriam's kangaroo rat produced a litter of three at the University of California, after a gestation period of 17–23 days (Chew, 1958). A pair of desert kangaroo rats (*D. deserti*), given their liberty in a large room with open cages for retreat, produced seven litters totaling twenty-three young at the University of Wichita after gestation periods of 29–32 days (Butterworth, 1961).

A banner-tailed kangaroo rat received here on April 30, 1958, was still living 4 years later, while Hooper (1956) reports over 4 years for Merriam's. Brattstrom (1960) records 5 years, 5 months for *D. deserti* in captivity, Rabb (1960) lists 6 years, 3 months for *D. agilis* in the Chicago Zoological Park, and Hill (1957) says that a specimen of *D. nitratoides* lived in the Zoological Gardens of London for $6\frac{1}{2}$ years.

Because of their small size and secretive habits, the pocket mice (*Perognathus*) seem to have seldom been kept by zoological gardens. Before the red light experiments of Davis (1961), several forms were received here, including the desert pocket mouse (*P. penicillatus*) and Bailey's (*P. baileyi*), but even when shown under blue light, none of these animals survived for more than two years. In 1962 we were exhibiting the desert, the Apache (*P. apache*), and the silky (*P. flavus*), and all appeared to be thriving in red light. Nothing could be more fascinating than to watch a tiny silky pocket mouse scrounging about in the sand of its cage floor, in the safety of obliterating red, oblivious to onlookers. The diet used consisted of small seeds, bits of canned or dry dog food, greens, and vegetables. Water was always available, but the animals were not seen to drink. Huey (1959) reports that a specimen of *P. parvus mollipilosus* lived for 4 years, 6 months and one of *P. fallax fallax* for 8 years, 4 months. Both were kept chiefly on canary seed with occasional greens, and neither received water.

FAMILY CASTORIDAE

BEAVERS

This small family, consisting of only one genus and two species, has been and probably still is of greater economic importance than any other rodent group. The beaver of the Old World (*Castor fiber*), which once extended across northern Europe and Asia, long persecuted for the value of its fur, has largely disappeared from its former haunts. The American beaver (*C. canadensis*), the many races of which furnished the pelts so important in the exploration and early development of North America, once appeared doomed to a similar fate. However, the continued efforts of conservationists to re-establish colonies in depleted areas have been so encouragingly success-ful that many skins are now taken annually, under strict supervision, in regions from which, at one time, the beaver had been almost completely extirpated.

Great though the monetary value of beaver products may be, general public interest is based on the animal's real and fancied abilities in tree-felling and dam-building. The beaver, therefore, is a most desirable zoo animal when it can be well shown and managed. It is true that individuals kept in indoor and outdoor cages even as small as 4 feet square, supplied with tanks barely large enough for total submersion, may live for several years and keep in good condition. However, much that is of paramount interest in beaver activities is lost in such exhibits and can be shown only in outdoor installations that simulate natural conditions.

A Beaver Pond was one of the first projects undertaken in the con-struction of the New York Zoological Park, with the erection of a 4-foot fence of $\frac{3}{8}$-inch iron rods on 3-inch centers with an inside overhang at the top. This rested upon the coping of a concrete wall, extending 4 feet into the ground. This barrier inclosed an area of about $\frac{1}{2}$ acre, including a shallow natural pond covering about one-half of the space. Small springs and seepage that supplied the water were deemed insufficient and the supply was artificially supplemented.

In the spring of 1901 the first American beavers were obtained and released in the inclosure. As anticipated, the fence provided adequate restraint, and for many years there were no escapes. The newly-installed beavers were soon busily engaged in felling the few small trees available, so that finally only two or three larger ones remained, protected at their bases by guards of heavy wire netting. After the animals had stripped the edible bark from the branches, they were used in the construction of a "lodge," about 12 feet in diameter and 3–4 feet high, at the edge of a small island near the center of the pond. Strongly reinforced with mud and the outer covering of stripped branches kept constantly in repair, this lodge provided shelter for many successive beaver groups (Anon., 1901).

Once the natural food had been consumed, maple and willow browse (the apparently preferred aspen not being available), bread, grain, especially whole corn (maize), and apples, white potatoes, carrots, celery, and such other vegetables and greens as might be obtainable were provided.

Between 1904 and 1946 ten litters of young were produced and reared, seven composed of three kits, two of two, and one of five. These numbers are lower than those found by Bradt (1938) among wild beavers in Michigan but surprisingly greater than the usual number of one in twenty-five births in the Zoological Gardens of London as reported by Zuckerman (1953). Beavers produce one litter annually, usually in April or May. The gestation period is commonly given as 3 months or 90 days, but an observation recorded by Bradt (1939) indicates that 4 months may be required. Bradt gives the average weight of sixteen kits as 15.4 ounces at birth. Born fully furred and with eyes open, kits mature at from 2 to $2\frac{1}{2}$ years (Seton, 1909).

This brings up the crucial point in the maintenance of a going beaver colony in captivity. Well-established groups will normally consist of the monogamous parents, their young of the previous year, and the current litter of kits (Bradt, 1938). As they approach maturity, the older young would normally leave, whether of their own volition or at the urging of their parents. In captivity colonies, therefore, it is necessary to remove the older youngsters in their second autumn as suggested by Ashbrook (1928). Failure to do so undoubtedly has disrupted many a colony (including our own) through fighting and overcrowding.

The sexing of living beavers is difficult, since the common opening of the cloaca in both sexes makes the external appearance identical (Pocock, 1922). Also, the large scent glands, lying at each side in both males and females, are often mistaken for testes. However, Bradt (1938) shows that the os penis of adult males can be felt by inserting a finger in the cloacal opening (while the animal is held, head down, in an inverted drainpipe!).

The determined efforts of captive beavers to dam the running outlet of their pool present a problem not easily solved. There is no difficulty, of course, if no browse is supplied and no mud is available. This method has been successfully applied in the Detroit Zoological Park, where a mother and kits in a moated, concrete inclosure had become so accustomed to artificial feeding that they would emerge from their small brick lodge at any time at their keeper's call.

However, when closer approximation to natural conditions is desired, browse must be furnished, not only to supply food but to provide branches for use in conjunction with mud for building activities. Some means must then be found to prevent the beavers from flooding the area by raising the dam level. This cannot be accomplished by daily reduction to the proper height, since an active colony will rebuild it nightly, probably to an even greater elevation. Something can be gained by shutting off or diverting the water supply in late afternoon, but this is not entirely desirable, because of the effect on the freshness of the body of water and also because heavy night rains may invalidate it.

When our pool was constructed, a standpipe outlet, set for the desired water depth and attached to a drainpipe that discharged outside the inclosure, was installed about 25 feet upstream from the dam. This was surrounded by a wire-mesh cylinder 3 feet in diameter which permitted free flow of water but effectively blocked all efforts to close it off. This scheme was entirely successful for years, until the outlet area of the drainpipe rose to a level that prevented runoff, through accumulation of silt which could not be removed. With the drainage plan no longer effective, the beavers soon succeeded in flooding the inclosure to a point that led to dissolution of the colony, in spite of our efforts to prevent it.

An alternative drainage plan in which a pipe, its upstream end inserted in a wire-mesh cylinder, is thrust through the dam and extended outside the inclosure is suggested by Ashbrook (1928:185–86). Either of these methods should be successful in preventing flow of water over the dam, thus avoiding an incentive for the raising of the pool level by the animals.

Exhibitional difficulties arising from the nocturnal habits of beavers are not readily overcome, of course, when the animals are kept in natural areas. While the structural results of their labors are always evident, the creatures themselves are seldom to be seen during full daylight. In our own exhibit activity usually began at about 4:00 P.M., although on heavily overcast days an occasional specimen might be seen abroad at almost any hour. The Detroit method, then, has the definite advantage of visibility, which must be considered.

When kept under favorable conditions, the beaver is capable of living in captivity for what appear to be reasonably long periods. The greatest longevity for an American beaver here was established by a specimen received on May 10, 1912, which died on August 22, 1925, a span of 13 years, 3 months, 12 days. Flower (1931) reports a female of the same species said to have been "at least 19 years of age" at the time of its death in the Hamburg Zoological Gardens.

FAMILY ANOMALURIDAE

SCALY-TAILS, OR AFRICAN "FLYING SQUIRRELS"

While the beautiful animals in this small group closely resemble the true flying squirrels in both habits and appearance, the squirrels and the members of the present family are considered not to be closely related. Four genera (*Anomalurus*, *Anomalurops*, *Idiurus*, and *Zenkerella*), all from the forests of central and west Africa, are recognized by Ellerman (1940). Members of the first two are rather large and comparable in size to the American gray squirrel, while the others are tiny creatures, hardly larger than house mice. All are distinguished by a plate of pointed horny scales on the underside of the base of the tail, which is thought to be of service in clinging to branches. The first three are provided with lateral skin folds, with which they make scaling leaps after the fashion of true flying squirrels. In *Zenkerella* the membranes are absent.

The life histories of the scaly-tails are not well known, beyond the fact that they are nocturnal and spend the days, presumably sleeping, in hollow trees. They have been kept in captivity so rarely that little has been recorded concerning their requirements.

An account of efforts to keep the pygmy scaly-tail (*Idiurus zenkeri kivuensis*) in captivity is given by Durrell (1952). Twenty specimens, smoked out of a hollow tree, were tried on a variety of food items, including fruits, cassava, sweet potato, groundnuts, corn, milk, and raw egg, but none was taken. Various insects also were rejected. It was later found that the animals would eat only groundnuts, on which the most resistant survived for 6 weeks. A second group was induced to eat avocado and potato as well as groundnuts, but none lived to reach England.

Our own experience with the family is limited to two specimens of the larger Jackson's scaly-tail (*Anomalurus j. jacksoni*). These animals were brought to us from the Belgian Congo by Charles Cordier, arriving in New York on June 15, 1949. They were in poor condition when received, and one died 5 days later, while the other survived for only 6 weeks. Opportunity for study was therefore limited and devoted largely to efforts to find an acceptable diet. The animals had been kept by Cordier on bananas, and these remained the preferred item. In addition they took small amounts of a mixture of raw chopped meat, bone meal, and cod-liver oil, and mealworms were eaten greedily. Throughout, stools were soft and fluid, a condition attributed by Cordier to the giving of drinking water, which he had withheld before arrival here. In an effort to correct this, apple peelings were given, in the hope that the pectin content might be effective as a corrective. The peelings were taken freely but there was no noticeable remedial effect. We have since thought that dog food, either canned or dry, might have been useful, but unfortunately this was not tried. While it is evident that no suitable over-all diet for the scaly-tails has as yet been developed, these sketchy notes may at least offer a beginning.

FAMILY PEDETIDAE

Cape Jumping Hare or Springhaas

The jumping hare (*Pedetes capensis*), of which numerous local races have been described, is found in high, dry areas of Africa, from Kenya and Angola south to the Cape Province. It is not, of course, a hare, and after various assignments is now considered to form a family of its own with no really close affiliations. It is a fairly large animal, with body and bushy tail each approximately 12 inches in length. It is not surprising that it should once have been considered to be a giant jerboa, for in appearance and habits of locomotion it does parallel the animals of that group, the long hind legs being well adapted for leaping progression.

A common enough animal in favorable regions of its range, it is strange that a creature so attractive in appearance should not be more commonly seen in zoological gardens. Its nocturnal habits, of course, present some difficulties, but these are no greater than those found in many other groups. The natural food is almost entirely of a vegetable nature, some damage being done to crops in cultivated areas (Shortridge, 1934).

Up to 1963, only two specimens were seen here, one in 1920, the next in 1922. The latter animal lived for only 4 months, the other for just short of 18 months. A more encouraging result was obtained in the Zoological Gardens of London, where a jumping hare lived for 7 years, 7 months, 20 days (Flower, 1931). Our animals were kept in indoor cages about 5 feet long by 3 feet deep, provided with the usual retiring boxes that seem satisfactory for most burrowing animals. Their food consisted of crushed oats, greens, raw vegetables, and bread. It seems probable that dog biscuit might prove a welcome addition to this diet.

The jumping hare appears to have been seldom bred in captivity, but Hediger (1950) gives an account of the birth and partial rearing of a single young (the usual number) in the Zoological Gardens of Basel in 1949.

FAMILY CRICETIDAE

Rats and Mice of the New World, with Some Old World Species

This immense aggregation of creatures, mostly of small size and furtive habits, has presented a great problem for the zoological garden. As already noted, most are nocturnal, so that until an efficient method of exhibition was devised little was to be gained by exhibiting them. Yet many are so beautiful in both form and color and adapt so readily to the conditions of captivity they they were often kept, even though not well shown. Actually, of course, the diverse life histories and adaptations of these small creatures are fundamentally just as important as those of larger animals, and making them available to a larger public under red light (Davis, 1961) is proving to be fully rewarding.

In laboratory work, often directed toward determination of value for experimental purposes, the smaller species are usually kept in wire-mesh or glass-sided cages, with removable wire tops. Glass or metal containers are provided as retreats, and water is furnished in drip bottles. In zoological gardens small cages of the type used here for ground squirrels and similar animals are more usual. A nest box or small hollow log is essential for most, although some species appear to be satisfied with a glass jar as a hiding place. If floor coverings and cage furnishing are properly adapted to the known habits of the animals, an attractive exhibition can be arranged.

Small grains such as canary and sunflower seeds, whole or rolled oats, greens, fruits, and raw vegetables are the staples. Dry or canned dog food fortified with cod-liver oil, with perhaps an occasional bit of raw meat or fish, will satisfy the animal protein needs of most. There are variations in requirements, of course, and carnivorous species, such as the grasshopper mice (*Onychomys*), seem to have the food needs of shrews. An account of the special food requirements and breeding habits in captivity of the brown grasshopper mouse (*Onychomys leucogaster fuscogriseus*) is given by Svihla (1936), and Egoscue (1960) gives an extended report on the northern grasshopper mouse (*Onychomys l. utahensis*), including maintenance and breeding in the laboratory. In 1958 a pair of southern grasshopper mice (*Onychomys torridus*) in our collection produced a litter of seven young in July and a second, number undetermined, in September. These animals were on exhibition under blue light, and frequently both parents were observed in the nest with the young. When the latter were approximately 3 weeks old they left the nest and were then removed, as the adults would no longer tolerate them. The female of the breeding pair lived here for 3 years, 3 months, 16 days.

Because of the great number of comparatively obscure forms involved and their relatively low value as zoological-garden exhibits, only a few can be mentioned here and these but briefly. Where possible, reference to laboratory work or to zoological-garden experience will be made.

The rice rats (*Oryzomys*) have not been kept here, but A. Svihla (1931) gives a thorough account of behavior in captivity. Worth (1950) gives further details, having bred captive animals to the fourth generation. Both papers relate to races of *Oryzomys palustris*. Flower (1931) reports a specimen of *Oryzomys longicaudatus* from southern South America as having lived in the Zoological Gardens of London for 2 years, 10 months, 3 days.

The white-footed or deer mice (*Peromyscus*) probably are kept more generally in this country than any other native mice. Most of the numerous forms accept captivity readily and are maintained and bred without difficulty. It is not necessary to remove the male following birth, as the female drives him from the nest and does not allow him to return until the young are several days old. However, rebreeding occurs almost immediately after parturition, and since the period of gestation is but 21 days (or sometimes slightly longer), multiplication is rapid.

Dice (1929) gives instructions for the housing and feeding of these and other mice under laboratory conditions and a later version of the feeding formula (1934). Results of a study of foods taken by captive deer mice, with extensive lists, are given by Cogshall (1928).

Various white-footed mice kept here have caused difficulties of disposal rather than of maintenance, the increase in numbers soon resulting in overcrowding of available space. Feeding and caging here are as indicated for the family. A specimen of the Canadian white-footed mouse (*Peromyscus maniculatus gracilis*) received here at an unfortunately unrecorded date in 1948 lived until March 14, 1953, so that its longevity was certainly well in excess of four years. Sumner (1922) reports 5 years, 8 months for a captive specimen of Gambel's white-footed mouse (*P. m. gambelii*).

Of the cotton rat (*Sigmodon hispidus*), Audubon and Bachman (1849–54, 1:231) say, "We have on several occasions known their young born and reared in cages." They note also that in addition to vegetable food, this rat will take flesh in almost any form, that it is partial to birds' eggs, and that cage mates are likely to fight fiercely. Since those early days, the willingness of the cotton rat to breed in captivity despite a rather truculent disposition has been developed to the point where it is now in general use as a valuable laboratory animal. A complete account of the management, feeding, and breeding of the cotton rat in the laboratory is given by Meyer and Meyer (1944).

While not especially attractive in appearance, the cotton rat does have an advantage over most other members of this family, in that it is not strictly nocturnal and may sometimes be seen stirring about during the day. A specimen received here on October 13, 1910, lived until September 27, 1912, just short of 2 years. It was fed as outlined for the group.

The wood rats or pack rats (*Neotoma*) are of special interest because of their habit of carrying to their storage places any portable bright or metallic objects they may come upon. All of the many forms are attractive, but especially so are the races of the bushy-tailed wood rat (*Neotoma cinerea*), which have greater appeal than those with more thinly haired tails. There are variations in disposition, too, the dusky-footed wood rat (*N. fuscipes*) being particularly hostile toward members of its own species when closely confined (Linsdale and Tevis, 1951). This species has been found difficult to breed in captivity, one success with the Portola wood rat (*N. f. annectens*) having been reported by Donat (1933) with a pair of animals at liberty in a large room, and two with the gentler large-eared wood rat (*N. f. macrotis*) in laboratory cages (Wood, 1935). Much better results in captivity breeding have been had with races of the Florida wood rat (*N. floridana floridana*) (Svihla and Svihla, 1933; Worth, 1950; Pearson, 1952; Hamilton, 1953) and with the Allegheny wood rat (*N. f. magister*) (Poole, 1936, 1940). Egoscue (1957) reports the establishment of a limited laboratory colony of the desert wood rat (*N. l. lepida*).

Wood rats shown here have made reasonably good exhibits, although too often concealed in the huge nest constructed when material is available. The usual food suggested for the group is adequate, although little flesh is eaten. A beautiful specimen of the gray bushy-tailed wood rat (*N. c. cinerea*) lived here from September 8, 1947, to May 23, 1952, or 4 years, 8 months, 15 days.

The hamsters, consisting of several Old World genera, are small, rather dumpy rodents provided with capacious internal cheek pouches and very short tails. They are essentially burrowing animals, living in loose colonies, but except for the brief periods of mating and rearing of the young by the female, solitary in habit.

This rather obscure group has been brought into prominence through the rapid and unprecedented development of the golden hamster (*Mesocricetus auratus auratus*) as a laboratory animal and popular pet. According to Bruce and Hindle (1934), an adult female and twelve young were dug from a burrow 8 feet deep near Aleppo, Syria, in 1930 by I. Abromi, of the Hebrew University at Jerusalem. It is presumed that the present numerous captive population was derived from these specimens. First bred in Jerusalem 4 months after their capture, two pairs were received in London by Bruce and Hindle in 1931 and methods of breeding and maintenance were worked out. Present procedures are described by Marsh (1948), and further notes, with descriptions of established color mutations, are given in an anthology edited by Folk (1958).

In practice, male and female are placed together only for breeding and are separated once mating has been accomplished. The gestation period is given by Asdell (1946) as 16 days, with possible variation up to 19 days. The young are weaned at from 3 to 4 weeks and maturity is reached in from 7 to 8 weeks. Feeding procedures approximate those already suggested for other small rodents, including dog food, game pellets, or other animal protein source. Life spans of golden hamsters kept here have not exceeded 2 years, but the expectancy is usually given as 3 to 4 years.

That the chance capture of a few living specimens of the golden hamster, a comparatively rare and little-known animal, should have produced such remarkable results, while the larger European hamster (*Cricetus cricetus*), well known for centuries, still proves resistant, is an interesting sidelight on the variability of characteristics in closely related species. Numerous examples of the European hamster have been kept here but no young have ever been born. The greatest longevity was 6 days over 2 years. Flower (1931) gives the best longevity of ten specimens in the Zoological Gardens of London as 2 years, 6 months.

Early efforts to establish the small Chinese striped hamster (*Cricetulus barabensis*) as a laboratory animal were not encouraging. A pair of the race *C. b. griseus*, received here in 1952, proved to be so antagonistic that no breeding was possible. The survivor escaped after 1 year, 11 months. Methods for maintaining and breeding this difficult species are given by Schwentker (1957). Two related species, the migratory hamster (*Cricetulus migratorius*) and the triton hamster (*Cricetulus triton*), have been bred in the Zoological Gardens of London (Zuckerman, 1953).

The muskrat (*Ondatra zibethicus*) is spread, in many races, over most of North America north of Mexico, except Florida and the Arctic regions. It has been introduced into Europe and elsewhere, usually with adverse effects on vegetation and waterways (Mohr, 1933; Bourdelle, 1939; Warwick, 1940). Since Colonial days muskrat skins have been of great importance in the fur trade, and so well has the animal withstood the onslaught that it still exists and is trapped annually in large numbers. Many areas within the limits of the city of New York are inhabited by muskrats. They have sometimes managed to invade our Beaver Pond, where they are frequently reported as young beavers, since the laterally compressed tail is not always visible in a swimming animal.

Efforts to breed the muskrat in pens for fur production have proved to be unprofitable, and attention has turned largely to increased production in natural areas (Ashbrook, 1928). As with the beaver, occasional specimens of the muskrat, especially if taken young, will give reasonably good results in small quarters provided with a water container deep enough for submersion. Svihla and Svihla (1931) report that penned muskrats of the Louisiana race (*Ondatra z. rivalicius*) ate, in order of preference, rolled oats, corn (maize), apple, lettuce, wheat, rice, and whole oats but did well on corn and marsh plants plus raw or boiled crabs and small fish. Here we have used crushed oats, carrots, celery, apples, any available greens, bread, and dry or canned dog food fortified, if necessary, with cod-liver oil. A single animal so kept lived here for 5 years, 10 months.

A natural inclosure on the order of that suggested for beavers, on a smaller scale, makes a suitable exhibition area for muskrats. A barrier of $\frac{1}{4}$-inch bars set on 1-inch centers or a barrier of concrete extending 3–4 feet underground and $3\frac{1}{2}$ feet above is adequate. No special provisions to protect the water overflow from obstruction are required, since the muskrat does not build dams. If rushes or other thick-stemmed material are furnished, a low, rough house for all-season use will be built in shallow water. Just as beavers will quickly fell any trees accessible, so muskrats will soon destroy edible growing plants, and daily supplies of food, as suggested, must be furnished.

Pairing customs of the muskrat in nature are still not fully understood, but in any case it is unlikely that the bond is as strong as it is in the beaver. Also, the muskrat, at least at times, is more social than the beaver, although precautions must still be taken against overcrowding.

Muskrats produce from one to three litters of young each season, usually between April and September. Asdell (1946) gives the gestation period as "probably 29 to 30 days."

The voles or meadow mice (*Microtus*) are holarctic in distribution, being found in North America, Europe, and Asia. Ellerman (1940) lists 238 forms, a number certainly subject to variation. The fluctuating populations of these small creatures are of great economic importance, since they provide the main food supply of many predators and may do immense damage to crops and other vegetation when their numbers reach periodic high levels.

The mounting search for laboratory animals has found in the meadow mouse an extremely useful subject. Under controlled conditions, various forms have been found to breed freely in captivity and are now produced in numbers. No mammal is known to be more prolific. Bailey (1924) reports that a female eastern meadow mouse (*Microtus pennsylvanicus*) produced seventeen litters within a year at three-week intervals. Greenwald (1956) found that a female California meadow mouse (*M. californicus*) had been impregnated at the age of 14 days. The gestation period is usually given as 21 days or in that order for all species of *Microtus* that have been studied.

While the meadow mice are essentially nocturnal, they are not exclusively so, and conditioned captive specimens are often active on dull days. The principles of maintenance are given by Bailey (1924), and further developments have been added by Selle (1928) and Poiley (1949). Meadow mice are almost entirely vegetarian in dietary requirements and in captivity will thrive on commercial mouse pellets or canned or dry dog food containing the necessary mineral and vitamin supplements, canary seed or rolled oats, fresh greens, raw vegetables, and fruits. Small retiring quarters and nest-building materials, of course, are required.

The gerbils and jirds are found in open, often sandy regions of Africa and much of Asia. Some of the numerous species are diurnal and many show a lengthening of the hind legs in accord with kangaroo-like leaping habits. Tails are usually haired, sometimes tufted, and ears are proportionately large.

These attractive desert creatures adapt well to captivity and are easily kept and bred. Cage floors should be sanded to a fair depth and sleeping boxes provided. Diets outlined for other small rodents, including some flesh, will suit them very well. Consumption of water varies with species, individuals, and diets. As noted in the *UFAW Handbook* (Worden and Lane-Petter, 1957), the Mongolian gerbil or clawed jird (*Meriones unguiculatus*) has been well established in this country as an experimental animal by Victor Schwentker of Tumblebrook Farm.

The only birth recorded here was that of a single young of Sundevall's jird (*Meriones crassus*), but related species have been bred with success elsewhere, notably in the Zoological Gardens of London (Zuckerman, 1953). Our best longevity is 1 year, 5 months, 15 days for the same species; Flower (1931) gives 4 years, 5 months, 17 days in the Giza Zoological Gardens. Our best result with a gerbil is 1 year, 2 months for *Gerbillus pyramidum*; Flower (1931) records 5 years, 14 days for *G. gerbillus* in the Zoological Gardens of London.

FAMILY MURIDAE

OLD WORLD RATS AND MICE

This family, sometimes enlarged to contain the Cricetidae (Ellerman, 1940), contains a large number of species, many of great economic importance. Most familiar, of course, are the house mouse (*Mus musculus*) and the brown or Norway rat (*Rattus norvegicus*), both of Old World origin but now spread world-wide to the serious disadvantage of mankind. Many members of the group because of their great size and others for their beauty or other special points of interest are of value to the zoological garden. As with the preceding family, only a few of the more usable species can be mentioned here. Most of the general notes on care and maintenance made under "Cricetidae" (pp. 230–36) will apply here as well.

The genus *Rattus*, of which more than 550 forms have been described (Ellerman, 1940), is best known through the ubiquitous Norway rat (*R. norvegicus*) and the less abundant black rat (*R. rattus*). No rodent has so adversely affected the human race, through the spread of disease and the destruction of food, as the Norway rat nor has any been of greater service, through the extensive use of its domesticated descendants in research in genetics, medicine, and related sciences. The smaller, darker and more arboreal black rat, constantly driven farther and farther afield by its more aggressive relative, seems no longer to be of great economic importance. Curiously, it appears never to have been domesticated. Neither of these species is ordinarily exhibited by zoological gardens, energies more usually being devoted to elimination. On the other hand, breeding colonies are sometimes maintained for the production of food animals. An excellent outline of current practice in this field, with an extensive bibliography, is provided by Farris (1950).

The house mouse (*Mus musculus*), in a smaller degree, is guilty of the same destructive and disease-carrying transgressions as the Norway rat. It deserves, too, the same praise, for the use of domesticated mice in research is of great importance. The establishment of standardized strains has been carried to a high level in various fields of investigation. Maintenance and care of domesticated mice under laboratory conditions are covered by Grüneberg (1943) and Strong (1950).

The Old World spiny mice (*Acomys*) are found from Africa to central Asia. Larger than the house mouse, they are most attractive in appearance, the back being covered with short, hardened spines, suggesting tiny hedgehogs. Although desert dwellers, they are often active by day. Conditioned specimens are gentle, and given sufficient space, groups of mixed sexes will live together amicably. The usual small grains and seeds, greens, vegetables, and fortified dog food make an adequate diet. The Palestine spiny mouse (*A. cahirinus dimidiatus*) has been bred here, and this form as well as Hunter's (*A. c. hunteri*) have reproduced in the Zoological Gardens of London (Zuckerman, 1953). Flower (1931) gives a maximum longevity of 4 years, 5 months, 12 days for this species in the same institution.

The giant pouched rat (*Cricetomys gambianus*), found in many races in the forested areas of Africa, is a giant indeed, for it may reach a total length of 30 inches or more. Although like a huge Norway rat in general appearance, the over-all effect is very much more pleasing. The light-brown fur is tight and smooth, and the suggestion of softness is borne out by the animal's gentle nature. The species appears to be largely vegetarian, but those that have been kept here took dry and canned dog food freely in addition to grains, greens, raw vegetables, and fruits. While individuals seem to get on well together—I have seen as many as four in a heap, sound asleep—the species appears to have been seldom bred in captivity, as remarked by Ellerman (1940). Flower (1931) reports two specimens as still living in the Zoological Gardens of London after 4 years, 5 months, 4 days. A female Emin's giant rat (*C. gambianus emini*) lived here for 5 years, 6 months, 11 days.

The giant or cloud rats of the Philippines (*Crateromys* and *Phloeomys*) apparently have been represented in zoological gardens only through the collection landed in New York on July 9, 1947, by Charles Wharton. These animals were distributed among the zoological gardens of Washington, Philadelphia, and New York and gave excellent results. Both are of very large size, with head and body lengths of from 15 to 18 inches. While they are nocturnal in habit, they are often about on dull days, and even in sleep are so large and conspicuously colored that they are always visible. Here both were fed on rolled oats, carrots, celery, lettuce, bread, and a small quantity of fortified dog food. In demeanor they were quiet, phlegmatic, and non-aggressive.*

The bushy-tailed giant rat (*Crateromys schadenbergi*) is one of the handsomest of the rodents, with long, soft hair on body and tail. The striking black and white color pattern is extremely variable in arrangement. A specimen lived here for 4 years, 3 months, 28 days. This attractive species was bred at the Philadelphia Zoological Garden in 1948.

In coloration Cuming's giant rat (*Phloeomys cumingi*) has a cream ground, varied with darker markings to such an extent that no two seem exactly alike. The body hair is fairly long but the tail is normally clothed, so that altogether this species loses something in beauty when compared with the bushy-tailed. However, it has proved to be longer-lived in captivity than the handsomer animal, as a specimen received here in the original shipment lived until September 18, 1955, or 8 years, 2 months, 9 days. A group of eight, including five adults from the same lot and three fully reared

*See Addenda, p. 733.

young, was seen at the National Zoological Park in February, 1956, living peacefully together. All the young represented single births.

As given by Troughton (1957), more than fifty species of rats and mice are native to Australia. It appears that their ancestors must have reached the island continent at a very early time, for the present representatives of the group have become widely dispersed and diversified. Many parallelisms to the rodents of other lands have developed, including the water rats (*Hydromys*). These interesting animals are suggestive of the muskrats (*Ondatra*) in their adaptation to aquatic habits, size, denseness of coat, and even partially webbed feet. However, unlike those comparatively harmless creatures, the water rats appear to be entirely carnivorous, feeding on mussels, snails, crayfish, fish, and water birds and their eggs (Troughton, 1957). Two specimens of the eastern water rat (*Hydromys chrysogaster*) were received here in 1917, but both were in poor condition and neither lived for more than a few days. However, Fleay (1949) recounts a much more successful experience, in which the animals were kept in combined pool and wooden burrows, reminiscent of a miniature platypusary. Here, fed on crayfish or "yabbies" and fish, a pair not only lived well but bred at least twice, the young numbering four and two, respectively, in each litter.

FAMILY GLIRIDAE

Dormice

The dormice, in several genera and many forms, are found in Europe, Africa, and much of Asia. For the most part they are gentle, attractive creatures, many being squirrel-like in habits and appearance. They are nocturnal in general, and the northern residents, at least, hibernate during the winter months.

Dormice are common pets of boyhood in Europe and do not have high standing as exhibits in the zoological gardens of that continent. However, in America they must be rated as rarities, since they are seldom imported. Only two species have been kept here: the common or hazel dormouse (*Muscardinus avellanarius*) and the fat, edible, or squirrel-tailed dormouse (*Glis glis*).

The common dormouse is a small, reddish-brown creature, somewhat larger than a house mouse, and with a well-haired but not bushy tail. It is found over most of Europe, from England to Asia Minor. Provided with a nesting box and branches for its nocturnal activities, the common dormouse is easily maintained on a diet of apples and other fruits, small nuts, grain, and fortified dry or canned dog food. The best longevity reached in our collection is 2 years, 6 months; Flower (1931) reports 2 years, 11 months for a captive in Italy. The gestation is listed by Asdell (1946) as 21 days.

The fat dormouse extends, in a number of races, across continental Europe to Persia. Introduced into England in 1902 (Thompson, 1953), it appears to have established a strong foothold there in spite of efforts to eradicate it because of possible damage to fruit. The fat dormouse is a much larger animal than the common, with a body length of about seven inches and a full, squirrel-like tail. This species thrives well in captivity on the method of maintenance suggested for the common dormouse. The best span recorded here is 2 years, 3 months, but Flower (1931) gives 4 years, 1 month, 20 days in the Zoological Gardens of London, and Hill (1955) has reported a rather surprising 7-year longevity in the same institution. The species appears reluctant to breed in captivity, and the gestation period seems not to have been recorded.

FAMILY ZAPODIDAE

JUMPING MICE

This family contains the American jumping mice (*Zapus* and *Napaeozapus*) and the little-known *Eozapus* of China. The American jumping mice are beautiful little creatures, much like the house mouse in general appearance but with tremendously long, slender tails and with the hind legs greatly lengthened. By their use and with the tail as a balance, leaps of from 8 to 10 feet are accomplished. Jumping mice are inclined to be nocturnal in habit and hibernate during the winter months.

The jumping mouse (*Zapus*) ranges widely, in three species and many races, over most of North America, except extreme northern and southern areas. It frequents grassy or lightly wooded regions from sea level to high elevations. The meadow jumping mouse (*Zapus hudsonius*) and the western jumping mouse (*Z. princeps*) have been represented here. Both are highly nervous and neither appears to become fully reconciled to captivity. In accordance with the natural diet of grass seeds, berries, and insects, we provide canary and sunflower seeds, berries, apples, fortified canned dog food, and an occasional mealworm, which is readily taken.

Although no dietary deficiency is indicated, none of our specimens has lived for more than a few months. Mann (1930) records a specimen of *Z. h. americanus* as having lived for 6 months in the National Zoological Park in Washington. Sheldon (1938*a*) reports no success in getting *Zapus* to breed in captivity. The gestation period is given by Palmer (1954) as about 18 days.

The woodland jumping mouse (*Napaeozapus insignis*), readily distinguished by its white tail-tip, inhabits woodlands of eastern North America. It has not been kept here, but Sheldon (1938*b*) was successful in keeping and breeding it in captivity. A diet of grass seeds, rolled oats, canary and sunflower seeds, and insects and berries was considered adequate.

FAMILY DIPODIDAE

JERBOAS

The jerboas are found in several genera and many forms from North Africa to southern Russia and from Arabia and Persia across China to Mongolia, being missing entirely from the plains of India. There are variations in body size, length of ears, and the number of hind toes, but they agree in great length of the hind legs and in possessing very long tails, well haired and usually tufted. Their coloration is that of the sand on which most of the species live, varying from reddish brown to pale yellow or buffy. They agree in being almost entirely nocturnal and in hibernating during the winter months.

The jerboas are social animals, at least to the extent of digging their burrows in small groups. Here the young are born and long periods of cold spent in sleep. The natural diet is that of most small rodents: plant materials of various kinds, insects, and sometimes the eggs and young of birds. Some species are said not to drink water in nature, but all that have been kept in captivity here drank it sparingly.

Jerboas are inoffensive creatures, seldom given to biting and quickly becoming tame in captivity. They require a fairly large space for their nocturnal gambols, with a retiring box in which, unfortunately, they will spend much of the day, although under dull or blue lights they may occasionally emerge. Cage floors should be sanded and dry, as jerboas appear to be miserable in dampness. Small seeds, grains, fruits, any available insects, and a dab of fortified dog food, dry or canned, make a suitable diet.

Jerboas are fairly long-lived in captivity under suitable conditions. Two specimens of the greater Egyptian jerboa (*Jaculus orientalis*) lived here for 4 years, 17 days; Flower (1931) gives 4 years, 16 days in the Zoological Gardens of London and 6 years, 4 months in the Clifton Zoological Gardens, both for the lesser Egyptian jerboa (*J. jaculus*).

No jerboa has been bred here, but two births, each of three young, of *J. orientalis* in the Zoological Gardens of London have been recorded by Zuckerman (1953). The gestation period of 42 days given by Jennison (n.d.) is often quoted.

FAMILY HYSTRICIDAE

OLD WORLD PORCUPINES

Most of Africa, southeastern Europe, and southern Asia are inhabited by the members of the family, which are assigned by Ellerman (1940) to four genera and many forms. They agree in having spines, weakly developed in some species and reaching their maximum in the genus *Hystrix*. Terrestrial in habit, they are also largely nocturnal, although Goodwin (1954:353) reports having seen a porcupine abroad at noon in Iran. Actually, the night-prowling habit is not too firmly implanted in porcupines, so that in captivity they frequently become practically diurnal. The natural diet appears to be entirely herbivorous, and extensive damage may be done to vegetable gardens in cultivated areas (Roberts, 1951). Bone-gnawing, which serves the double purpose of keeping teeth in order and supplying calcium and phosphorus, is a well-established habit (Blanford, 1888–91).

Most popular as a zoo animal is the African porcupine (*Hystrix cristata*). This species, in several races, is found in Italy and Sicily and northern and eastern Africa. Undoubtedly, in zoo practice it is ordinarily lumped with the nearly related *H. galeata* and *H. africaeaustralis*, the three being indistinguishable in life according to Ellerman (1940, 1:200). In any case, our possibly collective animal is much the largest of the porcupines. The back and rump are clothed in heavy spines, guarded by longer and softer ones which may exceed 20 inches in length. The stronger spines are really lethal weapons—one before me measures $13\frac{1}{2}$ inches with a maximum diameter of $\frac{1}{4}$ inch—sharply pointed and lightly grooved longitudinally but without hooks or other projections. Ordinarily the spines are used only in defense, the animal raising and spreading them and turning its back to an aggressor, waiting for it to risk becoming impaled or even making short, threatening backward rushes. No porcupine, of course, can "throw" its quills, but since these are shed at intervals, loose ones may be shaken out when the animal is aroused. The short tail is provided with broad, open-tipped spines with which the familiar rattling is accomplished.

Porcupines, of course, are powerful gnawers and must be inclosed with impervious materials. Retiring niches are not essential, although a darkened corner will be used. Food provided here consists of grain, especially corn (maize), lettuce, cabbage, celery, carrots, raw white or sweet potatoes, bananas, peanuts, and a dash of cooked or raw chopped meat mixed with dry dog meal, fine bone meal, and cod-liver oil. In spite of presumed purely vegetarian preferences, most individuals accept the latter mixture eagerly.

The African porcupine breeds well in captivity under favorable conditions, and families make excellent exhibits. Such a group, headed by a large male, with several females and a number of young in various stages of development, was recently seen in the National Zoological Park. The male, especially, was definitely defensive of the small youngsters, constantly pushing, with partly elevated spines, between them and pausing visitors. The young are born fully developed, with eyes open and the body clothed in soft spines which soon harden. The gestation period for *H. cristata* is given by Asdell (1946) as minimum 63 days, maximum 112 days.

Our best longevity for the African porcupine is just over 6 years, but Mann (1930) gives 13 years, 2 months in the National Zoological Park, and Flower (1931) reports 20 years, 4 months, 14 days in the Zoological Gardens of London.

The Indian porcupine (*H. indica*) is found in southwestern Asia and Asia Minor. Externally it resembles the African porcupine but is smaller, with somewhat weaker spines. Care and feeding here have been as outlined for the African. The species does not appear to have been bred in this country, but Zuckerman (1953) records five births of single young or twins in the Zoological Gardens of London, and doubtless success has been attained elsewhere. Simon (1943) reports a specimen of *H. leucura* (=*indica*) that lived for 22 years in the Trivandrum Zoological Gardens, India.

The brush-tailed porcupines (*Atherurus*) are represented in both Asia and Africa: the Indo-Malayan (*Atherurus macrourus*) being found from Sumatra to southern China and the African species (*A. centralis, A. turneri,* and *A. africanus*), as listed by Ellerman (1940), in central and western areas of that continent. The Indo-Malayan races lack the strong spines found in *Hystrix*, but these are usually present in animals from Africa.

I have before me a shed quill from the Congo form (*A. c. centralis*) measuring 4⅛ inches, with a maximum diameter of ⅛ inch. This quill is exceedingly hard and sharp, its under-surface covered with tiny projections directed toward the tip. These undoubtedly would have a tearing effect in penetration but would not interfere with removal—a condition opposite to that found in American porcupines (*Erethizon*). The tail in *Atherurus* is comparatively long and bears at its tip a cluster of bristles alternately broad and narrow, looking exactly as though the quill had been flattened at intervals with a hammer.

In general, the brush-tailed porcupines are smaller than the forms of *Hystrix* and much more active. They quickly learn to come to the hand for food and live well in captivity but seem more difficult to breed. Caging and feeding here are as indicated for *Hystrix*.

A male and female of the Congo form (*A. c. centralis*) received here June 15, 1949, although in perfect condition, had produced no young up to 1963. The Indo-Malayan species (*A. macrourus*) has been bred at the San Diego Zoological Garden (Stott, 1954), and breeding records for both this species and *A. africanus*, in the Zoological Gardens of London, are listed by Zuckerman (1953). When visiting here in 1961, Dr. Urs Rahm recounted the breeding of the Congo brush-tailed porcupine in captivity at the Institut pour la Recherche Scientifique en Afrique Centrale, in the eastern Congo, and gave the gestation period, apparently previously unknown, as from 100 to 110 days.

The pair of Congo brush-tailed porcupines referred to above were still living here in 1963, after 14 years, representing our best longevity for the genus. George H. Pournelle (*in litt.*) reports 13 years, 3 months, 15 days for the Indo-Malayan species (*A. macrourus*) in the San Diego Zoological Garden, and Jones (1958) gives 15 years, 29 days for *A. africanus* in the Philadelphia Zoological Garden.

FAMILY ERETHIZONTIDAE

NEW WORLD PORCUPINES

In this family, two groups are of especial importance to the zoological garden: the North American porcupines (*Erethizon*) and the prehensile-tailed or tree porcupines (*Coendou*) found from Mexico southward to tropical South America. Beyond the possession of quills, they have little in common with the porcupines of the Old World. Most of the forms are chiefly arboreal and nocturnal, although neither habit is inviolate. They are mainly herbivorous, but the North American species, at least, has a special fondness for salt and the gnawing of bones.

The North American porcupine (*Erethizon dorsatum*) is found coast to coast in forested areas from Labrador south to Tennessee and from Alaska to northern Mexico. Seven races are listed by Hall and Kelson (1959).

Although solitary for most of the year, porcupines may gather in groups during the colder months, in dens in hollow trees or rock crevices. They do not hibernate but remain active throughout the winter. Their food consists largely of the inner bark of trees, including conifers, maples, and aspens, with leaves and tender twigs when these are available.

Slow-moving, even sluggish in action, the porcupine has no need for haste, since few enemies dare attack him. When forced to assume a defensive attitude, the head is drawn down between the forelegs, the overlying guard hairs are drawn aside, and the sharp, slender quills of the back are broadly extended. There is an effective offensive weapon in the tail, which, thickly set with spines, may be driven with great force against an enemy. The spines, which may be as much as 4 inches in length, are furnished with tiny scales whose free tips are directed toward the base, thus enhancing penetration. I well remember an occasion when I had passed the night in a deserted woodsman's cabin that had been invaded by porcupines. I awoke to find a quarter-inch of quill projecting from the calf of one leg which it had entered during the night. One of my companions, using thumb and forefinger, jerked out the quill, 1½ inches of which had worked into the muscle. No swelling or other difficulty developed.

North American porcupines are kept, at least on occasion, by most zoological gardens of this country and not infrequently by those of Europe. Tooth-resistant restraining materials are required for inclosures, and climbing perches should be supplied, of sufficient strength to support the animals' weight, which may be as much as 35 pounds. A retiring shelter should be available, even though some individuals may not use it. Lack of aggressive tendencies makes it possible to establish groups with little risk of quarreling, except possibly during the autumn mating season. Porcupines seem to thrive equally well indoors or out but do not respond well to transfers either way during cold weather.

Food items provided here include whole grains, especially corn (maize), crushed oats, carrots, potatoes, apples, lettuce, cabbage and celery, bread, and a small portion of a mixture of chopped meat, scalded or raw, dry dog meal and finely ground bone moistened with cod-liver oil. Fresh branches of spruce, hemlock, maple, and willow are also furnished. This regimen approximates that described by Shadle (1950) for laboratory animals.

The classic instances of breeding North American porcupines in captivity are those accomplished in the laboratory at the University of Buffalo and recorded by Shadle (1951). Through them, the gestation period was definitely established as approximately 7 months. The usually single young are born well developed and with eyes open, as in Old World porcupines. The normal ventro-dorsal copulatory position common to quadrupeds is well described and figured by Shadle (1946).

Two births in the Zoological Gardens of London are recorded by Zuckerman (1953), but whether or not these were actually instances of captivity breeding is not stated. Mann (1930) also records births in the National Zoological Park. Numerous births in both the Canada porcupine (*E. d. dorsatum*) and the yellow-haired (*E. d. epixanthum*) have occurred here, but in most of these cases the mothers were presumably pregnant when received. However, an albino female Canada porcupine which arrived here on March 4, 1938, and was placed with a normally colored male produced a coal-black youngster on October 13, 1938. This span of 7 months, 9 days makes it possible that an actual breeding record was achieved.

There appear to be few factual records of longevities of North American porcupines in captivity. Our best result for the Canada porcupine was with a male which lived here for 5 years, 1 month before shipment to the Zoological Gardens of Antwerp. An albino specimen, one of a total of sixteen that have been received here, died after 4 years, 8 months, 17 days. Our best span for a yellow-haired porcupine is 3 years, 9 months, 5 days. Ten years and presumably still living in the laboratory, as reported by Shadle (1951) for the Canada porcupine, is undoubtedly the greatest longevity in captivity so far recorded.

The prehensile-tailed or tree porcupines (*Coendou*) are found in tropical regions from Mexico to Paraguay and southeastern Brazil. They are essentially tree dwellers and are readily distinguished from all other porcupines by their long, prehensile tails. These appendages usually bear spines at the base and are lightly haired on the balance of the under-surface, the upper side being bare, a condition opposite to that usually found in prehensile-tailed mammals. There are numerous forms which fall naturally into two groups: one in which the spines are not hidden by the hairs which lie between them, typified by the Brazilian tree porcupine (*Coendou prehensilis*), and one in which the spines are buried beneath a long, woolly coat, as in the hairy tree porcupine (*C. insidiosus*), also from Brazil.

In captivity the tree porcupines appear sluggish and inactive during the day, perhaps because in them the nocturnal habit is more firmly fixed than in other porcupines. They are less aggressive gnawers than others, too, but still cannot be safely restrained by barriers containing wood. Proper branches for climbing and a shelf above the floor level should be provided. All species are sensitive to cold and must have warm quarters.

The habits of the tree porcupines in nature are not well known, but they are said to be largely herbivorous. Here they are fed grains, including corn (maize), crushed oats, carrots, potatoes, apples, bananas, lettuce, celery, and bread, with branches and leaves, when available, of maple, willow, and Russian mulberry. They also receive a small portion of the mixture of raw or scalded chopped meat, dog meal, finely ground bone and cod-liver oil, which most individuals eat, if sparingly.

No tree porcupine has been born here, but Zuckerman (1953) records the birth of a single young of the hairy in the Zoological Gardens of London in 1878. Mr. Thomas R. Baines, curator of the zoo at Calgary, Alberta, informs me (*in litt.*) that the female of a pair of prehensile-tailed porcupines which are so far unidentified, received in 1958, produced a single baby early in 1961. This was deposited on the cage floor, where it was visited regularly by the mother. It was several weeks old before it was able to climb. A second offspring was born early in 1962. Newborn young of *Coendou* have been figured and described by de Miranda-Ribeiro (1936), establishing that the spines are well-developed at birth, as in other porcupines.

General experience with tree porcupines in captivity has not been favorable, and it seems certain that most specimens do not survive for long. However, some individuals have established satisfactory longevities, indicating that variations in treatment before and after arrival are responsible, rather than an inherent lack of resistance in the animal itself. A specimen of the Brazilian tree porcupine (*C. prehensilis*) lived here from May 1, 1908, to March 30, 1917, a period of 8 years, 11 months, lacking one day. Flower (1931) records 8 years, 11 months, 14 days for a hairy tree porcupine (*C. insidiosus*) in the Zoological Gardens of London, a remarkably close approximation.*

FAMILY CAVIIDAE

CAVIES

As detailed by Simpson (1945), this family includes the several genera of small animals typified by the domestic cavy or guinea-pig (*Cavia porcellus*) and the much larger Patagonian cavy (*Dolichotis patagona*) and its relatives. Found only in South America, the members of this family are vegetarian in diet and diurnal in habit. They usually live in small, loose colonies, burrowing into the earth or making use of cavities on rocky ledges.

*See Addenda, p. 733.

The small relatives of the guinea pig are assigned to several genera, but superficially they are much like solid-colored members of the domesticated form, in shades of gray or brown, with comparatively large heads, stout bodies, and short legs. None has a tail. All are uncommon in captivity and none has been kept here, although the Andean or Peruvian cavy (*C. tschudii*) has been exhibited in the National Zoological Park, where it lived for 6 years, 4 months (Mann, 1930). Various other cavies have been shown elsewhere, particularly at the Zoological Gardens of London (Flower, 1929).

The common cavy or guinea pig (*C. porcellus*) was found as a domesticated animal living in the houses of the Incas during the early visits to Peru by the Spanish conquistadors. After its introduction into Europe, it achieved great popularity as a household pet. Later, it drew the attention of fanciers, and by selective breeding, color varieties were established as well as distinctions in coat: the normal short-haired, the Abyssinian, with wiry coat arranged in rosettes, and the Peruvian, with very long, soft hair.

The guinea pig is not ordinarily used for exhibition purposes in zoological gardens, but for one reason or another, few are without them. They are easily maintained and will endure temperatures well below the freezing point, if they are gradually accustomed to low temperatures and are kept dry and well supplied with hay under which they can burrow. Adequate food consists of hay, crushed oats, greens, and vegetables. The latter are essential because of an especially great requirement of vitamin C. Water may not always be taken when greens are abundant but will be drunk on occasion, and so should be made available.

The guinea pig is commonly used as an example of rapid multiplication, but it is not actually a particularly fast breeder. Females may reach puberty at 2 months but are usually not allowed to breed until at least twice that age, when they will have reached more mature size. The period of gestation is given by Asdell (1946) as 67–68 days. Young per litter vary from one to six, the usual number being two or three. They are well developed at birth and are able to nibble at solid food after a day or two. Mothers are receptive to the male a few hours after parturition, but it is not good practice to allow them to be bred, unless the only objective is quantity of young. For this reason, as well as the fact that some males cannot be trusted with a newborn litter, it is safer to pen an expectant mother separately.

Widely used as an experimental animal, the guinea pig is bred extensively in laboratories and by supply houses. Treatment under these conditions is well described by Ibsen (1950).

Few authentic records of maximum longevities of guinea pigs seem to be available. Flower (1931) gives "over six years" for two individuals as the best known to him.

The Patagonian cavy or mara (*Dolichotis patagona*) is a very much larger animal than the preceding, head and body measuring 30 inches or more. The legs are long, the hind ones especially so, in accordance with the animal's leaping locomotion when moving at speed. The ears are long, broad at the base, and tapering abruptly toward the tip. There is a very small tail, practically bare and usually turned to one side. The typical race (*D. p. patagona*) is found from the wastes of Patagonia to the great pampas of central Argentina. At the northern end of the range the black band across the rump disappears, this being the definitive character of the race *D. p. centricola*.

The Patagonian cavy is a familiar zoo inhabitant. Usually it is kept indoors where, even in rather small quarters, it lives reasonably well. When such confinement is unavoidable, as much floor space as possible should be provided. It is not a troublesome gnawer but is a tremendous leaper, a point that must be kept in mind. Food provided here consists of hay, lettuce or other available greens, raw vegetables, and rolled oats. A salt block or spool is a useful adjunct. Drinking water is always made accessible but is little used when greens are abundant. Under indoor conditions the Patagonian cavy has lived here for 3 years, 5 months.

In 1942 a colony of Patagonian cavies was set up here in the inclosure described under "Prairie Dogs" (p. 217). Two pairs of animals were installed but it was soon found that when disturbed they were able to leap over the 4-foot barrier, overhang and all, with no difficulty. A 3-foot upward extension proved to be non-negotiable and put an end to too frequent escapes. At first, no shelter was provided, and the animals promptly took to earth, digging large and complicated burrows. Later, a low stone shelter with open front was built. This served the animals well, and tunnels were then dug sporadically if at all. This hut not only provided protection for the animals but served to keep dry the hay provided for food and bedding. Kept in this way, the cavies proved to be entirely hardy and indifferent to snow and cold at temperatures as low as 0° F. (−17.8° C.). The only difficulty experienced was occasional fighting of adult males, when one sometimes had to be removed.

From 1943 to 1956 there were thirty-nine recorded births, occurring in every month of the year except January and December. The greatest number (eleven) occurred in May, with eight in September and seven each in June and August. In twenty cases there was 1 young, with 2 in seventeen others and triplets in two instances. The total number of young born in this period was actually 67, but for 7 the definite birth date was not recorded. The data are well in accord with those furnished by Zuckerman (1953) for nineteen births in the Zoological Gardens of London. The animals are born fully developed and are carefully nursed and guarded by their mothers. Mann (1930:349) gives the period of gestation as 58 days.

Surplus specimens, of course, were disposed of from time to time. Two additional males were introduced, one in 1944, the other in 1949. Such moves must be made with caution, because of the antagonism of resident animals toward strange ones. Each of these males was kept in a small pen inside the inclosure for a few days, until the others had become accustomed to it, before liberation. In both cases the introduction was entirely successful.

Under these conditions of semi-liberty it is difficult to identify individuals, so that accurate longevities could seldom be established. The only definite one obtained was for a male, fully adult when received in 1949, which lived 5 years, 11 months, 9 days. Flower (1931) gives "nearly 14 years" in South Africa, probably the greatest recorded span.

The much smaller salt desert cavy (*Pediolagus salinicola*) of north central Argentina does not appear to have been kept in the United States, but it has been exhibited and bred in European zoological gardens (Mohr, 1949). Zuckerman (1953) records five births of this species in the Zoological Gardens of London between 1932 and 1934.

FAMILY HYDROCHAERIDAE
CAPYBARAS

Largest of the rodents, the common capybara (*Hydrochaeris h. hydrochaeris*) may measure as much as 4 feet in length and weigh 100 pounds or more—the largest specimen recorded here was a female weighing 92 pounds. The appearance is that of a gigantic cavy, with large head, heavy body, short but serviceable legs, and rudimentary tail. There are four toes on the front feet and three behind, partially webbed, a useful provision for an animal of semiaquatic habits. For while the capybara often seeks its food of grasses and other plant material on land, it is never far from water, into which it plunges if alarmed. This is well in accord with its inoffensive and harmless nature as well as with its ability as a swimmer.

The common capybara lives in the swampy or grassy areas that border the great rivers of eastern South America, from Brazil northward; another race (*H. h. notialis*) is found in similar regions of Paraguay, Uruguay, and northern Argentina. A considerably smaller form (*H. isthmius*) is known from Panama; Cabrera (1961) lists this as a race of *H. hydrochaeris*.

In many respects the capybara is well suited for life in the zoological garden. Although it is more active at night than by day, it is not inclined to hide even while sleeping, so that it is always visible to the public. In northern latitudes it will thrive at liberty during the summer in a grassy paddock provided with a pool and can safely be included in mixed groups of equally harmless creatures. In cold weather, which, of course, it cannot endure, heated quarters must be provided. These should be as roomy as possible, although space is not of paramount importance. A pool of some sort, deep enough for submersion, is essential. Without this, the capybara's skin and hair become dry and unsightly, finally resulting in severe ulceration. A diet of hay, rolled oats, abundant greens and raw vegetables, fruit, and bread seems to be adequate.

Capybaras are not frequently bred in captivity, at least in northern climates. Zuckerman (1953) reports a birth of two young in the Zoological Gardens of London in 1874, a litter of five bred in England was entered in competition for a medal in 1913 (Amateur Menagerie Club, *Year Book*, 1914:240), and successful reproduction has been achieved in the San Diego Zoological Garden (Stott, 1954). All of these references are to the South American species.

An excellent account of the breeding of the Isthmian or Panama capybara (*H. isthmius*) at the Gorgas Memorial Laboratory in Panama is given by Trapido (1949). This includes a definite gestation period of between 104 and 111 days, followed by the birth of three young. The comparable period for the South American capybara is usually given as 119–26 days. This seems to stem from Jennison (n.d.), who gives no further details.

The best longevity for the South American capybara recorded by Flower (1931) is 8 years, 10 months, 6 days in the Zoological Gardens of London. A female received here on September 4, 1929, lived until October 6, 1941, a period of 12 years, 1 month, 2 days.

FAMILY DINOMYIDAE

BRANICK'S RAT OR PACARANA

Variously known by the names above and also as "false paca," this rather unlovely creature (*Dinomys branickii*) superficially resembles the paca (*Agouti*). However, its coloration is grayish rather than brown, with white markings on the lower back and flanks, and it has a well-haired tail some 6 inches in length. Head and body of the adult measure about 30 inches. The head is proportionately large, giving the animal a somewhat formidable appearance. This aspect, however, is not borne out by its nature, for in captivity it is calm, almost phlegmatic, and non-aggressive. The range is usually given as Peru, Colombia, Ecuador, and western Amazonia (Ellerman, 1940). However, this is subject to revision, as much remains to be learned concerning the species in nature. Tate (1931), quoting the collector A. M. Olalla, says it lives in burrows, usually under rocks, the group generally consisting of male and female and two young.

Branick's rat is among the rarest of mammals in captivity. Mohr (1937) gives an account of its history in Europe up to that time. The first specimen to be received here was brought from the zoological garden at Pará (Belém) by William Beebe on May 28, 1915. This animal lived until April 24, 1922, or 6 years, 10 months, 27 days. It was kept in a hard-walled cage with wire-netting front, about 4 by 6 feet, and fed crushed oats, greens, raw vegetables, bananas, apples, and bread. It did not climb and was active by day. Three further specimens were purchased from a dealer on April 7, 1930, but, perhaps because of poor condition on arrival, none survived for more than a few months. A specimen received at the Philadelphia Zoological Garden on December 24, 1946, is reported by Jones (1958) to have lived until June 19, 1956, or 9 years, 5 months, 26 days.

FAMILY DASYPROCTIDAE

Pacas and Agoutis

The paca or spotted cavy (*Agouti paca*) and the agoutis (*Dasyprocta* and *Myoprocta*) are treated here as members of a single family in accordance with Simpson (1945), although they are sometimes considered as forming separate groups (Cabrera, 1961). Both are found in tropical regions of the Americas. They are generally but not exclusively nocturnal, and their food consists of plant materials.

The paca is found in several races, from Mexico to southern Brazil. It is a heavy-bodied animal, with head proportionately large, and may reach a length of 30 inches. The tail is obsolete. Coloration is in shades of reddish-brown, with rows of white spots along the sides. The paca is a forest dweller, living in cavities among the roots of trees or in the ground. It is almost entirely nocturnal, and in captivity here has adjusted well to reversal under red light. Those kept here have been fed on rolled oats, any available greens, raw vegetables, bananas, apples, and bread.

The paca does not breed readily in captivity, but successes have been recorded in the Zoological Gardens of London (Zuckerman, 1953), the San Diego Zoological Garden (Stott, 1954), and the National Zoological Park, Washington (Mann, 1930, 1953). The gestation period appears to be undetermined.

Average durations of pacas in captivity are not as good as might be expected—the best span recorded here is 3 years, 7 months—but Flower (1931) lists 12 years, 8 months, 22 days in the National Zoological Park, and a longevity of 13 years, 11 months in the Philadelphia Zoological Garden has been reported by Tobin (1936).

The agoutis (*Dasyprocta* and *Myoprocta*), in a number of species and races, range from Mexico to Paraguay, including the Lesser Antilles and Trinidad. Considerably smaller than the paca, they are graceful, active, and beautifully proportioned. The fragmentary tail is concealed under the long hair of the rump in *Dasyprocta*, but in the much smaller-tailed agoutis (*Myoprocta*) the short, spikelike appendage is plainly visible. Coloration varies from sooty black through gray and shades of reddish brown to light golden yellow.

Like the paca, the agoutis are forest animals, spending the days in holes or cavities and foraging at night for the plant products that form their food. However, the nocturnal habit does not seem to be as firmly implanted in the agoutis as in the pacas, for in captivity they adapt readily to daylight and become as fully diurnal as squirrels. Since they also soon lose the timidity which is pronounced in nature, they rank among the most desirable small mammals for exhibition purposes.

Being entirely terrestrial, agoutis require a reasonable amount of floor space, though this need not be excessive. Here we have found that pairs do well in glass-fronted cages 4 feet long by 3 deep which are heated in winter. True pairs or even two animals of opposite sex but different species get on well together in such quarters. However, if young are produced, we have found it necessary to remove them soon after weaning, as males will not tolerate possible rivals. Food provided is the same as that listed for the paca, and fresh water is always available.

Agoutis breed freely under such conditions, and family groups make most attractive exhibits. The young are born fully developed and are able to run about actively almost at once. Male parents are tolerant of their playful offspring, at least until they begin to approach maturity.

Seven births of various agoutis have been recorded here, occurring in the months of January, March, April, August, September, and November. This is in accord with the much more extended data supplied by Zuckerman (1953), showing that births of some species have occurred in the

Zoological Gardens of London in every month of the year. In each of our cases there were two young, although Zuckerman records many single births in London. Brown (1936) gives the gestation period of *Dasyprocta aguti* as 104 days, which is generally quoted.

Our longest-lived agouti was a Central American (*D. punctata*), born here on March 1, 1948, and died December 26, 1958, after 10 years, 9 months, 25 days. Flower (1931) records 13 years, 1 month, 21 days for a Mexican agouti (*D. mexicana*) in the National Zoological Park, and a golden (*D. aguti*) is stated to have lived for 15 years, 6 months in the Philadelphia Zoological Garden (Duetz, 1938).

FAMILY CHINCHILLIDAE

Viscachas and Chinchillas

The members of this South American family are unlike each other in general appearance, but in addition to anatomical similarities they agree in being terrestrial and in the possession of large ears and rather long, well-haired tails. All are vegetarian in diet.

The plains viscacha (*Lagostomus maximus*), in several races, is found on the pampas of Argentina, where it lives in large groups of burrows known as *vizcacheras*. It is a much larger animal than its relatives, adults measuring up to 20 inches for head and body. Once commonly imported into this country, the plains viscacha has become scarce in recent years and has not been seen here since 1925. Up to that time our specimens were fed the usual diet furnished for vegetarian rodents, consisting of rolled oats, greens, vegetables, bananas, apples, and bread. They were kept in wire-fronted indoor cages, about 3 by 6 feet, and provided with sleeping boxes in accordance with nocturnal habits. It seems probable that better results might be obtained in outdoor inclosures such as that in use here for the Patagonian cavy, since the species presumably is hardy at this latitude. Flower (1931) says that the species rarely lives over 5 years in Europe and gives 6 years, 8 months, 12 days in the Zoological Gardens of London. Our best here is 4 years, 10 months, 27 days, while Mann (1930) gives 4 years, 10 months in the National Zoological Park. Scattered births have occurred here, as well as at Washington. Zuckerman (1953) charts numerous young born in the Zoological Gardens of London, indicating that births in captivity may occur in practically any month. Asdell (1946) gives the gestation period as 145 days and the number of young as two or three— usually two.

The mountain viscachas (*Lagidium*) are intermediate in size between the plains viscacha and the chinchilla. They are found, usually at high altitudes, in the mountains of western South America. Ellerman (1940) lists twenty-one forms in four species, ranging from Peru and Bolivia to southern Chile. Mountain viscachas appear to be uncommon in captivity, but between 1941 and 1946 eight specimens, all of which were assigned to the Peruvian race, *Lagidium peruanum subroseum*, were received here. They were fed rolled oats, feeding pellets, greens, raw vegetables, apples, and bread. Hay also was provided but seemed to be used only as bedding. The animals were kept in glass-fronted indoor cages during the winter months, but in the spring were put out-of-doors in large wire-inclosed, earth-floored runs, where they burrowed beneath the rock backgrounds. Three single births occurred of very large, well-developed young, one each in May, June, and July. The gestation period seems not to have been determined. The greatest longevity established was 4 years, 8 months, 8 days. Rabb (1960) lists 8 years for *Lagidium peruanum* in the Chicago Zoological Park.

The chinchilla (*Chinchilla lanigera*), bearer of the silver fleece, has become so rare in nature, through the constant persecution by fur hunters, that it has almost disappeared. However, it is now so extensively bred in captivity that its name has become a household word. Some confusion of identity has arisen, for while Cabrera and Yepes (1940) recognize three forms, with distribution high in the mountains of Peru, Bolivia, Chile, and western Argentina, Ellerman (1940) synonymized them all under the name above and restricted the range to Chile and possibly Bolivia. Breeders claim the recognition of various types in their animals, but whether or not they correspond to the forms of Cabrera and Yepes now seems indeterminable. The latter authorities say that the eleven chinchillas collected by M. F. Chapman in 1923 and established in California the following year came from northern Chile and were "*Chinchillas costinas*" or *C. lanigera*. These animals were the foundation from which the present very large stock in this country was produced, although small importations were received later.

Chinchillas have been kept by zoological gardens, off and on, for many years. The first arrival at the Zoological Gardens of London was received in 1829 (Flower, 1929). The first specimens shown at the New York Zoological Park came here in 1901. Our feeding system has always been simple: timothy hay (which the animals will eat), rolled oats, feeding pellets, greens, raw vegetables, apples, and bread.

From 1958 to 1962 twenty-nine chinchillas were born here, births occurring in January, March, April, May, June, August, and September. Seven sets of twins and one of triplets were included. Zuckerman (1953) reports one instance of quadruplets in nineteen births at the Zoological Gardens of London.

The wide-spread breeding of captive chinchillas has resulted in the development of somewhat intricate but successful techniques, and much has been learned concerning the biology of the animal. Gathered from various sources, including an excellent summary by Kellogg (1953), pamphlets of supply houses, and conversations with breeders, the essentials appear to be as follows:

> Breeding animals are usually kept in pairs in pens with wood or metal frames supporting coverings of $\frac{1}{2}$-inch-thick wire mesh, with floors of the same material. Retiring boxes are provided and there is usually a box or tin of fine sand or fuller's earth used for dusting. In the larger plants the pens are placed in tiers on open racks to conserve space. Temperatures between 40° and 75° F. are considered to be most favorable. The animals are arranged in pairs as they approach maturity when 6–8 months old, and after settling down they do not later accept strange mates readily. However, experienced handlers are able to accomplish multiple mating, at least in some cases. Feeding is simplified by the use of commercial pellets and hay, placed in racks. This is supplemented by small allowances of greens, raw vegetables, and apples. Nursing mothers usually receive Pablum or some other prepared baby food. Fresh drinking water is provided.

The gestation period is variously given as 111–28 days (Kellogg, 1953), 125 days (Asdell, 1946), and 105–28 days (Kenneth, 1953). Breeders usually say 111 days is most nearly correct. The average number of young per birth is two and they are born fully developed and with eyes open. Males ordinarily are not troublesome when young appear but are sometimes removed for a day or two. The young are weaned at about 60 days.

References to longevities of from 12 to 20 years are found in the literature, but I have seen no supporting evidence for such claims. Flower (1931) gives 6 years, 8 months, 12 days as the longest span in the Zoological Gardens of London. Just over 4 years and still alive in 1963 is our best record here.

FAMILY CAPROMYIDAE

HUTIAS AND COYPU

All the species included here are of comparatively large size and are generally similar in appearance. Tails provide the greatest superficial variation, as they may be long or short, nearly bare or thickly haired, even prehensile.

Some of the members are arboreal, at least one appears to be terrestrial, and the coypu is semiaquatic. Their distribution is in the West Indies and South America.

The hutias, in several genera and forms, are known from Cuba and the Isle of Pines, Jamaica, Hispaniola, and the Bahamas, and one species (*Procapromys geayi*) has been described from Venezuela. Several of the hutias have been kept in collections, the common hutia (*Capromys p. pilorides*) of Cuba being most usually seen. This animal may measure 20 inches in length of head and body, with moderately long, well-haired tail. While it climbs well, it is less arboreal than some of its relatives. The food of all the hutias appears to consist of fruits, roots, and leaves.

In captivity, the common hutia is quiet, if not overly friendly. In indoor cages of tooth-resistant materials, measuring 4 by 6 feet and 8 feet high, provided with tree perches, it has done well here. The feeding schedule followed included apples, greens, vegetables, crushed oats, and bread. Our best longevity for the species is 8 years, 7 months, 15 days. Mann (1930) gives 9 years, 5 months for a specimen in the National Zoological Park, while Flower (1931) reports 9 years, 8 months, 3 days in the Zoological Gardens of London. The common hutia has frequently been bred in captivity, notably at the National Zoological Park (Mann, 1930) as well as at London (Zuckerman, 1953).

The island of Hispaniola has been the home, in fairly recent years, of two small hutias of the genus *Plagiodontia*. One of these, *Plagiodontia aedium*, described by Cuvier in 1836, was hunted so thoroughly as a food animal that it is now considered to be extinct. A living specimen is listed as having been received at the Zoological Gardens of London between April, 1855, and April, 1856 (Flower, 1929). In 1923 a series of thirteen hutias was collected by Dr. W. L. Abbott in the Dominican Republic and described by Miller (1927) as a new species (*Plagiodontia hylaeum*). In 1947 two living specimens of the new Hispaniolan hutia were offered to us by Dr. André Audant of the Department of Fisheries of the Republic of Haiti, with the statement that the animals had been taken in that country. When these hutias were received here on July 28, 1947, it was found that while one wore the normal coat of medium brown, the other was albinistic, being pale buffy in color and with the eyes pink. They climbed inexpertly and made little use of the tree perches provided for them, seeming to prefer the seclusion of a niche in the rock background. Provided with a wide variety of leaves, fresh greens and vegetables, fruit, crushed oats, and bread, the animals never fed well and neither survived for more than a few weeks. They are now preserved in the American Museum of

Natural History. That the species still persists in Hispaniola is evidenced by the fact that living specimens are still offered occasionally by residents of that island.

The coypu or nutria (*Myocastor coypus*) is found in southern South America from Paraguay and Chile to the Straits of Magellan. Four races are listed by Cabrera (1961). It is a large animal, as rodents go, with a total head and body length of 24 inches. The tail is long, rounded, and nearly naked, and the large incisors are conspicuously bright orange. The mammary glands are located so high on the female's sides that they are often said to be upon her back. Semiaquatic in habit, the coypu is not entirely at home on land and is seldom found far from waterways, in the banks of which its burrows are dug. It swims freely and well, making good use of the broadly webbed hind feet.

Because of the fine quality of its underfur after the removal of the long guard hairs, the coypu has long been persecuted almost to extinction in many parts of its range. The increasing scarcity of skins led to the establishment of "farms" for breeding the animals in captivity. Bourdelle (1939) gives a brief account of early efforts in France, dating from 1882. After a series of failures and partial successes, breeding plants are now operating in North and South America and Europe. This long-continued interest has resulted in the development of proper techniques, and several color variations, such as "albino" and "golden," have already appeared. In the course of time, escapes and apparently intentional liberations from captivity have occurred, both in this country and in Europe. Coypus have thus become established in many areas outside South America, a situation which has aroused mixed reactions (Bourdelle, 1939; Laurie, 1946; Howard, 1953; Gunderson, 1955). The race introduced into various regions of North America is listed by Hall and Kelson (1959) as *M. c. bonariensis*.

The coypu has long been a popular zoo animal, since it is active by day, easily maintained, and resistant to cold—it has withstood a temperature of −6° F. here without damage when provided with an unheated shelter (Ditmars, 1918). In properly balanced groups coypus make excellent exhibits, either indoors or out. In small quarters males are likely to quarrel, so that only one should be kept, with several females. Where there is sufficient space, fighting is less likely. An excellent indoor installation, with a large glass-fronted tank and extensive dry area at the back, houses a fine group of coypus in the Small Mammal House in the National Zoological Park. In the Philadelphia Zoological Garden coypus are shown in an outdoor inclosure including a large pond and extensive dry land, surrounded by a low stone wall. Small wooden igloos, set at intervals, provide as much shelter as required. For restraining coypus, a wall of stone or concrete or a fence of stout wire netting, set 3 feet into the ground and rising $3\frac{1}{2}$–4 feet above it, is sufficient. If the floor of the area is covered with concrete, then, of course, sinking of the barrier below the surface is not necessary.

Commercial breeders follow the group plan, as outlined, for mass production. Where animals of selected strains are concerned, it is usual to keep each female in a small compartment of her own, complete with pool and shelter box. Here she is paired with an approved male which is removed after mating, the female then being left to rear her brood in seclusion. General feeding procedures include hay, grains such as corn (maize) and crushed oats, greens, vegetables, apples, bread, and rabbit pellets.

The coypu breeds readily under zoological-garden conditions, the first birth in London having occurred in 1883 (Flower, 1929) and the first here in 1903. The gestation period is usually stated by breeders to be 120–35 days (Naether, 1954), but Palmer (1954) gives it as 100–125 days, Cabrera and Yepes (1940) as 127–32 days, and Asdell (1946) as 135–50 days. The number of young, born fully developed, may vary from 1 to 10 per birth. Zuckerman (1953), in analyzing thirty births in the Zoological Gardens of London, found the number of young in each to be from 1 to 9, with an average of 4.1. The young are usually weaned at 6–8 weeks and females are said to mature at 8 months (Bourlière, 1954).

The best longevity established by a coypu here is 4 years, 10 months, 24 days. Mann (1930) gives 5 years, 7 months in the National Zoological Park, and Flower (1931) lists 5 years, 11 months, 2 days in the Zoological Gardens of London.

· REFERENCES

ALCORN, J. R.
   1940. Life history notes on the Piute ground squirrel. Jour. Mammal., **21** (2):160–70.
ALLEN, ELSA G.
   1938. The habits and life history of the eastern chipmunk, *Tamias striatus lysteri*. New York State Mus. Bull., **314**:1–122.
AMATEUR MENAGERIE CLUB, THE.
   1914. Year Book. G. TYRWHITT-DRAKE, Hon. Secretary. Maidstone, Kent, England.

ANON.
    1901.   Our beaver and otter. News Bull. [N.Y.] Zool. Soc., No. 5, p. 6.
ASDELL, S. A.
    1946.   Patterns of mammalian reproduction. Comstock Publishing Co.,
            Ithaca, N.Y. 437 pp.
ASHBROOK, FRANK G.
    1928.   Fur-farming for profit. Macmillan Co., New York. 300 pp.
AUDUBON, JOHN JAMES, and JOHN BACHMAN.
    1849–54. The quadrupeds of North America. V. G. Audubon, New York.
            3 vols.
BAILEY, VERNON.
    1924.   Breeding, feeding and other life habits of meadow mice (Microtus).
            Jour. Agric. Res., 27 (8):523–36.
    1927.   Beaver habits and experiments in beaver culture. U.S. Dept. of
            Agriculture, Tech. Bull. 21. 39 pp.
BAUMGRAS, PHILIP.
    1944.   Experimental feeding of captive fox squirrels. Jour. Wildlife Manage-
            ment, 8 (4):296–300.
BLANFORD, W. T.
    1888–91. The fauna of British India. Mammalia. Taylor & Francis, London.
            617 pp.
BOURDELLE, E.
    1939.   American mammals introduced into France in the contemporary
            period, especially Myocastor and Ondatra. Jour. Mammal., 20
            (3):287–91.
BOURLIÈRE, FRANÇOIS.
    1954.   The natural history of mammals. Alfred A. Knopf, New York.
            363 pp.
BRADT, G. W.
    1938.   A study of beaver colonies in Michigan. Jour. Mammal., 19 (2):139–62.
    1939.   Breeding habits of beaver. Ibid., 20 (4):486–89.
BRATTSTROM, BAYARD H.
    1960.   Longevity in the kangaroo rat. Jour. Mammal., 41 (3):404.
BROWN, C. EMERSON.
    1936.   Rearing wild animals in captivity and gestation periods. Jour. Mammal.,
            17 (1):10–13.
BRUCE, H. M., and E. HINDLE.
    1934.   The golden hamster, Cricetus (Mesocricetus) auratus Waterhouse.
            Notes on its breeding and growth. Proc. Zool. Soc. London, pp. 361–66.
BUTTERWORTH, BERNARD B.
    1961.   The breeding of Dipodomys deserti in the laboratory. Jour. Mammal.,
            42 (3):413–14.
CABRERA, ANGEL.
    1961.   Catalogo de los mamiferos de America del Sur. Rev. Mus. Argentina
            Cienc. Nat. Bernardino Rivadavia, Zool., 4 (2):309–732.

CABRERA, ANGEL, and JOSÉ YEPES.
   1940.   Historia natural ediar. Mamiferos Sud-Americanos. Compañia
          Argentina de Editores, Buenos Aires. 370 pp.
CHASEN, FREDERICK NUTTER.
   1940.   A handlist of Malaysian mammals. Bull. Raffles Mus., 15:1–209.
CHEW, ROBERT M.
   1958.   Reproduction of *Dipodomys merriami* in captivity. Jour. Mammal.,
          39 (4):597–98.
COGSHALL, ANNETTA STOW.
   1928.   Food habits of deer mice of the genus *Peromyscus* in captivity. Jour.
          Mammal., 9 (3):217–21.
CRIDDLE, STUART.
   1930.   The prairie pocket gopher, *Thomomys talpoides rufescens*. Jour. Mam-
          mal., 11 (3):265–80.
CULBERTSON, A. E.
   1946.   Observations on the natural history of the Fresno kangaroo rat.
          Jour. Mammal., 27 (3):189–203.
DAVIS, JOSEPH A., JR.
   1961.   Red means go! Animal Kingdom, 64 (4):114–18.
   1962.   Red light pays dividends. *Ibid.*, 65 (1):3–5.
DAY, BILLY N., HAROLD J. EGOSCUE, and ANGUS M. WOODBURY.
   1956.   Ord kangaroo rat in captivity. Science, 124:485–86.
DICE, LEE R.
   1929.   A new laboratory cage for small mammals, with notes on methods of
          rearing *Peromyscus*. Jour. Mammal., 10 (2):116–24.
   1934.   An improved *Peromyscus* ration. *Ibid.*, 15 (2):160–61.
DITMARS, RAYMOND L.
   1918.   A test in acclimatization. Bull. New York Zool. Soc., 21 (3):1624.
DONAT, FAE.
   1933.   Notes on the life history and behavior of *Neotoma fuscipes*. Jour.
          Mammal., 14 (1):19–26.
DUETZ, GERTRUDE H.
   1938.   Comments on longevity and average exhibition ages during the year
          1937. In: Rept. Penrose Res. Lab., Zool. Soc. Philadelphia,
          pp. 31–34.
DURRELL, GERALD M.
   1952.   Pigmy scaly-tail. Zoo Life (London), 7 (1):12–15.
EGOSCUE, HAROLD J.
   1957.   The desert wood rat: A laboratory colony. Jour. Mammal., 38 (4):
          472–81.
   1960.   Laboratory and field studies of the northern grasshopper mouse.
          Ibid., 41 (1):99–110.
ELLERMAN, J. R.
   1940.   The families and genera of living rodents. British Museum (Natural
          History), London. 2 vols.

ELLERMAN, J. R., and T. C. S. MORRISON-SCOTT.
    1951.   Checklist of Palaearctic and Indian mammals. British Museum
            (Natural History), London. 810 pp.

FARRIS, EDMOND J.
    1950.   The rat as an experimental animal. In: The care and breeding of
            laboratory animals. Ed. EDMOND J. FARRIS. John Wiley & Sons, Inc.,
            New York. 515 pp.

FINLEY, ROBERT B., JR.
    1959.   Observation of nocturnal animals by red light. Jour. Mammal.,
            40 (4):591-94.

FLEAY, DAVID.
    1949.   The shy Australian water rat. Animal Kingdom, 52 (2):54-58.

FLOWER, S. S.
    1929.   List of the vertebrated animals exhibited in the gardens of the Zoo-
            logical Society of London, 1828-1927. 1. Mammals. Zoological
            Society of London. 419 pp.
    1931.   Contributions to our knowledge of the duration of life in vertebrate
            animals. 5. Mammals. Proc. Zool. Soc. London, pp. 145-234.

FOLK, EDGAR G., JR., ED.
    1958.   Hamster guide. All-pets Books, Inc., Fond-du-Lac, Wis. 80 pp.

GOODWIN, GEORGE G.
    1954.   The animal kingdom. Vol. I. Ed. FREDERICK DRIMMER. Greystone
            Press, New York. 680 pp.

GREENWALD, GILBERT S.
    1956.   The reproductive cycle of the field mouse, *Microtus californicus*.
            Jour. Mammal., 37 (2):213-22.

GRÜNEBERG, HANS.
    1943.   The genetics of the mouse. University Press, Cambridge. 412 pp.

GUNDERSON, HARVEY L.
    1955.   Nutria, *Myocastor coypus*, in Minnesota. Jour. Mammal., 36 (3):465.

HAAGNER, ALWIN.
    1920.   South African mammals. H. F. & G. Witherby, London. 248 pp.

HALL, E. RAYMOND, and KEITH R. KELSON.
    1959.   The mammals of North America. The Ronald Press Co., New York.
            2 vols.

HAMILTON, W. J., JR.
    1953.   Reproduction and young of the Florida wood rat, *Neotoma f. floridana*
            (Ord). Jour. Mammal., 34 (2):180-89.

HANLEY, GEORGE H.
    1944.   Housing of the pocket gopher in captivity. Jour. Mammal., 24
            (4):407-8.

HEDIGER, H.
    1950.   Gefangenschaftsgeburt eines Afrikanischen Springhasen, *Pedetes
            caffer*. Zool. Garten, Leipzig (N.F.), 17 (1/5):166-69.

HILL, W. C. OSMAN.
1942. Note on the breeding of the Malabar giant squirrel (*Ratufa indica maxima*) in captivity. Jour. Bombay Nat. Hist. Soc., 43 (3):521-22.
1949. The giant squirrels. Zoo Life (London), 4 (4):98-100.
1955. Report of the Society's prosector for the year 1954. Proc. Zool. Soc. London, 125 (3/4):533-39.
1957. Report of the Society's prosector for the years 1955 and 1956. *Ibid.*, 129:431-46.
HOOPER, EMMET T.
1956. Longevity of captive kangaroo rats, *Dipodomys*. Jour. Mammal., 37 (1):124-25.
HOWARD, WALTER E.
1953. Nutria (*Myocastor coypus*) in California. Jour. Mammal., 34 (4): 512-13.
HOWES, PAUL GRISWOLD.
1954. The giant cactus forest and its world. Duell, Sloan and Pearce, New York; Little, Brown & Co., Boston and Toronto. 258 pp.
HUEY, LAURENCE M.
1959. Longevity notes on captive *Perognathus*. Jour. Mammal., 40 (3): 412-15.
IBSEN, HEMAN L.
1950. The guinea pig. In: The care and breeding of laboratory animals. Ed. EDMOND J. FARRIS. John Wiley & Sons, Inc., New York. 515 pp.
JENNISON, GEORGE.
N.d. Table of gestation periods and number of young. A. & C. Black, Ltd., London. 8 pp.
JOHNSON, CHARLES EUGENE.
1926. Notes on a pocket gopher in captivity. Jour. Mammal., 7 (1):35-37.
JOHNSON, GEORGE EDWIN.
1927. Observations on young prairie-dogs (*Cynomys ludovicianus*) born in the laboratory. Jour. Mammal., 8 (2):110-15.
JONES, MARVIN L.
1958. Mammals in captivity. Mimeographed MSS (unpublished).
KELLOGG, CHARLES E.
1953. Chinchilla raising. Leaflet 266, U.S. Dept. of Agriculture. 8 pp.
KENNETH, J. H.
1953. Gestation periods. Oliver & Boyd Ltd., Edinburgh. 23 pp.
KLUGH, A. BROOKER.
1927. Ecology of the red squirrel. Jour. Mammal., 8 (1):1-32.
KOFORD, CARL B.
1958. Prairie dogs, whitefaces and blue grama. Wildlife Monographs. 3. The Wildlife Society (n.p.). 78 pp.
LAURIE, E. M. O.
1946. The coypu (*Myocastor coypus*) in Great Britain. Jour. Animal Ecol., 15 (1):22-34.

LINSDALE, JEAN M., and LLOYD P. TEVIS, JR.
   1951.   The dusky-footed wood rat. University of California Press, Berkeley.
           664 pp.
LYDEKKER, RICHARD.
   1893–96. The royal natural history. Frederick Warne & Co., London and
           New York. 6 vols.
MANN, WM. M.
   1930.   Wild animals in and out of the zoo. Smithsonian Sci. Ser., 6. 362 pp.
   1953.   Report on the National Zoological Park for the year ended June 30,
           1952. Smithsonian Inst. Report for 1952, pp. 94–129.
MARSH, ALBERT F.
   1948.   The hamster manual. By the Author, Mobile, Ala. 86 pp.
MEYER, BERT J., and ROLAND K. MEYER.
   1944.   Growth and reproduction of the cotton rat, *Sigmodon hispidus hispidus*,
           under laboratory conditions. Jour. Mammal., **25** (2):107–29.
MILLER, GERRIT S., JR.
   1927.   The rodents of the genus *Plagiodontia*. Proc. U.S. Nat. Mus., 72,
           Art. 16. 8 pp.
DE MIRANDA-RIBEIRO, ALIPIO.
   1936.   The new-born of the Brazilian tree porcupine (*Coendou prehensilis*
           Linn.) and of the hairy tree porcupine (*Sphingurus villosus* F. Cuv.).
           Proc. Zool. Soc. London, pp. 971–74.
MITCHELL, P. CHALMERS.
   1911.   On longevity and relative viability in mammals and birds; with a note
           on the theory of longevity. Proc. Zool. Soc. London, pp. 425–548.
MOHR, ERNA.
   1933.   The muskrat, *Ondatra zibethica* (Linnaeus), in Europe. Jour. Mammal.,
           14 (1):58–63.
   1937.   Vom Pacarana (*Dinomys branickii* Peters). Zool. Garten, Leipzig
           (N.F.), **9** (5):204–9.
   1949.   Eineges vom grossen und vom kleinen Mara (*Dolichotis patagonum*
           Zimm. und *salinicola* Burm.). *Ibid.*, **16** (3/4):111–33.
MOTTERSHEAD, GEORGE S.
   1958.   Nocturnal mammal exhibit. Our Zoo News (Chester), 128:2.
MUSACCHIA, X. J.
   1954.   Cannibalism and other observations of captive ground squirrels.
           Jour. Mammal., **35** (3):445–47.
NAETHER, CARL.
   1954.   Care of the nutria. All-pets Mag., **25** (9):40–42.
ORR, ROBERT T.
   1939.   Longevity in *Perognathus longimembris*. Jour. Mammal., **20** (4):505.
PALMER, RALPH S.
   1954.   The mammal guide. Doubleday & Co., Inc., Garden City, N.Y. 384 pp.

PEARSON, PAUL G.

1952. Observations concerning the life history and ecology of the woodrat, *Neotoma floridana floridana* (Ord). Jour. Mammal., **33** (4): 459–63.

PFEIFFER, E. W.

1953. Animals trapped in mountain beaver (*Aplodontia rufa*) runways, and the mountain beaver in captivity. Jour. Mammal., **34** (3):396.

POCOCK, R. I.

1922. On the external characters of the beaver (Castoridae) and of some squirrels (Sciuridae). Proc. Zool. Soc. London, pp. 1171–1212.

POILEY, SAMUEL M.

1949. Raising captive meadow voles (*Microtus p. pennsylvanicus*). Jour. Mammal., **30** (3):317–18.

POOLE, EARL L.

1936. Notes on the young of the Allegheny wood rat. Jour. Mammal., **17** (1):22–26.

1940. Life history sketch of the Allegheny wood rat. *Ibid.*, **21** (3):249–70.

POURNELLE, GEORGE H.

1960. Some longevity records of captive mammals. Jour. Mammal., **41** (1): 114.

RABB, GEORGE B.

1960. Longevity records for mammals at the Chicago Zoological Park. Jour. Mammal., **41** (1):113–14.

ROBERTS, AUSTIN.

1951. The mammals of South Africa. Trustees of the Mammals of South Africa Book Fund, Johannesburg. 700 pp.

ROSS, ROLAND CASE.

1930. California Sciuridae in captivity. Jour. Mammal., **11** (1):76–78.

SÁNYÁL, RAM BRAMHA.

1892. A hand-book of the management of animals in captivity in Lower Bengal. Bengal Secretariat Press, Calcutta. 351 pp.

SCHRAMM, PETER.

1961. Copulation and gestation in the pocket gopher. Jour. Mammal., **42** (2):167–70.

SCHWENTKER, VICTOR.

1957. The Chinese (striped) hamster. In: The UFAW handbook on the care and management of laboratory animals. Universities Federation for Animal Welfare, London. 951 pp.

SELLE, RAYMOND M.

1928. *Microtus californicus* in captivity. Jour. Mammal., **9** (2):93–98.

1939. Golden-mantled ground squirrels raised in captivity. *Ibid.*, **20** (1):106–7.

SETON, E. T.

1909. Life-histories of northern animals. Chas. Scribner's Sons, New York. 2 vols. 1267 pp.

SHADLE, ALBERT R.
  1940. A source of meat for diets of wild rodents. Jour. Mammal., **21** (4):460–61.
  1946. Copulation in the porcupine. Jour. Wildlife Management, **10** (2):159–62.
  1950. Feeding, care and handling of captive porcupines (*Erethizon*). Jour. Mammal. **31** (4):411–16.
  1951. Laboratory copulations and gestations of porcupine, *Erethizon dorsatum. Ibid.*, **32** (2):219–21.

SHAW, WM. T.
  1925. Breeding and development of the Columbian ground squirrel. Jour. Mammal., **6** (2):106–13.

SHELDON, CAROLYN.
  1938a. Vermont jumping mice of the genus *Zapus*. Jour. Mammal., **19** (3):324–32.
  1938b. Vermont jumping mice of the genus *Napaeozapus. Ibid.*, No. 4, pp. 444–53.

SHORTEN, MONICA.
  1951–52. Some aspects of the biology of the grey squirrel (*Sciurus carolinensis*) in Great Britain. Proc. Zool. Soc. London, **121**:427–59.

SHORTRIDGE, G. C.
  1934. The mammals of South West Africa. William Heinemann Ltd., London. 2 vols. 779 pp.

SIMON, E. S.
  1943. Life span of some wild animals in captivity. Jour. Bombay Nat. Hist. Soc., **44** (1):117–18.

SIMPSON, GEORGE GAYLORD.
  1945. The principles of classification and a classification of mammals. Bull. Amer. Mus. Nat. Hist., 85. 350 pp.

SNEDIGAR, R.
  1949. Day into night. Parks and Recreation, **32** (5):283.

SOUTHERN, H. N., J. S. WATSON, and DENNIS CHITTY.
  1946. Watching nocturnal animals by infra-red radiation. Jour. Animal Ecol., **15** (2):198–202.

STOCKARD, A. H.
  1929. Observations on reproduction in the white-tailed prairie-dog (*Cynomys leucurus*). Jour. Mammal., **10** (3):209–12.

STOTT, KEN, JR.
  1954. Baby food for thought. Zoonooz, **27** (6):5–6.

STRONG, LEONELL C.
  1950. The care of experimental mice. In: The care and breeding of laboratory animals. Ed. EDMOND J. FARRIS. John Wiley & Sons, Inc., New York. 515 pp.

SUMNER, F. B.
  1922. Longevity in *Peromyscus*. Jour. Mammal., **3** (2):79–81.

SVIHLA, ARTHUR.
1931. Life history of the Texas rice rat (*Oryzomys palustris texensis*). Jour. Mammal., **12** (3):238–42.

SVIHLA, RUTH DOWELL.
1930. A family of flying squirrels. Jour. Mammal., **11** (2):211–13.
1936. Breeding and young of the grasshopper mouse (*Onychomys leucogaster fuscogriseus*). *Ibid.*, **17** (2):172–73.

SVIHLA, ARTHUR, and RUTH DOWELL SVIHLA.
1931. The Louisiana muskrat. Jour. Mammal., **12** (1):12–28.
1933. Notes on the life history of the wood rat, *Neotoma floridana rubida* Bangs. *Ibid.*, **14** (1):73–75.

TATE, G. H. H.
1931. Random observations on habits of South American mammals. Jour. Mammal., **12** (3):248–56.

THOMPSON, HARRY V.
1953. The edible dormouse (*Glis glis*) in England, 1902–1951. Proc. Zool. Soc. London, **122** (4):1017–24.

TOBIN, VIOLET E.
1936. Analysis of high exhibition figures for five year periods and some records of long life in living specimens. In: Rept. Penrose Res. Lab., Zool. Soc. Philadelphia, pp. 25–30.

TRAPIDO, HAROLD.
1949. Gestation period, young and maximum weight of the Isthmian capybara (*Hydrochoerus isthmius* Goldman). Jour. Mammal., **30** (4):433.

TROUGHTON, ELLIS.
1957. Furred animals of Australia. Angus & Robertson, Ltd., Sydney. 374 pp.

WADE, OTIS.
1927a. Breeding habits and early life of the thirteen-striped ground squirrel, *Citellus tridecemlineatus* (Mitchell). Jour. Mammal., **8** (4):269–76.
1927b. Food habits of a pocket gopher. *Ibid.*, pp. 310–11.
1930. The behavior of certain spermophiles with special reference to aestivation and hibernation. *Ibid.*, **11** (2):160–88.

WALKER, ERNEST P.
1942. Care of captive animals. Smithsonian Report for 1941, pp. 305–66. Govt. Printing Office, Washington, D.C.
1948. They glide through the air with the greatest of ease. Fauna, **10** (3):82–84.

WARWICK, Tom.
1940. A contribution to the ecology of the musk-rat (*Ondatra zibethica*) in the British Isles. Proc. Zool. Soc. London, Series A, **110**:165–201.

WOOD, FAE DONAT.
1935. Notes on the breeding behavior and fertility of *Neotoma fuscipes macrotis* in captivity. Jour. Mammal., **16** (2):105–9.

WORDEN, ALASTAIR, and W. LANE-PETTER, Eds.
  1957. Some notes on species not dealt with in detail in the handbook. In: The UFAW handbook on the care and management of laboratory animals. Universities Federation for Animal Welfare, London. 2d ed. 951 pp.

WORTH, C. BROOKE.
  1950. Observations on the behavior and breeding of captive rice rats and wood rats. Jour. Mammal., 31 (4):421–26.

YOUNG, STANLEY P.
  1944. Longevity and other data on a male and a female prairie dog kept as pets. Jour. Mammal., 25 (4):317–19.

ZUCKERMAN, S.
  1953. The breeding seasons of mammals in captivity. Proc. Zool. Soc. London, 122:827–950.

ORDER CARNIVORA

.

WOLVES, BEARS, CATS, ETC.

Popularly, the carnivores are eaters of flesh. Systematically, they are distinguished by such anatomical characters as the form, number and arrangement of the teeth, the arming of the toes with claws rather than flattened nails, and the possession of shearing or carnassial cheek teeth in upper and lower jaws, functioning like scissors. Actually, some carnivores, such as the giant panda, are not known to eat flesh, while some members of other orders, such as the marsupials, the insectivores, even the rodents, do so. Nevertheless, the simple definition seems to serve as well as any. Carnivores of some sort are indigenous in most parts of the world except Australia and New Zealand, the Canidae, Felidae, and Mustelidae being especially extensive in distribution. In size they range from the great brown bears of Alaska to the comparatively diminutive weasels.

FAMILY CANIDAE
WOLVES, WILD DOGS, FOXES, ETC.

Long, sharp muzzles, more or less bushy tails, erect ears, and strong, non-retractile claws make the members of the family easily recognized. They are generally cursorial in habit and carnivorous in diet, although fruit and plant materials are eaten by some. Pair formations of usually constant nature seem to be the rule, males sharing in the duty of providing food and protection for the young. The distribution of the family approximates that of the order.

The Canidae are of importance to the zoological garden, since many of the species, notably the wolf and the fox, are well known to visitors as past or present factors in local livestock and wild-life economics or through the medium of legend and fable. Most members of the groups are easily maintained, many breed readily, and there is the added advantage that activity is almost equally balanced between day and night. Because of the wide prevalence of dog distemper in this country, all canines arriving here without a definite record of immunization, receive preventive treatment; those born here receive it immediately after weaning.

The wolves (*Canis*) are restricted to the Northern Hemisphere. The range of the gray wolf (*Canis lupus*), in its many races, once included most of North America as well as much of Europe and Asia. Its distribution in America has now become greatly reduced, and it is no longer found in the British Isles and parts of western Europe, although it still exists in Spain and Italy and from Sweden eastward to Sakhalin (Ellerman and Morrison-Scott, 1951). The smaller red wolf (*C. niger*) is found in the wilder parts of the south-central United States.

Wolves live well in captivity and can be useful and instructive exhibits when well shown. Unfortunately, this is not always the case, but two excellent installations come prominently to mind. One is a well-done concrete representation of a rock niche at Skansen, Stockholm. When I saw it last, this inclosure contained a pair of European wolves (*C. l. lupus*) with a litter of puppies 2 or 3 weeks old, plainly visible beneath an over-hanging ledge. This seemed to me an ideal arrangement for a small unit. On a different basis is the superb Wolf Wood at Whipsnade, where a pack of wolves is shown in large twin inclosures, one of which is always out of use. They are thickly planted with straight young pines and floored with thick deposits of dry needles. There are separate pupping dens at the back. Fencing is of 2-inch diamond mesh 7 feet high, with a 2-foot inward overhang at the top. The animals are transferred periodically from one section to the other for sanitary reasons. There is sufficient space to avoid serious fighting, and the glimpses of wolves skulking among the tree trunks are most effective. It was here that Lorenz (1952:185–89) observed the details of dominance and submission in male wolves which he has so well described. In any wire-inclosed exhibit, of course, where concrete flooring is not used, the wire should be run deeply into the ground or a coping of stone or concrete provided to prevent the animals from escaping by burrowing.

In this country, at least, the larger canines are greatly troubled by biting flies which attack their ears during the summer months. Sprays and other repellants are too difficult to apply to be useful, and we have found that the only practical protection lies in darkened shelters in the recesses of which the animals are able to escape their tormentors.

Wolves breed readily in confinement—sometimes too readily—and many American zoological gardens keep small groups of one sex only; even dog wolves that have been reared together or otherwise become familiar with each other get on perfectly well if there are no females about. The reason for this segregation is that surplus wolf pups are not readily disposable, and in quarters roomy enough for a pair but no more the father will not tolerate young males for long after weaning.

Two specimens of the northern Rocky Mountain wolf (*C. l. irremotus*), mother and daughter, are the only representatives of the species kept here at present. These animals are fed an average of 3 pounds of raw horse meat each, daily, the amount varying with the weather. In addition each receives a daily ration of ½ pound of a mixture of chopped raw meat, dog meal, powdered bone, and cod-liver oil. The mixture may be omitted altogether and the meat allowance reduced during hot weather. On the occasions when we have had mothers with young, whole milk has been added to the regular diet. The calcium and vitamin D content of the mixture above is essential if weaned pups are to develop free of rickets.

Since 1902 fifteen litters of various American races of the gray wolf have been born here: three in February, eight in March, three in April, and one as late as May 11. The number of pups per litter ran from 1 to 7, with an average of 3.8. This compares with the average of 5 for eleven births of *C. l. occidentalis*, the Mackenzie Valley wolf, in the Zoological Gardens of London between 1903 and 1929, as given by Zuckerman (1953). Some of these pups must have been of a group which R. I. Pocock, then superintendent, pointed out to me in 1912 as his "cancer-transmitting" family. I recall them well as very pale-colored animals with un-wolflike dark eyes. The gestation period for the gray wolf is given by Asdell (1946) as 63 days. Young and Goldman (1944:97) give the maturity age of males as 3 years and of females as approximately 2 years.

Our best record here for the European wolf (*C. l. lupus*) is 12 years, 5 months, 27 days, after which the animal, still living, was sent away in exchange. A pup received here from Wyoming in 1912 and recorded as a Great Plains wolf (*C. l. nubilus*) lived for 15 years, 7 months, 10 days. The greatest longevity reported by Flower (1931) is 16 years, 3 months, 5 days for an animal of the same race in the National Zoological Park, Washington.

The coyote (*C. latrans*) inhabits open or broken country of western North and Central America from above the Arctic Circle in Alaska to western Costa Rica, many local races having been described. Sometimes known as the prairie wolf, it is smaller and more slender than the true wolf, and less bold in habits.

Coyotes are kept in most American zoological gardens but too often do not meet with great favor, again largely because of the difficulties of surplus disposal. I know of only one proper coyote exhibit in this country, an attractive moated area in the Detroit Zoological Park. Coyotes are usually exhibited here and are kept and fed on the same basis as the true wolves. In quarters of ordinary size, say 10 by 25 feet, our experience has been that coyotes, both male and female, are even less tolerant than wolves of their weaned young. For this reason it is advisable that the pups be removed as soon as they are able to feed for themselves, not only to avoid persecution but to make certain that they receive the necessary intake of vitamins and minerals.

Between 1900 and 1945, nineteen litters of coyotes were born here: one in March, seven in April, and eleven in May, the latest date being May 21. The total number of cubs was 63, the number per litter running from 1 to 7, with an average of 3.3. In the Zoological Gardens of London, Zuckerman (1953) reports fifteen litters born between 1909 and 1937, varying from 1 to 11 pups per birth, with an average of 5. Asdell (1946) gives the period of gestation as 60–65 days.

A coyote received here on November 14, 1899, lived until August 10, 1912, or 12 years, 8 months, 27 days, while an albino specimen survived for 5 years, 6 months, 8 days. Flower (1931) lists 14 years, 5 months, 2 days for a coyote in the National Zoological Park. Manville (1953) reports just over 15 years for a specimen kept at Michigan State College, this and companion animals having been the subjects of investigations of food preferences and breeding habits (Whiteman, 1940). The greatest known longevity for the species appears to be 15 years, 10 months recorded by Mann (1930) for a coyote in the National Zoological Park.

The jackals, widely distributed in the Old World, have long been the subjects of doubt and uncertainty because of confusion concerning their relations to each other. However, it is now generally agreed that there are three species, each with numerous races (Allen, 1939; Ellerman and Morrison-Scott, 1951). The Asiatic or golden jackal (*C. aureus*) extends from southeastern Europe eastward to Siam and south through Africa to Kenya; the black-backed jackal (*C. mesomelas*) is found in East Africa from Somaliland to the Cape and South West Africa; the side-striped jackal (*C. adustus*), largest of the group, inhabits much of Africa from Ethiopia and the Cameroons southward.

In habits the jackals are much like the coyote, preying on such small game as they can capture and invading farmyards where these are available. The Asiatic jackal, at least, has become so conditioned to the presence of man that it freely enters villages at night to perform its function as scavenger. All jackals are known for their habit of being on hand, along with vultures and other bone-pickers, for their share of what may be left over from the kills of more powerful predators.

Jackals seem to be kept quite generally in European zoological gardens but are not frequently imported into this country. However, we have had both the Asiatic and the black-backed here and have found them to do very well in summer in runs approximately 8 by 20 feet with open shelters attached. It seems quite likely that both species might endure fairly low temperatures without heat, but rather than expose them to the deep cold that sometimes prevails here, we have always moved them indoors for the winter. In addition to the usual meat diet, jackals here have been given dog biscuit, rats, chicken heads, and an allowance of fruit and cooked vegetables for such individuals as will eat them.

Our only experience in breeding jackals was with a litter of black-backed born on February 27, 1910. The young did not survive for long, and unfortunately their number was not recorded. Zuckerman (1953) lists five births of this species in the Zoological Gardens of London, occurring in March and April, the average number of young being two. Zuckerman also reports two litters of side-striped jackals born in London, one each in March and April, the respective number of young being one and three. Haagner (1920:43) gives the gestation periods for two litters of this species born in the National Zoological Garden of South Africa as 57 and 60 days, respectively. In an account of the Asiatic jackal in the Zoological Gardens of Calcutta, Sányál (1892) says that "[Asiatic] jackals have never been bred in captivity." However, Zuckerman lists numerous births in London, dating from 1850. Births have been reported at Vincennes, 1956; Tokyo, 1959; San Diego, 1960; and doubtless elsewhere.

The Asiatic jackal has lived here for 9 years, 2 months, and the black-backed for 9 years, 21 days. Because of the confusion of names, the jackal longevities of Flower (1931) are difficult to unravel, but he gives definite records of 14 years, 7 months, 7 days for the Egyptian (*C. aureus lupaster*) and 13 years, 8 months, 3 days for the black-backed, both in the Zoological Gardens of London. Sányál (1892) says that a specimen of the Asiatic jackal received at the Calcutta Zoological Gardens in 1876 was still living at the time of writing, a period of approximately 16 years.

The dingo (*C. dingo*) of Australia is an animal of particular interest, its existence in the land of marsupials having long been the subject of speculation. It is generally agreed nowadays that the dingo must have been brought to Australia as the companion of very early human immigrants, presumably from the Malayan region (Troughton, 1951). It is supposed that it eventually became feral, finally becoming established over most of Australia. Following settling of the country by white men, the dingo proved a scourge on the great sheep stations of the interior, and bounties were offered for its destruction. Great numbers were destroyed by professional "doggers," so that the true dingo has now become scarce except in the most remote areas.

A rather tall, rangy animal with prick ears, somewhat bushy tail, and coarse hair of yellowish brown, the dingo is well known to zoo visitors everywhere. Early writers described the dingo as being red or black and marked with white, and it is true today that many zoo specimens have white legs, tail-tips, or even facial blazes and are further disfigured by hanging ears and tail curled over the back. Perhaps a plea for an upstanding solid red dog with strongly erect ears and thickly haired tail carried well down is a plea for a false image. But at least such an animal, even with a touch of white on a toe or two, is not an eyesore. How beautiful a really good dingo can be is shown in a photograph of a dog bred in England from Australian stock, published by Finn (1907). With a bit of polishing, our present pair, received from the Taronga Zoological Park, Sydney, in 1954, would not be far behind!

At the latitude of New York the dingo is perfectly hardy if provided with a snug but unheated shelter and has endured temperatures here as low as $-14°$F. (approximately $-25.5°$C.). To prevent digging and to promote sanitation, we use smoothly troweled concrete or macadam for the floors of runs. Feeding is as suggested for jackals, as many individuals will take vegetables and fruit in addition to meat and dog meal or biscuit.

In captivity the dingo breeds freely and with some degree of mateship. I have not noticed the persecution of weaned young that is likely to occur with rather closely confined wolves and coyotes, but we have always removed the young when they were a few months old.

Between 1933 and 1955 six litters of dingos were born here; two in January, two in February, one in March, and one in December. Numbers of pups per birth ranged from 1 to 9, with an average of 3.7. Zuckerman (1953) reports on forty-three births in the Zoological Gardens of London between 1830 and 1936, with an average per litter of 4.1. The gestation period is usually given as 63 days (Asdell, 1946).

A female dingo lived here for 13 years, 1 month, 7 days, while Flower (1931) reports 12 years, 10 months, 24 days in the Zoological Gardens of London. Mann (1930) gives 14 years, 9 months for a specimen in the National Zoological Park.

The place of the domestic dog in the genus (*Canis*) is undisputed, and the name *C. familiaris* assigned by Linnaeus in 1758 serves as a convenient handle, but the exact origin of the animal remains obscure. Much has been written concerning its possible ancestors, but knowledge has advanced little beyond the conclusions of Darwin (1868) and Mivart (1890) to the effect that it had a multiple origin from various canid ancestors, including the wolf, the jackal (notably races of *C. aureus*), and other locally available species such as the coyote in North America. All these animals are known to have produced hybrids, usually fertile, with domestic dogs (Gray, 1954). In this connection the comments of Lorenz (1952) concerning the characteristics of dogs which he considers to be of predominantly wolf or jackal descent are of special interest. The dingo has a place in the picture, too, for not only does it represent a primitive type but also it appears to have influenced the development of Australian breeds as well as the domestic dogs of nearby islands (Mivart, 1890). The village dogs of southeastern New Guinea are black or yellow, self-colored or pied with white. Although rather slim, they otherwise resemble dingos and, like them, do not bark. I have a clear recollection of an old, solid-yellow dog, grown paunchy with age and with a definite aversion to white men, that would pass anywhere as a dingo. Incidentally, these animals practically never receive animal protein but live almost entirely on a diet of coconut meat, sweet potato, taro, and boiled banana, which may account for their usual slenderness (Crandall, 1931).

The Arctic fox (*Alopex*) is circumpolar in distribution, usually keeping to the north of the tree line, the numerous races being assigned to *Alopex lagopus* (Ellerman and Morrison-Scott, 1951; Hall and Kelson, 1959). The typical animal is white in winter, changing to grayish brown for the brief Arctic summer. There is also a blue phase, bearing much the same relation to the white fox as the silver does to the red, which maintains its slate-blue in winter and assumes a grayish brown coat for the warmer months. Pelage changes in the Arctic fox have been described and figured by Pocock (1912).

In or near its own habitat the Arctic fox is obviously a hardy animal, following the polar bear at a respectful distance, jackal fashion, feasting on the occasional beached whale, and hunting birds and rodents, which it often hides in cold storage during periods of abundance. Arctic foxes are farmed to some extent in Alaska and its islands, as well as in other northern areas. Since pelts of the blue phase are more valuable than those of the white, strains have been developed by selection for the production of that color (Ashbrook, 1925, 1928).

At the latitude of New York and presumably farther south, experience in zoo maintenance of the Arctic fox has not been satisfactory. We have always supposed that inability to withstand high temperatures was the basic cause, but a check of our records shows that of a total of twenty-six deaths here, only eight occurred during June, July, and August, when the greatest extreme of heat is usually reached. Arctic foxes have been fed here on whole raw meat, raw fish, a mixture of dog biscuit, chopped raw meat, bone meal and cod-liver oil, and cooked and raw vegetables. No young have been born here, but Ashbrook (1925) gives the gestation period as 51–52 days followed by the birth of from one to fourteen pups from late April to June.

An Arctic fox of the blue phase lived here for 7 years, 1 month, 8 days. Flower (1931) reports a specimen destroyed at the Belle Vue Zoo, Manchester, "at the age of fourteen."

The red fox (*Vulpes*), legendary symbol of slyness and trickery, has a wide distribution; *Vulpes fulva*, in its many races, covers most of North America north of Mexico while the numerous forms of the Old World species, *V. vulpes*, extend over Europe and Asia to Japan, as well as to the fringe of North Africa above the Sahara. In spite of constant persecution by sportsmen, fur hunters, and defenders of the farmyard, the red fox continues to hold its own over most of its range. In America, besides the normal red pattern, at least three other color phases occur, all melanistic: the cross, a somewhat sooty red that carries stripes of black on back and shoulders, the black, and the silver, all retaining the white tail-tip. Increasing value of silver skins in the fur market led to efforts to domesticate animals of this color, the first successes having been achieved in 1894 by Robert T. Oulton and Charles Dalton on Prince Edward Island in the Gulf of St. Lawrence (Dearborn, 1915). Silver foxes are now bred extensively in northern areas of both North America and Europe. Methods followed on fox farms are described in detail by Dearborn (1915), Ashbrook (1923, 1928), and many others.

An important development of feeding practices on fox farms was the discovery that the enzyme thiaminase, an antivitamin found in carp and some other fishes, when fed to foxes in the raw state inactivates vitamin B_1 (thiamine) and causes a polyneuritic condition known as Chastek paralysis (Green and Shillinger, 1936; Green, Evans, and Carlson, 1937). The Atlantic herring (*Clupea harengus*) was reported by Wolf (1942) to contain thiaminase, a finding confirmed by Yudkin (1945). Cooking destroys thiaminase, and animals already affected by B_1 deficiency can be helped with brewer's yeast (Gorham, 1956). An extensive literature of the subject has been built up, and numerous references are listed by Halloran (1955). These findings are of great importance in the feeding of all captive fish-eaters, and references will be made to them where indicated.

In both American and European zoological gardens, red foxes, like too many other readily obtainable species, are not taken seriously. Those seen are usually pet animals that have grown out of hand and have been turned over to the zoo, which keeps them if it must. Foxes do have an advantage in temperament, so that numbers can be kept together in reasonably roomy quarters without serious quarreling. At one time the usual practice was followed here, gift foxes being accepted as they were offered and added to the group already living in a paved inclosure about 40 by 75 feet. This run was well shaded and provided with shelter boxes, so that the animals did perfectly well, and with daily hosing of the concrete floor odors were kept at a minimum. However, as might be expected, no young were ever born in this changing group, and it finally became obvious that something must be done in the interests of better exhibition.

The first step was to initiate firm refusal of unwanted gift foxes, always a difficult attitude for zoo management to take and maintain. We then accepted a beautiful silver vixen and let her wait, unmated, until a suitable young red was offered. These two animals were established in a fully inclosed area about 15 feet square, with a rock background and floor of sand over earth, and provided with hidden shelter boxes and scattered shrubbery. Here they bred yearly, looking carefully after their young—all cross foxes and making an excellent exhibit. The same problem of disposal holds for foxes as for many of their relatives. They do not seem to persecute their young, but since these will mate and produce young of their own in the spring following their birth, disposal is essential.

Foxes are fed here on small strips of raw meat, a mixture of dog meal, bone meal and cod-liver oil, and some fruit, especially diced apples and grapes. Mice, sparrows, and chicken heads, of course, are always well received.

Red foxes are usually born in April or May, after a gestation period commonly given as 51–52 days (Dearborn, 1915; Ashbrook, 1923). The number of cubs born here, per litter, has ranged from 3 to 6, with an average of 4.6.

A red fox (*V. fulva*) was accidentally killed after having lived here for 9 years, 4 months. Mann (1930) gives 10 years for *V. fulva* in the National Zoological Park. Flower (1931) reports 12 years, 21 days for *V. fulva* and 9 years, 9 months, 21 days for a white specimen of *V. vulpes*, both in the Zoological Gardens of London.

The kit and swift foxes, big-eared and pale in color, are the smallest of the New World foxes and usually are assigned to two species, *Vulpes velox*, the swift, and *V. macrotis*, the longer-eared kit, although Hall and Kelson (1959) suggest that the distinction may be only subspecific. Desert or at least arid regions are their preferred habitat, *velox* ranging

from New Mexico and Texas north to southwestern Canada, while
macrotis, in at least eight forms, is found from Baja California and northern
Mexico through much of the southwestern United States as far north as
southeastern Oregon. These little creatures are so extremely shy that they
are seldom seen. Once quite abundant, they are now thought to have
become much reduced in numbers, but observations are not easily made.
They are known to feed largely on small rodents as well as on snakes,
lizards, and insects.

Swift and kit foxes kept here have lived in the same sort of outdoor
inclosure as that described for the red fox. Both species are quite hardy,
and our specimens occupied these quarters throughout the year. Food
consisted of whole raw meat and a mixture of dog meal, bone meal, and
cod-liver oil with a little fruit, although the latter apparently has not been
established as part of the natural diet.

Neither has been bred here, and the only captivity records I have found
are one reported by Stott (1954a) for the desert kit fox (*V. macrotis arsipus*)
in the San Diego Zoological Garden, and one for *Vulpes velox* in the
National Zoological Park (Mann, 1930). The gestation period appears to
be undetermined.

Our best longevities for either species, established by three specimens
recorded as *Vulpes velox*, are 11 years, 4 months, 19 days; 12 years,
8 months, 17 days; and 12 years, 9 months, 13 days. Mann (1930) gives
10 years, 4 months for a specimen of the same species in the National
Zoological Park.

Smallest and most beautiful of the foxes is the fennec (*Fennecus zerda*),
a tiny, sand-colored creature with ears that are enormous, even for a fox.
The fennec is a dweller in the desert and lives in such regions in North
Africa from Morocco to the Sudan and across the Sinai Peninsula to
Arabia. Like many other desert animals, it is largely nocturnal, spending
the hours of greatest heat in its burrow and emerging at night to hunt the
mice, lizards, and insects on which it preys, making up for any scarcity
with such fruit as it can find.

In captivity the fennec fox has a reputation for delicacy. It seems probable
that much of the difficulty has been occasioned by lack of appreciation of
the fact that while the fennec is a basically gentle animal, it is also extremely
shy, making friends with its keepers only after its confidence has been
gained through a period of cautious advances. Until this happy situation
has been achieved, there is always risk of loss.

A female received here on August 17, 1953, had reached this stage well before her death on November 2, 1961, and was a most engaging little creature.

In summer she was kept out of doors in a cage like that described above for red foxes, where she spent most of the day curled up in a rock niche. In winter we took her indoors, not daring to risk a test of hardiness. Her food consisted of small strips of raw meat, a mixture of dog meal, milk powder, raw egg, bone meal, and cod-liver oil, diced bananas, apples, and grapes, and an occasional mouse or young rat.

Perhaps because of its extreme shyness, the fennec is seldom bred in captivity, and records are few. Nouvel (1952) recounts the birth of three young in the Zoological Park of Vincennes in May, 1950, all, unfortunately, devoured by the mother. The female noted above as having been received here in 1953 was born and reared in that year at the Zoo Wassenaar, Holland. Otto Koenig of the Biological Station at Wilhelminenberg, Vienna, has informed me (*in litt.*) that a birth occurred there in 1955, followed by two each in 1957 and 1958, only two young from the last litter having been safely reared. At the Tierpark Krefeld, Germany, a cub born on May 17, 1958, was fully reared (Günter Voss, *in litt.*). These notes give added importance to four births occurring in the Philadelphia Zoological Garden, the first in 1953 (Ulmer, 1955). This unique breeding pair was received at Philadelphia in 1952. In the following year pregnancy of the female was suspected, and she was removed to a secluded mink breeding cage. Two days later, on June 13, she gave birth to two young, which unfortunately were lost when over a month old by wedging their heads in the ¾-inch wire mesh of the cage. In 1954 a single youngster, born on June 16, was successfully reared in the same apparatus, and in 1955, a litter of three was again reared. A single cub was born in 1958 (Anon., 1958a). Close observation of the condition of the female and her removal to secluded quarters before parturition seem to be the essential points. The gestation period of 51 days given by Jennison (n.d.) is usually quoted. The best longevity record for a fennec fox seems to be 10½ years for a specimen in the Philadelphia Zoological Garden (Fox, 1936), although the 10 years, 5 months, 27 days in the Giza Zoological Gardens given by Flower (1931) is certainly a reasonable approximation.

The gray fox (*Urocyon*) is a smaller animal than the red, with proportionately longer legs. It is readily distinguished by its gray upper parts and the reddish markings on head, neck, and legs. Of the mainland species (*Urocyon cinereoargenteus*), the many races extend from southern Canada over most of the United States and Mexico south to northwestern South America. From various islands of the Santa Barbara group, off the coast of southern California, several races of a diminutive species, *U. littoralis*, have been described. The gray fox prefers wooded country, where it frequently ascends the trees. It is largely nocturnal and feeds on small mammals, birds, lizards, and various fruits. The species is well established within the limits of the city of New York and not infrequently invades the Zoological Park.

As far as American zoological gardens are concerned, the position of the gray fox is much the same as that of the red. Serious efforts to exhibit it properly are seldom made, and animals shown are usually those received only by chance. Caging and feeding here have been on the basis given for the red fox.

It seems probable that the gray fox has been bred in captivity more successfully than indicated by the only definite records I have been able to find. These are one each for the California gray fox (*U. cinereoargenteus californicus*) and the San Clemente gray fox (*U. littoralis clementae*) in the San Diego Zoological Garden (Stott, 1954*a*). The gestation period is given by Asdell (1946) as about 63 days.

A specimen of *U. cinereoargenteus* has lived here for 10 years, 5 months, 18 days. Flower (1931) gives 8 years, 5 months for a fox of the same species in the Zoological Gardens of London. I am informed by Miss Hattie Ettinger, administrative assistant, St. Louis Zoological Park (*in litt.*), that two specimens of the Guatemalan gray fox (*U. c. guatemalae*) received at that institution in April, 1944, were still living July 6, 1955, a period of at least 11 years, 3 months.

The raccoon-like dog (*Nyctereutes procyonoides*) is a small, grayish animal, usually with buffy flanks and with a black facial mask which is the basis for its name. While the legs are rather short, it stands well up on them, and the tail, of course, is not ringed. Distribution extends from eastern Siberia to northern Indochina and Japan. Several races have been described (Ellerman and Morrison-Scott, 1951), but there is much individual variation—albino and albinistic specimens have been exhibited here.

Previous to World War I, the raccoon-like dog was fairly frequently imported into this country, but from 1914 to 1945 it was seldom seen. Since the latter date, however, there have been a number of arrivals, mostly from Japan, and many American zoological gardens now exhibit the species. The animal is entirely hardy, and in the type of inclosure described as in use here for the red fox, will give satisfactory results, even though the species is largely nocturnal. Those kept here have been fed fish, for which they seem to have an especial fondness, whole raw meat, the usual mixture of chopped raw meat, dog meal, bone meal, and cod-liver oil, as well as peeled bananas and grapes. This diet is in accord with the scant reports of the natural food (Allen, 1938, 1:349).

Zuckerman (1953) lists the frequently mentioned litter of seven born in the Zoological Gardens of London in May, 1877. A litter of eight was born here in April, 1915, and a second birth of two cubs occurred here in June, 1918. More recent records are the rearing of a single cub in the Philadelphia Zoological Garden in 1950 (Anon., 1954a) and successful breeding in the Lincoln Park Zoological Gardens, Chicago, in 1952. The average gestation periods listed by Kenneth (1953) range from 59 to 79 days.

Flower (1931) records a longevity of 5 years, 10 months, 25 days for one of the raccoon-like dogs born in the Zoological Gardens of London in 1877. Two of our specimens, both received when adult, established almost identical spans: 9 years, 4 months, 6 days, and 9 years, 4 months, 21 days.

The South American wild dogs are comparatively small, jackal-like, grayish creatures, sometimes with an infusion of reddish. Many species and races have been described, and the nomenclature is much confused. Designations used here are those of Cabrera (1957).

Four specimens of the now extinct Antarctic "wolf," *Dusicyon australis*, of the Falkland Islands were exhibited in the Zoological Gardens of London, the last individual dying on March 2, 1876, after having lived there for 5 years, 3 months, 24 days (Flower, 1931). The Andean wild dog (*D. culpaeus*), known locally as *lobo* or wolf, is now the largest living member of the group, although its size hardly justifies its popular name. In a number of races, it inhabits the slopes of the Andes from Ecuador to the rocky shores of Tierra del Fuego. Much smaller and more familiar in zoological gardens are Azara's wild dog (*D. gymnocercus*), from the pampas regions of Brazil, Paraguay, and Argentina, and the crab-eating wild dog (*Cerdocyon thous*), a dweller in tropical forests from Colombia to Uruguay. Rarest of the group is the small-eared wild dog (*Atelocynus microtis*), from the forests of the basin of the Amazon in Brazil, Ecuador, Peru, and Colombia. The species was described and figured by Sclater (1882) from an animal living in the Zoological Gardens of London. A single specimen received here in poor condition on May 1, 1930, lived only until May 19, 1931, or 1 year, 18 days. The species is discussed by Hershkovitz (1961), and photographs of living specimens in the Chicago Zoological Park are given.

These dogs are often reared from puppyhood by Indians, whose women excel in such matters, and kept about their villages as pets. When such specimens reach the zoological garden, as they sometimes do, good longevity results may be expected. On the other hand, animals captured as adults are usually shy and difficult. While it is presumable that forms such as *culpaeus*, from the Andes and the extreme south, would prove hardy at this latitude, we have never risked any out of doors in winter, so that they have alternated between outdoor runs in summer and smaller heated quarters during the colder months. In addition to whole raw meat, the mixture of chopped raw meat, dog meal, bone meal, and cod-liver oil and such rats and mice as might be available, many, especially the more tropical forms such as *thous*, will take fruit, particularly banana.

The South American wild dogs seem seldom to have been bred in captivity, although two litters of Azara's (*D. gymnocercus*) born in the Zoological Gardens of London, of four and one young, respectively, are reported by Zuckerman (1953). The gestation period appears to be unknown.

TABLE 7
LONGEVITIES OF SOUTH AMERICAN WILD DOGS

	London*		
	Years	Months	Days
Dusicyon culpaeus	8	4	18
D. gymnocercus	9	1	12
D. griseus	7	5	14
	New York†		
D. culpaeus	7	9	5
D. gymnocercus	7	9	10
D. griseus	4	5	7
Cerdocyon thous	10	1	16

*Flower, 1931.
†Crandall.

The maned wolf (*Chrysocyon brachyurus*) is not only the largest of the South American canids but much the most beautiful as well. Its body size is comparable to that of a small wolf—Cabrera and Yepes (1940) give the length of the head and body as 125 centimeters or about 4 feet—but the bright bay color, large ears, and sharp nose are more suggestive of the fox. Actually, the extremely long, slender legs dispel the illusion of resemblance to either animal. The long hair rises to a crest on the neck and shoulders, giving the maned wolf its name. It inhabits open grassy areas with broken patches of brush and trees extending from northern Argentina across Paraguay to southern Brazil.

The maned wolf is among the rarities greatly sought by zoological gardens. It has seldom been imported into this country and was not received by the New York Zoological Park until 1962. In 1951 a fine pair was shown in the Antwerp Zoological Gardens in a large wire-inclosed run with unheated shelter attached, in which they spent most of the daylight hours. I was informed by the keeper in charge that the daily food for each animal consisted of a freshly killed pigeon and twelve peeled bananas, the latter given in two meals. I was also told that this regimen was sometimes varied with liver, but that muscle meat, if taken, was invariably regurgitated, and that milk and eggs were refused altogether. The diet is in general accord with the natural one, as outlined by Cabrera and Yepes (1940). During cold weather the animals were confined to the shelter, although no heat was provided. The precaution seems wise in view of the tropical and semitropical distribution of the species.

Of four maned wolves received at the San Diego Zoological Garden in 1951, three provided comparatively good longevities, and one female produced three litters of puppies which, while none was successfully reared, appear to be the only young of their kind that have been bred in captivity. In a letter dated November 26, 1956, George H. Pournelle, curator of mammals at San Diego, has provided full information concerning these animals, summarized as follows:

Two males, one of which lived only a few days, were received on September 16, 1951. On October 9, 1951, two females, one of which had a defective eye, were obtained. The three animals were kept together and at first would take only bananas. Later they were induced to take cubed horse meat, and as they began gradually to refuse bananas, that item was finally eliminated from the diet. On February 13, 1953, a litter of three was born, but the puppies were neglected by the mother and soon died, as reported by Benchley (1954). On January 7, 1954, the birth of a second litter of three occurred, but the young survived for only 2 days. Preceded by the death of the male parent on December 12, 1954, a third litter, consisting of one male and two females, was born on December 30, 1954. The male puppy lived only a few hours, while the two females, accepted by a nursing mongrel bitch, lived until January 4 and 6, 1955, respectively. An account of this event, with photographs, has been published (Anon., 1955a). All these births were to the female with normal vision.

The breeding female died on March 12, 1956, her death being preceded by that of the practically blind female on March 3, 1956. These dates work out to the following longevities for the three San Diego animals: the breeding male, 3 years, 2 months, 26 days; the non-breeding female, 4 years, 4 months, 22 days; the breeding female, 4 years, 5 months, 3 days. Flower (1931) says of the maned wolf that "no records of its having lived to even 5 years in captivity have been found." Mann (1945) reports the death of a maned wolf after it had lived in the National Zoological Park for 10 years, 6 months, certainly a remarkable span.

The South American bush dog (*Speothos venaticus*) is an almost complete antithesis of the maned wolf, with short legs, large head, and tail so brief that it appears to have been docked. The body coloration is dark brown, with shoulders, neck, and head light reddish-yellow and the tail, legs, and underparts black. Its range covers forested areas from Colombia to Paraguay. A second species, having the anterior portions of the body whitish, has been described from Panama by Goldman (1912) as *Icticyon* (= *Speothos*) *panamensis*. The following notes refer entirely to *venaticus*, as I find no records of *panamensis* in captivity.

Furtive and reputedly almost entirely nocturnal, the bush dog's habits in nature are little known, although they are well represented in Indian folklore. Many of these tales have been gathered together by Bridges (1954). Small though it is, the bush dog appears to justify some of these accounts of savagery and is said to follow the paca into the water and to kill it there (Tate, 1931).

The bush dog has always been rare in collections and up to 1953 had been represented here by a single specimen, which lived for only a few weeks. On October 9, 1953, we received a single male, collected in Dutch Guiana by Charles Cordier. This animal, which lived until May 4, 1957, was kept in an indoor cage about 8 feet square with a concrete floor. A wooden sleeping platform was placed in a darkened corner. While three sides of this cage were built of solid materials, the front was 2-inch mesh wire netting. The top, also, was wire covered, for it was found that the animal had the rather surprising ability to climb the wire front to a height of 6 feet and might easily have escaped.

When first received, this bush dog would take only whole raw meat and an occasional rat. After a considerable period of coaxing, he finally accepted the chopped raw meat, dog meal, bone meal, and cod-liver oil mixture. Fruits and vegetables were always refused. He was generally active during most of the day, often coming forward when visitors approached, although he did not allow himself to be touched. As mealtime approached, he scurried eagerly about, whining continuously in a thin, high-pitched voice.

In 1912 I was shown two bush dogs in the Amsterdam Zoological Gardens by Inspector A. F. J. Portielje, who told me they were "mother and child." I understood then that the young animal had been bred in the Gardens and later reported what I assumed to be the fact (Crandall, 1921). However, later efforts to obtain confirmation were not fully satisfactory, so that the record must remain in doubt. With this dubious exception, there appear to be no records of the breeding of the species in captivity until the birth of four puppies in the San Diego Zoological

Garden on January 7, 1954. The parents, collected by Charles Cordier, arrived in the same shipment as our single arrival of 1953. Two of the puppies, reported to have been ejected from the den by the mother when two weeks old, died from exposure (Stott, 1954*b*). The survivors were successfully reared by hand (Stott, 1954*a*). A female bush dog that arrived here on April 20, 1960, was paired with a male received in 1958 and produced a litter of six on October 20, 1961, after a definite gestation period of 65 days. Unfortunately, none survived for more than 2 days.

Mann (1930) reports 4 years, 8 months for a bush dog in the National Zoological Park. One of the puppies reared at San Diego in 1954 was still living in the Philadelphia Zoological Garden in July, 1961, having already established a longevity in excess of $7\frac{1}{2}$ years.

The dhole or Asiatic wild dog (*Cuon alpinus*) ranges, in several races, from eastern Siberia across most of Asia to Java and Sumatra. The general coloration is in shades of red, but there is much variation, as described in detail by Pocock (1936*a*). Dholes are primarily forest animals, sometimes living at high elevations. After the breeding season they hunt in packs, presumably formed by family parties or by the junction of such groups, and are reported as able to kill animals as large as domestic water buffaloes. Widely distributed but shy and furtive, dholes are so secretive that they are seldom encountered. The following notes, supplied to me by T. Donald Carter, assistant curator of mammals at the American Museum of Natural History, New York, are therefore of special interest:

November 11, 1934. Near Cheng Wei, on Chengu Creek, 25 miles west of Wenchuan, Szechuan, W. China, between 6,000 and 7,000 feet. Our camp was pitched in a deep valley facing a high cliff directly across the stream and steep forested mountain slopes behind us. It had been cold with some snow on the mountain sides and ice along the stream. We were up before daylight and were eating our breakfast beside a welcome fire just as dawn was breaking. Wong, our most experienced hunter, suddenly held up a finger for silence and far up the mountainside we heard a series of whining yelps. Wong said, "Wild dogs hunting, they are running after some animal." The sound came closer until it sounded from the forest almost directly over the cliff. Suddenly the sound changed to sharper, more excited "yaps." Wong jumped to his feet and from his gestures we inferred that the dogs had brought their quarry to bay and were attacking. Wong grabbed a gun, waded the icy stream and started climbing the cliff. That climb was too much for me so I went upstream and crossed over where a smaller stream had cut a small valley down the mountainside. By the time I had reached the top of the cliff Wong was no-where to be seen but I soon heard his call from farther up the mountain. I found him standing over the body of a large male serow. There was some hair scattered about, one of the front legs was quite badly mutilated and an eye was gouged out but otherwise the animal seemed in good condition. We skinned it and brought its skin and skull back to the Museum. Wong said that the dogs had killed the serow before he had arrived and that he had had a fleeting glimpse of two of the animals. It was evident that the serow was endeavoring to reach the cliff, where he would have a much better chance of defending himself, but the dogs overtook him before he could reach its safety.

Dholes have seldom been imported into this country. A single specimen of the Javan dhole (*Cuon a. javanicus*), the only representative of the species to have been received here, arrived on April 26, 1934, and survived for just under 1 year. It was fed as outlined for the red fox (p. 277).

Zuckerman (1953) records four births of the Indian dhole (*C.* [*a.*] *dukhunensis*) in the Zoological Gardens of London between 1833 and 1927, the average number of young per litter being 3.5. Steinmetz (1940) figures 4 of a litter of 7 Javan dholes born in the Zoological Gardens of Berlin. Blanford (1888–91) says the gestation period is "probably about 2 months," which is frequently quoted; Asdell (1946) gives it as 63 days.

While captive dholes in general have not given satisfactory results— Sányál (1892) says "they do not appear to thrive well in captivity"—Flower (1931) gives two creditable longevities. These are 6 years, 6 months, 10 days for the Javan in the Zoological Gardens of London and 9 years for the Indian in the Trivandrum Zoological Gardens. M. L. Jones (1958) reports 11 years, 1 month, 14 days for a Sumatran dhole (*C. a. sumatrensis*) in the National Zoological Park.

The Cape hunting dog (*Lycaon pictus*) was once found over most of Africa, except for the desert areas of the north and the heavily forested regions of the west. Because of its serious depredations on domestic stock, it has been extirpated or at least greatly reduced in numbers in the more settled parts of its former range. A great number of races have been described, but Allen (1939) has synonymized these to seven.

The general coloration is in blotches of black, gray, white, and yellow, so greatly varied that two animals exactly alike could hardly be found. These markings are somewhat suggestive of the spotted hyena (*Crocuta crocuta*), so that, while there is no relationship, the hunting dog is sometimes known as the hyena dog. A swift, relentless hunter, usually in packs, the hunting dog pulls down and devours the largest antelopes and is execrated by sportsmen and farmers wherever it still exists.

Although never a common species in captivity, the hunting dog has been kept from time to time by many institutions. Those shown here have had the freedom of large, paved outdoor runs in summer and have been confined to roomy, heated indoor cages during the winter. While certainly not inclined to be friendly, they are not particularly aggressive toward keepers or cage mates. Our specimens have been fed whole raw meat and also have taken the mixture of chopped raw meat, dog meal, bone meal, and cod-liver oil without hesitation.

Births of hunting dogs in captivity have occurred fairly often, several instances being enumerated by Windecker (1955). However, the young have seldom been successfully reared. Windecker reports on three litters of 9, 7, and 13 young, respectively, born to the same female in the Zoological Gardens of Cologne. None was reared by the mother, but 4 survived after having been given to mongrel bitches. They were removed from the foster mothers at 46 days and fed chopped meat, milk, and veal boiled with the bone. They were carried to 118 days, at least, and may have been fully reared. Windecker says that while the young were handleable up to the age of 110 days, they then became dangerous. He feels that "it is impossible to tame this animal."

A pair of hunting dogs was received here on August 8, 1941. On April 22, 1942, four puppies were born in a shallow straw-filled box, about three feet square, set in a darkened corner of the indoor cage. The birth had been anticipated and the male removed in advance as a precaution. (Hediger [1955] says the males "have no obligations whatever during the birth of the young.") The mother seemed to care for the puppies well, but one died on May 5, another on May 20, and a third on September 23. The fourth was fully reared but died of distemper on June 9, 1943.

On December 5, 1942, a second litter of eleven young was born, but while the father and the young female from the previous litter had been removed, all the puppies died within 6 days. Conditions seemed to be exactly the same, and we were able to find no explanation for this complete failure.

All hopes of breeding from this pair came to an abrupt end in June, 1943, when the parents and the young female, noted above, all succumbed to distemper. Following this disaster, our present policy of immunizing all canids against distemper immediately after arrival was initiated, and there have been no further outbreaks.

Since 1956 births and successful rearing of hunting dogs, once so unusual, have occurred so frequently in this country that surplus animals have actually become almost indisposable. In that year, on December 3, a litter of six was born at the San Diego Zoological Garden followed by another of the same number on December 12 at the Chicago Zoological Park. Further births occurred at San Antonio and Philadelphia in 1958 and at Washington in 1959.

On April 2, 1959, a pair of hunting dogs born at the San Antonio Zoological Park in March, 1958, was received here and placed in the quarters previously occupied by this species. Late in November, 1959, it was obvious that the female was pregnant, and in accordance with previous practice a large, covered nesting box with a single entrance was installed and the male was removed to the adjoining cage. The first birth occurred on November 25. The female did not lick the pup but took it in her mouth and leaped excitedly against the partition, solid below, wired above, that separated her from her mate. After perhaps an hour the male was admitted and went directly to the pup which, already dead, had been placed on the floor by the mother. He licked and mouthed it but finally abandoned it. Five further young were born at intervals on the bare floor of the cage. Successive puppies received no attention from the mother, but each was carefully cleaned and gently mouthed by the father. It was then picked up and carried into the nest box by the mother. The birth completed, she then showed intolerance of the male and he was run into the adjoining cage, but with the door left open. In following days the female sometimes visited him there, but he was obviously not welcome in her compartment and was never allowed to enter the nest box. On November 30 a dead puppy was carried to the male's cage by the mother and left there, but the male took no notice of it. On the morning of December 9, when the four surviving puppies were 14 days old, the eyes of all were found to have opened. On that day one stumbled out of the box. The male rushed into the cage, presumably bent on rescue, but this intrusion so disturbed the mother that she drove him back into his cage, the door of which was then closed. As long as this arrangement continued the animals remained calm, but if the male was moved while his cage was serviced, both became agitated, calling to each other in their strange, hooting voices.

By December 20 the puppies were coming out to the cage floor, where they were nursed by the mother. Early in January, 1960, they began taking chopped raw meat and dog meal in milk. During the weaning period they were frequently fed by the mother by regurgitation. On January 27 they were no longer nursing and were separated from the mother, wormed, and immunized. The parents were then reunited.

Although no further evidence of pregnancy was observed, on the morning of December 6, 1960, the female was seen carrying a puppy in her mouth. The nesting box had been removed, but when a bundle of hay was placed in a corner, the animals at once curled up on it together. Three more puppies were born; however, during the night, apparently disturbed by dingos in the adjoining outdoor run, the parents devoured all of the young.

Various authorities quoted by Shortridge (1934, 1: 185–86), as well as numerous others, consider the normal number of young per litter to be from two to six, and it is generally thought that when more occur they have been produced by two or more mothers occupying the same den. The litters of nine, eleven, and thirteen young noted above, all produced by single females under control, suggest the desirability of further study in nature.

Our best longevity for a hunting dog was established by a male received October 25, 1911, which lived until October 11, 1919, or 14 days short of 8 years. Flower (1931) gives 10 years, 1 month, 27 days in the Dublin Zoological Gardens, where, he says, the species was bred.

The long-eared or Delalande's fox (*Otocyon megalotis*) inhabits open or partly arid country from Somaliland and Ethiopia diagonally southward to South West Africa. The disproportionately large ears sometimes cause this animal to be confused with the fennec, but the long-eared fox is much darker in its brownish coloration and much larger as well. A number of races have been described, Allen (1939) recognizing four.

This gentle and attractive animal is largely nocturnal in habit. Its food in nature is given by Shortridge (1934) as consisting largely of insects, particularly termites, as well as small rodents, birds, lizards, and fruits. The species has been imported into this country fairly often; in general it has not lived too well. Four specimens have been received here, but none has survived for so long as a year. The diet followed was that outlined as in use here for the fennec and would appear to be reasonably adequate. Haagner (1920) notes a particular fondness for monkey nuts (peanuts), a point probably worth noting.

Better results than ours have been obtained at the National Zoological Park at Washington, where the female of a pair of long-eared foxes, received in 1950, produced a litter of three cubs in the same year and another of two cubs in 1951 (Mann, 1952, 1953). When seen in 1956, the parents and the 1951 cubs, the two pairs kept separately, were in fine condition. Haagner (1920) says that a female in the National Zoological Park of South Africa, at Pretoria, reared several litters of three cubs each. He gives the gestation period as 60 days, while Asdell (1946) gives it as 60–70.

The only longevity given by Flower (1931) is 5 years, 6 months, 9 days, established in the Zoological Gardens of London in the middle of the last century. Some at least of the Washington foxes certainly exceeded this span.

FAMILY URSIDAE

BEARS

So homogeneous are the bears that any given species is instantly recognized as a member of the family. Their obvious distinguishing characters— heavy bodies, short ears, plantigrade feet, and abbreviated tails—apply also to the giant panda (*Ailuropoda*) so aptly that early naturalists knew this strange creature as the parti-colored bear. But aside from this species, no mammal is likely to be confused with the bear, and no bear is likely to be mistaken for something else.

Bears are well distributed in North America, Europe, and Asia. One species, the spectacled, is found in northwestern South America, and Africa seems once to have been represented by the now presumably extinct Crowther's bear of the Atlas Mountains (Harper, 1945).

Much alike as bears are in general characters, there is great variation in size, ranging from the huge brown bears, the world's largest terrestrial carnivores, to the diminutive sun bears of the Malaysian region. Almost all are omnivorous in diet, eating flesh when it can be had and otherwise resorting to fruits, berries, roots, leaves, and even grass. A special fondness for honey seems to be a common trait.

Bears of the north usually pass a period of dormancy in a sheltered nook during the winter months. Males and unmated females occasionally arouse from sleep and wander about, while mothers with newborn young drowsily nurse their helpless offspring. The dormancy of bears is not the deep torpidity of true hibernation, so that they may not be disturbed with impunity. An exception to the rule is the male polar bear, which remains active during the months of deep cold and darkness.

Since the days when bears were used in the gory exhibitions of the Roman arenas, their treatment in captivity has progressed, through the centuries, to a better state. The famous Bear Pit of Berne, dating at least from 1480, was occupied, off and on, up to 1825, another and larger pit coming into use in 1857. It appears that these pits were of historical significance, beyond the mere exhibition of bears, in other Swiss cities as well as in Berne (Loisel, 1912, **1**:230–31; **3**:108–9).

When construction of the Bear Dens in the New York Zoological Park was begun on September 7, 1898, a new era was heralded. Bears were no longer to be housed in pits but would have the run of ample inclosures, fully exposed to fresh air and sunlight, with rocks for climbing, deep pools for bathing, and snug shelters against severe weather. Skeletons of old cedars, dried and seasoned, were set upright in beds of concrete for the benefit of the more agile species. Unaesthetic as the exhibit was, the planners were quite correct in their thinking, for basically these dens provided all, or almost all, that is required. The facts that the nine inclosures, each 70 feet long and 25–30 feet wide, were surrounded by barriers of $\frac{3}{4}$-inch steel bars set on 4-inch centers at the front and 2-inch centers in the partitions, that they were 9 feet high and were surmounted by inside overhangs 2 feet, 6 inches across, did constitute advanced design at that period. Doors of steel, operated from curiously complicated remote control points, confined the animals to their dens for the daily cleaning of runs and pools. Keepers were safe, and bears were living under the best imaginable conditions. Later, when skilful climbers like American black and sloth bears found means for circumventing the overhangs and were able to make nightly forays in the grounds and to return at dawn, great sheets of metal ended their activities but added nothing of beauty. When time and weather finally caused sagging of long runs of bars, they were supported by the addition of unsightly trusses, and when rust and wear ended the operation of the den doors, means were still found for insuring proper care of the animals if not the complete safety of the keepers. Today (1963) all but three of these dens, still in temporary use, have been leveled, ready for reconstruction on another basis. Belatedly, bars of steel are giving way to the open moat.

During the period through which these once superb bear dens functioned, great advances in ideas for the maintenance of this group were made. These stemmed from the innovations of Carl Hagenbeck, developed early in the present century and quickly given world-wide approval. Great mountains of rock-simulating concrete, concealing dens and passages, opening into runs divided by the same construction and separated from the public by broad open moats, soon became central features of many of the great zoological gardens. These structures were extremely costly and in some cases were so large that they completely dominated the gardens around them. On the other hand, they did provide superb exhibits, of great public interest, and at the same time usually included improved operational features that facilitated the care and transfer of the animals and gave complete safety to keepers. At the present time there seems to be a trend in newer construction toward detached, single inclosures as opposed to extended ranges. Excellent examples of this type are to be found in most of the larger American zoological gardens and notably in the beautifully simulated rock dens at Skansen, Stockholm.

Construction of bear dens, whether barriers are to consist of bars or of moats, concrete, and stone, depends largely on available funds. The essentials are effective restraint, a bathing pool, and retiring dens. If these last are accessible from a roomy, concealed service passage from which metal doors can be operated by remote control, so much the better. Floor levels in the exhibit area should vary, and there should be opportunity for climbing. If breeding is contemplated, maternity dens to which the expectant mother can be removed with a minimum of annoyance to the animal should be provided. Such dens must be so arranged that the mother will be completely undisturbed. The alternative, of course, is to remove the male, but absolute quiet is not always assured in an exhibition area. Even the scratching of a male on a den door may cause the female to neglect her cubs or even destroy them.

In most American constructions, widths and depths of bear moats for the larger species are considered to be safe at 14 feet. It is worth noting that in one instance where the original width was 10 feet, 6 inches, a brown bear not fully grown succeeded in escaping—on opening day!—by simply extending itself across the space. After the moat width had been increased to 14 feet, there was no further difficulty. Rough steps or holds on the moat wall, leading up to the exhibit area, will enable the animals to reach the level from the moat, in case of need, and will seldom be used in the opposite direction.

Because of their particularly variable temperaments, bears should never be fully trusted by keepers, and no den or inclosure containing animals should ever be entered. With a proper system of remote control, as already mentioned, by means of which the inmates of one area can easily be moved to another, feeding and cleaning operations can be carried on in complete safety.

The comparatively small spectacled bear (*Tremarctos ornatus*) is found in mountainous areas of western South America, from Colombia and western Venezuela to Bolivia and Peru, at altitudes up to 10,000 feet. It is black in color, with buffy or whitish areas of muzzle, throat, and chest. Narrow, light-colored streaks extend upward around the eyes, suggesting the common name. There is great variation in the extent of these markings, and sometimes they are almost absent. On the other hand, I cannot recall a specimen in which the "spectacles" were complete, although this may sometimes occur. These wide differences have led to the naming of several races, none of which is now considered to be valid (Cabrera, 1957).

The spectacled bear is extensively arboreal, ascending trees freely to obtain the fruits and young shoots which form its principal food. Tate (1931) reports being told by the collector, A. M. Olalla, that the species builds a nest of branches high in a tree, and the same statement is made by Cabrera and Yepes (1940).

The species has always been rare in collections, presumably because of the inaccessibility of its habitat. The first specimen to reach the Zoological Gardens of London was received in 1832 (Flower, 1929), while an animal that arrived at the New York Zoological Park on July 30, 1909, was thought to be the first to be seen alive in this country. Since that time eight others have been kept here, but none of the earlier ones survived for more than a year or two, presumably because the requirements of the species were not fully understood. Not until 1934, when a young spectacled bear was presented, was a fully vegetarian diet provided, with the result that the animal lived for just short of 8 years. This specimen was still living when, on November 12, 1940, another was received. Up to that time it had been considered here that the species should have heat during the winter months. However, since there was then no indoor space available, the new animal was placed in an outside den provided only with a snug but unheated shelter. Here it soon established the fact that the spectacled bear is entirely hardy at this latitude. It died on June 6, 1957, after 16 years, 6 months, 25 days. Flower (1931) gives a longevity of 13 years, 6 months, 24 days for a specimen of this species in the Zoological Gardens of London. Pournelle (1960) reports the remarkable spans of 20 years, 4 months, 5 days and 21 years, 4 months, 18 days for two specimens in the San Diego Zoological Garden.

The food furnished daily for our spectacled bear, a rather large and irascible male, consisted of one quart of reconstituted evaporated milk, eighteen apples, and seven loaves of raisin bread. At one time he took bananas but later rejected all fruits except apples. He never accepted meat or even a mixture of chopped meat and dog meal, although a young animal received in April, 1958, took small quantities of both. Unlike most northern bears, he was remarkably uniform in food intake, showing little seasonal variation. He showed no inclination to become dormant during the winter and was usually abroad, no matter how cold or foul the weather might be.

Concerning births of the spectacled bear in what appears to be a well-established colony in the Zoological Garden of Buenos Aires, Saporiti (1951) gives the gestation period as 8–8½ months, the number of young as one or two, and the times of birth as June, July, and September. I was informed by W. Wendnagel, vice-director, Zoological Gardens of Basel, in a letter of January 28, 1957, that a pregnant female received from a dealer on November 25, 1952, gave birth to three young on February 17, 1953.

The *Annual Report* of the Basel Zoological Gardens for 1959 records the birth of two spectacled bear cubs in that year and a single birth in the Zoological Gardens of Berlin is listed in the *Report* of that institution for 1960.

The Himalayan or Asiatic black bear (*Selenarctos thibetanus*) is a smaller animal than the American black bear (*Euarctos*), with the same black coat and tan muzzle but with a large white crescent on its chest. The hair of neck and shoulders is lengthened, forming a ruff which adds to a general impression of broadness. The range of the species extends, in forested areas, from Baluchistan across most of Asia to eastern Siberia and Japan. Seven races are listed by Ellerman and Morrison-Scott (1951). Those most usually seen in zoological gardens are the typical one, found from Nepal to Annam and to which the common name of the species is generally applied, and the Japanese black bear (*S. t. japonicus*).

Both have been kept here and have proved to be hardy and attractive. They are able climbers and may be capable of escaping from inclosures which safely confine clumsier species. Here they become intermittently dormant during very cold weather, but, like many bears at this latitude, will usually rouse themselves at feeding time, take what they like, and return to their dens.

In spite of the statement by Blanford (1888–91) to the effect that this is the most carnivorous of the Indian bears, Himalayan bears kept here have never taken meat, though I have no evidence that this is general experience. The daily regimen of a female specimen that was received here on April 8, 1936, and died February 10, 1963, consisted of 4 pounds of butterfish (*Poronotus*), 6 pounds of apples, and 3 loaves of bread. This she took with great regularity, regardless of weather conditions.

Neither the Himalayan nor the Japanese black bear has bred here. Reuther (1961) reports that the birth of a single cub of the Japanese race in the Cleveland Zoological Park on January 27, 1961, is believed to have been the first recorded in America, although he also mentions forty-five births as having occurred in Japanese zoological gardens between 1953 and 1961. Two Himalayan black bears are reported to have been born in the St. Paul Zoo, Minnesota, on January 11, 1961 (*Internatl. Zoo News*, 8 [1]:26).

Our best longevity for the species (26 years, 10 months, 2 days) is represented by the female noted above. Flower (1931) gives "about 27 years" in the Mysore Zoological Garden and also lists the report of Sányál (1892) that a specimen living for 15 years in the Calcutta Zoological Gardens had lived in captivity for 18 years before coming to that institution, a total of 33 years. M. L. Jones (1958) gives 26 years, 11 months, 11 days for a Himalayan bear in the National Zoological Park.

The American black bear (*Euarctos americanus*), once found in forested areas of North America from Labrador to southern Alaska and south to Florida and northern Mexico, has been extirpated from parts of its former range but still persists in some numbers in less settled regions. Typically it is a black animal with tan muzzle and occasionally a white spot on the chest. Eighteen races are listed by Hall and Kelson (1959) under the generic title *Ursus*. Numerous color phases occur, the best known of which are shades of cinnamon and brown, found mostly in the West. A nearly white variant known as Kermode's bear (*E. a. kermodei*) appears in a restricted coastal area of British Columbia, while the glacier or blue bear (*E. a. emmonsii*) is found in southeastern Alaska and northeastern British Columbia. A female cub, light bluish-gray in color with tan muzzle and ears, was received here as the gift of the New York State Conservation Department on July 5, 1946 (Crandall, 1946). She had been taken in the Catskill Mountains of New York State, along with two black litter mates, and reared by hand. At the time of her death a year later her coat had become chocolate brown, a change apparently not experienced by the true glacier bear.

The only record of Kermode's bear in captivity appears to be that of an animal in the white phase kept at the Beacon Hill Zoo in Victoria, Vancouver Island, where she is reported to have lived from 1924 to 1950 (Yocum, 1961). At least two specimens of the blue phase of the glacier bear, both from the Yakutat Bay area of Alaska, have been received. One was acquired by the National Zoological Park on July 25, 1917, and is reported by M. L. Jones (1958) to have lived until July 26, 1941. A female cub, presumably born early in 1950, was received at the Detroit Zoological Park on April 14 of that year (Greenhall, 1951). I am indebted to Walter Stone, formerly curator of mammals at that institution, for her subsequent history. Paired to a Michigan black bear of the typical race (*E. a. americanus*), this female produced a single cub on January 10, 1953, two cubs on January 2, 1955, and three on January 29, 1956. All six cubs were black, although the latter three showed scattered silver hairs on muzzle, ears, and body. In 1960, when paired with a black son, only black cubs were produced.

A male glacier bear cub in the black phase, taken June 3, 1955, at Elinor Cove, Yakutat Bay, by Oshin Agathon and presented to us in the same month, was later transferred to the Highland Park Zoological Gardens at Pittsburgh. It was hoped that plans to mate this animal with the blue female at Detroit would result in the production of blue offspring, but breeding could not be accomplished.

Like most of its relatives, the black bear is omnivorous, feeding on fruits, nuts, roots, leaves, young grass, and such fish and small rodents as it may be able to catch. At the same time it is not averse to larger game if available, and individuals may become destructive to domestic stock. In northern areas, at least, both sexes undergo varying periods of dormancy during the winter months.

In this country the black bear is the species most commonly kept in captivity. Since it is an especially skilful climber, extra precautions must be taken to prevent its escape. Barred dens should be topped and possible clawholds carefully avoided in rock or concrete barriers.

Daily food per animal provided here averages 3 pounds of butterfish, 4 pounds of horse meat, and 3 loaves of bread, with apples, carrots, celery, etc., as available. Some regulation of food quantities is required, of course, since there is wide variation in size and weight in this species. Probably 200–300 pounds would represent a fair average for black bears, but much heavier individuals have been recorded. Hornaday (1922) reports the weight of a male from Anticosti Island, Quebec, as 635 pounds, and Hamilton (1953) gives 671 and 680 pounds for specimens from Louisiana and the Yosemite, respectively.

The mating season of black bears occurs in June and July, the young being born in January or February, about 7 months later. Birth occurs while the mother is dormant, and the lightly haired young are very small, with eyes closed. Reventlow (1953) gives the birth weight of the heaviest of four cubs born in the Copenhagen Zoological Gardens as 362 grams (approximately 12.7 ounces) and the lightest as 265 grams (approximately 9.3 ounces). The long apparent gestation period and the comparatively small size of the young suggest delayed implantation of the fertilized ova (see Asdell, 1946). Cubs usually remain with their mothers until the second spring so that young are produced only in alternate years. Young black bears are easily and commonly reared on whole cow's milk heated to body temperature and administered from a nursing bottle. They must, of course, be kept both warm and dry.

Black bears breed readily in captivity, but the managements of few zoological gardens in this country consider it worthwhile to provide suitably isolated quarters for expectant mothers. When this is done, most females rear their young well. The species has been bred here on only one occasion and that purely by accident. A cinnamon male that had been living with a black female since 1942 died suddenly on June 26, 1954. The female continued to occupy the inclosure alone and became dormant with the onset of cold weather. On January 31, 1955, she gave birth to two cubs, indicating a minimum gestation period of 219 days. The two cubs left the den for the first time on April 15, when they were $2\frac{1}{2}$ months old, and were seen nibbling at scraps of meat on April 20. Both were dark cinnamon.

The best longevity for a black bear here is 19 years. The longest span given by Flower (1931) is for a specimen in the Frankfurt Zoological Gardens that was killed by an Asiatic black bear after 25 years, 11 months, 6 days.

The great brown and grizzly bears (*Ursus*) include the largest and most powerful of the living carnivores. In the Old World the distribution of *Ursus arctos* extends from mountainous regions in France and Spain across Europe and Asia to Siberia, Manchuria, and Japan. Seven races, most of which have captivity histories, are listed by Ellerman and Morrison-Scott (1951). The Alaska brown bears, which excel in size their congeners of the Eastern Hemisphere, inhabit coastal regions and nearby islands of Alaska. The grizzlies once inhabited mountain and plains areas of western North America from northern Mexico to Alaska. Today only a scattered few are to be found within the boundaries of the United States, principally in the government reserves in Montana and Wyoming. From British Columbia to Alaska, particularly in the interior, they still are fairly abundant.

After years of study, Merriam (1918) listed seventy-one full species and fifteen subspecies of brown and grizzly bears from North America. Couturier (1954) advances well-organized material to support his opinion that all brown and grizzly bears are races of a single species, *U. arctos*. It seems probable that this view will eventually be generally accepted, at least in part, but to avoid confusion, pending revision of the group, the names used here for the North American forms are those given by Hall and Kelson (1959).

Because of their great size and potential ferocity, the brown and grizzly bears are well represented in the folklore of their native lands and have been considered as among the most desirable of sportsmen's trophies. Their food includes the usual items of fruits, leaves, roots, grass, and, at least in North America, salmon and other fish. Rodents and other small creatures are hunted or dug from their burrows, and the great size and strength of the hunters permit them, occasionally, to kill much larger prey. In the north both sexes den for the winter months, but farther south, males do not always pass this period in dormancy.

Brown and grizzly bears, when taken young, accept captivity well and are kept by most zoological gardens. Young animals are able to climb, but as they grow older this ability is lost, so that effective confinement may actually be accomplished with greater certainty than with more active species. Food for growing cubs should include milk and chopped raw meat, dog meal, finely ground bone meal, and cod-liver oil, to insure sound bone formation. The quantity required to keep an adult animal in good condition is rather formidable, the average daily provision here being 10 pounds of raw horse meat, 5 pounds of whole fish, and 5 loaves of bread, with apples, vegetables, and greens as available. Males are usually larger than females, so that food intake varies with individuals. Also, animals inclined to dormancy during cold weather may emerge from their dens at feeding time but will seldom take their full normal ration.*

Some Alaska brown bears may achieve surprisingly great weights, although estimates made in advance of the use of scales are seldom supported. Commonly quoted is the 1,656 pounds given by Ward (1922:502) for a specimen from Kodiak Island (*U. middendorffi*). Details concerning a very large male Kodiak bear are furnished me (*in litt.*) by Roland W. Giggey, secretary-treasurer of the Cheyenne Mountain Museum and Zoological Society at Colorado Springs, Colorado. The bear was received at Colorado Springs as a cub, directly from Kodiak Island, on June 29, 1940. It died on September 22, 1955, and by means of derrick and truck was transported to the scales at the nearby Broadmoor Hotel, where it was found to weigh 1,670 pounds. A photostatic copy of the official tally-card, signed by L. E. Chapman, weigher, was inclosed with Mr. Giggey's letter.

The heaviest brown bear weighed here was recorded, immediately after its death, at an even 1,100 pounds. This animal was just over 10 years old, a son of the well-known breeding pair of Kodiaks (*middendorffi*) in the Chicago Zoological Park, and thought, while still living, to be much heavier. The average weight of Alaska brown bears in captivity is certainly much less. A male from Admiralty Island, listed in our records as *U. eulophus*, weighed 800 pounds while still living, at the age of 13 years. A male peninsula brown bear (*U. gyas*), destroyed following an accidental injury and in excellent condition, weighed only 650 pounds.

Our greatest weight here for a grizzly (*U. horribilis*) is 995 pounds. This animal was a male which had lived here for just over 26 years. He had never impressed us as being particularly large, nor was he overly fat. Seton (1925–28, 2:8) quotes 1,153 pounds for a grizzly once living in Union Park, Chicago, as the greatest authentic weight for a grizzly up to that time.

Couturier (1954) gives the weight limit of Russian specimens of the

*See Addenda, p. 733.

European brown bear (*U. a. arctos*), which are the largest of this race, as about 400 kilograms or 880 pounds. Our greatest record here is 630 pounds for an aged male of uncertain origin.

The mating season for brown and grizzly bears occurs normally in June and July, with some latitudinal variation. Production by individual females may take place at intervals of 2 or 3 years, according to the dependency period of the current young. The cubs, from one to three in number, are usually born to the dormant mother in January or February, after a gestation period of 7–8 months in which delayed implantation appears to be involved (Asdell, 1946; Couturier, 1954). The young are sightless at birth and lightly haired. For the American forms the weight is usually given as about 1½ pounds and the length as 8–9 inches. A female cub born in the Copenhagen Zoological Gardens to a mother bred from the Chicago Kodiaks measured 27 centimeters (approximately 10½ inches) and weighed 600 grams (approximately 1 pound, 5 ounces) at birth (Reventlow, 1954). The birth weights of six European brown bear cubs born at the Jardin des Plantes, Paris, are given by Couturier (1954) as ranging from 265 grams to 380 grams (approximately 9–13 ounces).

It is a rather curious fact that while breeding successes with grizzly and Alaska brown bears have been few, the European brown bear reproduces so freely and the mothers rear their young so well that disposal has sometimes become a problem, as with American black bears. It seems probable that a much longer and more abundant captivity history in the case of the European form may be responsible. Captivity-bred specimens are readily obtainable and should be expected to be more amenable than animals bred in nature, even though hand-reared. The latter accomplishment is not difficult, since, if kept warm and dry, cubs can be reared on whole cow's milk given from a nursing bottle. Reventlow (1954) gives a full account of the successful rearing of the Copenhagen Kodiak cub already referred to. She received 15 grams (approximately ½ ounce) of milk with butter fat enriched to 6 per cent, heated to 28°C. (approximately 82°F.), at 3-hour intervals. Small supplements of honey and "Mammysan," a prepared food, were also included but do not seem essential. No vitamin supplement was used until the cub was 90 days old, when she began to receive 4 drops of cod-liver oil every third day. She drank milk from a dish at 70 days, and solid materials were added gradually. "Ursula" appears to have been the first Alaska brown bear to be reared outside North America.

In the course of years, six European brown bears have been reared here, by their mothers, births occurring on January 15, 17, 19, and 24, and on February 1. Most of the larger institutions in this country have had similar experiences, and the San Diego Zoological Garden, at least, has bred the race to the third generation (Stott, 1954a). Three racial intergrades between a male hairy-eared bear (*U. a. beringianus*) and a female European were fully reared here (Hornaday, 1907), but more important was a cub born to a female European in 1916, sired by a male sloth bear (*Melursus ursinus*) (Anon., 1916). This animal became so savage at the age of 2 years that it had to be destroyed. Various bear hybrids produced in captivity are listed by Gray (1954), including the American black bear by European brown bear crosses born in the Zoological Gardens of London in 1859 (Bartlett, 1860).

Most interesting of bear hybrids are those of polar (*Thalarctos maritimus*) by brown. This cross appears to have been first produced in a small zoo in Stuttgart, Germany, where a female European brown bear (*U. a. arctos*) paired to a male polar gave birth to twin cubs in 1876. At least three further births are recorded, and the young are reported to have been fertile *inter se* and when paired back to the parents or animals of the same species. Full accounts of these experiments are given by Rorig (1903) and Scherren (1907). Present interest in such hybrids is focused on those produced in the National Zoological Park. A female Alaska brown bear noted as *gyas* (Mann, 1937), after having been mated with a polar bear, gave birth to three cubs in February, 1936. A second litter of three was born in 1939 to the same parents, although the female was then listed as *middendorffi* (Mann, 1940). These cubs showed exceptional vigor and size, one male having reached a weight of 1,160 pounds (Davis, 1950). Two of these hybrid females, when paired to a brother, have produced several litters of cubs, at least some of which have been fully reared. A detailed account of these matings has been given by Davis (*loc. cit.*).

Two cubs, listed as *middendorffi*, which failed to survive, are the only representatives of the Alaska brown bear group to have been born here. As already noted, few breeding successes with these great animals have been achieved, so that the accomplishments of the Chicago Zoological Park in breeding the Kodiak bear (*U. middendorffi*) are especially important. The recorded history of these bears (Anon., 1951a) is to the effect that six cubs, three of each sex, captured on Kodiak Island, Alaska, were received in Chicago in 1933. Two of the females died, but the surviving female and the three males continued to live peacefully together. At maturity (time not stated but presumably at the age of 4–5 years) the female paired with one of the males, apparently with no objection on the part of the two others, a curious relationship which continued for the lifetime of the animals. Chicago is blessed with excellent cubbing dens, and here the female gave birth to her cubs and reared them well. The authority quoted states that thirteen cubs in all were born and eleven reared. However, Robert Bean, director, has informed me that the total number fully reared was actually eight. The breeding female died in 1952, and in 1957 only "Erskine," one of the rejected suitors, survived. Pairs of the offspring, sent to Copenhagen and Whipsnade, both produced young in their new homes.

Continued breeding of Alaska brown bears is now being carried on by the Highland Park Zoo in Pittsburgh, concerning which Edward J. House (*in litt.*) has given me the following information: The male (*middendorffi*) from Kodiak Island and the female (*shirasi*), captured on Admiralty Island, both believed to have been born early in 1942, were received at Pittsburgh in that year. No cubs were produced until 1952, when a litter of two was born. These were lost, but in 1953 and 1954 two further births of two cubs each occurred, and in 1955 another, this time of three. All of these births took place in January and all cubs, except the first two, were fully reared.

No grizzly bear cub has ever been reared here, but successes have been achieved by the National Zoological Park (Mann, 1930), the San Diego Zoological Garden (Stott, 1954*a*), and probably others. Excellent results have been obtained in the Highland Park Zoo, Pittsburgh, and again I am indebted to Mr. House (*in litt.*) for particulars. When Mr. House took charge of the zoo, in 1941, one male and five female grizzlies (*horribilis*) were already in the collection. No young had been reared, but in that autumn one of the females was removed to a cubbing den. In January, 1942, twins were born and safely reared. Mr. House says: "She has had a litter of cubs practically every year since and had a litter of two in January, 1956." Most of these cubs were reared, and no disposal difficulty had so far been encountered. Mr. House attributes his success in breeding bears to his policy of withholding food from females that have been moved to cubbing dens at the onset of cold weather. This does serve to break the habit of leaving the den at regular feeding hours and could be an important factor in successful rearing.

Brown and grizzly bears are long-lived in captivity, and excellent records have been reported. The best longevities established here for the group are as follows:

	Years	Months	Days
Peninsula brown bear (*gyas*)	36	10	6
Kodiak bear (*middendorffi*)	34	0	13
Hairy-eared bear (*U. a. beringianus*)	31	11	7
Grizzly bear (*horribilis*)	31	5	10
European brown bear (*U. a. arctos*)	28	9	18

Flower (1931) gives about 34 years for *U. "behringi"* at Schönbrunn, Vienna, and 30 years for a grizzly at the Cologne Zoological Gardens. Ratcliffe (1953) reports 32 years, 3 months for a Yezo bear (*U. a. yesoensis = lasiotus*) in the Philadelphia Zoological Garden, and Arthur Watson, director of the Druid Hill Park Zoo in Baltimore, Maryland, informs me (*in litt.*) that a grizzly bear lived 33 years, 8 months, 7 days in that institution. Flower (1931) mentions the brown bear born in the Berne Pits, said to have completed a span of 47 years in the Jardin des Plantes, Paris. He takes a doubtful view of the record, which is not mentioned by Bourdelle and Mouquet (1930). However, Kai Curry-Lindahl, director of the Zoological Department of the Nordiska Museet och Skansen, Stockholm, informs me (*in litt.*) that a European brown bear has lived for 47 years in that institution.

The polar bear (*Thalarctos maritimus*) is circumpolar in distribution and is found in arctic areas of North America, Europe, and Asia. Whether or not the several races that have been described can be maintained requires further study. It is more aquatic in habit than other bears, and most of its life is spent on the ice or in the sea. Its white coat, sometimes tinged with yellow, is distinctive enough, but the long neck, comparatively small head, and hairy soles are additional characters. The polar bear is almost entirely carnivorous, its food consisting largely of seals, young walruses, fish, and carrion, a stranded whale being a special attraction. However, vegetable material, such as seaweed and grass, is also eaten when available. Males and non-pregnant females remain active throughout the dark arctic winters, but expectant mothers burrow into crevices in ice and snow, where they become dormant and give birth to their helpless young.

In size, the male polar bear, which is considerably larger than the female, closely approaches the big browns. Seton (1925–28, 2:197) quotes the statement of Captain George F. Lyon that a male killed in Hudson Strait weighed in excess of 1,600 pounds. This weight is generally accepted but certainly is far above the average. Using the figures of Captain James C. Ross, Seton (*loc. cit.*) gives the average weight of nine males as 900 pounds, the heaviest being 1,028 pounds, and the average of seven females as 700 pounds. "Silver King," a very large male lassoed off the coast of Ellesmereland by Paul J. Rainey (1911) weighed 880 pounds on arrival here a month later—probably somewhat below his normal level. Another male, apparently considerably smaller, destroyed after having lived here for 25 years, also weighed 880 pounds. A female, also captured by the Rainey Expedition and known as "Silver Queen," weighed 425 pounds at death, nearly 30 years later. A male that had lived here for 14 years died following accidental injury in 1960 and was found to weigh 1,030 pounds.

In captivity no bear is more popular or more sought than the polar. Its unique white pelage, great size, and skilful water play make it most attractive. If furnished a pool of sufficient size and depth to give space for a full display of its aquatic abilities, an engaging exhibit is always assured. The pool in the present polar bear inclosure here is roughly circular and about 20 feet in diameter. Its depth is 8 feet, and it is filled with water to the 7-foot level. It provides ample facilities for a group of three adults, all females. As they plunge through the floating ice cakes in winter, visitors shiver in delighted astonishment, and the bears' obvious enjoyment of bathing in hot weather arouses both approval and envy. At such times a floating toy, such as a small aluminum keg, will always receive the animals' attention.

Unfortunately, the temper of the polar bear is more unpredictable than that of any other, so that it is especially important that visitors, made incautious through admiration, be prevented from approaching the exhibit area too closely. The adult polar bear does not climb but can leap to a considerable height from the water, a point which must be considered in planning.

As already noted, the polar bear is almost entirely carnivorous. The daily diet provided here for a single adult consists of 10 pounds of raw horse meat, 3 pounds each of butterfish (*Poronotus*) and mackerel (*Scomber*), and 4 or 5 pounds of stale bread. Polars are often reported to take vegetables, fruit, and greens but here such items are rejected, perhaps because more acceptable foods are made available in sufficient quantity.

The mating season for the polar bear in captivity is given by Prell (1930) as March and April, with recurrence in July, and the time of birth as November and December. These data are in accord with our own experience, except that we have not noted mating in July. The only births recorded here occurred on November 9 and November 15 (two). Zuckerman (1953) reports ten births in the Zoological Gardens of London, all in the months of November and December. The gestation period is given by Asdell (1946) as 8 months and by Kenneth (1953) as 240 days. Young born here have been well clothed in fine white hair. One measured, at birth, $10\frac{1}{4}$ inches from tip of nose to base of tail and weighed 1 pound, 3 ounces; another was only $9\frac{1}{2}$ inches long but weighed 1 pound, $10\frac{3}{4}$ ounces. The eyes were closed.

Polar bears are frequently born in captivity but are seldom reared. We have never been successful here, probably because of the lack of suitable cubbing dens. Occasional successes have been scored, however, by some other American institutions, including the San Diego Zoological Garden, the Detroit Zoological Park, and the Cincinnati Zoo, and by various European institutions, by natural means. The value of such events is exemplified by the immense popularity of "Brumas," born in the Zoological Gardens of London in November, 1949, the first polar bear to be reared in captivity in Great Britain (Cansdale, n.d.).

The outstanding successes in the natural rearing of polar bears in captivity are those of the Washington Park Zoological Garden at Milwaukee, Wisconsin, the Detroit Zoological Park, the Nuremberg Zoological Gardens, and the Nordiska Museet och Skansen, Stockholm.

The history of the Milwaukee polars has been well documented (Heller, 1930; Speidel, 1949; Anon., 1953). Some slight discrepancies and omissions in these reports have been adjusted and results brought up to the date of March 27, 1957 (*in. litt.*), by George Speidel, director of the Washington Park Zoological Garden, to whom I am greatly indebted. Four cubs, three males and one female, presumably born in November or December, 1911, were captured on the coast of Greenland and arrived in Milwaukee on August 12, 1912. They lived peaceably together as they grew, one of the males, called "Silver King," gradually becoming dominant. The female, "Sultana," first became cyclic in the spring of 1919, at the apparent age of 7 years and 4 or 5 months. She then mated with Silver King, the two other males maintaining a respectful distance, a situation similar to that of the Chicago Kodiaks. In the autumn of that year, Sultana became dormant, for the first time, in a den from which the males could be excluded and on December 2, 1919, gave birth to a single cub. This cub was successfully reared and was believed to have been the first polar bear to be reared in captivity. From then until 1935 Sultana continued to produce one or two cubs, in alternate years, in November or December, twelve in all. Of these she reared eleven, only the last, born on December 27, 1935, failing to survive. Silver King sired the first seven of Sultana's cubs, and after his death on October 16, 1928, the second male, "Borealis," took his place, siring the last five young.

The third of the original males, "Clown," was shot after having escaped from his inclosure on April 11, 1921. But Borealis lived until April 19, 1939, when he was killed by a younger male. It appears, then, that Sultana was not mateless following the loss of her last cub in 1935, but in any case she produced no more up to April 13, 1947, when she was destroyed.

A female named "Sultana II," daughter of Borealis and Sultana, born December 5, 1931, produced her first cub on November 29, 1944, having been mated with her brother, "Borealis II," born December 12, 1929. Five single cubs were born to this pair in alternate years, the last on December 3, 1952, and all were reared by the mother. The parents were still living in 1957 but there were no further births. The female, born November 29, 1944, known as "Cirrus," having been paired to her father, Borealis II, gave birth to a single cub on December 3, 1955. Efforts to rear this youngster by hand were unsuccessful, and it died on December 16, 1955. It did, however, represent the third generation born in Milwaukee. In all, from 1919 to 1955, eighteen cubs were produced and sixteen fully reared. Six members of this prolific family were still living in 1957.

The polar bears at Stockholm are kept in strikingly fine dens of simulated rock. When seen in the spring of 1950, the stock consisted of an adult female, which had been reared there, living with her two daughters, one three years old, the other five. In another inclosure were a male and two females, all very large. These females, presumed to be pregnant, were to be removed to cubbing dens in autumn. Captain Gustave W. Lilliehook, our guide, informed us that six cubs had been reared up to the time of our visit.

Hand-rearing of polar bear cubs seems to be especially difficult. In the first place, they seldom can be removed before they have suffered from injury or exposure or, for that matter, have disappeared altogether. Also, there appears to be a possibility that such young animals are more susceptible to infections than those reared by their natural mothers. Probably best known of such undertakings and certainly best documented is the rearing of the female polar cub, "Ilun," born at the Zoological Gardens of Prague on December 20, 1942 (Duncan, 1947; Hindle, 1947–48; Vlasák, 1950). Ilun, with a sister, was separated from the mother immediately after birth and placed in a basket with an electric heating device. The sister died 3 days later, but Ilun lived for nearly 10 months, when she died unexpectedly from "paralysis of the lungs."

Room temperature of the nursery was maintained at approximately 77° F., and the sterilizing effect of a quartz lamp was applied several times daily. The basic food was whole cow's milk fortified with Scott's Emulsion to 9–10 per cent fat, on the assumption that bear's milk was most likely to approximate the better-known product of the bitch. This mixture, heated to body temperature, was administered with a nursing bottle at the rate of 10 cc. per meal, every 2 hours, the quantity gradually increased to keep pace with the cub's growth. At about 80 days she began to feed from a dish. Cereals were then added, followed by solids in the form of bread, vegetables, and meat, which she did not take until she had reached about

$7\frac{1}{2}$ months. Ilun's eyes opened on the thirty-third day, although they were not fully functional for some time. Her weight at birth was 648 grams (approximately 1 pound, 6 ounces) and at death, on October 7, 1943, it was 79.7 kilograms (approximately 175 pounds).

Baldwin (1953, 1955) gives an account of an attempt to hand-rear a polar bear cub born at the San Francisco Zoological Gardens on December 11, 1952. This cub was removed from the mother promptly and was found to weigh 1 pound, 5 ounces. It was fed reconstituted evaporated milk with Viosterol, heated to body temperature, and given at the rate of 1 ounce every 2 hours, day and night. At the end of the first month the quantity of milk was increased to 3 ounces and 1 tablespoonful of Pablum and 3 drops of Pervinal were added; 12 drops of cod-liver oil were substituted for the Viosterol and feeding intervals were changed to every 3 hours. At the age of 4 months the cub weighed 24 pounds, 8 ounces and was eating meat, boiled sweet potatoes, and bread and milk, as well as other unlisted oddments. Mr. Baldwin, who is director of the San Francisco Zoological Gardens, informs me (*in litt.*) that the young polar died at the age of 4 months, 3 weeks, 1 day. Death followed a week of dysentery and vomiting, thought to have been caused by a *Salmonella* infection. A cub born at the Philadelphia Zoological Garden in the winter of 1959–60, was successfully hand-reared by Frederick A. Ulmer, Jr., curator of mammals, probably the first accomplishment of this feat in America.

Our own attempts at hand-rearing polar bear cubs, so far without success, have been limited to the two whose weights and lengths have already been given. The first of these, born on November 15, 1951, lived only 1 day and was found to have received severe head injuries, presumably inflicted by the mother before it could be removed. The second, born to the same female on November 9, 1956, was separated without difficulty and appeared to be normal. Treated under the Prague system, as outlined above, it thrived for 10 days, when it suddenly died and was found to have had an aggravated intestinal invagination.

Longevity records for polar bears approximate those of their relatives. Our best here is 29 years, 10 months, 15 days, established by Silver Queen, captured in the Arctic as an adult, while Flower (1931) gives 33 years, 4 months, 9 days for a female in the Zoological Gardens of London. Milwaukee's Sultana, as noted above, lived there for 34 years, 8 months, 1 day. George S. Mottershead, director-secretary of the North of England Zoological Society, informs me (*in litt.*) that a male polar bear which died in the Zoological Gardens of Chester on July 20, 1946, had been in captivity for approximately 41 years at death.

Smallest of the family is the sun bear (*Helarctos malayanus*), adults averaging 4 feet or less in total length and seldom reaching a weight of 100 pounds. Two races are generally recognized: the Malayan (*H. m. malayanus*), ranging from Burma, Indochina, and Thailand through the Malay Peninsula to Sumatra, and the somewhat smaller Bornean form (*H. m. euryspilus*). Both are clothed in short, tight black hair, with grayish-tan muzzle and a white crescent, sometimes tinged with yellow, on the chest.

The sun bear is largely arboreal in habit, the strongly incurved forelegs and long claws being well adapted to the purpose. Beyond reports that it feeds extensively on fruits and has a special liking for honey, its wild habits seem to be little known.

Probably because of the playful and attractive nature of the young cubs, they frequently are kept as pets in their native countries and many find their way to the world's zoological gardens. Unfortunately, however, their playfulness soon gives way to the irascible temper of the adult, which certainly is among the most ill-natured of bears.

In zoological gardens they are sometimes kept in skilfully contrived moated inclosures, but our attempts to do so here have resulted in failure, since we have found them perfectly able to climb walls that seemed to us unscalable. Our more recent specimens have lived behind bars. In spite of the tropical nature of its natural habitat, the sun bear is quite hardy, at least in the latitude of New York, and requires only an unheated shelter during the winter months. It does not hibernate.

Sun bears here receive a daily average of 2 pounds of raw horse meat, 1 pint of milk containing Pablum and sweetened with syrup or honey, and $\frac{1}{2}$ pound of a mixture of chopped raw meat, dog meal, fine bone meal, and cod-liver oil. They also take fruit, including bananas, apples, and raisins.

The sun bear seldom breeds successfully in captivity but has done so in the San Diego Zoological Garden (Stott, 1954*a*). Hutzelsider (1940) gives an account of several births in the Aarhus Zoological Gardens, Denmark, all of which resulted in the death of the cubs. A single cub born at the Cleveland Zoological Park on September 20, 1960, is reported by Reuther (1961) to have been destroyed by the mother. Single births of sun bears are reported to have occurred in the East Berlin Zoological Gardens, on April 4 and in late August, 1961, to the same mother (Michaelis, 1961).

Our best longevity for the species here is 12 years, 6 months, 12 days. Miss Hattie Ettinger, administrative assistant at the St. Louis Zoological

Park, informs me (*in litt.*) that a sun bear lived for 18 years, 9 days at that institution, and Flower (1931) reports 20 years, 6 months, 29 days for a specimen in the Zoological Gardens of London.

The sloth bear (*Melursus ursinus*) is an animal of medium size with a maximum weight of perhaps 300 pounds. It is black in color, with grayish muzzle and a white crescent on the chest, the hair being longer and shaggier than that of any other bear. The lips are mobile and the tongue extensile, providing unique equipment for securing food. It has a peculiar rolling gait which, with the heavy coat, makes this bear unlikely to be confused with another, although the Himalayan black bear, when in full coat, has some resemblance. The typical race (*M. u. ursinus*) is found in hilly and forested areas of the Indian peninsula, with some extension toward the northeast, while the form inhabiting Ceylon is usually distinguished as *M. u. inornatus*.

The natural food consists largely of fruits, honey, and insects, termites being a major item. These are obtained by tearing open the nest with the heavy claws and drawing out the inhabitants by the sucking action of the lips and protrusion of the lengthy tongue. The sloth bear apparently seldom kills warm-blooded prey but has been reported to eat the remains of animals killed by other predators or by hunters (Blanford, 1888–91).

The sloth bear is a persistent climber and, whether confined by moats or bars, is not easily restrained. We have been able to keep it within proper bounds here, with certainty, only when its inclosure was barred across the top as well as at the sides. Like the sun bear, the present species is perfectly hardy at this latitude if provided with an unheated winter shelter and it also does not hibernate. The feeding regimen of the sloth bear here is that listed for the sun bear, with the addition of bread and an increase in amounts commensurate with much greater size. Liquid foods are drawn into the mouth by suction.

Possibly because the species is not commonly kept, at least in this country, there appear to be few records of the breeding of the sloth bear in captivity. Two cubs born here on November 30, 1941, were neglected by the mother and failed to survive. A single cub born at the San Diego Zoological Garden on December 5, 1958, was fully reared by the mother (Anon., 1959).

The maximum longevity for a sloth bear here is 13 years, 10 months, 25 days. Flower (1931) gives 18 years, 2 months, 13 days for a specimen in the Trivandrum Zoological Gardens, and Baker (1926) reports one which lived in the National Zoological Park for 21 years, 6 months.

FAMILY PROCYONIDAE

CACOMISTLES, RACCOONS, COATIS, KINKAJOUS, OLINGOS, AND PANDAS

Typified by the raccoons, this small family is largely American, although there are two Asiatic members, the lesser and the giant pandas. The feet are plantigrade in all, and with a single exception they are animals of small size, with long tails which are often bushy and sometimes ringed. The exception, of course, is the giant panda (*Ailuropoda*), which may equal a small bear in bulk and has only a rudimentary tail.

The cacomistle (*Bassariscus astutus*), sometimes known as the ringtail or civet cat, is found, in numerous races, from southern Oregon to Mexico. With grayish body, black facial markings, and thick tail strongly barred with black, the cacomistle might almost pass for a diminutive raccoon except for the absence of the black mask across the eyes. Small, furtive, and nocturnal, it is seldom seen, even though it may be locally abundant. In spite of its particularly innocent expression, the cacomistle is a fierce and relentless hunter, preying extensively on small mammals, birds, reptiles, and insects, but also taking a variety of vegetable food (Taylor, 1954).

In spite of its natural shyness, the cacomistle accepts captivity readily enough. Kept indoors here, under blue light, it was perfectly content to pass the day in sleep, stretched horizontally on a convenient branch. On the other hand, it is thoroughly hardy and does well in an outdoor cage without heat. It must, however, be provided with a shelter, in which, unfortunately, it will spend the daylight hours, seldom being visible to visitors. Given reasonable space, groups of mixed sexes will live together with little quarreling.

Any inclosure meant to restrain a cacomistle must be tight indeed, for this little animal can run, leap, or ferret its way out if the slightest opportunity offers. I can recall one that managed this and during a single night destroyed an entire breeding colony of mourning doves in an aviary which was several hundred yards away across a large pond and supposedly fully protected from such marauders.

Cacomistles here are fed a mixture of raw chopped meat, dog meal, finely ground bone meal, egg, and cod-liver oil, with small bits of whole raw meat, bananas, and apples.

There are few actual breeding records for the species, and I can report only a near miss here. On June 1, 1945, the female of a pair kept caged indoors gave birth to three young. She had chosen a rock crevice for a nest and cared for the young well, without interference by the male. However, on the morning of June 4, the cage was found in wild confusion, the tiny, sightless, fluff-covered young dead, the parents dishevelled, and on the floor the mangled remains of a very large rat buried under the dry leaves. How this intruder had managed to get in is still a mystery, but loss of the young undoubtedly resulted from the ensuing struggle. A young cacomistle, stated in the caption to have been born in the Rome Zoological Gardens, is figured in *Giardino Zoologico*, 1 (4):26, 1959.

M. L. Jones (1958) gives 11 years, 21 days as the longevity of a cacomistle in the Philadelphia Zoological Garden, while Mann (1930) lists a specimen that lived for 11 years, 11 months in the National Zoological Park. A cacomistle lived in the New York Zoological Park from December 29, 1921, to April 9, 1936, or 14 years, 3 months, 11 days.

The raccoon (*Procyon lotor*), of which many races have been described, is found from southern Canada over most of the United States and southward through Mexico and Central America to Panama. In spite of its nocturnal habits, so ubiquitous is this attractive animal that it is well known to almost everyone and need hardly be described as grayish in general, with a black mask across the eyes and black-ringed tail. Few of the world's zoological gardens have missed including the raccoon in their collections, and those of North America, at least, have had to contend constantly with the problem of oversupply. Hand-reared raccoons make especially attractive pets, but unless kept under close surveillance and control are likely to get out of hand as they mature. It is then that the owner seeks to transfer his problem to the local zoo, which cannot always refuse to accept the donation.

In nature the raccoon eats practically any sort of animal or vegetable food that it can secure. Small mammals, birds, reptiles, fish, crayfish, and insects, as well as nuts, fruits, and cultivated vegetables—all have a part in its menu. The habit of immersing its food in water before eating it is well known.

The raccoon is as much at home in the trees as on the ground and is likely to spend the day curled up in a crotch or cavity. In the north it may remain in its den in a state of dormancy during cold weather, emerging only at intervals to search for food.

In captivity the raccoon is completely hardy and indifferent to cold if the sketchiest sort of shelter is provided. An open, moated inclosure makes the most suitable exhibition area, for where wire netting is used it must be extended overhead, and the animals are inclined to spend too much time in climbing and hanging from it. Our present raccoon inclosure is perhaps 30 feet in diameter, fronted by a dry moat 4 feet across and surrounded by a rough concrete wall 5 feet high with a slight inside overhang. From this, no raccoon has yet escaped. There is a small, shallow pool, much used for food-washing, and a dead cedar set up for climbing. Other trees in the area are covered with camouflaged metal for several feet up their trunks to prevent the animals from ascending and clearing the walls by dropping from overhanging branches. A very large hollow log, 3 feet through and 12 feet long, laid on the ground at right angles to the viewing area, provides sufficient shelter and prevents the inmates from hiding completely.

The bulk of food provided for our raccoons consists of a mixture of chopped raw horse meat, dog meal, fine bone meal, and cod-liver oil. In addition they are given small allowances of fish, fruit, principally apples, and fresh vegetables in season. The latter items are usually given in the morning to induce the animals to leave their shelter, the main meal being given in the evening. This results in a fair amount of activity during the day, since if raccoons are fed heavily too early, they will soon seek seclusion.

In a mixed group of raccoons breeding presents serious problems. If nesting dens are provided for each female, the production of young will soon raise the disposal problem. When individual seclusion is not possible, the mothers must do the best they can, and under such circumstances this certainly will not be very good. This situation forced us, some years ago, to find a solution in keeping females only. Since that time we have maintained a group of from twelve to fifteen of that sex, which get on well together, make an interesting exhibit, and present no problems. Introductions may be made from time to time, and while strangers may be subjected to mild hazing for a day or two, they quickly become integrated with the group.

When the breeding of raccoons is desired, this is easily accomplished. At this latitude mating usually occurs during February and March, followed by a gestation period of 63 days (Asdell, 1946). The young, from 1 to 6 in number, are sightless and very lightly furred but are able to leave the den with their mother when they are from 6 to 8 weeks old. Provided with a suitable nesting den, the mother is usually able to defend the young against any designs of the father, but if quarters are small he is best removed. Once they are out of the nest, the father usually accepts them or at worst is indifferent. In the course of years twenty-five raccoon births have occurred here, from March through July, the later births presumably being accounted for by young females, which may become cyclic later than normal. These births produced a total of 55 young in litters ranging from 1 to 5, with an average of 2.2.

So many raccoons, including albino and melanistic individuals, come and go here that it has been impossible to keep longevity records. The best I have been able to find in our files is 8 years, 6 months and still living. Flower (1931) reports 13 years, 9 months, 21 days for an albino in the Zoological Gardens of London.

The crab-eating raccoon (*P. cancrivorus*) ranges from Costa Rica to northern Argentina, several races having been described. It resembles its northern relative in general, except that it is thinly and coarsely haired, a condition particularly noticeable in the tail. Its food requirements in captivity are similar, but, unlike *P. lotor*, it must have heated quarters in winter. The species has never been particularly successful here; however, Flower (1931) gives 15 years, 10 months, 5 days for a specimen in the Zoological Gardens of London.

The coatis (*Nasua*) are somewhat raccoon-like in appearance, the body being generally uniform in color, with light markings about the face. The strongly ringed, tapering tail is usually carried erect, and the mobile nose is noticeably prolonged. Color varies among the many described forms, from gray to brown or bright bay. The coatis are forest animals, ranging from the southwestern border of the United States through Mexico and Central America and over most of South America at least as far south as Paraguay.

Less nocturnal than the raccoon, the coatis prefer morning and evening for their forays, often hunting in small bands perhaps composed of mother and young. Trees are ascended freely in search of fruit, although the ground below is thoroughly covered. Nothing edible is overlooked, small mammals, birds, reptiles, insects, and fruits entering into the diet. With sensitive noses constantly testing, the coatis give an impression of implacable ferocity, well confirmed by their nature. Hand-reared young animals make charming pets, but as they grow older they are likely to become untrustworthy.

Since most of the specimens that reach zoological gardens have been taken when young and at least partially tamed, they make excellent exhibits. They must have heated quarters in cold weather, of course, and while they are unlikely to damage barriers, these must be of unclimbable nature, as an escaped coati could wreak havoc among small creatures.

Feeding here is largely on the mixture of chopped meat, dog meal, bone meal, and cod-liver oil, as recommended for raccoons, with the addition of fruit, especially bananas and any available raw vegetables.

Coatis do not breed often in captivity, and there have been no births here. However, young of both the white-nosed coati (*Nasua narica*) and the red (*N. rufa* [=*nasua*]) have been born at the National Zoological Park (Mann, 1930), and at least two generations of the former have been bred in the San Diego Zoological Garden (Stott, 1954*a*). Zuckerman (1953) also records births of both species in the Zoological Gardens of London. Asdell (1946) gives the gestation period of *N. nasua* as 77 days. Gander (1928) reports a definite 71-day period for an undetermined form of *Nasua*.

Mann (1930) gives 8 years, 10 months as the longevity of a specimen of *N. narica* in the National Zoological Park, while Flower (1931) reports an unidentified coati as having lived for 10 years, 1 month in the Belle Vue Zoological Gardens, Manchester. A female red coati (*N. nasua*) lived here from March 15, 1907, to May 15, 1917, or 10 years, 2 months. M. L. Jones (1958) gives 14 years, 9 months, 1 day for this species in the Philadelphia Zoological Garden.

The kinkajou (*Potos flavus*), known popularly as "honey bear," is found in forested areas of the American tropics from southern Mexico to central Brazil. Several races, not readily recognizable in living specimens, have been described. In general this is a uniformly light-brown animal with short, soft hair. The head is round, the muzzle short, and the eyes comparatively large. The most characteristic feature is found in the tail, which is long, tapering, and strongly prehensile.

Perhaps because of its nocturnal habits, the ways of the kinkajou in nature are not well known. Its food is said to consist largely of fruits, although insects and small birds are also taken (Cabrera and Yepes, 1940). It lives almost entirely in the trees of the forest, seldom descending to the ground.

Most of the many kinkajous seen in captivity have been reared by hand or at least were taken while very young and so make gentle and confiding pets. This, however, should not be taken as indicative of the basic nature of the animal, for the occasional wild-caught adult is savage enough. Even a perfectly tame kinkajou, if sufficiently frightened or annoyed, can inflict a painful bite.

In the zoological garden the kinkajou is usually shown in indoor cages because of its need for warmth. Pairs will live together peacefully, but males are likely to quarrel fiercely, at least in small quarters. Branches for climbing should be provided, but a sleeping box is not required, for the kinkajou is content to pass the day sleeping quietly in plain view, if the light is not too bright. Kinkajous have reacted well here when shown under red light (Davis, 1962).

Kinkajous here are fed largely on fruit, especially oranges, apples, bananas, and grapes, with small allowances of bread, carrots, and peanuts, which they especially like. They also take a mixture of raw or cooked chopped meat, dog biscuit, cooked or raw egg, bone meal, and cod-liver oil, the lot sweetened with condensed milk. A favored item is ice cream, which is drawn into the mouth with the extensile tongue.

In spite of the frequency with which kinkajous are kept in captivity, it appears that they are seldom induced to breed. A reference often quoted is that of Goodwin (1946, 1954), who says that a pair that had lived together for nine years in the Milwaukee Zoological Garden produced a litter of two young, in September (year not given). However, Mann (1943) reports a single birth in the National Zoological Park; more recently, several such events have occurred. The *International Zoo Yearbook*, Volume 2, 1960, published by the Zoological Society of London, 1961, lists births as having occurred in 1960 at the following zoological gardens: Albuquerque, New Mexico, West Berlin, Frankfurt, Dublin, and Manchester. In the first three institutions, at least, the event recorded was one of a series.

On November 5, 1961, one of four female kinkajous kept with a male under red light in our Small Mammal House gave birth to a single baby (Davis, 1962). In the general activity of the group, the young animal appeared in some danger, for while none of the occupants seemed to threaten, neither did the mother offer it protection. Eventually, however, the identity of the female responsible was determined and the others were removed. When a section of hollow log about 18 inches high was stood on end in the cage, the mother seized the baby in her mouth by its neck and deposited it in the log. Here she cared for it well and eventually fully reared it.

Kinkajous are long-lived in captivity, and several have lived here for periods in excess of 10 years. A male known as "Jimmy," received here on August 6, 1937, died on September 24, 1959, after 22 years, 1 month, 18 days. M. L. Jones (1958) lists a kinkajou as having lived in the Zoological Gardens of London from February 8, 1911, to June 26, 1933, or 22 years, 4 months, 18 days. Dr. E. F. Jacobi, Director at "Artis," the Zoological Gardens of Amsterdam, informs me (*in litt.*) that a specimen received at his institution on September 17, 1935, lived until April 17, 1959, or 23 years, 7 months, apparently the greatest longevity so far recorded for a captive kinkajou.

Closely allied to the kinkajou and apparently often confused with it is the olingo (*Bassaricyon gabbii*). Several forms of this genus have been described, extending from Nicaragua to northwestern South America, but few specimens appear to have found their way into captivity. An olingo received at the National Zoological Park in 1956 was thought probably to be the first exhibited in this country (Mann, 1957). It does seem possible that the animal is less rare than has been supposed, for its resemblance to the kinkajou certainly leads to confusion. In fact, an olingo received on June 5, 1956, and the first to have been kept here, was obtained from a pet-seeker who had bought the animal as a kinkajou and was disappointed by its unfriendly nature (Manville, 1956).

The olingo is a grayer brown, over-all, than most kinkajous, with pale gray face and noticeably longer and more pointed muzzle. Its most obvious character is the long tail, which is very faintly ringed, somewhat bushy, and non-prehensile. It is far more active, even by day, than the kinkajou, running and leaping with an agility seldom shown by its relative.

Even less known than the wild habits of the kinkajou are those of the olingo. It is largely arboreal, nocturnal, and frugivorous, as shown by Goldman (1920), who shot both animals from the same tree in Panama, where they had been feeding on fruit at night.

The basic habits of olingos here are generally in accord. They sleep quietly during the day but quickly become active if disturbed. As the light begins to fade, they come down from their sleeping branches in search of food. In the choice of items they are far more particular than kinkajous. Bananas are favored, but they also eat grapes, taking only the pulp. They take small amounts of chopped meat, raw or cooked, and nibble at lettuce and the mixture of chopped meat and dog meal. This somewhat limited diet appears to be adequate.

The Zoological Gardens of London exhibited an olingo (*B. alleni*) in 1894 (Flower, 1929). Since 1956 olingos have been imported with some frequency into this country.*

The lesser panda (*Ailurus fulgens*) is suggestive of a particularly attractive raccoon, with full coat of bright chestnut, light-colored face, black legs and abdomen, and bushy, sharply ringed tail. There are two recognized races: *A. f. fulgens*, from the eastern Himalayas in Nepal and Sikkim, and the slightly larger *A. f. styani*, found in the mountains of southeastern China and the borders of northern Burma. The former, of course, is the form most likely to reach the zoological garden, native collectors not infrequently bringing it down to Calcutta during the winter months.

The lesser panda is essentially diurnal, although it is inclined to sleep during the day, becoming most active in morning and evening. It is not at its best on the ground but is thoroughly at home in the trees, the semi-retractile claws being well adapted for climbing. Even when taken adult,

*See Addenda, p. 733.

as most zoo specimens seem to have been, it soon accommodates to changed conditions. Especially gentle and non-aggressive, it will allow some familiarity on the part of its keeper, but if actually touched, usually shows its resentment by emitting explosive coughing sounds.

The species has long been a popular, if not common, zoological-garden inhabitant. London received its first specimen in 1869, and the inimitable Bartlett (1900), then superintendent and known for his enterprise and independent methods, has left some interesting observations concerning it. The earliest arrival here, quite possibly the first to be seen in this country, came on July 10, 1911. Since that time lesser pandas have arrived here occasionally but certainly not in any numbers. Once kept in our Small Mammal House, where they were coddled as rarities are likely to be, the animals could not be made to thrive. Later, the moated inclosure now devoted to raccoons and described above was occupied by lesser pandas with much better results. The species, of course, is completely indifferent to cold, so that it certainly does not require heat in winter. On the other hand, it is likely to show signs of distress during periods of excessive heat, often refusing food at such times.

At liberty in this inclosure, the animals spent much of the time in their climbing tree. It was in this tree that the only offensive gesture seen here was observed, when one male crowded another from the tip of a branch, so that he fell to the ground and was killed. They showed a definite distaste for wetting themselves, and when, apparently by accident, one got too far into the pool, it hastily scrambled out and shook itself with vigor, lifting its feet gingerly like a cat. Here, at least, the lesser panda has shown no inclination to winter dormancy.

Most accounts of the feeding habits of the lesser panda in nature list bamboo leaves and fruits as the principal items, although some include birds, eggs, and insects. Here, we have never been able to get a lesser panda to take flesh in any form, raw meat, mice, birds, and insects being completely ignored. The principal food has been diced fruit, especially oranges, bananas, and apples, with the addition of carrots. Second choice was a pan of the mixture supplied to our giant pandas, the formula for which is given under that species (p. 321). This semiliquid was lapped up with the tongue. In addition, of course, a supply of fresh bamboo tips with tender leaves has always been available. At first these were shipped to us twice weekly from the south, but later clumps of a hardy species, *Pseudosasa japonica*, were established here and found to be fully acceptable.

While we have not been successful in breeding the lesser panda here, better results have occasionally been scored elsewhere. Wall (1908) gives an account of the birth of two young, on July 7, 1908, to a female received at the Darjeeling Horticultural Gardens in May and presumably pregnant when captured. He describes the young as pale in color, measuring 6 inches from nose to vent and the tail $1\frac{7}{8}$ inches. The eyes, closed at birth, opened on August 6.

Zuckerman (1953) records three births in the Zoological Gardens of London, occurring in June of 1919, 1920, and 1921, and numbering one, two, and two young, respectively. Some, at least, were fully reared, for in 1920 I brought one of them to New York as a gift from the Zoological Society of London.

A really remarkable success has been achieved by the San Diego Zoological Garden in the maintenance and breeding of the lesser panda. One male and three females, obtained from the Zoological Gardens of Calcutta, were received at San Diego in May, 1940. Dittoe (1944) reports that the first young, two in number, were born in June, 1941, but failed to survive. In the following year one was successfully reared. Breeding continued for a number of years, and George Pournelle, curator of mammals at San Diego, informs me (*in litt.*) that the total young born numbered thirty-one, of which fifteen were fully reared. The last birth occurred on July 6, 1954, but the cub lived for only 3 days. The parents of this ill-fated youngster were bred in the collection and were the only survivors. Still living in 1957, they had produced no further young since 1954. All births recorded occurred in June, as did those already noted in the Zoological Gardens of London, the young numbering one or two. Dittoe (*loc. cit.*) assumes the mating season to be February and the gestation period to be 112 days, although neither seems to have been fully determined. She gives the San Diego feeding formula as a mixture of 1 pint of milk, 1 egg, $\frac{1}{8}$ cup of Pablum, and 1 tablespoonful of Karo corn syrup per animal, plus peanuts, fruit, and an abundance of fresh bamboo leaves. When seen in September, 1947, the pandas were living in groups, some of mother and young, in wire-netting inclosures about 12 feet in each dimension, equipped with trees for climbing and attractive rock work. In small wooden shelters at the back, shelves with partly boarded-in fronts were set at a height of about 6 feet and served as brood boxes. Each outside inclosure contained a stalk of freshly cut bamboo, 2 inches in diameter and at least 10 feet tall, set in a bucket of water. Kenneth (1953:39), quoting Osman Hill, gives the gestation period as 90 days.

Flower (1931) considers that the scant longevity records for the lesser panda are such that "no conclusions can be drawn." Mitchell (1911) gives 5 years, 4 months as the maximum reached, up to that time, in the

Zoological Gardens of London. This is in excess of our own best, which is 4 years, 11 months, 9 days. Dr. Pournelle tells me (*in litt.*) that one of the females received at San Diego in May, 1940, lived until March 3, 1953, approximately 12 years, 10 months. This is the best longevity achieved by a lesser panda at San Diego, and I do not know of another captivity span to approach it.

The giant panda (*Ailuropoda melanoleuca*) is a monotypic species, found only in the province of Szechuan in western China, directly north of Yunnan. Here it lives in the dense thickets of bamboo that cover the precipitous mountain slopes at elevations of from 5,000 to 10,000 feet. As already noted, the giant panda is a somewhat aberrant member of this family, and only its anatomical characters indicate its relationship. Superficially it is bearlike, so that early naturalists assigned it to that group and called it the "parti-colored bear." Adults may measure 6 feet in length, disregarding the stumpy tail, and may weigh in excess of 300 pounds. The general coloration is white, with legs, shoulder band, and eye patches deep black.

Made known to the outside world in 1869 by the French missionary, Père David, the first living giant panda to leave China was brought to New York in December, 1936, by Mrs. Ruth Harkness (Carter, 1937). When seen soon after arrival, "Su-Lin" was still an infant, fat, pudgy, and unable to walk with facility, so that he spent most of the time lying happily on his back. Eventually acquired by the Chicago Zoological Park, Su-Lin was received at Brookfield on February 8, 1937, and was then found to weigh 14 pounds (Bean, 1937). His arrival created great interest, and his cuddly appearance and attractive markings soon gave rise to the still popular "panda doll." As Su-Lin grew, his amusing ways increased his popularity, so that his untimely death in 1938 resulted in widespread sadness. Before his death, Mrs. Harkness had brought him a "mate" which, however, eventually proved also to be a male. "Mei-Mei" arrived at Brookfield on February 18, 1938, and lived until 1942. The third and last of the Chicago pandas was "Mei-lan," again a male, which came in November, 1939, and achieved fame by living until September 5, 1953 (Robert Bean, *in litt.*). This span of approximately 13 years, 10 months appears to be the greatest so far accomplished by a captive giant panda.

The St. Louis Zoological Park acquired its two giant pandas in 1939, "Happy," a male, coming on June 24, and "Pao-Pei," a female, on September 12. Happy weighed 240 pounds on arrival and Pao-Pei only 60. However, by the following year, Pao-Pei's weight had increased to 165 pounds and the two animals were then placed in the same inclosure, where they lived peacefully together until Happy's death on March 10, 1946. Pao-Pei went on alone until June 24, 1952, the span of 12 years, 9 months, 12 days being only a year short of that of Chicago's Mei-lan (Miss Hattie Ettinger, *in litt.*).

Experience with the giant panda in the New York Zoological Park has involved four animals. The first of these, "Pandora," was received on June 10, 1938, through the co-operation of Dean Sage, Jr., a trustee of the New York Zoological Society, Frank Dickinson, of the West China Union University at Chengtu, and Roy C. Spooner, of the same institution, the latter of whom accompanied the panda on the voyage to San Francisco (Sage, 1938). Pandora, a thoroughly delightful creature, weighed 35 pounds on arrival. She spent the summers of 1939 and 1940 as the star attraction of the Zoological Society's exhibit at the New York World's Fair and the intervening periods in a large cage in the Lion House. When her life ended on May 13, 1941, from an undeterminable cause, she weighed 230 pounds. She had reached a maximum of 265 pounds on October 28, 1940.

Pan, the only male among our four giant pandas, came to us on May 1, 1939, as the gift of Mr. Sage. Pan was unlike the other young pandas received here in that he was unfriendly, even surly, in his reactions to his keepers. Although his weight increased from 72.5 pounds on arrival to 170 pounds at the time of his death on May 5, 1940, he never adapted fully to captivity conditions.

"Pan-dee" and "Pan-dah"—named through the sometimes unfortunate medium of a public contest—were received as the gifts of Mme Chiang Kai-shek and Mme H. H. Kung. John Tee-Van went to Chengtu to receive the animals, which had been secured by David C. Graham of the West China Union University (Graham, 1942). After an exciting wartime journey by airplane and steamer beginning on November 14, 1941, the animals were finally landed safely in New York on December 30, 1941 (Tee-Van, 1942).

As negotiations for the anticipated arrivals progressed, plans for a suitable giant panda inclosure were formulated, and construction was under way before Dr. Tee-Van's departure on his quest. On his return, a moated inclosure, 60 by 75 feet, surrounded by a stippled concrete wall 8 feet high at its lowest point, was ready to receive his charges. A huge, smooth, glacier-scored outcrop of rock occupied one corner, and a pool 15 feet across lay near the center, shaded by a tall hickory tree. Several slender cedars, set in openings in the natural rock and tile floor, enhanced the desired effect, that of a Chinese garden. Hidden behind the wall was a small shelter house containing two compartments with raised wooden sleeping platforms, each large enough for a single animal. Behind these was a keeper's room of ample size, containing a small oil-burning heater. Sliding doors of steel bars separated the animals from the keeper's room, so that ready and convenient access was provided.

Since the pandas had come through warm climates only to reach New York in midwinter, they were kept confined in their mildly heated indoor quarters for the remainder of the cold season but were given their liberty in the outer inclosure on increasingly frequent warm days. In following years this precaution was no longer taken, for the giant panda has no fear of cold and appears to enjoy frolicking in snow.

On one of the earlier visits to the outer precincts, Pan-dee gave us a demonstration of the giant panda's tree-climbing abilities. She climbed the tall hickory to a height of 40 feet, where she remained for 41 hours before she could be persuaded to come down. This sort of thing was ended by the installation of camouflaged metal "pants" on the trunk, extending upward beyond panda reach (Anon., 1942).

On arrival and for some time thereafter, Pan-dee was considered to be a male and Pan-dah a female. Later it was determined that both were members of the latter sex.

The food of the giant panda in nature is reported to consist solely of leaves, stems, and even fairly heavy stalks of bamboo (Carter, 1937; Sheldon, 1937). McClure (1943) gives a list of bamboo species known to be palatable to the panda. Included is *P. japonica*, referred to above under the lesser panda and most used here for both species. In addition to bamboo, giant pandas in both St. Louis and Chicago have taken whole vegetables, fruit, and sliced bread. Bean (1948) gives the following items as included in the diet: green corn stalks, green soybean plants, spinach, chard, raw carrots, apples, whole-wheat bread, milk, and porridge. In reporting on the newly arrived Pandora here, Blair (1938) says that in addition to milk, egg, Pablum, honey, orange juice, and fish oil, she was given green corn stalks, willow sprigs, celery, lettuce, Swiss chard, beet tops, and baked potato, which she took readily. This willingness, however, may have been only the eagerness of a young animal to investigate strange offerings, for she soon refused to eat anything beyond bamboo and a semi-liquid formula to which ground vegetables might be added. This routine was followed almost exactly for all of our giant pandas. None, incidentally, would take flesh in any form.

In 1940, when Pandora weighed between 240 and 265 pounds, her diet, in addition to bamboo sprays, was as follows:

Morning:	1 cup Pablum
	1 cup powdered milk
	2 raw eggs
	2 tbsp. honey
	1 pt. water
Noon:	6 oranges (juice only)
	2 tbsp. honey
	1 qt. water
Night:	1 pt. Cerevim (prepared cereal)
	½ cup Pablum
	½ cup powdered milk
	2 raw eggs
	2 tbsp. honey
	1 tbsp. cod-liver oil
	½ tsp. brewer's yeast
	½ tsp. fine bone meal
	1 pt. water

Dr. Tee-Van brought Pan-dee and Pan-dah from China while feeding them a porridge composed of boiled corn meal, Pablum, evaporated milk, honey, and water, together with such bamboo sprays as were available. This diet was adhered to for some time after their arrival here, but later some changes and additions were made (Goss, 1942). In December, 1944, when Pan-dee weighed 289 pounds and Pan-dah 199, the following formula was prepared for the two animals, twice daily. Pan-dee, of course, received the larger share.

> 13½ oz. cornmeal (boiled)
> 7 oz. Cerevim
> 2 cans evaporated milk
> 2 cans water
> 5 tbsp. Calcitose
> 3 tbsp. honey
> 15 drops Vipenta (multiple vitamin concentrate)
> 40 sprays of bamboo

Variations in quantities were made, of course, as the animals grew and changed in condition. However, this formula was adhered to fairly closely, and was in use for both giant and lesser pandas.

From the beginning, Pan-dee and Pan-dah were taught to enter weighing crates from their sleeping compartments, and their weights were recorded monthly during their lifetimes. The following figures are extracted at intervals of approximately 6 months, fractions having been equalized:

Date	Weight (in Pounds)	
	Pan-dee	Pan-dah
Dec. 30, 1941	62	57
June 18, 1942	128	117
Dec. 21, 1942	169	171
June 21, 1943	165	229
Dec. 20, 1943	179	261
June 21, 1944	185	287
Dec. 18, 1944	199	289
June 19, 1945	202	277
Oct. 4, 1945	173*	—
Jan. 19, 1946	—	304
June 20, 1946	—	309
Jan. 18, 1947	—	341
July 19, 1947	—	379
Oct. 31, 1951	—	360*

*Died

The two animals showed practically parallel gains in weight until 1943, when Pan-dee began to lose ground. This could be accounted for by fairly frequent periods of refusal of food relieved, often after several days, by the evacuation of large accumulations of mucus from the bowel. She suffered less often from impaction of the intestine with bamboo stems, which she cleared with difficulty. At necropsy she was found to have suffered an "acute idiopathic intestinal paralysis" (Goss, 1945). Pan-dah was afflicted with the same mucous and bamboo-stem blocks that troubled Pan-dee, but these were of less serious nature, although her weight records reflect periods of food refusal. No cause of death was determined at necropsy (Goss, 1951).

Giant pandas here have appeared to be uncomfortable during periods of greatest heat but, unlike lesser pandas, had no aversion to water as a cooling agent. When a fine spray was directed across the tile floor of the outdoor inclosure, they walked slowly to and fro through it. Their reaction to the pool was curious. They seemed to regard standing water as merely another obstacle and waded directly through it to reach an objective, in the usual panda fashion. However, when the weather was hot, they often sat down in the pool for a brief soaking, although this always seemed to be an afterthought and not deliberate bathing, as commonly practiced by bears.

Sheldon (1937) thinks that the giant panda in nature feeds mostly in the morning and evening, perhaps also late at night. Our specimens were usually fed early in the morning and late in the evening. After meals they generally slept for an hour or so, at least in the morning, and then resumed their normal activity. At night they were confined to their sleeping compartments, so we have no records of possible nocturnal activity. None ever showed a tendency toward winter dormancy.

While there can be no question that the giant panda is among the most desirable of zoological-garden exhibits, much of its attraction is lost as it advances in age. Older animals of both sexes become lethargic, sometimes even potentially or actually savage, so that they must be handled in cages operated by remote control.

All the nine living giant pandas so far received in the United States arrived in the 5 years from December, 1936, to December, 1941. During the same period several specimens were brought to Europe, including "Ming," who died in the Zoological Gardens of London in December, 1944, and others in Germany (Schneider, 1939). Since 1941 only two living specimens are known to have reached the West. One was "Lien-Ho," who arrived at the Zoological Gardens of London on May 11, 1946, as the result of a student-training agreement with the Provincial Government of Szechuan (C. Hill, 1946). Lien-Ho died in 1950. The second specimen, known as "Chi-chi" was obtained from the Peking Zoo in May, 1958, on an animal exchange basis, by Heini Demmer (1958). Chi-chi was exhibited, temporarily, in various Continental zoological gardens and in September was purchased by the Zoological Gardens of London, where she was still living in 1963. A note by Fu-Jen (1956) reports three specimens living in the Peking Zoo in 1956.

No giant panda has so far been born in captivity, and little is known of the breeding habits of the species in the wild state. Carter (1937) discredits native reports that the panda does not mature until it is 6 years old, yet Pan-dee reached her maximum weight of 379 pounds in what was presumably her seventh year. Carter believes the number of young per birth is one and reports the statement of a guide that young are born only in alternate years. Sheldon (1937) quotes native reports that mating occurs in spring and that births take place in January.*

FAMILY MUSTELIDAE

WEASELS, MINKS, MARTENS, WOLVERINES, BADGERS, SKUNKS, AND OTTERS

Although none of the members of this extensive family is of really large size, most are fierce hunters and important as destroyers of rodents. Included are the smallest of all the carnivores, the least weasel (*Mustela rixosa*), as well as the wolverine (*Gulo*), large and powerful enough to over-

*See Addenda, p. 734.

come prey of the size of sheep and deer. Many of the world's richest furs are furnished by the otter, the sable, the ermine, and the mink. While the greatest concentration of the mustelines is in the Northern Hemisphere, representatives of the family are found on all the continents, excepting only Australia.

The genus *Mustela* includes the weasels, polecats, ferrets, and minks. The weasels are seldom exhibited in zoological gardens, and because of their furtive habits and high excitability are not really suitable for the purpose, as exposure to light beyond the animals' threshold of endurance is likely to result in convulsions from which they may not recover. Flower (1931) lists very creditable records of 5 years, 10 months, 18 days and 7 years, 9 months, 16 days for the common weasel (*M. nivalis*) of Europe and Asia in the Zoological Gardens of London. However, it seems unlikely that these animals were on exhibition, in the proper sense.

We have never made serious efforts to exhibit weasels here, although a specimen of the New York long-tailed weasel (*M. frenata noveboracensis*), received after having lived 2 years in the care of W. J. Hamilton, Jr., of Cornell University, survived in our own laboratory for a further year and 3 months. This animal was the subject of investigation and photography concerning its change of coat from brown to white and vice versa, a phenomenon exhibited by northern members of the group (Noback, 1935).

Reasonably good results have been obtained with weasels in the laboratory, where the essential seclusion can be assured (Hamilton, 1933; Hall, 1951). A full coverage of speciation and life histories of the American forms has been provided by Hall (1951), while P. L. Wright (1942, 1948) has reported on delayed implantation in the long-tailed weasel (*M. frenata*) and the short-tailed weasel or ermine (*M. erminea cicognanii*). In the former it was found that the principal breeding season is in July and August, births occurring an average of 279 days after mating. Fertilized ova do not become implanted until about 4 weeks before birth, full development of the embryos being completed during that period.

Weasels are intense predators, feeding largely on small mammals and birds, although cold-blooded vertebrates and invertebrates, including earthworms, are sometimes taken (Hamilton, 1943). Vertebrate victims are usually bitten at the base of the skull, and the killer does not suck the blood, as commonly believed. I was once watching an adult silver pheasant cock feeding along a small brook, at a distance of perhaps 20 feet, when a weasel leaped at the bird's head, to which it clung. The attacker fled as I rushed forward, but the pheasant was already in its death throes, its skull bitten through.

In captivity weasels will take raw meat but certainly thrive better if fed mice, sparrows, and similar small game. Suitable cages, consisting of wired runs and darkened retiring boxes, have been described by Hamilton (1933) and Bissonette and Bailey (1940).

Larger, stronger, and perhaps even more rapacious than the weasels are the minks. Two species are known: the American (*M. vison*), found in many races over most of the United States and Canada, and the slightly smaller European (*M. lutreola*), the several races of which extend from central and northern Europe to western Siberia. The minks divide their time impartially between land and water, hunting small mammals and birds in the forests and pursuing fish and other aquatic creatures in lakes and streams. Bold and fearless, the minks seem ready to face any potential enemy, however large. In the Adirondack Mountains of New York I once was challenged by a mink for possession of a row of trout I had caught and laid on a log behind me. Only a sharp tap on the nose with the tip of my fly rod finally caused the animal to relinquish its claim.

The great demand for mink pelts by the world's fur trade once placed a serious strain on the natural supply, but the establishment of the American mink in captivity has relieved much of the pressure. According to Kellogg, Bassett, and Enders (1948), the undertaking began in 1866 and now has grown to an industry of great economic importance. These authors give a complete résumé of the methods used in present-day production, and much of the same ground is covered by Ashbrook (1951). Two points of particular interest are discussed: the necessity for guarding against vitamin B_1 deficiency, which may follow the feeding of certain kinds of fish (already mentioned under "Foxes," p. 276), and the gestation period. The mating season occurs in March, forced ovulation following copulation. The actual term of gestation after implantation is given as 30–32 days, but the fertilized ova may remain unattached for varying periods, so that birth does not occur until after an average of 51 days from mating.

In the zoological garden the mink has seldom been considered as a suitable exhibition animal. Wild-caught native specimens are subject to the same difficulties as the weasel, and the wire-floored pens in which ranch-bred animals are housed are too unsightly for our purpose. However, a really attractive and interesting exhibit recently installed in the Chicago Zoological Park offers definite possibilities. This structure is a long, low unheated building divided into seven glass-fronted compartments, each about 4 feet by 6, floored with wire cloth concealed by a front molding 6 inches high. The glass fronts are separated from each other by wooden panels about 2 feet wide which conceal retiring boxes. When seen in 1957, each pen contained a single mink, each representing one of the recent mutational color varieties. All were in excellent condition and showed no unfavorable reaction to crowds of visitors. In such an installation successful breeding should be entirely feasible. Reflections from the glass caused some interference with visibility but this could readily be overcome by a simple walk-through gallery built outside.

Our most recent experience with the mink had to do with a beautiful male "sapphire" that lived here from August 9, 1954, to June 30, 1957. This animal was kept indoors in our Small Mammal House in a glass-fronted cage about 3 by 4 feet, with running water for drinking. However, there was no pool for bathing, which brings up the point that while the mink is perfectly at home in the water, immersion is not essential to its well-being. While various diets in use on mink farms are listed by the authors quoted above, our specimen was kept in excellent condition on a mixture of dog meal, chopped raw meat, fine bone meal, brewer's yeast, and cod-liver oil, with an additional allowance of meat and one or two small smelts daily. This approximates, in a general way, the carefully developed diets used commercially.

M. L. Jones (1958) gives a longevity of 5 years, 5 months, 25 days for an American mink in the National Zoological Park. Our best here is 3 years, 6 months for a presumably wild specimen. These figures probably are considerably less than those achieved by ranch animals which, according to Palmer (1954), are considered old at 10 years.

The polecat (*M. putorius*) is found over most of Europe and northern Asia, many local races being recognized. Like its relatives, it is a notorious killer, despised and hunted by farmers and gamekeepers alike. It is largely terrestrial in habit, its food consisting of such small mammals, birds, reptiles, and invertebrates as it can catch and kill. Comparable in size to the American mink, its underfur is yellowish, obscured by black or dark brown guard hairs. Like most of its congeners, the polecat is able to eject a foul-smelling fluid from the scent glands beneath the tail. This probably accounts for the application of the name to the skunk by early English-speaking settlers in America, in spite of the fact that the polecat is much less free with offensive gestures. The polecat has never been kept here, and I find no record of it in other American zoological gardens. It certainly is sometimes shown in Europe. Flower (1931) says it appears not to live long in zoological gardens, although he mentions a polecat said to have lived in private hands for 13 years. Zuckerman (1953) charts twelve births of the species in the Zoological Gardens of London.

The polecat is probably best known in this country as the ancestor of the domestic ferret (*M. p. furo*). The dark form of the ferret is hardly distinguishable from the polecat, but there is an albinistic breed, yellowish-white with pink eyes, that is perhaps even more common. Once popular in America for use in hunting rats and rabbits, ferrets are now prohibited in many states. Much work has been done on the reproduction of the ferret, as summarized by Asdell (1946). The litter size may range from five to thirteen, and gestation from mating is given as 42 days.

The black-footed ferret (*M. nigripes*), once fairly abundant in the Great Plains region of North America from Alberta and Saskatchewan to Texas and Arizona, now appears to be on the verge of extinction. This is generally thought to have been brought about by reduction in the numbers of the once widely distributed prairie dog, on which the black-footed ferret depended for shelter and presumably for at least part of its food supply. Efforts have been made to transfer the occasional survivors to prairie dog colonies in protected areas (Cahalane, 1954). In days of greater abundance black-footed ferrets occasionally found their way into captivity, and an excellent account of a semi-tame specimen is given by Aldous (1940). Mann (1930) gives a longevity of 5 years for an individual in the National Zoological Park, but of three specimens kept here, our best record is 1 year, 11 months. Feeding was on the basis suggested for the mink, with the addition of occasional rats and mice.

The martens and sables (*Martes*) are found in forested northern areas of North America, Europe, and Asia. They are more arboreal than other members of this family, climbing and leaping with great agility. Not only do they bear fur of great beauty and value, but the animals themselves are noted for their graceful forms. While various martens, as well as the fisher (*Martes pennanti*) of North America and the sable (*Martes zibellina*) of northern Asia, have been bred in captivity (Ashbrook and Hanson, 1930; Brassard and Bernard, 1939), this seems to have been accomplished only with difficulty. Work in this field is continuing, and commercial production levels may yet be achieved. Already much has been learned concerning the breeding habits of several species; as summarized by Asdell (1946), delayed implantation results in very long gestation periods, which may vary from 220 to 265 days in the American pine marten (*Martes americana*) and last up to 358 days in the fisher (*Martes pennanti*). Ashbrook (1928) gives detailed instructions for the care and housing of martens and fishers under fur-farm conditions, while later developments are covered by Bassett (1957).

Both martens and fishers are almost omnivorous, for in addition to the fare of flesh common to the weasel tribe, both will eat fruits and nuts when preferred food is scarce. Both are confirmed enemies of squirrels, which they pursue and catch in the treetops. The fisher is further noted as one of the few predators able to kill the porcupine with impunity.

The members of this genus are particularly attractive exhibits in the zoological garden but require sufficient space for their energetic activities. Several of the American forms, as well as some of those of the Old World, have been shown here. Their food has been that of the minks, with the addition of occasional rats, mice, grapes, and diced apples.

An American pine marten has lived here for 2 years, 3 months, and a fisher for 4 years, 11 months. Very much better records, however, have been achieved elsewhere, Flower (1931) giving 13 years, 7 months for a European pine marten (*Martes martes*) at Basel and 10 years, 3 months, 1 day for a fisher in the Zoological Gardens of London. He also quotes Ashbrook and Hansen (1930) concerning two male American pine martens that showed signs of age when "about 10 years old." From the records of the United States Fur Animal Experimental Station, Bassett (1957) reports a span of over 18 years for an American pine marten.

The tayras (*Eira*) and the grisons (*Galictis*) are large, weasel-like creatures, ranging from southern Mexico through Central America to Argentina. The tayra may measure as much as 3 feet from tip to tip, although the body alone may be no more than 2 feet. It is very dark brown or black in color, with the head and neck paler in most of the several races. The smaller grison is grizzled gray above, with face, underparts, and legs black, the color areas separated anteriorly by a band of white. Both animals are essentially terrestrial in habit, but while the grison seems to maintain this preference, the tayra takes to the trees freely in search of food. They are exceedingly rapacious and, like their relatives of colder climates, will kill any mammal or bird they can overcome; they feed also, to a lesser extent, on various fruits.

Tayras and grisons are frequently reared as pets in the countries to which they are native, and consequently the occasional specimen that reaches the zoological garden is reasonably steady, if not fully trustworthy. Those that have been kept here have been fed a mixture of chopped raw meat, dog meal, fine bone meal, and cod-liver oil, with some fruit, especially banana. Odd rats, mice, etc., are always welcome.

The only captivity breeding record I have come across for the tayra (*Eira barbara*) is a birth of two young in the Zoological Gardens of London on September 5, 1878, reported by Zuckerman (1953). Clayton Freiheit, curator of the Zoological Gardens of Buffalo, New York, has informed me (*in litt.*) that two grisons (*Galictis vittata*) were born at his institution on

July 27, 1961. Unfortunately, the birth occurred in an exhibition cage, and although the young appeared to be well cared for by the mother, they survived for only a few days.*

Both tayra and grison have done fairly well here, the former having lived for just 4 days under 6 years. However, Mann (1930) reports 14 years, 8 months for a tayra in the National Zoological Park, and Flower (1931) gives 17 years, 4½ months and still living for a specimen in the Frankfurt Zoological Gardens. The best record for a grison appears to be the 7 years, 7 months, 3 days reported by Flower (*op. cit.*) in the Zoological Gardens of London.

The zorilla or striped polecat (*Ictonyx striatus*) of Africa is strongly suggestive of the striped skunk, both in appearance and habits. From Senegal and Ethiopia to the Cape it is among the most common mammals; Allen (1939) lists a total of twenty-one local races. The zorilla is a small, slender animal, handsomely marked in alternating stripes of black and white. When disturbed, it is capable of emitting an evil-smelling fluid, comparable to that of the skunk. The zorilla is nocturnal and highly carnivorous. Once commonly imported into this country, it is now seldom seen and has not been represented in our collection since 1935. The best survival here was only 14 months but Flower (1931) reports 5 years, 5 months, 8 days for a specimen in the Zoological Gardens of London.

Largest of the ground-dwelling mustelids is the wolverine (*Gulo*). Confined to the arctic and subarctic regions, it is found in the Old World from Norway to Manchuria and in North America from Alaska and northern Canada to the borders of the United States, with southern extensions in the western mountains to Colorado and California. While it seems probable that all the wolverines are races of a single species, *Gulo gulo*, as suggested by Ellerman and Morrison-Scott (1951), we here follow Hall and Kelson (1959) who retain *G. luscus* for the American forms. Now greatly reduced in numbers throughout its range, the wolverine is close to extermination in the United States, although it seems still to hold its own in western Canada and Alaska. Few mammals have a more unsavory reputation, much of it justified, than the wolverine. The broad, squat body may reach a weight of 50 pounds, perhaps even more, which, combined with immensely powerful jaws and the grim determination common to all members of this group, makes it indeed a formidable adversary. Robber of trap lines, killer of prey many times its size, the wolverine thoroughly justifies the dread and dislike it inspires wherever it makes human contacts.

*See Addenda, p. 734.

As a zoo animal, the wolverine has not been universally successful, perhaps because it does not thrive when closely confined, nor does it like hot weather. However, when roomy outdoor, all-weather areas have been available, much better results have been obtained. The beautiful moated wolverine inclosure at the Detroit Zoological Park is well known and most satisfactory. The St. Louis Zoological Park has been remarkably successful with wolverines in similar, though somewhat smaller, quarters.

Previous to 1952 no proper accommodations for wolverines were available here, and our results were mediocre. However, our giant panda inclosure, already described, was unoccupied when, on May 13 of that year, we were able to obtain a litter of four young wolverines of the European species (*G. gulo*). These had been taken from a den in northern Finland and hand-reared by C. af Enehjelm, director of the Zoological Gardens at Helsingfors (Crandall, 1952). A male and three females, these young animals were still completely tame and most engaging. They throve on whole cow's milk, which they drank by lapping, and a mixture of raw chopped horseflesh, dog meal, fine bone meal, and cod-liver oil. Their growth rate was surprisingly rapid. Weights on arrival were 6, $6\frac{1}{2}$, and 8 pounds for the three females, 8 pounds for the male. On September 13, exactly 4 months later, they were recorded at $25\frac{1}{2}$, $26\frac{1}{2}$, $27\frac{1}{2}$, and 38 pounds, respectively. No further weights were taken, as, having been immunized to dog distemper (to which all mustelids seem susceptible), the animals were removed to the former giant panda inclosure, where they soon became unhandleable. While they never attacked their keeper, they stood their ground so resolutely when approached that it seemed expedient to work around them, rather than test their tempers further.

As adults they alternated periods of activity with short naps, by day and at night. While they adhered to the wolverine reputation for solitary living and seemed to have no attachment for each other, there was no serious quarreling. On the other hand, it was found to be impossible to introduce an adult female of the same form, obtained in 1954. This stranger was subjected to mild but continuous hazing, so that eventually she had to be removed. The reaction of the wolverines to the water of their pool and to a spray used during hot weather was curiously like that of the giant panda. They splashed doggedly through standing water or swam if they had to, treating it as a mere obstacle between them and an objective; they stalked stoically through the spray with apparently complete indifference.

The food requirements of the wolverine seem fairly high in comparison to its weight, although the name "glutton," sometimes applied to it, seems hardly justified. The daily diet of an adult male here, probably weighing in excess of 40 pounds, consisted of approximately 2 pounds of our standard mixture of raw ground horse meat, dog meal, bone meal, and cod-liver oil, and 1 pound of raw horse meat. Once or twice weekly $\frac{1}{2}$ pound of butterfish was given in addition. Ordinarily, the wolverine does not take fruit, but on one occasion an animal that had refused all food for several days and was causing us great concern suddenly and unaccountably devoured a peeled banana. The next day it resumed its customary diet but rejected bananas and other fruit offered.

There are few records of the breeding of the wolverine in captivity. Several young have been born to wild-caught pregnant females from Alaska (*G. l. luscus*) received at the Detroit Zoological Park but none has been fully reared (Smits, 1956). A. F. Oeming of the Alberta Game Farm, Edmonton, Alberta, Canada, has informed me (*in litt.*) that a female received from the Yukon Territory in January, 1958, produced four young on March 6, 1958, and successfully reared them. While actual breeding does not appear to have been accomplished in this country, successes in Europe have been scored at Stockholm and Copenhagen, at least. Mohr (1938) gives an account of the Copenhagen events, which may be summarized as follows: the female of a pair (*G. gulo*) received in 1914 gave birth to a litter of three young on March 6, 1915, but all died within 48 hours. The parents were seen to copulate between July 17 and 22, 1915, and the male was then removed. On February 27, 1916, three young were born, two of which appear to have been reared. On February 24, 1917, a birth of two young occurred. On April 17, following the death of the mother, the young were removed and reared by hand.

For information concerning the Stockholm wolverines, I am indebted to Kai Curry-Lindahl, director at Skansen (*in litt.*). The female of a pair (*G. gulo*) gave birth to four young on February 20, 1944. The male was allowed to remain in the inclosure and caused no trouble. Copulation was observed on March 23–25, and three young were born on February 17, 1945. Copulation was again noted on the following March 30. Dr. Curry-Lindahl gives no report on the results of this mating, but two cubs were born in 1953 (whether or not to the same parents is not stated). One at least of these was fully reared, for it was sent to the Philadelphia Zoological Garden in October of the same year.

These notes include definite observations of captivity mating of *G. gulo* in March and July, with four birth dates in February and one in March. The Copenhagen record indicates a gestation period between 30 and 31 weeks, as pointed out by Mohr (1938). The span noted at Skansen, from March 23–25 to February 17, is approximately 47 weeks. It is possible that in this case further unnoticed copulation may have occurred, since the male appears to have remained in the inclosure, but it seems likely that delayed implantation may have been responsible for the variation in periods, as suggested by the investigations of Wright and Rausch (1955) on Alaskan specimens.

An investigation of longevities of wolverines in American and Canadian zoological gardens has been made by Woods (1944). This showed that forty-five animals which had survived for more than 6 months averaged about $5\frac{1}{2}$ years. This author notes that a male Alaskan wolverine kept for 9 years in the Detroit Zoological Park and then transferred to the University of Michigan was still living after a total of 14 years in captivity. He also mentions five specimens of the same race (*G. l. luscus*) received at the St. Louis Zoological Park on January 10, 1929, one of which died in April, 1943, thus exceeding 14 years. Miss Hattie Ettinger, administrative assistant at St. Louis, informs me (*in litt.*) that one of the four survivors died on October 20, 1943, another in July, 1944, and two in February, 1946. These show respective spans of 14 years, 9 months, 10 days, approximately 15 years, and approximately 17 years. The latter appears to be the best recorded longevity for a wolverine in captivity.

The ratel or honey badger (*Mellivora capensis*) is widely distributed from southern Asia and Asia Minor over most of Africa to the Cape Province. Badger-like in form, it is a large and powerful animal, with strong claws and heavy jaws. The back is gray or white, varying in the numerous races, while the face, underparts, and legs are black, suggestive of the coloration of the grison. Basically nocturnal, it is catholic in its choice of habitat, dwelling in heavy bush, open plains, or even in partly arid regions. Although primarily terrestrial, it climbs ordinary obstacles with ease. It is practically omnivorous in feeding habits, taking small mammals, birds, reptiles, fruits, and berries (Shortridge, 1934). It also has a fondness for honey and bee larvae, in the finding of which it has long been said to receive aid, at least in Africa, from the honey guides (Indicatoridae). Friedmann (1955) provides ample proof of this association as well as of the ability of this clumsy, terrestrial animal to climb trees to reach bees' nests.

In captivity the ratel is hardy and vigorous, so quickly accommodating to zoological-garden conditions that it is likely to be active by day. Since it will test the strength of confining materials and take advantage of any weakness, strong restraining barriers are required. Ratels kept here have been allowed the freedom of a large outdoor cage with concrete floor during the summer months but have been kept indoors during cold weather. I cannot recall an instance in which the fetid discharge of which the animal is capable was produced. Food has consisted of the mixture of chopped raw meat, dog meal, bone meal, and cod-liver oil, with fruit, vegetables, an occasional rat or chicken neck, and now and then a treat of honey.

I know of no record of the captivity breeding of the ratel. Asdell (1946) gives the gestation period as 6 months and the number of young per birth as two.*

A ratel from South Africa (*Mellivora c. capensis*) lived here from September 4, 1920, to September 15, 1943, or 23 years, 11 days. Bourdelle and Mouquet (1930) give 21 years, 1 month for a ratel in the Jardin des Plantes, Paris; Flower (1931) lists 23 years, 6 months, 12 days for a specimen in the Zoological Gardens of London; and M. L. Jones (1958) gives 24 years, 4 months, 1 day for a ratel in the Zoological Gardens of Basel.

The badgers are squat, terrestrial creatures, noted for the digging power of their forefeet and the strength of their jaws. Two of the species are well known in zoological gardens: the Eurasian badger (*Meles meles*), which extends, in a number of races, from Ireland across Europe and northern Asia to Japan, and the American badger (*Taxidea taxus*), of which five subspecies, extending over much of central and western North America from northern Mexico to southwestern Canada, are listed by Hall and Kelson (1959). Both are grizzled gray above, with black legs. The face is black in the American badger, with a white line on the forehead and nape, while in the Old World species the head is white, with a black streak along each side, through the eyes. The latter is a fairly upstanding animal, stout though it may be, compared with the broad-bodied, flattened, American species. The badgers are mainly nocturnal in habit, spending the days in deep underground burrows. They are not true hibernators but may remain torpid during periods of extreme cold. Like other mustelids, they feed on such small mammals as they can catch by surprise or dig from their holes, birds, reptiles, and insects. The Eurasian badger extends its diet to include fruits, roots, and nuts, a habit in which the American species seems to indulge less freely, if at all.

Badgers kept here have done best in an outdoor inclosure of heavy wire netting—a low moat-and-wall arrangement would have been more attractive—containing 3 or 4 feet of sandy soil above a sunken floor of concrete, provided with small drainage openings. In this the animals burrowed and at first remained invisible. Later, however, they usually partly abandoned their nocturnal ways and were often active during the day. Food for the American species has consisted of whole raw meat, the mixture of raw chopped meat, dog meal, fine bone meal, and cod-liver oil, with occasional

*See Addenda, p. 734.

rats and chicken necks. A similar diet was provided for the several races of
M. meles we have had, with the addition of fruits and vegetables for those
that would take them.

Badgers have rarely been bred in captivity, although there are scattered
records. Stott (1954*a*) reports success with the western badger (*Taxidea
taxus neglecta*) in the San Diego Zoological Garden. Zuckerman (1953)
lists eleven births of *M. meles* in the Zoological Gardens of London, all
in the months of February and March, between 1842 and 1914. Kai
Curry-Lindahl, director at Skansen, Stockholm, informs me (*in litt.*) that
the first recorded birth of the European badger (*M. m. meles*) in his collection occurred in 1957. Delayed implantation plays an important part in
reproduction. Asdell (1946) gives the mating time for the American
badger as August to September, with implantation following in February
and birth in April, dates varying somewhat with localities. The European
badger appears to have two breeding seasons, April to May and July to
September, with implantation in December and birth about 60 days later.
However, there have been instances in which captive females have given
birth after 12–15 months of complete isolation. Further ovulations may
occur before the already fertilized ova have become implanted (Neal, 1947;
Harrison and Neal, 1956). The number of young varies from one to four
with two the most usual.*

An American badger lived here for 6 years, 7 months and a European
badger for 8 years, 10 months. Flower (1931) gives 13 years, 10 months,
14 days as the maximum for an American badger in the Zoological Gardens
of London, 14 years, 3 months for a European badger privately kept in
England, and 14 years, 9 months, 9 days for a Japanese badger (*Meles* [*m.*]
anakuma) in the Zoological Gardens of London. Mann (1930) reports
15 years, 5 months for an American badger in the National Zoological
Park, and Ratcliffe (1948–49) says an American badger lived in the Philadelphia Zoological Garden for 242 months or 20 years, 2 months.

The hog badger (*Arctonyx collaris*) is a squat, heavy animal found, in a
number of races, from China south to Sumatra. It is dull grayish above,
with black markings about the generally white head. Its habits are little
known, though Blanford (1888–91) says it is nocturnal and feeds on flesh,
fish, fruit, and earthworms. The species is uncommon in collections and has
never been kept here. M. L. Jones (1958) reports a specimen as having lived
in the National Zoological Park for 6 years, 10 months, 5 days.

The ferret badgers (*Melogale*) are smaller and considerably more attractive animals than the foregoing. They extend, in three species and numer-

*See Addenda, p. 734.

ous races, from western China to Nepal and south through Indochina and Thailand to Java and Borneo. In general, coloration is in shades of brown and gray, with head markings of black and white. Rarely seen in captivity, none of the forms is well known in nature, beyond the fact that all are nocturnal. Of a pair of Chinese ferret badgers (*Melogale moschata* subsp.) received here on March 12, 1958, one lived until March 4, 1962, just short of 4 years. They fed well on the usual mixture of chopped raw meat, dog meal, and cod-liver oil and also took carrots and sweet potatoes, both raw. All fruits were refused.

The skunks are found only in the Americas, ranging from southern Canada to Patagonia, keeping to open or broken country, and usually avoiding deep forest. The striped skunks (*Mephitis*) are found from southern Canada across the United States to northern Mexico; the attractive little spotted skunks (*Spilogale*) range from southern British Columbia and southern Pennsylvania south to Costa Rica, while the beautiful white-backed hog-nosed skunks (*Conepatus*) are distributed from the extreme southwestern borders of the United States to Chile and Patagonia. All are patterned sharply in black and white, fair warning of their extraordinary ability to eject and even direct the irritating, foul-smelling fluid for which they are famous. Confident of their ability to defend themselves, the skunks are quiet, inoffensive creatures, going into action only as a last resort. Their basically gentle nature has brought the skunks some popularity as pets, a situation which makes "de-skunking" imperative. Quick results may be had by mere severance of the ducts of the scent glands which lie at either side of the anus but only complete removal of these glands can be permanently effective. When the subject has been anesthetized, a single incision will expose gland and duct. The latter is then tied off and the gland removed. The operation must be repeated, of course, on the opposite side. If ordinary antiseptic precautions are taken, there should be no adverse aftereffects, although youngsters of 6 weeks seem to make easier recoveries than older animals do. Detailed instructions are given by Ashbrook (1928) and by Enders and Paxson (1946).

Really tame individuals, even though in full possession of their powers, may never use them, even under pressure. We once received a female striped skunk which had been a pet of its donor for two years or more. It was a really beautiful animal, docile and friendly, its coat full and well brushed and, of course, completely odorless. The owner reported that while the skunk had been descented, she had noticed that when she playfully threatened it with a broom for some slight infraction, a faint odor could sometimes be detected. This animal had been a charming attraction in our Children's Zoo for some months when detection of a slight aroma led to the discovery that its scent apparatus was intact—a condition quickly remedied!

Skunks are generally nocturnal and terrestrial in habit, leaving their dens in earth tunnels, rock piles, or hollow logs in evening and returning at dawn. Their food consists of the usual musteline fare of small mammals, birds and their eggs, reptiles, and insects, with various fruits and insects in season. Even in the frigid north, skunks do not truly hibernate in winter, and while they are likely to undergo short periods of dormancy, are often about searching for food during clement periods. While skunks may den together during the winter, they are otherwise solitary, the males traveling for considerable distances in search of receptive females during the mating season. In the striped skunk (*M. mephitis*) this occurs in February and March. The gestation period, from the first mating, is given by Wight (1931) as 62 days, the number of young varying from four to seven. Care of the young is undertaken by the female alone.

At one time striped-skunk fur was in great demand, preference being shown for all-black pelts or for those showing only a small white "star" on the head. Skunk farms were put into operation and strains of "star" animals established (Ashbrook, 1928). However, diminishing popularity quickly made the venture unprofitable.

Skunks are frequently kept in zoological gardens, although it must be said that tame, descented individuals, maintained as "keepers' pets," are most common. It is sometimes found that a pair or even several females and one male will live together reasonably well, but even then some quarreling is bound to occur. If trouble is taken to separate the females after they have been bred, interesting groups of mother and young are practically assured. As winter approaches, the animals become sluggish and inordinately fat, and do not fully regain their attractiveness as exhibits until spring comes again.

Skunks of the north are best kept in outside inclosures, low walls of stone or concrete or wire netting of ordinary strength being sufficient to restrain them. The floor should be of concrete or wire netting, covered with a few inches of earth or sand, to prevent the animals from digging extensively enough to get out of hand or even to escape entirely. Rock work concealing straw-filled retreating dens should be installed. The tropical species, of course, require heated quarters in winter. Skunks kept here are fed the mixture of chopped raw meat, dog meal, fine bone meal, and cod-liver oil, with small quantities of fruit, especially diced grapes, apples, and bananas. An occasional egg, raw or boiled, and an odd mouse or chicken neck round out the diet.

Numerous striped skunks of various races have lived here for periods exceeding 5 years, the best longevity being 6 years, 10 months, 14 days for an eastern striped skunk (*Mephitis m. nigra*). Mann (1930) gives 7 years for a specimen of the same race in the National Zoological Park.

Most aquatic of the mustelids, the otters are widely distributed, occurring on all of the continents, excepting only Australia. The river or land otters (*Lutra* and allies) live near fresh water, with some invasion of the sea in coastal areas, while the great sea otter (*Enhydra*) spends much of its life afloat.

Best known and most familiar of the otters are the American (*Lutra canadensis*), the races of which cover most of North America from the Rio Grande to Canada and Alaska, except desert areas and the treeless Arctic, and the Eurasian otter (*L. lutra*), which extends from Ireland, Morocco, and Algeria across Europe and most of Asia to Japan. Long, sinuous bodies, short legs, and broadly webbed feet are ideally adapted for the swift movement and agile turns in the water in which the river otters excel. Cahalane (1947) says they are capable of swimming under water for a quarter of a mile, and Scheffer (1953) records the capture of two American otters in one crab pot at a depth of 60 feet in Alaskan waters. On land no otter is at its best, yet river otters walk with undulating grace and gallop more awkwardly but at fair speed, so that overland trips of considerable distances are sometimes undertaken. The habit of sliding down mud banks into water or tobogganing on snow, apparently in playful spirit, is well known. Otters in the north do not hibernate but remain active throughout the winter.

The food of the river otters includes fish, frogs, crayfish, insects, and any small mammals or birds they may be able to capture. They are sometimes accused, in America, of serious destruction of muskrats, and certainly they will play havoc among confined waterfowl. The *Report* of the Royal Zoological Society of Ireland for the year 1956 (1957) contains an account of the entry of wild otters into the waterfowl inclosure in the Zoological Gardens of Dublin, resulting in decimation of the collection.

Otters in general are most attractive exhibits in the zoological garden, their antics in the water being especially engaging. The races of *L. canadensis* and *L. lutra* are best suited for northern institutions, since their hardiness permits them to be shown in permanent outdoor installations. The first essential is a pool of fresh, clean water, deep and long enough for swimming, diving, and play. Moderately running water is certainly preferable, if not actually essential. There should also be sufficient land area to allow reasonable space for the explorations in which the otter seems to delight. For, while we tend to think of the otter in terms of water, the animal really spends much more time out of that element than in it. A dry, clean shelter, well packed with clean straw, will complete the requirements, at least as far as the welfare of the otters is concerned. An unclimbable wall or fence, 4 feet, 6 inches high, will contain any river otter, provided snow does not raise the level inside it, a point that must always be considered in more northern latitudes.

The inclosure at present in use here for river otters is approximately thirty feet in diameter, fronted by a dry moat 4 feet wide and surrounded by a concrete wall 4 feet, 6 inches high, with a slight inner overhang at the top. A natural rock outcrop covers most of the floor and the balance of the area is filled in with asphalt and concrete, to prevent the persistent digging in which otters seem to take particular delight. This floor rises gradually toward the back, where the wall conceals a small shelter containing individual dens, readily accessible to the keepers by a rear entrance. A trickle of running water crosses the area in front of the shelter, finally ending in a pool about 15 feet long, 4 feet wide, and 2½ feet deep. Just behind the pool is a natural rock 3 feet high, on the face of which we built a "slide" of steel-troweled concrete which, made slippery by a flowing film of water, was intended to convey playful otters to the pool itself. Only once, as far as I know, has this slide been used for its intended purpose, and that quite by accident. On that occasion an otter carelessly attempting to walk across it, missed its footing on the glassy surface and slid ignominiously into the water on its back. Captive otters will slide in snow with abandon, but I have never seen one make proper use of the artificial chutes customarily provided.

Since otters are usually considered to be unable to climb trees, we once were greatly surprised to find that a female of the Florida race (*L. canadensis vaga*) had developed the habit of ascending to a height of 6 feet or more in a small cherry which diverged slightly from perpendicular. She accomplished this by hugging the trunk with her forelegs and inching herself upward. This she did easily enough, but when she attempted to descend by reversing the process, she was awkward and uncertain. A final fall to the concrete floor fortunately caused no injury but led to providing the tree with metal "pants," ending the otter's escapades.

For animals rarely exceeding 25 pounds in weight and often considerably less, otters are heavy feeders. The daily allowance per animal for river otters here averages 2 pounds of butterfish (*Poronotus*), ¼ pound smelts, ½ pound whole raw meat, and ½ pound of the chopped raw meat, dog meal, bone meal, and cod-liver oil mixture. Liers (1951) recommends a mixture consisting largely of ground horse meat, with liver, bone meal, bran, grated carrots, tomato, lemon or orange juice, rolled oats, mink meal, cod-liver oil, and brewer's yeast added. This is reduced to a soft mash by the addition of milk. Emil Liers' success with river otters is too well known to question the efficacy of the diet used. Since otters do well here on a somewhat divergent schedule, particularly in the use of fish, it is obvious that if the basic food requirements are met, a fairly wide variation in the choice of items is unimportant.

On December 1, 1950, we received four young Florida otters, a male and three females, presumably siblings of the year. The introduction of these animals was complicated by the presence of an older female of the same race which appeared, at first, to accept them with good grace. It was not until two of the young females had been lost that it was discovered that the older animal was slyly but determinedly persecuting them; after her removal there was no further difficulty. We had feared that otters of the Florida race might not be hardy at this latitude, but they have proved to be indifferent to temperatures down to 0° F.

This experience is typical of the risk in the introduction of strange otters to an area already occupied by one or more older residents, which are bound to resent intrusion into their territories. On the other hand, animals that have been reared together or are familiar with each other, even though of mixed sexes, often get on perfectly well as long as no breeding is attempted. In 1947 the Philadelphia Zoological Garden received a litter of young Florida otters consisting of three males and one female. These four animals were still living together in perfect amity in 1957, although Freeman Shelly, director, informed me that it was necessary to remove the female when she was in season to avoid serious quarreling among the males at such times.

It seems curious that so little should have been learned concerning the breeding habits of animals otherwise so well known as the river otters. This presumably is because of the secretive ways of the animals in nature and the rareness of the occasions on which they have bred in captivity. Hediger (1952) says of the European otter (*L. l. lutra*) that there has been "no birth in captivity up till now." However, two births in the Zoological Gardens of London, one on August 13, 1836, the other on August 11, 1856, each of two cubs, are reported by Zuckerman (1953). The first two are said by Flower (1929), who gives the birth year as 1846, to have lived for over 6 years. Then there is the classic account of Cocks (1881a) of the mating of a pair of otters of this race which were kept in captivity in England. Copulation, in the water, was observed on July 17 and again on August 12. Two young were born on October 12, 1880, 61 days after the last observed mating, and both were fully reared by the mother.

The American otter (*L. canadensis*) appears to be more readily bred in captivity than does the European species (*L. lutra*). The earliest records for *L. canadensis* appear to be those established in the National Zoological Park, according to particulars furnished by Theodore H. Reed, director (*in litt.*). The first birth occurred on December 15, 1913, when a single male was born but failed to survive. The origin of the parents is uncertain. The second litter, of four cubs, was born on January 5, 1915, to a female of the Florida race (*L. c. vaga*), the father being undesignated. These cubs were fully reared, and one lived until November 27, 1928 (see also Mann, 1930). On February 1, 1922, a litter of three, listed as *L. c. vaga*, was born, one of which lived until December 11, 1939.

The unique contribution of data on the controlled breeding of river otters compiled by Liers (1951) makes a record of great interest. The animals involved were mostly Canadian otters (*L. c. canadensis*), so conditioned and trained by their owner as to be completely tractable. Seven births are recorded from 1940 to 1948, in November, December, and January, the number of young per litter ranging from two to four. Elapsed periods from observed copulation to birth are given as ranging from 9 months, 18 days to 12 months, 15 days, although, if stated dates are correct, the minimum period was actually an even 10 months, as shown by dates in the last record listed. As Liers suggests, delayed implantation appears to be involved.

One of two females obtained from the Liers collection by the Detroit Zoological Park, having mated with a male from the same source, produced a litter of two young in 1942. Frank McInnis, director, informed me at the time that these cubs were accidentally drowned in their pool at an early age. Subsequently, however, several litters were fully reared. The practice now followed, as outlined verbally by Mr. McInnis, is to remove the male when young are born, usually in January, and to return him to the family group in April, when he is accepted by the female and allowed to play with the young. Water in the pool is reduced to an inch or two before the young emerge from the nest and gradually increased in depth after they have begun to play in it, usually at about the age of three months. The young are removed from the inclosure in October or November.

A pair of Liers otters, privately owned by Arthur E. Hoffman, of Kansas City, Missouri, proved to be prolific. Mr. Hoffman reports (*in litt.*) that a litter of four was born to the female in January, 1956, and safely reared. The parents were seen to copulate on April 29, 1956. The male died in the following June, and the female, continuing to live alone, gave birth on March 26, 1957. This period approximates those gathered by Liers, although it is not definitely established that there were no further matings.

Our own experience in breeding otters is limited to the activities of the pair of Florida otters (*L. c. vaga*) mentioned above as having been received here as young of the year on December 1, 1950. No signs of mating activity were noted, but in December, 1952, the female began working on a well-constructed nest of small branches, dry leaves, and straw in one of the compartments in the shelter. We anticipated a birth, but on January 13, 1953, an ambitious relief keeper removed the nest material as unsightly, and on the morning of the fourteenth two female cubs, evidently born during the night, were found dead on the bare wire mesh of the compartment floor. While the loss was disappointing, the incident does serve, loosely, to support the statement of Liers (1951) that otters mature at 2 years. Beginning about a week after the birth and death of these cubs, copulation was noted over a span of several days. No further sexual activity was observed during the year; on January 12, 1954, a litter of three was born. Eight days later the young had disappeared, perhaps destroyed by the mother following disturbance by incautious keepers.

A single mating was seen on March 29, 1955, and a renewal occurred during the period of May 25 to June 8. Copulation sometimes took place several times daily, the male holding the female's neck with his teeth, 10–15 minutes being required for completion of the act. Mating was seen only during the day and always in the water but, of course, may have taken place unobserved at night. On December 1, while the animals were out of the pool, the male was seen to seize the female's neck several time in succession and to attempt to mount, but when she refused to accept service by simply moving sideways away from him, he relinquished his grip on her neck. On January 5, 1956, a litter of four cubs, two males and two females, was born in a well-prepared nest in the shelter. Care was taken to prevent any possible disturbance of the mother by keepers or others, so that number and sex of the young remained unknown for some weeks.

First notice of the birth was the ejection of the male from the shelter by the female. During the first day he was seen to re-enter several times but always emerged, hurriedly, after a brief period of excited squealing. He finally gave up the attempt and sought refuge in a small wooden hutch placed in the inclosure for his use. The female's food was placed outside the entrance to her shelter, and when she came out to eat, the male remained discreetly in his box. A set ritual soon developed: when the female was about, the male remained hidden and came out only when she was tending her cubs. If he happened to be outside or even in the pool, the slightest sound from the nursery sent him scuttling for shelter. Later, when the mother began coming down to the pool to bathe, she did not disturb the male as long as he kept to his box but drove him to it furiously if she chanced to find him outside it. Obviously, he should have been removed entirely, had other quarters been available.

The first youngster to be seen outside the shelter came out alone on February 12, when it was 38 days old. It wandered nearby for a minute or two, when the mother rushed out, threatened the male, which had looked out from his box, seized the cub by the neck, and dragged it, walking backward, into the shelter. Such excursions soon became daily events, and all four cubs, always accompanied by the mother, often ventured several feet from the shelter. On March 9, 1956, at the age of 63 days, they were first seen eating the chopped meat and dog meal mixture and drinking water from the tiny flow. Neither mother nor cubs would accept milk. On March 22 the cubs were seen playing together in the flowing water, less than 1 inch deep. On the thirty-first, when just short of 3 months old, the cubs were frolicking at the neck of the pool in 4 inches of water, and we decided to double the depth. All went well until April 9, when the outlet became blocked and mother and brood were found swimming and diving in water 14 inches deep. That brought an end to our caution, and the full depth of $2\frac{1}{2}$ feet was restored, with no unfavorable results.

During this entire period the male seemed much interested in the young, but the female never allowed him to approach them. When the wandering of the cubs brought one near his shelter, he cowered within it. This resistance by the female gradually broke down, however, as she busied herself carrying food to her active offspring, and the male was permitted more freedom. On May 3 he was seen to pick up a fish near a feeding youngster, which immediately attacked him and inflicted a wound in his back which was slow to heal. The male defended himself as best he could and retreated to his hutch at the first opportunity. The mother did not participate in the fracas. From that time she became more tolerant of the male, and by early June he was accepted as a member of the group, all six frequently playing and tumbling in the water together. The young were separated from the parents on November 25.

No signs of mating behavior were observed during 1956, although the male and female were on good terms during the second half of the year, and no birth occurred in 1957. From March 19 to April 5, 1957, copulation was noted almost daily, sometimes several times in one day. On July 1, 1957, a single completed copulation was observed. This isolated occurrence, like the similar one recorded on March 29, 1955, is not easily reconciled with a general pattern, since the animals were always under close observation by their keepers during the day and any further activity must have been seen.

These data check reasonably well, in general, with those recorded by Liers (1951), although they are not fully in accord regarding the lapse between mating and birth. The shortest period given by Liers, if dates are correctly printed, is 10 months, while our minimum is in the area of 6 months, suggesting a very wide variance in time elapsing before the ova become implanted. If the period of 61 days given by Cocks (1881a) for *L. lutra* should be substantiated, it would appear to indicate a wider specific distinction than can be established by physical characters only.

Life expectation for the Eurasian otter (*L. lutra*) in captivity was found by Flower (1931) to be rather short, the greatest longevity recorded by him for the species being 11 years, 2 months, 23 days in the Zoological Gardens of Basel. However, Simon (1943) reports a specimen of *L. vulgaris* [=*lutra*] as still living in the Trivandrum Zoological Gardens on January 12, 1943, after 22 years in the collection.

While the American river otter (*L. canadensis*) probably also has a rather low average span in zoological gardens, it nevertheless has established some excellent records. The best of these are undoubtedly those of the National Zoological Park, as furnished to me by Theodore H. Reed, director of that institution (*in litt.*). Some have already been given above for animals bred in Washington, the longest being February 1, 1922, to December 11, 1939, or 17 years, 10 months, 10 days, for *L. c. vaga*. Other notable Washington records are 13 years, 7 months, 27 days for *L. c. canadensis* and approximately 19 years for a specimen of *L. c. vaga* that lived in the Park from 1936 to 1955.

Of the scattered examples of Old World otters that have been kept in this country, best results seem to have been obtained with the Asiatic clawless or small-clawed otter (*Aonyx cinerea*). Specimens of this small species kept here have been gentle and quiet but have consistently refused to enter water more than an inch in depth. The same peculiarity has been experienced in the National Zoological Park, Washington. Feeding and treatment here have been the same as for river otters, except that clawless otters have not been exposed to cold. Theodore H. Reed (*in litt.*) informs me that a specimen of *Aonyx cinerea* lived in the National Zoological Park for 10 years, 2 months, 11 days, while our best record for the species here is 10 years, 10 months, 1 day.*

*See Addenda, p. 734.

The giant otter (*Pteronura brasiliensis*) inhabits the great river systems of eastern tropical South America, the typical race coming from eastern Venezuela, the Guianas, and northeastern Brazil and *P. b. paranensis* from southern Brazil to northeastern Argentina and Uruguay. It is probably the largest of the fresh-water otters, Cabrera and Yepes (1940) giving a general length of 190 centimeters (approximately 6 feet, 3 inches), with reports available of old males as long as 2.20 meters (approximately 7 feet, 2 inches). Other distinguishing characters, as compared with its South American relatives, are the facts that the space between the nostrils of the giant otter is haired instead of naked, and the tail, thick and muscular for its basal two-thirds, is broadly flattened at the tip.

A young giant otter received at the National Zoological Park in December, 1952, was considered by Mann (1954:111) to be the first of the species seen alive in the United States. Unfortunately, it was in poor condition on arrival and lived for only a few weeks. In December, 1953, two young males arrived at the Chicago Zoological Park, followed soon afterward by a female. Robert Bean, director (*in litt.*), says they appeared to be about 3½ months old and were fed milk, Pablum, and boned fish with multiple vitamin concentrate added. Later, fresh shrimp and ground whole fish, minus heads, tails, and fins, were substituted for boned fish. The young animals thrived on this diet, and two of them, a male and a female, were in perfect condition when seen in the autumn of 1956; in October, 1961, Mr. Bean informed me that the male was still living. This pair spent the winter of 1956–57 in an unheated shelter, to which they were confined only during periods of cold weather. The water of their pool was prevented from freezing by agitation with compressed air. Later, mild indoor heat was provided. The next arrivals were two males which reached the National Zoological Park in October, 1954 (Mann, 1956). Dr. Mann says (*in litt.*) that these young animals were fed at first on mice, raw chopped meat, and a milk-and-egg mixture. Later, fresh fish was furnished, at the rate of 1½ pounds, three times daily for each specimen. The survivor of this couple, seen on June 11, 1957, appeared to be in perfect health.

The first giant otter to be exhibited here arrived on February 22, 1955, and was still living in 1963. This was a well-grown but immature female, weighing 28.16 pounds and measuring 43 inches in total length. She was perfectly tame and gentle and obviously accustomed to human companionship. Fed at first on a mixture of chopped raw meat, dog meal, bone meal, and cod-liver oil with bits of fish and milk-and-egg, she grew rapidly. She was kept indoors in a large exhibition cage with a glass-fronted pool and an elevated duckboard on which she could dry her coat. A small sleeping compartment was attached to which she was admitted at night. She spent much of her time in the pool, her great agility in making twists and turns being most attractive to visitors. By July, 1957, she had reached a length of 56 inches and had greatly increased in bulk, although no actual weight was obtainable. At this time her daily food ration consisted of 4 pounds of butterfish (*Poronotus*), 1 pound of the dog-meal mixture, and 1 pound of whole meat.

In 1961 a large outdoor inclosure equipped with pool and shelter became available. With the thought that the otter should have more freedom than her rather cramped quarters offered, she was moved, with some difficulty, at the onset of warm weather. However, the effort proved fruitless, for she protested continuously in a loud, whining voice, refused her food, and walked to and fro without ceasing along the restraining wire netting. After a few days she was returned to her accustomed home, to her obvious satisfaction.

After arrival the only weight it has been possible to obtain was 45 pounds, on October 1, 1958. The otter's total length on May 29, 1962, determined as accurately as possible in a living animal, was $57\frac{1}{2}$ inches, small gain since 1957.*

The sea otter (*Enhydra lutris*), once hunted to the verge of extinction for its exquisite fur, is now slowly increasing in numbers under strict protection. The northern race (*E. l. lutris*) is found from Kamchatka to the western Aleutian Islands and south to the coast of British Columbia, while the larger and browner southern subspecies (*E. l. nereis*) extends locally from the coasts of Washington to Baja California. Great size, small webbed forefeet, and large, broadly webbed hind ones are distinguishing superficial characters. Most of the animal's life is spent in the water, although it may come ashore, where it is awkward and slow-moving, during stormy weather. The sea otter is often said to be the largest of the mustelids, Scheffer (1951) giving 58 inches in length and about 80 pounds in weight as probable maxima for males of the northern race. However, even females of the giant otter (*Pteronura*) may attain similar length, and until weights for this species are better known the question cannot be answered.

The food of the northern sea otter is given by Murie (1940) as consisting principally of sea urchins, with mollusks, crabs, etc., making up 23.30 per cent, crabs 10 per cent, and fish only 6.70 per cent. Abalones are added to the list by the southern race and apparently are the preferred item. Feeding seems to take place while the animal floats quietly on its back. The habit of breaking hard shells by pounding them against large stones held on the chest has been well described by Fisher (1939).

*See Addenda, p. 734.

Recent efforts to establish the sea otter as a zoo animal resulted from experiments conducted by the United States Fish and Wildlife Service with a view toward the transfer of members of the Amchitka herd in the Aleutians to other nearby areas from which the species had been extirpated (Stullken and Kirkpatrick, 1955). Three otters, which apparently had been successfully maintained in captivity for 3 months before shipment, were sent to the Woodland Park Zoological Gardens in Seattle, Washington, to be rested and forwarded to the National Zoological Park. They arrived at Seattle on June 1, 1954, and remained there until June 13, when they were shipped by air to Washington. Edward J. Johnson, former director at Seattle, says (*in litt.*) that the otters were placed in a vacant bear grotto containing a pool 10 feet long, 8 feet wide, and 3 feet deep. About 30 feet distant was a den, the floor deeply covered with dry hay. The animals reached this retreat without difficulty, once they had learned its location, and spent much time there in careful grooming of their fur. They showed no fear of man and fed readily from the hand. The otters were fed at intervals of approximately three hours, the first feeding being at 9:00 A.M., the last at 10:00 P.M. The bulk of the food consisted of fish of several kinds, including smelts, various cods, herring, and whiting, all of which were taken well. Flat fishes were taken less readily. Fresh land crabs, clams, and frozen squids were accepted eagerly. In the light of the preferred diet listed above, it is somewhat surprising to find that fish can so readily be substituted for what appear to be the normal food sources.

On June 13, 1954, the three sea otters left Seattle aboard a specially cooled airplane and arrived at Washington the next day. Quickly transported to the National Zoological Park, they were placed in an air-conditioned cage (Mann, 1955). They swam freely, groomed their fur frantically, and fed well on fish, crabs, and clams. However, within a few days, all ceased feeding and died soon afterward, autopsies revealing only blood-filled intestines (Wm. M. Mann, *in litt.*).

The disappointing results of the Amchitka–Seattle–Washington experiment may be explained, at least in part, by the results of the studies of Stullken and Kirkpatrick (1955). These investigators give the annual variation of sea water temperature at Amchitka as ranging between 38° and 47°F. and that of the air as between 15° and 55°F. It was found that sea otters kept in captivity at Amchitka showed a very narrow temperature tolerance, evidencing distress at points below or above the indicated range. These authors recommend air temperatures between 30° and 60°F. and water temperature not colder than 40°F. as being most favorable for captive animals. It was also determined that a food intake averaging

25–35 per cent of body weight per day, preferably given in four meals at 6-hour intervals, was required to keep captives in good condition. When the quantity of food ingested was inadequate, black tarry feces resulted, and when death followed, the intestines were often found to contain quantities of extravasated blood.

With these findings in mind, it would appear that better results with sea otters in captivity might be obtained. Actually, a notable advance has already been made. On October 10, 1955, a pair of young sea otters from Amchitka arrived at the Woodland Park Zoological Gardens, Seattle. Placed in the same empty bear grotto and treated in the same way as those received in 1954, the male, estimated to be only 6 months old, lived but 2 weeks, quite possibly because he had not yet reached the weaning age. The female, on the other hand, considered to be 18 months old, readily adapted to the environmental change. Soon after arrival she was found to be heavily infested with internal parasites which yielded to treatment with the vermifuge Caracide. Mr. Johnson (*in litt.*) reported that the animal's weight on August 5, 1957, was 40 pounds and that she was then receiving a food allowance averaging 8–9 pounds daily, with a variation of 7–11 pounds, given in three meals. Nine pounds of food would represent about 22 per cent of the body weight of 40 pounds, somewhat less then the requirement suggested by Stullken and Kirkpatrick (1955), but apparently adequate. The preferred food items were still those listed for the 1954 specimens.

The water in the pool was fresh, not salt, and constantly running, and in it the otter spent most of the daylight hours. At night she retreated to the den, 30 feet distant, where she remained until morning, snug in a bed of shredded paper. The temperature of the water on August 10, 1957, was 60° F., which Mr. Johnson considered to be its high point; air temperature on the same day was 74° F. In winter ice has sometimes formed, but when this was broken the otter entered the water freely and showed no discomfort. Mr. Johnson said that summer air temperature in Seattle seldom rises above 80° F., although it did reach 100° F. in June, 1956. The animal withstood this without apparent distress by remaining in the water. Air temperatures in winter may be as low as 10° F., but no difficulty was noted. The letter ended with the statement that the sea otter "is an excellent exhibit—constantly moving about and very energetic." This experience suggests that, if the comparatively high food requirement is supplied and the animal is able to keep its coat in proper condition through alternate periods of immersion and drying, the temperature-tolerance span of the sea otter is greatly increased.

A young male received at Seattle on December 14, 1957, was readily accepted as a companion by the established female. He appeared to be thriving but lived only to September, 1958. The older animal, locally well known as "Susie," died on October 27, 1961, after 6 years, 17 days at Seattle (Frank Vincenzi, director, *in litt.*).

FAMILY VIVERRIDAE

CIVETS, BINTURONG, GENETS, MONGOOSES, AND FOSSA

Short legs, long, slender bodies, and rather lengthened muzzles are the superficial characters that distinguish the members of this Old World family, which extends from southwestern Europe and southern Asia through most of Africa to the Cape. They are comparatively small creatures, for the most part, the binturong, with a tip-to-tip measurement of about 60 inches, being the largest. Some forms have the catlike ability to retract the claws, and others are noted for the value of the secretion of the anal glands, used in the manufacture of perfumery.

Many of the species have been kept in zoological gardens, where most have proved to be long-lived and easily maintained. The Zoological Gardens of London and the National Zoological Park are especially noted for the fine series they usually maintain. While there are extensions into northern or southern temperate regions at the extremities of the range, suggesting that some of the forms might prove to be hardy in fairly cold climates, the majority live in tropical areas, and it is customary to treat all members of the group as requiring heated quarters when temperatures are low. As compared with the mustelids, the viverrine animals are less active in general and less inclined to be aggressive or to damage their inclosures. On the other hand, the more carnivorous species, such as the genets and the mongooses, lose none of their intense ferocity by comparison when the need for such activity arises.

Best known and certainly most often seen in collections are the civets. Typical of this group are the African civet (*Viverra civetta*), in which the grayish body is heavily spotted with black, and the somewhat smaller Indian civet (*V. zibetha*), which has the gray sides clear or only faintly marked. The latter species, in several races, is found from southern China west to Yunnan and southward through the Malay Peninsula. The forms of the African civet occur irregularly, avoiding arid regions, from Senegal in the west and Somaliland in the east as far south as the Transvaal. Both civets are noted for the copious glandular secretions basic in the making of some perfumes, and in some districts are said to be kept in captivity for the purpose of gathering this material (Roberts, 1951:128).

Civets are nocturnal and terrestrial, feeding on any small creatures they may come upon and making up any lack with fruits and vegetables. They have seemed quite contented here in glass- or wire-fronted cages approximately 8 feet long by 4 feet wide, provided with elevated sleeping boards placed in darkened corners. Our mixture of dog meal, chopped raw meat, bone meal, and cod-liver oil with an egg added now and then, supplemented with fruit and an occasional rat or chicken head, has appeared to be adequate. Neither species has bred here, but Zuckerman (1953) records two births of the African civet in the Zoological Gardens of London in 1862.

Results with the Indian civet here, as far as longevity goes, might have been better, 7 years, 8 days being our greatest record, although a specimen of the closely related Sumatran civet (*V. tangalunga*) lived here for 10 years, 6 months, 27 days. Flower (1931) gives 15 years, 4 months, 25 days for an Indian civet in the Trivandrum Zoological Gardens. Our best longevity for the African civet is 12 years, 3 months, while Flower reports 13 years, 9 months, 21 days for this species in the Basel Zoological Gardens.

The palm civets are considerably smaller than the preceding species, with long, slender, and well-haired tails. They are chiefly nocturnal and arboreal, feeding largely on fruits but also taking any animal prey, including insects, that may be readily available. Best known in zoological gardens are the members of three genera: *Paradoxurus* and *Paguma*, from southern Asia, and *Nandinia*, found in tropical Africa.

Palm civets should be kept in cages high enough to give space for branches for climbing, as well as for an elevated sleeping platform shielded from bright light. If a birth is anticipated, an open-topped box, well supplied with straw and placed in a sheltered corner or recess, should serve its purpose well, for palm civet mothers do not seem particularly shy. Specimens kept here are fed quartered oranges, bananas, and apples, small pieces of raw meat, the mixture of chopped raw meat, dog meal, bone meal, and cod-liver oil, with an egg added two or three times weekly. Occasional rats, mice, and chicken heads complete the menu.

The palm civets seem to adapt particularly well to the conditions of captivity, and several of the forms have been bred. Zuckerman (1953) records births of the Indo-Malayan (*Paradoxurus hermaphroditus*), masked (*Paguma larvata*), and two-spotted (*Nandinia binotata*) in the Zoological

Gardens of London, mostly in the nineteenth century. Similar results with the same species have been obtained here. Three Indo-Malayan palm civets were born on September 27, 1914, but failed to survive. Two two-spotted palm civets, born on April 22, 1945, were fully reared. Our experience in breeding the masked palm civet is more extensive. The first birth, on June 2, 1939, consisted of three young which did not live, presumably because of our failure to remove the male. When later births were anticipated, the male was transferred and not returned to the female's cage until the young had been weaned and removed. Two born on April 17, 1940, were reared, as were a further two born on February 24, 1941. Only one of twins born on August 24, 1941, was reared, as was a single female born on March 7, 1942. This female, when paired to her father, produced a single young on February 5, 1945, and safely reared it. Single young born on November 30, 1961, and May 12, 1962, were fully reared. The two-spotted palm civet has done particularly well here when reversed under red light (Davis, 1962).

Generally creditable longevity records have been established by captive palm civets. The best listed by Flower (1931) are 15 years, 5 months, 17 days for *Paguma larvata*, and 10 years, 4 months, 1 day (still living) for *N. binotata*, both in the Zoological Gardens of London. He also gives 14 years, 5 months, 12 days for *Paradoxurus niger* [= *hermaphroditus*] in the Trivandrum Zoological Gardens. Our best results for these species here are 11 years, 3 months, 27 days for *Paguma larvata*, 9 years, 3 months, 24 days (from birth) for *N. binotata*, and only 4 years, 10 months for *Paradoxurus hermaphroditus*. Our greatest span for the group is 11 years, 6 months, 10 days for the white-tailed or Jerdon's palm civet (*Paradoxurus jerdoni*).

Closely related to the palm civets is the binturong or "bear-cat" (*Arctictis binturong*), the several races of which are found from Burma, with possible extensions to the northwest, through the Malay Peninsula to Sumatra, Java, Borneo, and the Philippines. As already noted, this is the largest of the viverrids and is further unique in the possession of a tail at least partially prehensile. Grizzled black in color, rough in coat, and sluggish in action, the binturong is both nocturnal and arboreal.

Housing requirements for the binturong are similar to those for palm civets, with due allowance for greater size. During the summer months a small outdoor moated inclosure can be made use of to great advantage. One of the most striking exhibits I can recall was an installation of this sort in the Detroit Zoological Park. In it a group of five or six binturongs, presumably a family, slept soundly in a tight cluster on crossed poles high above the ground, each animal with its thick, clublike tail hanging straight down.

Binturongs here are given the same food as that provided for palm civets. With both groups some allowance must be made for individual preferences, which may show rather wide variation.

Breeding records for the binturong must be fairly numerous. Three births, occurring in March, July, and November, in the Zoological Gardens of London are recorded by Zuckerman (1953), and the species is listed by Stott (1954a) as having been bred in the San Diego Zoological Garden. A birth of three young occurred in the New York Zoological Park on April 24, 1942. The death of the father preceded this event by several days, so that no paternal reaction to the young could be recorded. Also, no data concerning the period of gestation were obtained, a situation that still exists in the case of most viverrids. The mother cared for the young well in a shallow, open-topped nest box, and all were fully reared. One was transferred to the Staten Island Zoological Society, New York, at the age of 6 months, but the remaining two, as well as the mother, succumbed to canine distemper in June, 1943 (Goss, 1944). This loss coincided with the outbreak of this scourge that decimated our Cape hunting dogs, as already noted under that species (p. 287). It points to the fact that some, at least, of the viverrids are susceptible to this disease.

Comparatively long life spans have been recorded for captive binturongs. The young animal noted above as having been born here on April 24, 1942, and transferred to Staten Island before the fatal outbreak of canine distemper occurred, lived there until January 16, 1957, or 14 years, 8 months, 23 days. Flower (1931) reports a specimen as having lived 16 years in the Singapore Gardens and died in the Zoological Gardens of London "when about 18 years of age." Fox (1941) records the death of a binturong after an exhibition period of 18 years in the Philadelphia Zoological Garden.

The genets (*Genetta*) are small, sinuous creatures, with sharp faces and pale gray or tawny coats, sharply spotted and striped with black or brown. The partially retractile claws are serviceable for tree-climbing, for the genets are as much at home above the ground as on it. As well as being more or less arboreal, the genets are also largely nocturnal. Three species and many races are usually recognized, the range of the genus extending from southern Europe, Arabia, and Palestine over most of Africa to the Cape.

Genets are seen fairly frequently in zoological gardens, where they usually are quiet and inoffensive, perhaps because those that reach us have generally been hand-reared or at least taken when very young. On the other hand, if they are disturbed or frightened, their fierce and active natures are at once aroused, so that their potentialities should never be underestimated. A cage 8 feet long by 4 feet wide and 6 feet high provides ample space for a single specimen or a pair—larger groups are almost certain to result in serious quarreling. Stout branches and a sleeping platform above floor level should be provided, and there must be provision for heat in cold weather. A female Equatorial genet (*Genetta tigrina aequatorialis*), received here from the Belgian Congo in 1949 and still living in 1963, is fed the mixture of chopped raw meat, dog meal, bone meal, and cod-liver oil and small pieces of whole raw meat, with rats, mice, chicken heads, and a raw or boiled egg two or three times weekly. Fruits, vegetables, and greens are refused, as they have been by genets kept here previously.

Genets have not bred in our collection, but Mann (1930) reports the birth of two Neumann's genets (*G. g. neumanni*) in the National Zoological Park. Zuckerman (1953) lists the pale genet (*G. g. senegalensis*), the blotched genet (*G. tigrina*), and various hybrids as having been born in the Zoological Gardens of London, all in the last century. A more recent birth of the latter species in London is reported by Kelham (1955).

A specimen of *G. tigrina* from South Africa lived here from June 15, 1907, to April 18, 1922, or 14 years, 10 months, 3 days. Mann (1930) gives 11 years, 4 months for *G. genetta* in the National Zoological Park, and Flower (1931) records 12 years, 4 months, 16 days for *G. pardina* [=*maculata*] in the Zoological Gardens of London.

The mongooses are natives of the Old World, extending, in many genera and species, from southern Europe and southern Asia over most of Africa to the Cape. Gray, brown, or reddish coats, grizzled or occasionally barred with black, are the rule. The hair is coarse and rather long, while tails are well furnished, sometimes even bushy. Claws are non-retractile. Most of the species are diurnal and terrestrial, their food consisting of small mammals, birds, and reptiles. However, some, such as the crab-eating mongoose (*Herpestes urva*) of Asia and the water or marsh mongoose (*Atilax paludinosus*) of Africa, are at home in the water, feeding largely on fish, frogs, and crustaceans. The latter species has the further distinction, according to Shortridge (1934), of being essentially nocturnal.

Because of regulations instituted by the United States Department of Agriculture, later enforced by the Treasury Department, prohibiting the importation of mongooses into this country, the experience of American zoological gardens, aside from the National Zoological Park, has been very limited. However, before this prohibition was effective, some of the more readily obtainable species were occasionally seen here. In northern Europe, where there is little danger that essentially tropical species may become established through the escape of caged specimens, many kinds of mongooses are kept. The Zoological Gardens of London are especially fortunate in this respect.

Typical of the group and probably best known, at least in America, is the Indian or gray mongoose (*Herpestes edwardsi*), the several races of which are found from Arabia east to Assam and south through peninsular India to Ceylon. Famous as the "Rikki-tikki-tavi" of Kipling, the Indian mongoose stands as a symbol of courage and tenacity. There is no doubt of its ability to kill a cobra, as well shown in the several staged combats that have been filmed and widely exhibited. On the other hand, it is ordinarily satisfied with less difficult fare, which may include small mammals, birds and their eggs, snakes, lizards, and even insects. Incidentally, the animal introduced into the West Indies and Hawaii with such disastrous results (De Vos, Manville, and Van Gelder, 1956) is now considered to be the small Indian mongoose (*H. a. auropunctatus*) and not *H. edwardsi*, as once supposed.

Mongooses of various sorts kept here have been housed indoors in cages averaging 4 feet by 8, which seem to provide ample space for exercise. A sleeping platform set above floor level has given variation, and sleeping boxes or rock crevices have been provided. Food has consisted of small pieces of whole raw meat, the mixture of chopped raw meat, dog meal, bone meal, and cod-liver oil for those that would take it, with milk and egg for some and rats, mice, and chicken heads for all. Blanford (1888–91) says that fruit is sometimes included in the diet of the Indian mongoose, but I cannot recall a captive specimen that would take it.

It is hardly to be expected that marked success should have been scored in breeding mongooses in this country, and in fact the only records appear to be those of water mongooses (*Atilax paludinosus*) born and reared at the National Zoological Park in 1955 and 1956 (Mann, 1956, 1957). The Zoological Gardens of London, as might be anticipated, have had excellent results, and in addition to the water mongoose, Zuckerman (1953) lists births in that institution of the Indian mongoose (*Herpestes* [*edwardsi*] *nyula*), the small Indian mongoose (*Herpestes auropunctatus*), the banded mongoose (*Mungos mungo*), the "true" meerkat or suricate (*Suricata suricata*), and the yellow or bushy-tailed meerkat (*Cynictis penicillata*). Kelham (1954) mentions births of the last species in London in four successive years. Taylor and Webb (1955) give a most interesting account of the breeding of dwarf mongooses (*Helogale vetula*) kept as pets in Kenya. Six litters of from two to six young each were born within a period of less than 14 months, the shortest gap between births being 9 weeks. Not only the father but young from previous litters assisted in looking after successive infants. A closely related species (*Helogale parvula*) is reported as having produced two litters of young in the National Zoological Gardens of South Africa, Pretoria (Haagner, 1920).

The best longevities established here for members of this group are: the Indian moongoose (*Herpestes edwardsi*), 9 years, 8 months, 11 days and 10 years, 8 months, 19 days, and the suricate, "true" meerkat or slender-tailed meerkat (*S. suricata*), 8 years, 6 months, 29 days. The highest figures recorded by Flower (1931) are: the Indian or gray mongoose (*Herpestes* [*edwardsi*] *nyula*), 8 years at the Trivandrum Zoological Gardens; the zebra or banded mongoose (*Mungos mungo*), 8 years, 7 months, 5 days at the Giza Zoological Gardens; the white-tailed mongoose (*Ichneumia albicauda*), 10 years, 29 days at the Zoological Gardens of London; the puisa mongoose (*Bdeogale* [*crassicauda*] *puisa*), 10 years, 10 months, 18 days at the Zoological Gardens of London, and the yellow or bushy-tailed meerkat (*C. penicillata*), 12 years, 10 months, 2 days, also at London.

These spans, of course, were established by exceptional specimens of a group having a rather low captivity potential, and make all the more remarkable two records for the Ceylon ruddy mongoose (*Herpestes smithi zeylanius*), published almost simultaneously. W. C. O. Hill (1956) reports that a fully adult female received by him in April, 1931, lived in his private collection in Ceylon until 1944. Two years later it was sent to the Zoological Gardens of London, where it died on June 19, 1947, after approximately 16 years, 2 months in captivity. Phillips (1954, 1956) gives an account of a male of the same form kept as a family pet in Ceylon. Obtained in January, 1938, when it was thought to be 3 months old, this animal died on September 8, 1955, after 17 years, 8 months in captivity.

Few mammals have been the subject of more controversy, at least as far as its relationships are concerned, than the fossa (*Cryptoprocta ferox*) of Madagascar. Its catlike appearance and retractile claws have sometimes led to its inclusion in the Felidae or even in an intermediate family. However, its partly plantigrade manner of walking and other viverrine characters have led to present general agreement that it should be assigned to the Viverridae.

The fossa is a short-legged, long-bodied animal said to reach a total length of 5 feet. Its coat is short and fine, of a uniform rich brown. The eyes are large and dark and the head small, so that it suggests an overgrown, very dark jaguarundi of the red phase, commonly known as eyra. The fossa is a forest dweller, at home in the trees, where it hunts, usually at night, for the lemurs and birds on which it feeds. Since it is the largest carnivore of Madagascar, it naturally is regarded with some awe by the natives, but Rand (1935) found that its reputation for ferocity, as reported in the literature, is somewhat exaggerated.

The fossa has rarely been seen in living collections, but some of the few specimens received have done remarkably well. It seems probable that these long-lived individuals have been hand-reared or at least taken while very young, since otherwise it is difficult to account for the wide temperamental variations in captives. The single short-lived specimen kept here was savage and intractable, as was a particularly truculent animal I once saw in the Zoological Gardens of London. On the other hand, a fossa received at the National Zoological Park on October 6, 1954, lived until January 6, 1962, and was a truly beautiful specimen. When seen by day, he was likely to be sprawled on his back in the middle of his cage floor with feet in the air, fast asleep. Toward evening he became more alert, prowling stealthily about, fully aware of visitors but indifferent to their presence, an excellent example of a perfectly adjusted captive.

The fossa appears to be wholly carnivorous and should receive pieces of whole raw meat, chickens, pigeons, rats, mice, and any other small creatures available. Beyond these items, my recollection of the diet of the specimen that lived here briefly in 1913–14 is not entirely clear, but if we should ever have another, I should certainly like to see it tried as well with our mixture of raw chopped meat, dog meal, bone meal, and cod-liver oil— just in case! The Washington fossa appeared to have no need for a darkened retreat for daytime use, but for most, such a haven is indispensable.

The longevity records for captive fossas reported by Flower (1931) do not appear to have been exceeded since that time. The best of these are 14 years, 2 months, 12 days in the Zoological Gardens of London, 16 years, 2 months, 24 days in the Berlin Zoological Gardens, and approximately 17 years in the old Hamburg Zoological Gardens. The latter animal was the survivor of a group of four received in 1909, the last, a male, dying in 1926. A full account of these animals, with notes on behavior and anatomy, is given by Vosseler (1929) and briefly summarized by Mohr (1942). The fossa is reported to have bred successfully in the small Zoological Garden at Tananarive, Madagascar, in 1956, 1957, and 1958 (M. L. Jones, 1958).

FAMILY PROTELIDAE

AARDWOLF

The aardwolf (*Proteles cristatus*), of which several races have been described, is found in eastern and southern Africa from the Sudan to the Cape and in the west from Angola to South West Africa. A small, harmless creature, vaguely hyena-like in appearance, its relationships have long been in dispute. Although Simpson (1945) assigns it to the Hyaenidae, we here follow Ellerman, Morrison-Scott, and Hayman (1953) in considering it as the sole member of the present family. Spending the day below ground, usually in the abandoned burrow of some other animal, the aardwolf comes forth at night to feed on termites, such other insects as it may come upon, and occasional small mammals and birds. Its small cheek teeth and comparatively weak jaws are adequate for this regimen.

The aardwolf is rarely seen in zoological gardens, largely because it has usually proved difficult to maintain in captivity. Alwin Haagner (1920) came to this conclusion after ample experience gained through his position as director of the National Zoological Gardens, Pretoria. However, very creditable records established by scattered individuals suggest that better results might be obtained. Only two specimens have been received here, both in poor condition following long sea voyages, and neither survived for more than a few months. A diet of raw chopped meat, dog meal, bone meal, and cod-liver oil, alternated with milk, egg, and raw chopped meat failed to save these animals, but it is presumable that in these days of fast air transportation, greater success might be anticipated. The aardwolf is not only nocturnal but extremely shy, so that a darkened retiring shelter of some sort is essential.

Mann (1930) reports an aardwolf as having lived for 6 years, 9 months in the National Zoological Park, while Duetz (1939) records 9 years, 7 months for a specimen in the Philadelphia Zoological Garden. What is apparently the greatest longevity for the species in captivity is the 12 years, 10 months, 21 days given by Flower (1931) for a male in the Zoological Gardens of London. These figures indicate that not all aardwolves are difficult to maintain in captivity.

FAMILY HYAENIDAE

HYENAS

The hyenas are natives of both Asia and Africa and are assigned to two genera and three species. Largest is the spotted or laughing hyena (*Crocuta*

crocuta), which may reach a weight of 175 pounds. The ground coloration is dull buff, heavily spotted with blackish brown. Its races extend from Senegal, the Sudan, and Ethiopia southward to the Cape, with greater abundance in the east. The striped hyena (*Hyaena hyaena*) is a much smaller animal, grayish in color, with transverse stripes of black or brown on body and legs. Its subspecies range from India through Palestine and Arabia to Africa, as far south as Tanganyika. The brown hyena (*H. brunnea*), which is dark brown with stripes confined to the legs, is found in South Africa below the Zambesi River in the east and Angola in the west.

In all the hyenas the foreparts are heavy and powerful, the shoulders sloping sharply downward to the shorter and relatively weaker hind legs. The jaws and teeth are immensely strong, so that even heavy bones are crushed with ease. Nocturnal, skulking, and "cowardly" in habit, the hyenas are scavengers, relying for their food largely on the kills of bolder carnivores. However, they are not adverse to living prey too weak to make strong resistance and frequently devour young or injured game or domestic stock. Even sleeping men are not immune from attack, and there are records of children having been carried off by hyenas.

A curious misunderstanding, apparently of ancient origin, concerning sex in the spotted hyena still persists. This is the belief that an individual animal may change from male to female or vice versa. This confusion has arisen from the fact that the external sex organs of the virgin female are superficially identical with those of the male and show only slight changes after the birth of young, beyond enlargement of the nipples. The anatomical details were described long ago by Watson (1877, 1878, 1881) and have been clearly summarized by Matthews (1949), but the conviction still persists. Incidentally, the sexual differences in striped and brown hyenas are easily recognized.

In spite of their unsavory reputation, hand-reared hyenas under favorable conditions may remain perfectly tame, even after they have become adult. Butler (1914) gives a particularly illuminating account of a female striped hyena that, after 13 years, still remained a household pet.

While easily kept in the zoological garden, the hyenas are not always entirely satisfactory. Since they are naturally shy and retiring as well as essentially nocturnal, they are inclined to keep out of sight during the day, and if forced to expose themselves to light, they may become restless and overexcited (see Hediger, 1950:84). At such times males are likely to display in a manner offensive to the visiting public. On the other hand, if allowed to come and go as they like with opportunity to secrete themselves when they wish, hyenas can be useful exhibits.

Because of the great power of their jaws, stout bars or heavy wire mesh are required for restraining hyenas. Although they are not particularly active, even at night, they require almost as much space as wolves for normal exercise. While ordinarily hyenas are kept in heated quarters in the colder areas, a brown hyena of unknown origin once lived out of doors here for nearly 12 years in a run approximately 20 by 50 feet which was equipped only with a small, unheated shelter. During this period a temperature of − 14° F. (approximately − 25.5° C.) was recorded (February 9, 1934), with no apparent ill effect on the animal.

Hyenas here have been fed whole meat, occasionally with bone attached, and the mixture of chopped raw meat, dog meal, bone meal, and cod-liver oil. When whole bone is given, it is readily crushed by the animal and large pieces are excreted, so that the feces may then be highly calcareous.

Both striped and spotted hyenas, when kept in pairs in suitable quarters, breed readily in captivity, but the brown seems more reluctant. Matthews (1939) reports the gestation period of the spotted as 110 days, and Asdell (1946) gives 3 months for the brown. The period for the striped appears not to have been recorded. Zuckerman (1953) lists three births of the striped hyena in the Zoological Gardens of London, numbering 2 young in one instance, 3 in another. The same author plots nine births of the spotted hyena in London between 1868 and 1873, well distributed throughout the year, with an average of 1.5 young per litter. Lang (1958) gives a detailed account of several births of brown hyenas in the Zoological Gardens of Basel from 1953 to 1957. Gestation periods recorded ranged from 92 to 98 days. There seem to be no American records. Hyenas have not been bred here, but various American institutions have been successful. A pair of spotted hyenas received at the Pittsburgh Zoological Gardens in 1946 is reported to have produced 2 cubs annually for 7 years, the first litter having been born in 1947 (Anon., 1954b). The author makes a point of the necessity for removing the male to prevent him from devouring the young.

Hyenas have an excellent longevity potential in captivity, with high average expectation. For some reason, perhaps because the species is not common in captivity, maximum records for the brown are less than those established by the others. The only brown hyena that has been kept here lived in unheated quarters, as already noted, for 11 years, 11 months, 1 day. Brown (1925) gives 12 years, 7 months, 20 days for a specimen in the Philadelphia Zoological Garden, while the 13 years, 5 months, 10 days reported by Flower (1931) for a brown hyena in the Zoological Gardens of London does not appear to have been exceeded. Flower (*op. cit.*) lists

20 years for a striped hyena in the Copenhagen Zoological Gardens and 22 years, 11 months, 24 days for the same species in the Giza Zoological Gardens.

Of the two spotted hyenas that we have exhibited, one was sold a few years after arrival. The other, captured in Kenya by Paul J. Rainey and presented to us in 1911, died in 1929, after 17 years, 11 months, 12 days. Of a pair received at the San Diego Zoological Garden in December, 1934, the female lived until April 18, 1958, or approximately 23 years, 4 months (George H. Pournelle, *in litt.*). Flower (1931) lists an animal of this species as having lived 24 years, 1 month in the Hamburg Zoological Gardens and gives an account of the varied career of another that lived in England for about 25 years. Ratcliffe (1948–49) states that a spotted hyena was exhibited in the Philadelphia Zoological Garden for 24 years, 10 months, a well-authenticated record that closely approximates Flower's best figures.

FAMILY FELIDAE

CATS

Easily recognized by over-all general appearance, not readily defined, the members of this group are distinguished, on closer examination, by several characters. All cats are digitigrade, with four toes on the hind feet and five on the front, although in the latter case the inner toe or thumb, while armed with a claw, does not touch the ground in walking. In all but the cheetah, the claws are retractile, so that when they are not in active use they are withdrawn into protective sheaths. Since their principal function is to seize and hold prey, they are fully extended at the instant the attack is made. The claws are kept clean and sharp by scratching, usually on the trunks of trees. For this reason sturdy woody material is essential for installations used for these animals in captivity.

The upper surface of the tongue bears sharpened papillae, directed backward, which are of use not only for dressing the fur but for removing remnants of flesh from bones. This is a useful compensation, for the cheek or carnassial teeth of the cats are adapted for cutting rather than for crushing. In order to bring the shearing carnassials to bear, the head is turned sideways, not for mastication but simply for cutting. The great canine teeth, especially well-developed in this group, serve only to hold the prey and sometimes to kill it.

Nocturnal habits are the general rule in the family, although occasional individuals of most of the species may prowl by day. Many kinds of cats are at home in the trees, but the lion, the tiger, and the cheetah are essentially terrestrial. There are curious variations in attitude toward water. The lion, the leopard, and many of the smaller species are reluctant to enter it, although all, of course, can swim if necessity demands and there are numerous accounts of their having done so. On the other hand, the tiger and the jaguar, at least, will go into water freely and swim with apparent pleasure.

The cats are widely distributed over most of the world, except the Australian region and Madagascar, being most numerous in warm areas. In size they vary from the lion and the tiger to the tiny black-footed cat (*Felis nigripes*) of South Africa, which is no larger than a small domestic cat.

The systematics of the Felidae have long been subject to controversy, but the arrangement proposed by Simpson (1945) and followed in general by many later authors (*cf.* Ellerman and Morrison-Scott, 1951) seems most natural. On the other hand, Haltenorth (1953) takes strong exception and argues vigorously for a more complicated system, with revival of many generic terms reduced to subgenera by Simpson. However, for the sake of simplicity, at least, we here follow the latter. This leaves us with but three genera: *Felis*, *Panthera*, and *Acinonyx*. *Panthera* includes the great "roaring cats," the lion, the tiger, the leopards, and the jaguar. In this group the flexibility of the hyoid support of the larynx permits the freedom of movement necessary for the roaring that is so characteristic. All the smaller cats, from the puma down, with the exception of the cheetah, are assigned to *Felis*. In this genus the larynx is less mobile, precluding the ability to roar. The third genus, *Acinonyx*, is reserved for the cheetah.

The cats, of course, are among the mainstays of the zoological garden, and few general collections would find the group without representation. Caging and housing may run the full gamut from the small, iron-barred cage to moated inclosures of the most elaborate sort. These will be considered under the groups.

It is the larger species that seem to be most concerned in the development of the "squeeze cage," the many types of which have been evolved for controlling the animals for minor operations, usually on teeth or claws. When our present Lion House was opened in 1903 it was provided with a traveling shifting-cage, by means of which animals could readily be moved from one cage to another. One side of this cage could be moved toward the other, so reducing the space that the inmate eventually was immobilized. Even in the early days "squeezing" was rarely undertaken, largely because of the danger of self-inflicted injury on the part of the frightened animal. In present practice even the largest cats can so readily be rendered immobile by drugs now in general use that the "squeeze-cage" no longer seems to serve a useful purpose.

The great scourge of cats in captivity is "cat enteritis," or feline panleucopenia. The ever present domestic cat provides the great reservoir for the transmission of this usually fatal disease so that, at least in this area, it is impossible to avoid occasional exposure. For this reason all felines, young or old, immediately after reception here, are started on a course of treatment with a commercial vaccine, readily available. This protection is usually fully effective, but occasional loses of presumably immunized specimens occur (Ratcliffe, 1953; Goss, 1956). A long list of references relating to this subject is given by Halloran (1955).

As is well known to breeders of domestic cats and to most custodians of zoological collections, cat animals are especially sensitive to coal-tar products, which may cause fatal results if they come into contact with the skin. Hilty (1932) defines cresylic acid as the responsible agent. To avoid risk of the trial by overenthusiastic keepers of such disinfectants or others that might be equally dangerous, it is a fixed rule here that all cleaning or disinfecting materials must be approved by the veterinarian before use.

The best known member of the genus *Felis* is, of course, the domestic cat (*F. catus*). Descendants of local races of the kaffir cat (*F. libyca*) and the jungle cat (*F. chaus*), domesticated and held sacred by the ancient Egyptians and carried, in the course of time, to Europe and Asia, are believed to have been interbred there with indigenous species, so that our familiar household pet presumably has a heterogeneous origin. A report on the remains of cats mummified by the Egyptians is given by Morrison-Scott (1951–52). While the domestic cat in itself is not of particular interest to the zoological garden, its habits are so typical of those of the group that they reveal much concerning the ways of its relatives. The studies of Leyhausen (1956a, 1956b) on the behavior of the domestic cat and some others have broad application.

Closely related and suggestively similar in color to the "striped tabby" pattern of domestic cats but with shorter and thicker tail is the European wild cat (*F. silvestris*). The races of this species extend from Scotland, where it still exists, across Europe to Asia Minor. Reputed to be fierce and untamable, it certainly could be no more savage than a truly feral domestic cat. The only specimen that has been kept here was noticeably quiet, perhaps because special efforts were made not to disturb it. It was fed whole meat which had been steamed, a practice in vogue here at that period (1915), and with rats, mice, and small chickens. In a large outdoor cage provided with an unheated shelter it appeared indifferent to cold. The European wild cat has been bred at least once by the Zoological Gardens of London (Zuckerman, 1953). The gestation period is given by Cocks (1881b) as 68 days, while that for the domestic cat is 63 days (Asdell, 1946). Hybrids between the European wild cat and the domestic cat, as well as between the former and the kaffir cat (*F. libyca*) are listed by Gray (1954). Flower (1931) reports a specimen privately kept in England that lived in captivity for 16 years.

The lynxes, sometimes treated as forming a separate genus, *Lynx*, but here included in *Felis*, are natives of forested areas of the Northern Hemisphere. Short tails and elongated hind legs are typical, while the ears are tufted in varying degree. Largest are the Old World lynx (*F. lynx*), the races of which extend, in suitable localities, from Norway and Sweden to Asia, and the closely related Canada lynx (*F. canadensis*), found from the northern United States over most of Canada to Alaska. The smaller bay lynx, bobcat, or wildcat (*F. rufa*) is widely distributed from southern Canada to Mexico, many local races having been described. While the lynxes are agile climbers, they hunt much on the ground, feeding largely on rabbits and birds. They are said to take to water freely and to swim well.

In captivity the lynxes usually thrive well, and unless unduly disturbed, their naturally savage natures are seldom aroused. All are perfectly hardy and indifferent to cold, so that roomy outdoor quarters, fully inclosed and provided with sleeping dens, are entirely suitable for year-round use, even in northern latitudes. A shift cage to which the inmates can be confined during cleaning periods should be provided as a safety precaution. Natural branches, including some level enough for resting, will be much used. A male Bailey's bobcat (*F. rufa baileyi*) that was received here on November 20, 1948, and lived until March 22, 1960, was fed daily about 3 pounds of whole raw horse meat which had been deeply scored with a knife, with fine bone meal and cod-liver oil rubbed well into the incisions. This was alternated with rabbits, rats, and chicken necks, as these were available.

Lynxes are not commonly bred in zoological gardens, perhaps because true pairs are not kept as often as they might be. Zuckerman (1953) reports a birth of the Old World lynx in the Zoological Gardens of London, and Mann (1930) lists the Texas bobcat (*F. rufa texensis*) as having produced young in the National Zoological Park. That better results might be obtainable is indicated by a note by Carter (1955) concerning a pair of Eastern bobcats (*F. r. rufa*), privately owned, which produced and reared three or four litters. The most remarkable successes in lynx breeding appear to be those reported by Behm (1933). From 1905 to 1933, Old World lynxes (*F. lynx*) at Skansen, Stockholm, produced nineteen litters of young, numbering from one to four per birth and totaling forty-three. Gunter Voss (*in litt.*) reports the birth of five kittens of the Canada lynx (*F. canadensis*) at the Assiniboine Park Zoo, Winnipeg, Manitoba, in 1960, and an account of the breeding of this species at the Alberta Game Farm, Winnipeg, is given by Oeming (1962). Asdell (1946) gives the following gestation periods: *F. lynx*, 63 days, *F. canadensis*, 2 months, and *F. rufa*, about 50 days.

Longevities established by captive lynxes compare favorably with those of other cats. The Canada lynx appears to be adversely affected by hot weather and has never done really well here, our best record for the species being 7 years, 8 months. However, Mann (1930) reports 11 years, 4 months in the National Zoological Park and Flower (1931) gives 11 years, 7 months, 1 day for a specimen in the Zoological Gardens of London. A Canada lynx is stated to have lived for 16 years in the Quebec Zoological Gardens (Anon., 1955*b*). Flower's best for the Old World lynx is 16 years, 1 month, 6 days in the Zoological Gardens of London, but Behm (1933) says that a male of this species, born in 1910, lived at Skansen, Stockholm, until March 8, 1932, approximately 22 years. The bay lynx, perhaps better adapted to variations in temperature, probably shows a greater average longevity in captivity than either of the other species. Mann (1930) gives 15 years, 4 months for a northern bobcat (*F. r. uinta*) and 15 years, 10 months for a bay lynx (*F. rufa*) in the National Zoological Park. Carter (1955) states that of the breeding pair of eastern bobcats referred to above as having been privately kept, the female died in 1950 and the male in March, 1953. As these animals were captured as adults in the autumn of 1928, approximate captivity spans are 22 years for the female and 24 years, 6 months for the male. A summary of bobcat longevities is given by Young (1958).

The caracal (*F. caracal*) is lynxlike in many ways, with abbreviated tail and well-developed ear tufts. It is reddish or tawny in color, the coat is short, without ruffs, and the legs are noticeably long. It is an inhabitant of open, even desert, country and is found from southeastern Asia throughout Africa, except the great forest areas of the west, south to Cape Province. Once abundant, the caracal is now becoming scarce throughout its range, so that, while at one time a familiar exhibit in zoological gardens, it is now seldom obtainable. In captivity it is best treated as sensitive to cold and provided with heated quarters in winter. Caracals kept here have been fed as suggested above for lynxes (p. 362). The species does not appear to breed freely in captivity, but Zuckerman (1953) records three litters born in the Zoological Gardens of London between 1908 and 1912, the number of young in each being two or three. The Zoological Gardens of Amsterdam, Rotterdam, and Stuttgart are listed in the *International Zoo Yearbook* for 1960 (Jarvis and Morris, 1961) as having bred the caracal in that year. The gestation period seems not to have been determined. Available longevity records are not too satisfactory in general, our best here being 8 years, 2 months, 25 days. However, Flower (1931) reports two caracals that lived in the Dublin Zoological Gardens for 16 years, 22 days and 16 years, 10 months, respectively, spans certainly seldom achieved.

The serval (*F. serval*) is a slender, long-legged animal, found in Africa south of the Sahara, many races having been listed. It is normally yellowish or reddish in ground color, well marked with bold black spots. Specimens with markings reduced almost to dots were once distinguished under the name of servaline cat (*F. brachyura* or *servalina*) but are now usually considered to be variants of *serval* (Ellerman, Morrison-Scott, and Hayman, 1953). The serval seems to prefer forested or at least bush-covered country rather than open plains and usually frequents the vicinity of water. Swift on the ground in pursuit of the small mammals and birds on which it preys, it climbs trees with equal facility. Graceful lines and bright coloration make the serval one of the most beautiful of the cats. Specimens kept here have been fed as described for the lynxes, with the quantity of whole meat reduced in favor of an increase in rabbits, rats, and chicken necks. The serval appears not to breed freely in captivity, and I have found few records. Three kittens were born and fully reared in the St. Louis Zoological Park in 1956 (Vierheller, 1957), and Stott (1954a) reports the birth of a litter in the San Diego Zoological Garden, the young unfortunately not surviving. Of three kittens born at the National Zoological Park, on May 2, 1961, two were successfully reared by hand (Theodore H. Reed, *in litt.*). A pair of servals in the Zoological Gardens of Basel is reported to have reared its eighteenth kitten in 1958 (Anon., 1958b). O. G. Jones (1952) gives the gestation period as 68–74 days.

The best longevity given by Flower (1931) is 8 years, 6 months, 13 days for an animal of the "servaline" type in the Zoological Gardens of London. Miss Hattie Ettinger, administrative assistant at the St. Louis Zoological Park, informs me (*in litt.*) that a serval lived in the St. Louis collection from June 9, 1938, to October 2, 1950, or 12 years, 3 months, 23 days.

Among the remaining Old World members of *Felis*, best known in zoological gardens are the tiny leopard cat (*F. bengalensis*) and the larger golden cat (*F. temmincki*). In the former the ground color is pale yellowish, thickly marked with rounded black spots. Its range, in several races, extends from eastern Siberia west to Baluchistan and south through India, the Malay Peninsula, and the larger islands to the Philippines. The golden cat is a much larger animal, normally unspotted reddish-brown in color, with black and whitish markings about the head and face. Wendnagel (1938) figures a fine captive melanistic specimen along with a normally colored companion. The range of the forms of the golden cat extends from Tibet to southern China and south through the Malay Peninsula to Sumatra.

The leopard cat, like many others, has a reputation for untamable ferocity, but it is natural to suppose that hand-reared specimens would be more responsive. A female kitten of this species, no more than a few months old, was received here on November 4, 1946. This little animal was extremely savage and could only be kept quiet by providing her with a darkened sleeping box in which she spent most of the day. During the period for which she was kept in quarantine while receiving her anti-feline panleucopenia treatment, she went into convulsions so frequently that the chances of reconciling her seemed slim. However, she was finally removed to a glass-fronted cage about 10 by 4 feet, in the Small Mammal House. Here she quickly learned to enter a shift cage when the door was opened by remote control, while her quarters received their daily cleaning. She soon became so accustomed to this routine that she spent her days sleeping quietly on a large log conveniently placed and had no further occasion to exhibit savagery. While most small cats seem to require a diet consisting largely of whole small mammals and birds, with very little beef or horseflesh, this leopard cat ate only 4–8 ounces of whole raw horse meat daily, well scored and rubbed with fine bone meal and cod-liver oil. She consistently refused rats, mice, rabbits, and pigeons. She maintained excellent condition until her death on May 8, 1960, after 13 years, 6 months, 4 days with us. Flower (1931) gives "12 or 13 years" for a specimen in the Singapore Zoological Gardens.

The golden cat has not done well here, and none has survived for more than 2 years. This poor showing perhaps can be accounted for by the fact that all of our specimens were received before means for protection against panleucopenia were available. Certainly our results should not be taken as a reflection on the durability of this handsome species, for Flower (1931) gives a longevity of 10 years, 9 months, 3 days for an animal in the Zoological Gardens of London. Miss Hattie Ettinger, administrative assistant at the St. Louis Zoological Park, informs me (*in litt.*) that a golden cat lived at that institution from August 20, 1927, to May 15, 1945, or 17 years, 8 months, 25 days. The species has been bred at the San Diego Zoological Garden (Stott, 1954a) and doubtless elsewhere.

The black-footed cat (*F. nigripes*) of South Africa is considered to be the smallest member of the Felidae, the total length of three specimens, measured in the flesh, ranging from 506 to 528 millimeters (Pocock, 1907). It has seldom been imported and has never been received here. One of the females of a trio received by the Catskill Game Farm, New York, in June, 1960, produced a litter of kittens in August of that year and another in September, 1961, each of two young. One of the latter lived for 8 weeks but none was fully reared (Roland Lindemann, personal communication).

Largest of the members of the genus *Felis* is the puma (*F. concolor*), known also as the mountain lion, cougar, panther, and catamount. This great, solidly brown, tawny, or grayish cat once ranged, in numerous races, over most of North and South America from southern Canada to Patagonia. In North America it is now restricted, except for possible stragglers, to Louisiana and Florida and the wilder parts of the west, from southern Canada to Mexico. B. S. Wright (1961) gives a photograph of the mounted skin of a puma killed in Maine in January, 1938, believed to be the last taken in the northeast. As in most members of the family, males exceed females in size and may weigh as much as 200 pounds and occasionally even more. Musgrave (1926), in reference to pumas in Arizona, says "the heaviest lion taken in this state weighed 276 pounds." Specimens from the northern and southern extremes of the range average larger than those from the tropics. The habitat may vary from broken plains to mountain elevations of 10,000 feet or more, usually in forested areas.

The puma hunts much on the ground, although it takes readily to the trees. Deer seem to provide a favorite food, while domestic stock may pay heavy toll where the range of the puma is involved. This animal seldom becomes a confirmed man-eater, although there are authentic accounts of instances of persons having been attacked and even devoured.

With the possible exception of the African lion, the puma is probably more often seen in zoological gardens than any other of the larger cats. Those from the cooler parts of its range, at least, are indifferent to cold, so that no provisions for winter heat are required. Most specimens that become available have been bred in captivity or reared by hand from an early age, so that they are fully accustomed to restraint. Inclosures of heavy wire mesh or steel bars, provided with rocks and logs for climbing and with secluded sleeping quarters, make adequate housing. A female of the Rocky Mountain race (*F. c. hippolestes*), largest of the North American pumas, was received here on December 15, 1947, and lived until September 29, 1958. This animal received an average of 4 pounds of whole raw horse meat treated by scoring with fine bone meal and cod-liver oil, 6 days weekly.

Pumas here are fasted on the seventh day, as are all of our larger cats. This diet was supplemented with occasional rabbits or similar food and appeared to be adequate.

Pumas breed readily in captivity and are kept and bred in so many institutions all over the world that enumeration is not necessary. While there is evidence that pumas in the wild may sometimes remain mated, it appears that such relations are usually of short duration, the pair soon separating. In any case, it is customary with captive animals to give the pregnant female seclusion and to allow her to rear the young before she is returned to the male. Asdell (1946) gives the gestation period as 90–93 days and the number of young per litter as from one to four. The kittens are spotted at birth, with ringed tails.

Our greatest longevity record for a puma here is 11 years, 11 months, 19 days. Flower (1931) reports 16 years for a specimen in the Hamburg Zoological Gardens, and Ulmer (1951) says a puma lived for 19 years in the Philadelphia Zoological Garden.

In tropical and subtropical regions of North, Central, and South America are found a number of small cats, most though not all of which are handsomely striped and spotted. Best known of these is the ocelot (*F. pardalis*), which is distributed in forested areas from the southwestern borders of the United States to northern Argentina. Although there is much variation in color, not only between the numerous races but among individuals of each, ocelots in general are buffy-yellow, the head and neck striped with black and the body heavily marked with spots of the same color. The spots frequently are centered with brown and may coalesce on the sides to form elongated chains. Size seems to increase toward the southern end of the range, the banded ocelot (*F. p. mitis*) of Brazil, northern Argentina, and Paraguay being an immense animal, as ocelots go. It is strongly marked with black, has heavy forelegs and large feet, so that, but for its color, it might well be mistaken for a small jaguar.

Closely related is the dainty margay (*F. wiedii*), which ranges in several forms from southern Texas to northern Uruguay. It is smaller than the ocelot, with a comparatively longer tail, and the spots ordinarily do not form bands along the sides.

Both animals are frequently taken when very young and reared by hand, so that they make tame and attractive pets. However, as they approach maturity they are likely to become unpredictable, even dangerous, and serious accidents have occurred when such animals have been privately kept. For the zoological garden, of course, these specimens are ideal and are frequently exhibited.

The jaguarundi (*F. yagouaroundi*) is a small, slender, long-tailed animal, strangely musteline in appearance. It occurs in two color phases, dark gray and reddish brown. At one time red individuals were considered to represent a separate species, designated as *F. eyra*. The many races extend from border areas of the southwestern United States to northern Argentina. The jaguarundi is a shy, secretive creature, an inhabitant of tropical or subtropical forests, and its natural habits are little known. Young kittens seem to be seldom found and reared, for most of the specimens that reach zoological gardens appear to have been captured at an age when the ways of the jungle have become so firmly fixed that the animals are difficult to establish in captivity.

Several others of the small South American cats are seen on occasion but none is commonly available. Geoffroy's cat (*F. g. geoffroyi*), found from Argentina to southern Brazil, and the salt desert cat (*F. s. salinarum*), from western Argentina, are among these. Certainly one of the most beautiful of the smaller spotted species is the pampas cat (*F. colocolo*), widely distributed in southern South America. A magnificent specimen was living in the National Zoological Park in 1958.

In the zoological garden all of these small American cats should be considered as sensitive to cold and dampness, so that their quarters should be both warm and dry. Cages should be sufficiently roomy to provide space for exercise and should contain logs, shelves, and sleeping retreats. Shift cages for use during cleaning periods are indispensable. Food should consist, as far as possible, of small mammals and birds: chickens, pigeons, sparrows, rabbits, rats, and mice. Raw meat, either ground or scored and fortified with fine bone meal and cod-liver oil, should be given only when other foods are not available. In this area, at least, these cats have little chance for survival unless promptly immunized against feline panleucopenia.

With the exception of the ocelot, most of these small species are seldom bred in captivity. While even the ocelot cannot be said to reproduce freely, there are scattered records of their having done so. Young were born and reared here as long ago as 1901 and 1902, while Zuckerman (1953) reports several early births in the Zoological Gardens of London. Benchley (1943, 1945) reports two such events in the San Diego Zoological Garden, and an anonymous writer (Anon., 1954c) gives an account of the rearing of a single kitten at the Calgary, Alberta, Zoological Gardens. The breeding of two races, one of which was *F. p. chibiguazu* [= *mitis*], at the Zoological Gardens of Buenos Aires is reported by Saporiti (1951). The number of young per birth is usually given as from one to three but the gestation period appears to be undetermined.

Geoffroy's cat (*F. geoffroyi*) is reported by Mann (1950) as having produced young in the National Zoological Park, and Saporiti (1951) lists both this species and the pampas cat (*F. colocolo*) as having bred in the Zoological Gardens of Buenos Aires. A single margay cat born in the National Zoological Park was successfully reared by the mother in an exhibition cage (Reed, 1961*a*).

The greatest longevity for an ocelot here is 6 years, 8 months, while Mann (1930) reports 6 years, 9 months for a specimen in the National Zoological Park, and Flower (1931) gives 9 years, 8 months, 7 days for an animal in the Zoological Gardens of London.

The following records are listed by Flower for other New World species: margay, at the Basel Zoological Gardens, 13 years, 1 month, 21 days; eyra (jaguarundi), at the Zoological Gardens of London, 9 years, 1 month, 23 days, and Geoffroy's cat, also at London, 8 years, 6 months, 28 days.

To the zoological garden the great cats—leopard, lion, tiger, jaguar, clouded leopard, and snow leopard, all here included in the genus *Panthera* —are of the greatest importance. The first four are to be found in most of the large collections, and even the clouded (*P. nebulosa*) and the snow leopards (*P. uncia*), rare and difficult though they may be, are sometimes seen. Traditionally these animals have been housed in large buildings, variously known as the Lion House, the Great Cats House, the Carnivora House, and so on. Such buildings, often architecturally imposing, have been focal points in most of the world's great zoological gardens. The basic plan is a "walk-through," with barred cages, on one or both sides, connected with outdoor compartments for use in clement weather. The Lion House in the New York Zoological Park, opened to the public in January, 1903, and then an advanced model of its kind, is still an excellent and serviceable building. It is 240 feet long and 110 feet wide, with six interior cages measuring 18 by 22 feet and six smaller ones measuring 12 by 22 feet. These connect directly with an outdoor series ranging from 38 by 42 feet, 6 inches to 12 feet, 6 inches by 24 feet in dimensions. Complete details of construction are given in the *Zoological Society Bulletin* for January, 1903, but salient points only need be considered here. At the back of each indoor cage is an elevated structure, rising 8 feet above the cage floor, containing a direct passage to the outer cage, flanked by retaining dens. The top forms a high platform, accessible by a series of "jump shelves," providing useful exercise as well as a much used retreat. Transfer of animals is facilitated by the use of a traveling shift cage, already described, and by direct communication between compartments. The larger outdoor cages are backed with rock-work, again providing variation from the floor level, and are also provided with small but deep pools for the use of those species that enjoy bathing. All cages, both indoors and out, are supplied with the scratching logs essential for keeping claws in order.

The most important innovation in the construction of this building was the use of wire mesh instead of bars for cage fronts. This was installed in spite of wide objection and, it must be said, with some qualms, on the basis that wire would never restrain lions and tigers. The wire used was 5-gauge steel, American Standard, and the mesh was 3 inches. It is still in use (1963), slight replacements having been required only because of occasional rust damage. It has never been damaged directly by any cat nor has it ever permitted any animal to escape. It is my personal feeling that this wire, painted black, provides better visibility than bars can possibly give. Also, it insures complete safety without the heavy appearance and unpleasant implications of bars.

Originally the indoor cages were floored with oak 2 by 4 strips, set on edge. However, these eventually became so saturated with urine that they had to be replaced. Later wood was abandoned entirely and the floors were covered with very fine steel-troweled concrete. In use for 30 years or more, this material has caused no trouble by abrading the feet of the animals. An oak duckboard, measuring 4 by 6 feet, is placed on the floor of each cage, to insure a warm and dry sleeping place. This reversion to concrete, of course, is in direct opposition to the long-established feeling that floors for big-cat cages must be of wood. However, wood quickly becomes foul-smelling, an objection that outweighs any favorable qualities it may have. Theoretically, at least, a composite material that would be constant, resilient, warm, and water-resistant without being slippery when wet would be more desirable than concrete, but all of the many substitute floor-covering materials that we have tried, while both warm and resilient, have either rolled into troughs after being walked upon steadily or have disintegrated under the action of water and urine. In the new Lion House at the Jardin des Plantes, floors are made of grooved teak blocks which, while presumably expensive, might prove to be effective.

Unless the ancient custom of poking meat through the bars with a long-handled fork is to be followed, a better and safer method for feeding the big cats must be devised. In our Lion House there is a space about 5 inches high beneath the wire at one end. This opening is closed by an iron bar which is removed at feeding time, so that the keeper is able to push the meat through without risk. This method, clumsy though it may be, has served us well. The only improvement I have seen is a device in use in the Jardin des Plantes. This consists of a V-shaped steel trough, hinged at the bottom, which can be tipped toward the keeper's space for filling, then inward to the cage, one side always closing the opening. The trough can be locked, of course, in either position.

The open moat, based largely on the experiments of Carl Hagenbeck at the beginning of this century, is now widely used. The method is effective for both lions and tigers but is less practical for the smaller members of *Panthera* because of their leaping and climbing ability. I have not seen a successful open inclosure for these animals. The salient point in the construction of such exhibit areas, of course, is the width and depth of the surrounding moats. Hagenbeck (1910:235) suspended a stuffed pigeon 10 feet above the ground and allowed various cats to attempt to bring it down. He found that lions and tigers could jump upward only about 6 feet, 6 inches and that leopards could not quite reach the pigeon. These figures were once confirmed to me by the late Theodore Schroeder, a former Hagenbeck employee and later head keeper in the Detroit Zoological Park. Nevertheless, they seem to me somewhat short of the animals' leaping ability, as I have seen a tigress, carrying a 10-pound piece of meat, leap cleanly to a shelf 8 feet above the floor and have measured the claw marks of a leaping lion, left 12 feet, 4 inches above the ground level. Hagenbeck also found that both tigers and leopards could cover 10 feet, on the flat, from a standing start but felt both might have done 13 or 14 feet with a run. He therefore made his trench at Stellingen 28 feet wide, a figure somewhat reduced in later practice.

Noted examples of the moated inclosure for lions and tigers in America are those in the Detroit and Chicago Zoological Parks. In the former the water moat used for confining tigers is 25 feet across and 16 feet deep, while that for lions is 21 feet wide by 12 feet deep. At Chicago the dimensions for tigers are the same as those at Detroit, but the Chicago lion moat is 20 feet across and 16 feet deep. The slightly concave back wall of the Detroit tiger exhibit is 20 feet high, as is that for lions, while at Chicago this wall, for lions, is only 16 feet. In all cases the land area of the inclosure slopes gradually downward from front to back, so that the moat wall on the visitors' side is higher than the inner one. In use for years enough to establish their efficacy as safety devices, these dimensions are now generally accepted as standard. In the superb tiger exhibit at the Parc Zoologique du Bois de Vincennes, Paris, the moat is 40 feet wide and 23 feet deep. These measurements are in accord with the colossal dimensions of the simulated rock background but do have the effect of somewhat dwarfing the animals exhibited.

Our own Lion Rock, opened to the public in 1941, comprises an exhibit area roughly triangular in shape and measuring about 50 feet on the viewers' side and approximately 65 feet to the apex. At front and back it is inclosed by dry moats 20 feet wide and 16 feet deep, while at the sides rows of wooden palings rise to a height of 16 feet, forming efficient barriers. At the left these palings conceal a low building containing seven individual cages, to which the animals are confined during periods of snow and cold. Since there is no backstop and the front moat is concealed by low shrubbery, the lions appear to be entirely free. Beyond them, antelopes may be seen grazing quietly on the African Plains, and from the opposite direction, with the antelopes in the foreground, the distant lions appear to be integrated in the same exhibit. As first constructed, no provision was made for the return of an animal reaching the moat bottom by accident. When such an incident finally happened, the unfortunate lion failed in its efforts to extricate itself and was securely trapped. As an emergency expedient, a wooden ramp was quickly built and lowered into the moat at a concealed point, giving access to the shelter building. This contrivance was barely in place before the frustrated lion climbed it, and the ramp has now become a permanent part of the operation.

The most recent development in the exhibition of the Felidae brings the formal building and the moated outdoor area into a single unit. This unification has been used in the Feline House in the Woodland Park Zoo, Seattle, Washington, built in 1951 (Johnson and Hall, 1954) and in the great Carnivora House in the Philadelphia Zoological Garden, opened to the public on April 14, 1951 (Anon., 1951b). Each of these fine buildings has two open moated areas, one for lions and one for tigers, to which the animals may be admitted from the indoor exhibition cages. The Philadelphia house, which is 300 feet long with two wings, each 83 feet in length, is equipped for the showing of small cats as well as the members of *Panthera*, so that fourteen forms were exhibited at the opening. At Seattle, in addition to the large moated inclosures, there are outdoor cages of conventional type. In front of these cages and between them and the guard rail is a moat, intended to restrain overenthusiastic visitors from attempting closer contact with the animals. Another innovation, perhaps of greater importance, is the use of glass cage fronts for the larger cats. This glass is Herculite, built in three layers, with an over-all thickness of $\frac{3}{4}$ inch and a calculated resistance to a blow of 300 pounds delivered at a speed of 30 miles per hour. As a safeguard in the unlikely possibility of complete collapse of the glass, an electrical trip installed in the middle layer of plastic will drop a steel mesh panel across the opening, precluding the escape of an animal.

In considering the great cats in detail, we come first to the leopard

(*P. pardus*), found in Asia from the Caucasus to eastern Siberia and south through Africa to Cape Province. A great many races, not always recognizable in the living animal, have been described. Pocock (1930, 1932) has described and discussed both the Asiatic and the African forms, while Ellerman and Morrison-Scott (1951) and Allen (1939) have given later opinions on the nomenclature.

In general, the ground color is tawny-yellow, marked with rounded black or dark brown spots, arranged in rosettes. There is much variation in both markings and ground color, the latter varying from gray or reddish to pale buff. Black individuals are found with some frequency in parts of the Asiatic region but are rare, though not unknown, in Africa (Pocock, 1930:68–69). Both normally colored and melanistic examples are said to occur in the same litter in nature (Blanford, 1888–91). In my own experience, captive pairs in which both animals were black have produced only black young, and I do not recall an instance in which black young have been born to spotted parents. The late Axel Reventlow once told me that a pair of leopards in the Zoological Gardens of Copenhagen, one spotted, the other black, bred cubs of both color phases. An albinistic specimen of the tall East African race (*Panthera pardus pardus*), recently living in the Central Park Zoo, New York City, was a beautiful creature. Its ground color was pale buff, almost white, its spots were very light brown, and its eyes were pink. This animal, a male, was brought from Mombasa with a normally colored male companion, as a "leopard-by-lion hybrid."

There is wide variation in the weights of leopards, which may be of racial or merely individual significance. As in most cats, males are substantially larger and heavier than females. The greatest weights given by Ward (1922) are 154 pounds for an Indian leopard and 140 pounds for a specimen from Somaliland. Sex is not stated in either case. Meinertzhagen (1938) gives the following weights, obtained in the field, for freshly killed animals: Mysore, India, male, 142 pounds, female, 129 pounds; Kenya, East Africa, males (five), 131–144 pounds, females (three), 98–129 pounds. The latter figures are of special value since they do not represent specimens selected for size but taken as they came.

The leopard is a bold and resourceful hunter, lurking in the foliage of forest trees or springing from ambush on the ground. It feeds on animals up to the size of deer, antelopes, and domestic cattle. Although it is not generally given to attacks on human beings, the literature abounds in accounts of man-eaters. One of the most remarkable is the statement by Sterndale, quoted by Finn (1929), concerning an Indian leopard that killed more than two hundred persons within a period of 3 years.

As already noted, moated inclosures in which leopards may safely be exhibited are not easily devised, and it is customary to keep them in cages of the conventional Lion House type. The provisions of our own building, as described, have proved fully satisfactory for leopards. While the statement of Blanford (1888–91) that leopards swim well is presumably correct, his objection to Blyth's account of a tame animal that was adverse to wetting its feet is not well founded. Captive leopards evidence as much dislike for water as any house cat, except only for drinking purposes.

Two leopards, a black male and a spotted female now (1963) living here, are estimated to weigh approximately 100 pounds each, no definite figures being available. On 3 days in the week each of these animals receives $2\frac{1}{2}$–3 pounds of whole raw horse meat, given without the bone. This is our practice with all of the larger cats, because of the risk of bone splinters becoming caught between teeth or causing damage in the intestinal tract. Twice weekly about 1 pound of scored raw meat, with fine bone meal and cod-liver oil rubbed into the cuts, is substituted for an equal amount of whole meat. On the sixth day muscle meat is omitted entirely and approximately 2 pounds of raw liver and 1 pound of kidneys are given instead. In accordance with long established custom there is no feeding on the seventh day in our Lion House, except to very young animals.

Properly adjusted and well-mated pairs of leopards breed freely in captivity, and many zoological gardens have been successful with them. That more are not produced may be because of the high nervous tensions that seem to pervade the species and the difficulty of obtaining or establishing reliable pairs. The best and surest method, of course, is to accustom young animals to living together. Any effort to introduce mature specimens to each other will bring the risk of injury and should be attempted only after the animals have become familiar with each other through a dividing barrier and have given evidence that its removal will be well received. Hand-reared individuals, of course, are more likely to be steady enough for breeding in captivity, but an exception to this generality is provided by Mann (1930) who gives an account of two pairs of wild-caught adults that each produced litters of two in the National Zoological Park only a year after their capture in Tanganyika. Zuckerman (1953) records twenty-seven births of leopards in the Zoological Gardens of London from 1839 to 1937. These occurred in every month of the year, except only January, the number of cubs per birth varying from one to three. The gestation period is given by Kenneth (1953) as 98–105 days.

A pair of adult black leopards, received here on April 3, 1941, had already become adjusted to each other. The male was a rather quiet, timid animal and the female, bold and aggressive in the true tradition of the supposedly more dangerous black leopard, was completely dominant. A single cub was born to this pair on November 1, 1942, and a litter of two on July 23, 1943. During the entire period the parents continued to live together. When birth was impending, the female retired to the den, which she did not permit the male to enter. When the cubs finally wobbled into the outer cage, she continued to protect them, but as they grew stronger, the male was gradually allowed to become familiar with them and finally to indulge in strenuous play. During the period of early cubhood the male was never seen to make an offensive gesture toward the cubs, although this may have been due to the defensive attitude of the dominant mother. However, when the youngsters reached the age of approximately 9 months, the male began to evidence impatience with their lively antics, and when he finally was seen to cuff them severely, it became necessary to remove them. This was a serious step, for the cubs, suddenly deprived of the protection of their parents, were as frightened as any wild-caught animals could be, and became reconciled only after considerable periods.

Because of this difficulty, it was decided that the next litter should be reared by hand. Therefore, when a single male cub was born on February 23, 1945, after an observed period of 90 days from the middle of the mating span, it was promptly removed and turned over to Mrs. Helen Martini, wife of the Lion House keeper. This cub, like its brothers and sisters, was black and naturally was named "Bagheera." At birth it was 14 inches from tip to tip and weighed 20 ounces. Fed at first on $\frac{1}{2}$ ounce of a mixture of one part evaporated milk and two parts water, given from a nursing bottle at 3-hour intervals, the cub progressed well, his blue eyes opening on the sixth day (Martini, 1955). At about 3 months he was given scraps of raw meat and was soon taking a mixture of chopped raw meat, fine bone meal, and cod-liver oil. Selections from a carefully compiled weekly record of Bagheera's weight growth are as follows:

Age (weeks)	Pounds	Ounces
Birth	1	4
4	2	8
8	4	8
12	6	0
16	10	8
24	21	0
32	32	0
40	49	0
52	71	0
78	88	0
96	98	0

At the age of 96 weeks, weighing was thought to be no longer safe or practical. However, it was considered that Bagheera had then reached his maximum, although not quite 2 years old, nor does his weight appear to have increased since that time.

The temperamental progress of Bagheera was most interesting. As a small cub, his disposition was friendly enough, as might have been expected, but gradually he began to concentrate on the Martinis and to withdraw from others. When he had reached the maximum recorded weight of 98 pounds, at the age of 96 weeks, Bagheera was removed to a cage in the Lion House which the Martinis did not enter. Completely friendly relations between them and the leopard were maintained through the wires. Others who crossed the guardrail were always cautioned to give Bagheera's cage a wide berth, for a black paw would shoot out through the wire like lightning if there seemed to be the slightest hope of striking home.

Our best longevity for a spotted leopard here is 17 years, 1 month, 18 days, established by a female of Asiatic origin. Bagheera, still living in October, 1963, had already exceeded this span. Flower (1931) gives 18 years each for animals in the Lisbon and Giza Zoological Gardens, respectively, and 21 years for a specimen in the Mysore Zoological Gardens. Twenty years for a leopard in the Philadelphia Zoological Garden is reported by Ulmer (1951).

The very anthropomorphizing that long ago designated the lion (*P. leo*) as the "king of beasts" has been employed, in later years, to dethrone him. A "king" has certain standards from which he may not deviate, so that when a starving lion soothes his hunger by eating small rodents or even carrion his position comes into question. But the lion, in spite of arguments that are no concern of his, is still an impressive animal. His most striking characteristic, I think, is that he is unafraid. A bold, powerful hunter, with no enemies of consequence, he has no sly tricks but goes straight to his business of firm attack. Zebras have usually been rated as the African lion's favorite prey, but a check made in the Kruger National Park, Transvaal, by Stevenson Hamilton, quoted by Shortridge (1934), revealed that wildebeests were first, waterbuck second, and zebras third. Five buffalo, two giraffes, a young hippopotamus, and an ostrich are also listed as victims. Since food animals of these types are mostly dwellers on open plains where grass is abundant, the lion lives there also, avoiding large deserts and dense forests.

This way of life brings the lion into contact with man and his herds of domestic stock, which graze over the same lands as antelopes and zebras. Depredations are a natural result, and man himself has not been exempt from the toll. Stories of the misdeeds of man-eating lions are too well known for repetition here. Nevertheless, the realization that, even in these days, the loss of human lives to wild animals is almost a commonplace comes as something of a shock. But a statement in the *Annual Report* of the Game and Fisheries Department of the Uganda Protectorate, January, 1955, to June, 1956 (1957), that at least seventeen deaths of natives from attacks by lions have occurred during that period is proof enough.

Once, the lion ranged across the plains of western and central India, southward from Sind, and from Greece, Turkey, and Persia to Africa, where it avoided only the Sahara and the great forests of the west. At the present time the species probably does not exist outside Africa, except for the remnant of the Indian lion (*P. l. persica*), which still persists, under strict governmental protection, in the Gir Forest, Kathiawar, India (Gee, 1956). Wynter-Blyth (1956) reports the result of a census of the Gir lions made in April, 1955, as showing 141 males and 100 females, for a total of 241 animals. In Africa itself the lion has been eliminated from the extreme north and south but still is found in most areas south of the Sahara, except the forested regions of the west and, of course, the Cape Province. Its numbers, however, are rapidly becoming reduced, for as the game goes, so must the lion.

The physical characters of lions vary greatly. The mane of the male makes its first appearance at the age of about 18 months, as a ridge along the nape, growing gradually downward and backward, reaching full development at from 5 to 6 years. It may be tawny, dark brown, or black, and may be very full with extensions along the belly line, scanty, or even lacking entirely, maneless males being not uncommon. Body color may also be of almost any shade of brown, and some individuals carry through their lives the dark markings of infancy. Some of these characters have been considered to be sufficiently stable for the designation of local races, ten being listed for Africa by Allen (1939). The "thorn" concealed in the tuft of hair at the tip of the lion's tail is a horny attachment of the skin, which has no known function.

Living male lions weighed here have been recorded as registering from 330 to 410 pounds, a single female 250 pounds. Fourteen freshly killed males are listed by Meinertzhagen (1938) as weighing from 329 to 421 pounds, while five females weighed from 269 to 409 pounds. The greatest weight for a male given by Shortridge (1934) is 516 pounds, for a female 260 pounds.

Zoo lions have been bred in captivity for so many generations that physical changes are likely to occur. Shortness of leg, "pushed-in" face, known as "bulldog," and sway backs are points to avoid in selecting breeding animals. Males almost invariably develop very heavy manes, usually considered a feature of beauty. However, an overdeveloped mane does obscure the suberb lines of the neck and head and is likely to become ragged and unsightly. Three of the largest and finest lions I have ever seen were part of a performing troupe. Their powerful, gracefully curved, maneless necks, long faces, and great size were particularly striking. Later investigation showed these animals to have been castrated.

The history of the lion in captivity is so interwoven with the early civilization of man that it is inextricable. Much of the available information is given by Loisel (1912), and an abridged account is furnished by Steyn (1951). Present-day methods of housing and exhibition have been discussed above, but some futher notes on the formation of moat groups may be of interest. Since such areas are usually of some size and often separated from visitors by considerable distances, a number of animals are required to make a suitable exhibit. Such animals, of course, must be attractive in themselves, and since they live almost in freedom, must get on well together. This means, of course, that males are the more useful and that no females can be included, as otherwise serious fighting will result. To introduce five or six adult male lions to each other and to get them to live peaceably together is no simple task. A much more workable method is to secure the required number of sound, well-reared cubs, aged from 6 to 9 months, and let them grow up together. This method has been followed here, successive groups of males occupying our Lion Rock up to 1959. All went well with a "pride" of five, all born in 1949, until they reached sexual maturity. When the group was liberated on the Rock in the spring of 1953, an unusual amount of quarreling and segregation occurred. Investigation showed that a rather small, pale-colored animal had developed a mate-relationship with the dominant male and was kept apart from the group by his protector, which would not allow another male to approach. This situation finally settled into routine, accepted by all, with a minimum of disturbance. This continued until the sudden death, on November 6, 1956, of the dominant male. After that time the surviving member of the couple was accepted as a member of the group on equal terms with the others and did not make another attachment. When these lions were shown to Konrad Lorenz on October 29, 1957, and the episode related to him, he recalled having heard of similar situations in European zoos, so that our experience is certainly not unique.

In 1959 these animals were considered to have become too inactive and were dispersed. Male cubs being unavailable at the time, a young pair

born in 1958 was introduced to the Rock. On January 29, 1962, the female
produced two cubs. There was some doubt about the safety of allowing
them their freedom on the Rock, for fear they might fall into the moat.
However, when they were liberated with their parents in early spring,
the solicitude of the mother removed all doubts, for she would not allow
them to approach the brink, a situation to which they quickly became
conditioned.

Lions are fed here on much the same basis as that already outlined for
leopards. In earlier times, beef was in common use for all of the carnivores
and horse meat, perhaps because it was not then subject to official inspection, was considered unsatisfactory. However, rising costs of beef eventually brought more serious consideration, and inspected, approved horse
meat is now generally used in the zoological gardens of this country. As
judged by the health, condition, and longevity of animals fed over long
periods on horse meat, it appears that beef offers no advantages. Cats that
have been accustomed to one or the other usually are reluctant to change
over and often will fast for some time before doing so.

Adult male lions here receive an average of 10–12 pounds of raw horse
meat, with no bone, daily on three days of the week. Allowances are made,
of course, for size and condition, very large animals sometimes requiring
as much as 15 pounds. One of our lionesses, an animal inclined to obesity,
receives only 6 pounds, on which she manages to maintain some degree
of obesity. A more normal lioness could be expected to require from 8 to
10 pounds. On two days about one half of the meat allowance is scored and
rubbed with fine bone meal and cod-liver oil, while on the sixth day an
equivalent amount of raw liver and kidneys is substituted for muscle meat.
Occasional individuals refuse liver or kidneys, sometimes both, so that
compensatory adjustments must be made. Adult lions are fasted on the
seventh day. Animals living together are separated at feeding time, not
only to control weight and condition but to prevent the fighting that otherwise might occur.

The breeding of lions in captivity, nowadays commonplace, was once
an undertaking of consequence, in which the Zoological Gardens of
Dublin and Leipzig, especially, achieved early fame. From 1857 to 1950,
502 cubs were produced in Dublin, and at Leipzig approximately 700
from 1878 to 1912 (Steyn, 1951). In their heyday these great centers
supplied lions to the zoological gardens of the world, but gradually
breeding successes elsewhere became so general that large scale operations
were no longer worthwhile. In the Report of the Royal Zoological Society of
Ireland for 1954 (1955), it is stated that because of increased feeding costs

and lack of demand, the once great breeding stock had been reduced to eleven. The *Report* for 1955 (1956) lists only six lions in the Dublin collection. At the present time few zoological parks attempt to breed lions, except on rare occasions, since the weaned cubs bring about a serious disposal problem.

It appears that in nature the lion is basically monogamous, although the rule is not inviolate and males have been reported as consorting with as many as four females and their cubs (Shortridge, 1934). These family parties may sometimes unite to form large "prides," while bands of several females only with their cubs, or of submature or unmated males, are not uncommon. The large natural inclosure in the National Zoological Gardens, Pretoria, described by Steyn (1951), is inhabited by a single adult male and four or more females. There are hidden individual cubbing dens, to which pregnant females are admitted well in advance of parturition; the cubs are removed as soon as they have been weaned.

If given reasonably roomy quarters, well-mated pairs of lions live peaceably together in captivity. The female produces and rears her cubs without interference by the male, which usually takes a kindly interest in his offspring as soon as they are about. A pair of lions with their cubs make a wonderfully attractive exhibit but one in which few zoological gardens are able to indulge, for the first litter will not be the last, and a surplus of hungry lion cubs can be economically serious. For this reason the sexes are usually kept separately in present-day zoological gardens, and breeding is permitted only on occasion.

Young female lions usually become cyclic when about 3 years old, while males appear to require several months longer to achieve sexual maturity. The female is polyestrous, periods occurring without regard to season, at 3-week intervals (Asdell, 1946). It is thus simple to introduce, at the appropriate time, a familiar male or even a stranger that has previously made himself known through intervening bars. After the period of heat has passed, the male may be removed or allowed to remain, depending on the temperaments of the animals. The gestation period for lions is just over 100 days, exact figures being difficult to derive because the period of estrus may extend over several days. Asdell (1946) gives the spread as 105–13 days. The only determination recorded here is 106 days from last noted copulation. Steyn (1951) presents figures from four institutions that show the number of cubs per litter to be from 1 to 6, with an average of 3.04. He quotes Cedric L. Flood as having reported that a lioness in Dublin gave birth to 4 living cubs and was later found to have retained 3 dead ones. This total of 7 appears to be unique.

At birth, lion cubs are more or less strongly spotted and striped, these dark markings sometimes persisting into adulthood. Schneider (1953) has made an extensive study of the variations in these markings. Lydekker (1893–96, 1:367) says that lion cubs are born with their eyes fully open, and this statement has frequently been repeated. It is possible that this may happen on occasion, but certainly all of the many newborn cubs I have seen had the eyes closed. Each of two females born here on December 22, 1944, opened one eye on the fifth day and the other on the next.

Each of these cubs measured $21\frac{1}{2}$ inches, tip to tip; one weighed 2 pounds, 12 ounces, the other an even 3 pounds. A male born dead in the same litter weighed 3 pounds, 15 ounces. The mother of these cubs was a notoriously nervous animal which had previously neglected her young, and since we were anxious to attempt hand-rearing lion and tiger cubs together, the two little females were lifted. One died from an intestinal infection 6 months later, but the other was fully reared and was still living in 1963. The growth of this animal, to the age of 9 months, was recorded as follows:

Date	Pounds
Dec. 22*	3
Jan. 6	$6\frac{1}{2}$
Feb. 3	8
Mar. 8	17
Apr. 7	24
May 5	31
June 2	45
July 7	60
Aug. 4	78
Sept. 22	99
*Birth	

The methods of feeding and care followed in the rearing of this cub were exactly the same as those used for tigers and will be considered under that species (pp. 385–86).

The problem of "star-gazing" has long troubled breeders of the great cats. Young animals so afflicted turn their heads to one side or even invert them, at the same time exhibiting general lack of muscular co-ordination. Tyrwhitt-Drake (1914) considered the disability to be the result of excessive feeding and insufficient exercise. Schneider (1933) describes and figures the condition in young lions, tigers, and leopards. With some reservations about hereditary possibilities, he considers dietary deficiencies to be responsible. The conviction is supported by Scheunert (1933), who attributes the difficulty to vitamin B_1 avitaminosis and describes the relief of the affliction in two lion cubs by the administration of dried yeast.

On the other hand, the possibility that a hereditary factor may be responsible seems now to be receiving increasing support, since "star-gazers" have been known to occur in succeeding litters of certain females. The late C. L. Flood told me in 1950, when he was director of the Dublin Zoological Gardens, that his dwindling stock of lions was producing so many "star-gazers" that he was seeking an unrelated male in the hope of improving the situation, which he attributed to inbreeding. Appelman (1956) says "everybody in charge of a zoological garden knows the 'star-gazing' lions and tigers which always occur after lengthy inbreeding, for which reason he will always look for refreshment of blood."

There is a general feeling, too, that while progress of the affliction, once developed, may be checked by dietary supplements of vitamins and minerals, damage already incurred cannot be corrected. I can contribute nothing from our experience here, since no "star-gazing" cub has so far appeared in our collection. Obviously, much more work in this field will be required before a final solution is reached.

It has often been said that a lion over 10 years old has passed his peak of usefulness as an exhibition animal and is on the downgrade. Severe though this restriction may seem, it is certainly true that somewhere between that age and 15, signs of senility are bound to appear. Because of the actually pathetic appearance of noticeably aging lions, 14 years, 3 months is the longest period a male has been retained here. That much greater ages can be attained is shown by the numerous records given by Flower (1931), which run from 15 to 29 years. The latter, accredited to the Cologne Zoological Gardens, apparently lacks full documentation, but the 25 years, 18 days achieved in the Dublin collection is certainly authentic.

Rivaling or perhaps even surpassing the lion in size and strength, the tiger (*P. tigris*) is the typical great cat of Asia. Its striking pattern of black or brownish stripes on tawny coat undoubtedly has concealment value to an animal that is a confirmed forest dweller, seldom venturing into the open. Tigers are found from the Caucasus across Asia to eastern Siberia and south over the forested areas of China, India, and the Malay Peninsula to Sumatra, Java, and Bali. There are no tigers in Ceylon or Borneo. While the tigers of the frigid north are large, long-coated, and pale in color, there is a gradual reduction in size and length of coat as well as a deepening of color toward the south, so that the island races are noticeably small, dark, and short-haired. The races have been thoroughly discussed and figured by Pocock (1929). A revision of the names assigned by Pocock has been made by Ellerman and Morrison-Scott (1951), who recognize six races. The three accepted island forms are listed by Chasen (1940). Melanistic and albinistic individuals have been reported. A description and figure of an example of the latter, followed by editorial comment, are given by Robinson (1928). On November 30, 1960, a "white tiger" that had been presented to the National Zoological Park by John W. Kluge of the Metropolitan Broadcasting Company arrived here for an overnight stay. It was forwarded to Washington on December 1. This animal, bred in the collection of the Maharajah of Rewa, in central India, was a well-grown female about 2 years old. Its ground color was nearly white with faint cream overcast, and the stripes were sooty black. The eyes, reported as blue, appeared pale green to me. A general account and description have been given by Reed (1961b).*

Useful standing heights and weights of tigers are not easily come by, most of the figures given in the literature having to do with more or less controversial tip-to-tip measurements of dead animals. Pocock (1929) says a very large male Manchurian tiger, measured by sighting in his cage in the Zoological Gardens of London, stood 38 inches at the shoulder. A large male Bengal, measured by the same means in our collection, stood 36 inches and a fine female 30 inches. Goodwin (1954) says a Siberian tiger may weigh over 650 pounds. The actual weight of a male Bengal, killed in central India, is given by Hornaday (1910) as 495 pounds, while the greatest size given for the race by Lydekker (1893–96, 1:375) is 540 pounds. The general average of male Bengal tigers is probably in the area of 400 pounds. Two exceptionally fine males reared here, each within a few days of 2 years old weighed 436 and 438 pounds, respectively. At the same time a female litter mate weighed 311 pounds.

Unlike the lion, the tiger is essentially a solitary animal, and the small groups that do occur are usually formed of mother and young, the latter sometimes nearly fully grown. The tiger is even more nocturnal in habit than the lion, so that most of its hunting is done at night. Deer and pigs form the bulk of the natural prey, but larger animals, even young elephants, are sometimes attacked. In times of food scarcity the tiger, like the lion, eats whatever it can get, even down to the level of insects. Near native villages, of course, the tiger is a notorious killer of domestic cattle and even, on occasion, becomes a man-eater; Corbett (1945) gives a list of sixty-four persons killed during 5 years by a single tiger.

In captivity the tiger appears to have been as well known to the ancients as the lion. Certainly it took its place in the combats of the Roman amphitheater (Loisel, 1912). It had its part, too, in the gradual development of the zoological garden and in present times has assumed a position superior to that of its ancient rival. For while the tiger thrives well in captivity,

*See Addenda, pp. 734–35.

under proper conditions, its life span appears to be somewhat shorter than that of the lion, and young are produced and reared much less readily. Also, in spite of the great expanse of its range, the tiger is nowhere locally abundant, so that wild-caught specimens are never freely available. For these reasons the market price of tigers has not fallen as has that of lions, remaining at a high level, so that no indisposable surplus seems ever to have existed.

Housing for tigers has already been discussed under "Lions" (pp. 362–79), so that little need be added here. There is the point that tigers not only swim well but appear to enjoy water-play, so that either a water-filled moat or a large pool should be provided. At least one side should have a shallow approach to insure easy emergence, as otherwise a water-soaked tiger may readily become exhausted or even drown. It has been our experience that if a Bengal tiger goes to sleep on a cold rock or concrete floor after a heavy meal, gastric disturbance is likely to result, so that in winter our animals are kept confined to heated quarters. Siberian tigers, however, if properly acclimated, seem impervious to the effects of cold and hence are most suitable for all-year exhibition in outdoor inclosures.

The feeding of tigers here follows the system already outlined for lions and leopards. Two large adult males, considered but not definitely known to exceed 500 pounds in weight, received an average of 13 pounds of horse muscle meat daily, with the appropriate exceptions mentioned under "Leopards" and "Lions" (pp. 374, 379). Our breeding tigress, "Dacca," an animal of good size, receives 12 pounds daily when carrying or feeding young and 10 pounds during resting intervals. A smaller, non-breeding sister keeps in good condition on 8–9 pounds. In providing ground bone for cat animals it appeared to us, probably with some justification, that fresh bone might be more desirable than a dried product. We therefore ground the bone that remained after the meat had been trimmed for each day's feeding. However, we soon found that the use of this material quickly produced blood in the feces, particularly in tigers, and that we were unable to grind it fine enough to avoid this condition. Since then we have used only commercial sterilized bone meal, which seems to furnish the required calcium and phosphorus, with no ill effects.

The mating habits of tigers in nature do not appear to be thoroughly well known, but the general impression is that the sexes live separately through most of the year, meeting and consorting during the female's period of estrus only, and separating once she has become pregnant. Locke (1954) says that this appears to be the case with the tigers of Malaya. On the other hand, this rule may not be entirely inviolable, for Blanford (1888–91:61) says that males may sometimes associate with mother and young. In any case, it is customary in zoological gardens to remove the male as soon as the female is no longer cyclic and not to return him until the young are no longer with her. Where more than average space is available, this method may have exceptions. The well-known pair of tigers kept in the large chalk-pit den at Whipsnade made a beautiful exhibit when seen in 1938 with a litter of cubs about 3 months old. Vevers (1948) says that the female, received in 1932, gave birth to thirty-seven cubs from 1933 to 1941 in this pit and successfully reared nineteen, while paired with two successive males. Such an experience with breeding tigers must be rare indeed.

The estrus cycle in the tiger seems not to have been thoroughly investigated, but experience here indicates that the female is polyestrous, heat recurring at intervals of about 3 weeks, as reported for the lion by Asdell (1946), receptivity continuing for about 5 days. Asdell (*loc. cit.*) gives the gestation period of the tiger as 105–9 days; our figures here, from last observed mating, are 100–108 days. Numbers of cubs per litter born here have varied from 1 to 4; the average for the Zoological Gardens of London, as given by Zuckerman (1953), for seventeen litters, is 2.3. Schomberg (1957:99) says that a litter of 6 was born in the Edinburgh Zoo in 1954.

Up to 1944 our experience in breeding tigers had been anything but good. From time to time cubs had been born, it is true, but no mother had ever succeeded in rearing her offspring. In that year we had a small, very nervous, jungle-bred female named "Jenny" that had been with us for 10 years, paired with a very large but decrepit male. Jenny had produced several litters of cubs but had lost them all. We determined, therefore, to lift the next litter and attempt hand-rearing. When small squalls were heard coming from the cubbing den on February 8, 1944, Jenny was coaxed out and the den was entered from the back. With the use of cotton gloves well soaked in Jenny's urine and carefully dried, the three beautiful cubs were sexed, weighed, and measured. One was removed and the others were taken during the two following days, Jenny having again demonstrated her inability or unwillingness to care for them. The cubs were turned over to Mrs. Helen Martini, whose husband, Fred, is keeper of our Lion House. Details concerning the rearing of these cubs have been reported by Martini (1955) and Crandall (1944a, 1944b) and will be treated more briefly here.

The cubs were kept, at first, in a box about 2 feet in each dimension, with open top and padded sides and floors. An electric heating pad was attached upright on one side, to provide warmth without risk of overheating. It was soon found that the cubs had a tendency to attach their mouths to feet or tail-tips of each other, sucking vigorously, so that separate boxes had to be provided.

Food, at first, consisted of a mixture of 13 ounces of evaporated milk to 26 ounces of water, with 3 drops of a multiple vitamin preparation and 1 teaspoonful of dicalcium phosphate added. Two to 3 ounces were heated to body temperature and given from a nursing bottle with a small rubber nipple, at 3-hour intervals, from 6:00 in the morning to midnight. After each feeding the anus was massaged gently with a moistened gauze pad, usually resulting in evacuation. Occasionally there would be evidence of diarrhea, but this condition usually corrected itself when the formula was changed to one part evaporated milk and three parts water. As growth progressed, the quantity of food taken naturally increased, but the relative proportions of the ingredients remained the same.

When the cubs were about 5 weeks old, $\frac{1}{2}$ teaspoon of liver juice was added to the formula, chiefly with the idea of preparing the cubs for a meat diet. At the age of 8 weeks each cub was given a small ball of chopped raw meat. This was eaten greedily but the results were appalling: severe gastric disturbance resulted, in one case so serious that we feared the cub might not recover. As soon as they had returned to normal, we substituted meat juice for the liver extract, with satisfactory results. When the cubs were just short of 11 weeks old, each was given a section of rib, to which bits of raw meat adhered. These were greedily licked clean, and as this time the meat caused no ill effects, the quantity was gradually increased. The cubs were 18 weeks old before they could be induced to drink by lapping, and even then they did so reluctantly. At that time each cub's total daily consumption was 3 pounds of chopped raw horse meat, to which had been added $\frac{1}{2}$ teaspoon fine bone meal and $\frac{1}{4}$ tablespoon cod-liver oil, in addition to approximately 1 pint of the milk formula.

At birth on February 8, 1944, each of these three cubs measured exactly 20 inches from tip to tip. Eyes, of course, were closed. Growth records of these animals are given in Table 7. No further weights were obtained, but it is assumed that all the animals eventually well exceeded the figures reached at 2 years of age.

There is much variation in elapsed time before the eyes of tiger cubs open. Of these three cubs, Dacca opened one eye on the ninth day, Rajpur on the eleventh, and Raniganj not until the seventeenth day. In most cases the second eye does not open until the day after the first. On the eleventh day all were cutting their first incisors.

In remarking on the strong temperamental differences in tigers, Sterndale (1884) says the local villagers know "that such a one is daring and rash;

another is cunning and not to be taken by any artifice; that one is savage and morose; another is mild and harmless." Very obvious characteristics were noticed in our three cubs at an early age. At 4–5 weeks, Raniganj was recorded as "definitely bad tempered," Rajpur as "fat and indolent," and Dacca as "bright and friendly" (Crandall, 1944a). Four months later, it was noted that Raniganj was "furtive and unpleasant," Rajpur "slow, fat, lazy and good-natured," and that Dacca "remains the hoyden" (Crandall, 1944b). It is interesting to observe that these characteristics, in more mature form, it is true, persisted in these animals in adulthood.

TABLE 7

GROWTH RECORDS OF THREE TIGER CUBS

Date	Rajpur (Male)		Raniganj (Male)		Dacca (Female)	
	Pounds	Ounces	Pounds	Ounces	Pounds	Ounces
Feb. 8, 1944*	2	9	2	8	2	11
Feb. 17, 1944	4	0	—		—	
Mar. 13, 1944	9	3	7	8	8	0
Apr. 24, 1944	29	0	29	6	28	0
July 19, 1944	59	0	59	0	52	0
Aug. 23, 1944	82	0	83	0	75	0
Oct. 1, 1944	118	0	124	0	108	0
Nov. 11, 1944	147	0	153	0	128	0
Feb. 7, 1946	438	0	436	0	311	0

*Birth

When the cubs had reached the age of approximately 3 years, Dacca began to show a strong preference for Rajpur and made life so unpleasant for Raniganj that he was removed to another cage. At about 3 years, 8 months, Dacca reached menarche. Periodically, she sought the attentions of Rajpur, rolling on her back, licking him, and striking him playfully with her paw. When she assumed the copulatory position, Rajpur attempted to complete the act but, at least at first, was incapable of doing so. We were taken entirely by surprise, therefore, when she gave birth to a cub, on May 4, 1948, in an open cage. As we watched, she leaped to a shelf and dropped another, which died later of a ruptured spleen. Dacca was quickly moved to the adjoining cage and the cubs placed in a nest box in the den. Dacca accepted the change readily and later in the day gave birth to two more cubs. From these facts it is easily discerned that while Dacca became sexually mature soon after passing the age of $3\frac{1}{2}$ years, Rajpur did not do so for some time but certainly had done so, without our knowledge, at least 15 days before he reached the age of 4 years.

From the first Dacca showed the greatest devotion to her cubs and gave no evidence of disturbance at being fastened out of the den daily while

Mrs. Martini checked and handled the cubs. In fact, on one occasion when Mrs. Martini was calling to her from the cage front, Dacca brought a cub and placed it in Mrs. Martini's hands, extended into the cage through the wire front. The tiger then walked toward the den, but when Mrs. Martini called frantically for her to come back and take the cub, she calmly did so and returned it to the den.

The introduction of these cubs to raw meat and then to the mixture was accomplished without much difficulty at an age between 11 and 12 weeks. At about this time Dacca began to show evidence of impatience with the playful antics of her brood and finally cuffed one with too much vigor, bowling it over and breaking one of its legs. This injury eventually mended, but in the meantime we provided a 3-foot barrier, over which Dacca could leap but which the cubs could not negotiate. This barrier became standard, and there were no further accidents. We adopted, too, the practice of weaning cubs when they were between $3\frac{1}{2}$ and 4 months old. This not only made certain that each received its proper allotment of food but relieved the mother of the necessity of avoiding their constant attentions.

From 1948 to 1959 Dacca produced eleven litters (not bred in 1955) totaling thirty-two cubs, of which twenty-eight were fully reared, some by the mother, some by Mrs. Martini. Young per litter varied from one to four, the division of sexes being nineteen males and thirteen females. One litter of four consisted of females only, while another of the same number contained only males. Weights at birth varied from 3 pounds, 1 ounce to 3 pounds, 9 ounces for males, and from 1 pound, 8 ounces to 2 pounds, 12 ounces for females. In spite of the fact that this was a brother–sister mating, all the cubs were strong and vigorous. However, a pair, litter mates, born in 1949 and sold to the Zoological Gardens at Baltimore, Maryland, were allowed to breed, and the female failed to produce viable young, stillbirths occurring in 1953, 1954, and 1955 (Arthur Watson, *in litt.*).

Because of friendly relations existing between Rajpur and Dacca, we were able to plan times of birth with some accuracy. Put together about January 15, the animals lived in perfect amity, and pregnancy usually occurred during the first following estrous period. A month or so later Dacca would become less tolerant of Rajpur's presence, finally treating him with such vixen-like severity that to save him from the actual persecution to which he meekly submitted, he was removed. Our hope was for births in May, so that the cubs might have favorable growing weather and could be shown out of doors. Actually, eight of Dacca's first nine litters were born in May, the ninth on June 3. Later, conception became more irregular and the two final births occurred in November.

All our tiger cubs, as well as the young of other cat animals, were immunized against feline panleucopenia or cat enteritis. The process of treatment applied by Dr. Leonard J. Goss, then our assistant director and veterinarian, was as follows: Tiger cubs reared naturally and presumably protected by the antibodies of the mother's milk while nursing received 10 or 12 cc. of commercial cat vaccine at the age of 3 months, followed by a similar dose 3 months later. Hand-reared cubs were given ½ cc. per pound of body weight of homologous enteritis serum as soon after birth as possible, repeating every 10 days until they reached the age of 3 months. Fourteen days later the procedure followed for naturally reared cubs was instituted. This treatment, of course, does not give permanent immunity but the expectation is that before the protective effect of the vaccine has waned, the cubs will be exposed to the virus of the disease and so acquire permanent resistance. To make certain that this will occur, small doses of live virus have sometimes been administered, but since this method presents obvious dangers it has not been practiced here.

The ages known to have been reached by captive tigers are less than those which have been recorded for lions. Flower (1931) says that there "appears to be no definite record of a Tiger living to twenty years," and the greatest longevity listed by him is that of a Siberian tiger that lived for 19 years in the Cologne Zoological Gardens. Nair (1957) reports the death of a tiger that had lived for 19 years in the Zoological Gardens of Trichur, Travancore-Cochin. Jenny, the female Bengal tiger referred to above, was received here on April 11, 1934. On December 13, 1948, she was sent on loan to the Staten Island Zoo, New York, where she died on December 4, 1953, after 19 years, 7 months, 23 days in New York.*

While both distributional and biological barriers presumably make hybridization between lions and tigers in nature improbable, such cross-breeding with captive animals is not uncommon. Hagenbeck (1910:115–16) says "I have bred many [hybrid] young from lions and tigers" and notes in a particular case that "one male hybrid weighs as much alone as the two parents together," an increase in size apparently being characteristic of such animals. One of these Hagenbeck products was deposited here in 1903.

The offspring of male tiger and female lion is referred to as a "tigon," or "tiglon," while in the reciprocal mating the term "liger" is applied. A male liger, bred in captivity in India and exhibited in the Zoological Gardens of London, is described and figured by Pocock (1935). The young are strongly spotted and striped, some of these markings usually persisting in adults, in which the ground color is usually darker than that of either

*See Addenda, p. 735.

parent species. Fully adult males may show cheek tufts and some indication of mane.

There seems to have been little interest in the production of lion–tiger hybrids in this country. While there may have been other instances, the only successful case known to me is the birth of a female liger in the Salt Lake City Zoological Gardens in 1948. The cub was removed and reared by hand (Sloan, 1949).

In 1935 four ligers, from two litters, were reared in the Zoological Gardens of Bloemfontein, South Africa. Three of these animals, a male and two females, were still living in 1953 (Van Ee, 1953). In a mimeographed sheet, undated but probably 1953, Dr. A. J. Louw, municipal veterinarian of Bloemfontein, reports the weight of this male as 750 pounds, and his shoulder height as $1\frac{1}{2}$ feet greater than that of an adult male lion. These animals are of particular interest, since Van Ee (*loc. cit.*) reports that frequent mating between the hybrids and of the male with three different lionesses proved fruitless. This is in accord with the general belief that such hybrids are sterile (Hagenbeck, 1910). However, Leyhausen (1950) gives an account of a cub born at the Hellabrunn Zoological Gardens in 1943 to a female lion–tiger hybrid paired to a lion. This cub, successfully reared, was later sent to Wuppertal, where, mated with a lion, she produced nine cubs in five litters, from 1948 to 1950, gestation periods varying from 103 to 113 days (Kemna, 1953). These notes seem to support the suggestion that male hybrids are "usually, if not invariably, sterile" (Gray, 1954), while indicating that females may sometimes, at least, be fertile.

A reference to a lion–leopard hybrid reported to have been bred at Schönbrunn is given by Gray (*loc. cit.*). Flower (1929) says that "a hybrid between a male Lion and a female hybrid Jaguar–Leopard, which had been bred in America, was deposited [in the Zoological Gardens of London], 14 April, 1908." Doi (1960) reports the birth of two cubs to a male leopard and a lioness in the Koshien Hanshin Park, near Osaka, Japan, on December 2 and 3, 1959. The parents, born in the Zoo in 1955, were brought up together and shared in the rearing of the cubs.

The jaguar (*P. onca*) is not only the largest member of this family found in the Americas but in the world is exceeded in size only by the lion and the tiger. As compared with the leopard, the jaguar is much larger and heavier, with especially powerful forelegs and massive head. Rings or rosettes of spots are arranged on the body in much the same manner in both species, but while the center of the circle is usually clear in the leopard, it generally includes one or more small spots in the jaguar. More or less complete melanism seems to occur as frequently in the jaguar as in the leopard, so that black individuals are not uncommon. Differences in size, coloring, and cranial characters are the principal distinctions on which the several races are based (Nelson and Goldman, 1933). At the northern extremity of its range the jaguar is not a particularly large animal, probably seldom reaching a weight of 250 pounds. However, size increases toward the south, and I am informed (*in litt.*) by Sasha Siemel, whose jaguar-hunting exploits are well known, that he has killed male jaguars in the southern Mato Grosso of Brazil that weighed in excess of 350 pounds.

Ranging from the southwestern borders of the United States through Mexico and Central America to northern Patagonia, the jaguar has been greatly reduced in numbers or even completely extirpated from many of its former haunts. It is essentially a dweller in lowland forests, climbing and leaping with skill and agility, at least until increasing weight hampers such activities. However, it may venture to fairly high altitudes in some areas and has invaded the open pampas in southern South America, where it finds shelter in clumps of reeds or low bush. Most of its hunting is done on the ground, where it kills deer, peccaries, and domestic stock. However, it does not hesitate to enter water in pursuit of tapirs and capybaras or to capture fish, turtles, and even crocodiles.

In captivity the jaguar seems more inclined to be morose, even occasionally savage, than does the more alert and active leopard. This tendency persists even in hand-reared animals, which, while perhaps perfectly tame, nevertheless seem less responsive. In spite of these characterizations the jaguar is, of course, a perfectly satisfactory zoo subject. Although it undoubtedly experiences fairly low temperatures at the extremities of its range, the jaguar is generally considered as sensitive to cold and is provided with heated quarters where the need is indicated. Accommodations already described in our Lion House serve very well, outdoor cages being provided with pools for summer use.

Because of the leaping and climbing abilities of the jaguar, moated inclosures for them have seldom been attempted. However, Jean Delacour has described to me a large area of this type, in the general order of the lion inclosures at Whipsnade and Pretoria, used for jaguars at the Zoological Gardens of Rio de Janeiro, Brazil. It was inhabited, at the time of Mr. Delacour's visit in 1957, by a large male and four or five females and was most successful, pregnant females being closed into feeding cubicles and removed to cubbing dens.

Our feeding schedule for jaguars is the same as that used for other big cats. A large male now living here receives an average of 7 pounds of raw, boneless horseflesh daily and a female 5 pounds, the variations already noted for other species being observed proportionately.

Well-established pairs of jaguars will breed regularly in captivity, and more than one small zoological garden has found means for the purchase of new animals through the sale of the offspring of such a pair. In establishing reliable breeders, best results are certainly obtained by introducing young animals and allowing them to mature together, for strange adults are not always amenable. In an early experience here a female was admitted, perhaps without a sufficiently long introductory period, to the cage of an apparently friendly male, which promptly killed her by biting her neck and crushing two cervical vertebrae (Anon., 1903).

At least in captivity, the jaguar is polyestrous and breeds at any season, as indicated by the widely spread dates of six births in the Zoological Gardens of London (Zuckerman, 1953). Our experience in breeding jaguars here has been limited to the offspring of a pair of litter mates born and reared by hand in the Cleveland Zoological Park. These animals, born on July 11, 1950, were received here on November 21 of that year. Their course of immunization against feline enteritis, to which jaguars seem especially susceptible, had already been completed.

As the cubs grew, they lived peacefully together and continued friendly relations with their keepers. As they approached the age of 3 years, the presumed time of maturity, they were kept under close surveillance but no mating behavior was seen. However, on November 10, 1953, a single male cub was found in the den and the father was promptly removed from the cage. The cub appeared normal, its total length on day of birth being 16 inches, its weight 1 pound, 14½ ounces. Its eyes opened on the thirteenth, but when the den was inspected on the following day it was missing, presumably having been devoured by the mother. Taking the gestation period as about 100 days—Asdell (1946) gives it as from 93 to 110—then mating must have occurred early in August, when the animals were approximately 3 years and 1 month old.

For 2 weeks following the birth the jaguars remained separated. During this short time the male developed marked truculence, even toward his keepers. At the end of this period he was allowed to enter the female's cage under observation, but usually could be permitted to remain for a few minutes only because of his increasingly rough treatment of his mate. This continued until mid-December, when friendlier relations were established, copulation occurring on December 23. Further matings were observed, sometimes several times daily, through January 3, 1954, when the female ceased to be receptive and the male was removed. On April 11,

1954, one male and two female cubs were born. No exact gestation period can be derived from these dates and term can be given only as from 98 to 109 days.

The cubs were allowed to remain with the mother until April 18, when she began to evidence uneasiness by carrying them about the cage. They were then removed and placed in the care of Mrs. Martini, who successfully reared them. Tip-to-tip measurements of the cubs on that date (age 7 days) were: male, 20 inches, female, $20\frac{1}{2}$ inches, and female, 21 inches. The body ground color was pale buffy, heavily marked with rounded, solid black spots, some showing faint indication of pale centers. Faces bore narrow black stripes which, a month later, had broken into small, solid spots. At that time, however, the body markings remained unchanged. All had their eyes open at the time (age 7 days), but no specific dates were noted. Care, feeding and immunization schedules were the same as those outlined above for tiger cubs (p. 389). Growth records of the three jaguar cubs are given in Table 8.

TABLE 8
GROWTH RECORDS OF THREE JAGUAR CUBS

Date	Male		Female		Female	
	Pounds	Ounces	Pounds	Ounces	Pounds	Ounces
Apr. 18, 1954*	2	$14\frac{1}{2}$	3	2	3	3
Apr. 29, 1954	3	$14\frac{1}{2}$	3	$15\frac{1}{2}$	4	0
May 26, 1954	5	1	4	8	4	$9\frac{1}{2}$
July 1, 1954	11	9	10	4	10	2
Aug. 5, 1954	23	8	18	8	20	0
Apr. 6, 1955	—		110	0	101	0
Feb. 20, 1956	166	8	—		—	

*Age 7 days

A jaguar is reported by Mann (1930) as having lived for 13 years, 1 month in the National Zoological Park, while our best record here is 13 years, 8 months. Flower (1931) records two specimens that lived for 20 years each, one at the Zoological Gardens of Hamburg, the other at Cologne. The greatest longevity given by him is that of an animal which, born at Leipzig in 1902, died in the Zoological Gardens of Rotterdam in 1925, "at least 22 years, 4 months, 25 days, probably 23 years old."

The clouded leopard (*P. nebulosa*) is here assigned to this genus in accordance with Simpson (1945), although Ellerman and Morrison-Scott (1951) retain *Neofelis* for the species. Three subspecies are recognized by the latter authorities, ranging from Nepal and Burma to Indochina, southern China, and Formosa. The clouded leopard is a long-bodied, short-legged animal, its gray or pale-tawny coat heavily striped and spotted with black, so that the general effect is very dark. It is a comparatively small animal, Blanford (1888–91) quoting a weight of 44½ pounds for an adult male. Little seems to be known of the natural habits of the clouded leopard, beyond the statements that it is nocturnal and arboreal, seldom coming to the ground.

Although Sányál (1892) mentions a very tame specimen that once lived in the Zoological Gardens of Calcutta, this handsome cat is usually extremely shy in captivity and attempts to avoid exposure to bright light. Perhaps failure to adjust housing to these characteristics may account for the animal's reputation for delicacy in captivity.

In the early days of this century the clouded leopard was a fairly frequent arrival in this country aboard freighters from the East. Nowadays it is a real rarity and seldom available. Those that were kept here were fed on the basis outlined for other great cats, with an occasional small fowl, pigeon, or rabbit. None survived for long, our best being 4 years, 8 months. George Pournelle informs me (*in litt.*) that a clouded leopard lived for 10 years, 8 months, 3 days in the San Diego Zoological Garden. M. L. Jones (1958) lists 15 years, 10 months, 19 days in the National Zoological Park, and 16 years, 11 months, 1 day for this species in the Philadelphia Zoological Garden.

There appear to be few records of the breeding of the clouded leopard in captivity. Robert V. Menary reports (*in litt.*) that two cubs were stillborn in the Cheyenne Mountain Zoo at Colorado Springs, Colorado, on March 29, 1955. A further birth of a single full-term cub occurred in late March, 1956. This cub lived for 10 days, when it disappeared, presumably having been devoured by the mother. A female clouded leopard received at the Dallas (Texas) Zoo and Aquarium on October 2, 1958, gave birth to a litter of four cubs on March 4, 1963. Three failed to survive, but the fourth, lifted for hand-rearing, remained in good condition on April 5, 1963 (Pierre A. Fontaine, *in litt.*). Three cubs born at the Frankfurt Zoological Gardens on April 20, 1963, were reared by the mother and were growing well when seen by William G. Conway, director of the New York Zoological Park, in September of that year.

Certainly among the finest of the great cats is the snow leopard or ounce (*P. uncia*). This beautiful animal is found at altitudes of from 6,000 to 18,000 feet in central Asia, from Tibet and Turkestan north to the Altai Mountains. Its most attractive feature is its long, soft pelage, gray or faintly yellowish in color, marked with dark spots and rings. The head, which is rather short with well-marked "stop," seems disproportionately small, perhaps because the very long body hair throws it out of perspective.

The snow leopard has always been uncommon in captivity, the remoteness of its habitat and its sensitivity to extreme heat being contributory causes. Sányál (1892) says that while up to that time no snow leopard had ever been kept at the Calcutta Zoological Gardens, a specimen received for transshipment to the Zoological Gardens of London died from "heat apoplexy" within a week. He also remarks that "the best time to bring them down is during the height of the cold weather in the plains and even then it is necessary to be extremely careful." Nowadays importations by air avoid this difficulty.

A male snow leopard, received here on May 8, 1946, was a lovely, tame animal that had accompanied an American Air Force pilot in flights "over the hump" in Burma during World War II. Brought to this country by its owner after his discharge, "Bowser" soon became "too much animal," and so found his way into our collection. He remained quite gentle during his stay here and always welcomed visitors in his cage by purring audibly. However, his temper took a different turn when the guest attempted to leave. Bowser would then wind himself around the visitor's feet, biting and clawing with mounting vigor. For this reason all petting and stroking soon took place only through intervening bars.

Bowser was kept, the year around, in one of the outside cages of our Lion House. During cold weather he always appeared quite content, but in the high temperatures of his first summer here he gave indications of distress, breathing heavily and treating his meals with indifference. To relieve this we gave him access to one of the dens, which, cooled by air from the passage below, was much more to his liking. He was fed on the basis of 4 pounds of raw horse meat daily, with the proportionate variations already mentioned for other great cats. However, this schedule was not followed rigidly, for Bowser received a fowl or perhaps a brace of pigeons two or three times weekly, items which we believe to have been essential to his well-being.

Bowser lived here until January 23, 1955, or 8 years, 8 months, 15 days. Mann (1930) gives 6 years, 5 months for a snow leopard in the National Zoological Park, Brown (1925) reports 7 years, 10 months, 10 days in the Philadelphia Zoological Garden, and M. L. Jones (1958) lists 8 years, 6 months, 23 days in the latter institution.

There are several well-authenticated records of the breeding of the snow leopard in captivity. Hagenbeck (1910:112) says that two young were born in 1906 to the female of a crippled pair kept at Stellingen. The parents were allowed to remain together, and although the male died 4 weeks after the birth, the female continued to care for the cubs. A single female cub was born at the Leipzig Zoological Gardens on May 28, 1912. It was left with the mother for a few days, but when it appeared not to be thriving, it was transferred to a dog foster mother. The cub lived until September 2, 1912 (Schneider, 1937). In 1938, three snow leopard cubs were born in the Dresden Zoological Gardens. The episode is noted and the mother and two young are figured by Petzsch (1939). While visiting here in June, 1956, Sven Andersen, director of the Copenhagen Zoological Gardens, was apprised of the birth of two snow leopards in his institution. Later, one of the cubs died, presumably because of the mother's neglect, and the survivor was removed for hand-rearing (Jorgensen, 1956). Further births occurred at Copenhagen in 1957, 1958, and 1959, and several of the young were hand-reared. A cub born at the National Zoological Park on May 18, 1958, was successfully reared on the bottle (Reed, 1959), but one born in 1960 and left with the mother failed to survive (Reed, 1961a). Two cubs born at the Cheyenne Mountain Zoo, Colorado, in 1959 met a similar fate (Don Davis, *in litt.*). Nickon (1960) reports that two cubs born at the Lincoln Park Zoo, Chicago, on May 12, 1960, were being reared by hand, while a further pair, born at Whipsnade in the same year, were fully reared by the mother, an apparently unique event.*

Jennison (n.d.) gives the gestation period of the snow leopard as 93 days and the number of young per birth as three to four. These figures, frequently quoted, do not appear to have been verified.

The cheetah or hunting leopard (*Acinonyx jubatus*), once found in plains areas over much of Africa and northward through Arabia and Persia to India, has now practically disappeared from the Asiatic parts of its range and is rapidly becoming reduced in Africa. A tall, slender animal, its yellowish-buff body color is thickly marked with small, round spots of black, which do not form rosettes or lines. Lengthened hair on the nape gives a suggestion of a mane. In size the cheetah approximates the leopard, Meinertzhagen (1938) giving the weights of four males, freshly killed in Kenya, as from 127 to 143 pounds and that of a single female as 139 pounds. In addition to a number of subspecies of *A. jubatus*, a beautiful animal marked with irregular stripes, largely horizontal, known as the king cheetah (*A. rex*), has been reported and figured in color by Pocock (1927). Whether this animal is to be regarded as a distinct species or merely as a color mutant of *A. jubatus* is still not entirely clear.

In many ways the cheetah is as un-catlike as a cat can be. For, instead of the usual creep-and-pounce method of capturing prey, the cheetah is cursorial, pursuing and overtaking its victims with unequaled bursts of

---

*See Addenda, p. 735.

speed. While this can be maintained for short distances only, the swiftest antelope is usually pulled down within a few hundred yards. The cheetah is reputed to be the swiftest land mammal and has been reported as capable of speeds up to 70 miles per hour. Three checks with a stopwatch on a cheetah pursuing a mechanical hare on a dog racetrack gave a speed of only 44 miles per hour (Meinertzhagen, 1955), but this is still faster than similarly accurate records for any other mammal, including the race horse and the greyhound. The fact that the claws cannot be fully retracted, as in other cats, makes them available for necessary traction.

The combination of superlative speed, predatory habits, and curiously amenable nature makes the cheetah particularly adaptable to training for sport, and since very early times it has been used by man for controlled hunting. This sport was highly developed in India on much the same lines as falconry. Although the reduction of the cheetah in India has caused restriction of this practice, it still continues through the importation of suitable animals from Africa. Just as wild-caught birds are preferred to hand-reared ones by the falconer, so is the cheetah with natural hunting experience esteemed by the trainer. A hand-reared hawk can be given partial liberty for "hacking" and then be returned to its block, but this is a practice hardly suitable for a cheetah. Once trained, the hooded animal is taken to the field on bullock cart or jeep and unhooded and released when game is sighted. The blackbuck, of course, is the favorite object of pursuit in India.

Cheetahs received by zoological gardens have usually been at least partly hand-reared and ordinarily are quite tame. For this reason they make especially attractive exhibits and seem quite at home in the cages of Lion Houses, where they are usually kept, as ours are. On the other hand, they are seen to great advantage in natural inclosures, which are easily constructed, since the animals are unlikely to damage restraining devices and have little ability as climbers. At Whipsnade, in 1950, a pair of cheetahs was kept in a large grassed inclosure surrounded by rather light wire netting 9 feet high, with a slightly down-turned internal overhang, 3 feet wide. A small shelter hut, electrically heated, served for winter protection. I was informed by the keeper in charge that the animals never leaped against the fence unless pressed and even then had never been able to escape. They were allowed the freedom of the inclosure during moderately cold weather, sometimes when snow covered the ground, and were considered to be at least somewhat hardy.

A pair of cheetahs, living in our Lion House, received a basic daily ration of 4 pounds of whole raw horse meat, daily, for the male and 3 pounds for the female. The usual variations were practiced, the animals taking liver, kidneys, and the mixture of raw chopped meat, bone meal, and cod-liver oil without reluctance. Whole chickens and pigeons were supplied frequently, so that the schedule was not followed closely.

In spite of the long captivity history of the cheetah, it appears that up to 1956 no instance of breeding in captivity had been recorded (Hediger, 1950:144; 1952:74). For this reason two successive births in the Philadelphia Zoological Garden, as reported by Ulmer (1957), are of particular interest. On March 24, 1956, a female cheetah, received 6 months previously, gave birth to three young, two males and one female. Since her residence was of longer duration than the presumed gestation period (Asdell [1946] gives it as 95 days), there could be no question of possible pregnancy before arrival. The male had been removed and a covered nest box provided, in anticipation of the birth. However, the female refused to enter this and gave birth on the bare floor of the cage. One cub was almost immediately killed by the mother, and although the others were removed and bottle-fed, they died 3 days later. In 1957, when the female was again thought to be pregnant, a wooden tray 5 by 3 feet, with sides 6 inches high and well packed with straw was provided. In this, on April 25, 1957, the female gave birth to two cubs, one of each sex. She cared for them well for 2 weeks when, excited by noisy school children, she began carrying them about. The cubs were then removed and their rearing continued by hand. Unfortunately, although their course of immunization had been completed, the young cheetahs died of panleucopenia at the age of 3 months.

It is of interest to note that these unique records were established by a pair of cheetahs that were confined to indoor and outside cages, each 8 by 10 feet, and did not have the presumed advantage of an outdoor inclosure such as Whipsnade's. Ulmer estimates the gestation period as about 92 days, which is well in accord with the expectation. He considers that the principal factor in these successes may have been a multiple vitamin supplement furnished in the diet, a suggestion previously offered by Hediger (1952:76).

Two cheetah cubs born at the Tierpark Krefeld, Germany, on April 25, 1960, were reared by hand, apparently the first successful captivity record ("Cover picture," *International Zoo News*, 7 [4]:99, 1960). Of two cubs born at the Oklahoma City Zoo on April 7, 1962, and two born on November 14, 1962, none survived (Warren Thomas, director, *in litt.*).

Perhaps because of what seems to be a special susceptibility to panleucopenia, the cheetah has usually not achieved satisfactory longevity spans, at least in European and American zoological gardens. Flower (1931) says that the cheetah "seldom lives for more than 6 years in captivity," a figure certainly higher than the usual result. However, he lists two specimens that lived respectively 13 years, 6 months, 9 days and 14 years, 28 days in the National Zoological Park, and another that established a record of 15 years, 7 months, 14 days in the Giza Zoological Gardens.

· REFERENCES

ALDOUS, SHALER E.
  1940. Notes on a black-footed ferret raised in captivity. Jour. Mammal., **21** (1):23–26.

ALLEN, GLOVER M.
  1938, 1940. The mammals of China and Mongolia. American Museum of Natural History, New York. 2 vols. 1350 pp.
  1939. A checklist of African mammals. Bull. Mus. Comp. Zool. Harvard, 83.

ANON.
  1903. A tragedy in the Lion House. Bull. New York Zool. Soc., No. 8, p. 65.
  1916. A hybrid bear. Bull. New York Zool. Soc., **19** (4):1375.
  1942. Panda up a tree. Animal Kingdom, **45** (5):79.
  1951a. Mostly about bears. Brookfield Bandar-Log, Chicago Zool. Soc., **6**:1–4.
  1951b. [Carnivora House in Philadelphia Zoological Garden]. America's First Zoo, **3** (2):1–3.
  1953. 17th polar bear born at the Zoo still in "nursery." Milwaukee Zoo News, **2** (9):3–4.
  1954a. The next time you visit the zoo: see the raccoon dog. America's First Zoo, **6** (3):8.
  1954b. Pittsburgh Zoo hyenas prove prolific. Parks and Recreation, **37** (9):32.
  1954c. The "eyes" have it! The Honker, **5**:1.
  1955a. Maned wolf pups. Zoonooz, **28** (2):30.
  1955b. Note. Internatl. Zoo News, **2** (4):66.
  1958a. Birth and death. America's First Zoo, **10** (2):1.
  1958b. Basle—Switzerland. Internatl. Zoo News, **4** (5):121.
  1959. Zoo briefs. Zoonooz, **32** (7):10.

APPELMAN, H. G.
  1956. The importance of zoological gardens for the protection of wild life. Minutes of the Conference of the International Union of Directors of Zoological Gardens, Chicago, 1956.

ASDELL, S. A.
  1946. Patterns of mammalian reproduction. Comstock Publishing Co., Ithaca, N.Y. 437 pp.

ASHBROOK, FRANK G.
    1923.   Silver fox farming. Bull. 1151. U.S. Dept. Agriculture, Washington,
            D.C. 60 pp.
    1925.   Blue fox farming in Alaska. Bull. 1350. U.S. Dept. Agriculture,
            Washington, D.C. 35 pp.
    1928.   Fur-farming for profit. Macmillan Co., New York. 300 pp.
    1951.   Raising small animals for pleasure and profit. D. Van Nostrand Co.,
            Inc., New York. 260 pp.
ASHBROOK, FRANK G., and KARL B. HANSON.
    1930.   The normal breeding season and gestation period of martens. Circ.
            107. U.S. Dept. Agriculture, Washington, D.C. 6 pp.
BAKER, A. B.
    1926.   Report of the Superintendent of the National Zoological Park for the
            year ended June 30, 1926. Ann. Rept. Smithsonian Inst., 1926,
            pp. 91–107.
BALDWIN, CAREY.
    1953.   On raising baby polar bears. Parks and Recreation, 36 (7):16–17.
    1955.   Bear cub diets. Parks and Recreation, 38 (6):19.
BARTLETT, A. D.
    1860.   Notes on some young hybrid bears bred in the Gardens of the Zoo-
            logical Society. Proc. Zool. Soc. London., Pt. 28, pp. 130–31.
    1900.   Wild beasts in the "Zoo." Ed. EDWARD BARTLETT. Chapman & Hall,
            Ltd., London. 375 pp.
BASSETT, CHARLES F.
    1957.   The martens. In: The UFAW handbook on the care and management
            of laboratory animals. University Federation for Animal Welfare,
            London. 951 pp.
BEAN, ROBERT.
    1937.   Giant panda. Guide Book, Chicago Zool. Park, 1937. 104 pp.
    1948.   Giant panda. Guide Book, Chicago Zool. Park, 1948. 108 pp.
BEHM, ALARIK.
    1933.   Zucht von Luchsen in Gefangenschaft. Zool. Garten, Leipzig (N.F.),
            6 (7/9):196.
BENCHLEY, BELLE J.
    1943.   Note. Zoonooz, 16 (1):4.
    1945.   Note. Ibid. 18 (8):3.
    1954.   1953 the year 'round. Ibid. 27 (2):3.
BISSONETTE, T. H., and E. E. BAILEY.
    1940.   Den and runway system for weasels and other small mammals in the
            laboratory. Amer. Midland Nat., 24:761–63.
BLAIR, W. REID.
    1938.   Pandora in her new home. Bull. New York Zool. Soc., 41 (4):119–22.
BLANFORD, W. T.
    1888–91. The fauna of British India. Mammalia. Taylor & Francis, London.
            617 pp.

BOURDELLE, E., and A. MOUQUET.
  1930. La longévité des mammifères à la Ménagerie du Muséum National d'Histoire Naturelle. Bull. Mus. Hist. Nat. Paris, 2d ser., 2 (5):488–97.
BRASSARD, J. A., and RICHARD BERNARD.
  1939. Observations on breeding of marten, Martes a. americana (Kerr). Canadian Field Nat., 53 (2):15–21.
BRIDGES, WILLIAM.
  1954. It's the "fearsome warracaba tiger." Animal Kingdom, 57 (1):25–28.
BROWN, C. EMERSON.
  1925. Longevity of mammals in the Philadelphia Zoological Garden. Jour. Mammal., 6 (4):264–67.
BUTLER, ROSE.
  1914. "Ebby," a tame striped hyaena. Year Book, Amateur Menagerie Club, 1914.
CABRERA, ANGEL.
  1957. Catalogo de los Mamiferos de America del Sur. 1. Rev. Mus. Argentina Cienc. Nat. Bernardino Rivadavia, Zool., 4 (1):1–307.
CABRERA, ANGEL, and JOSÉ YEPES.
  1940. Historia natural ediar. Mamiferos Sud-Americanos. Compañia Argentina de Editores, Buenos Aires. 370 pp.
CAHALANE, VICTOR H.
  1947. Mammals of North America. Macmillan Co., New York. 682 pp.
  1954. Status of the black-footed ferret. Jour. Mammal., 35 (3):418–24.
CANSDALE, GEORGE.
  N.d. George Cansdale's Zoo Book. Phoenix House Ltd., London; British Book Center Inc., New York. 64 pp.
CARTER, T. DONALD.
  1937. The giant panda. Bull. New York Zool. Soc., 40 (1):6–14.
  1955. Remarkable age attained by a bobcat. Jour. Mammal., 36 (2):290.
CHASEN, FREDERICK NUTTER.
  1940. A handlist of Malaysian mammals. Bull. Raffles Mus., Singapore, 15.
COCKS, A. H.
  1881a. Note on the breeding of the otter. Proc. Zool. Soc. London, pp. 249–50.
  1881b. Wild cat breeding in confinement. Zoologist, Ser. 3, 5:307.
CORBETT, JIM.
  1945. Man-eaters of Kumaon. Oxford University Press, New York. 235 pp.
COUTURIER, MARCEL A. J.
  1954. L'ours brun, Ursus arctos L. By the author, Grenoble, France. 904 pp.
CRANDALL, LEE S.
  1921. Rarities in European zoological gardens. Bull. New York Zool. Soc., 24 (1):20–24.
  1931. Paradise quest. Chas. Scribner's Sons, New York. 226 pp.
  1944a. Three tiger cubs. Animal Kingdom, 47 (2):46–48.
  1944b. The cubs are growing up. Ibid., 47 (4):95–97.

1946.   "Blue" or "Cinnamon" ? *Ibid.*, **49** (4):154.

1952.   Welcome to the Zoo. *Ibid.*, **55** (4):108–13.

DARWIN, CHARLES.

1868.   The variation of animals and plants under domestication. Vol. 1. Orange Judd & Co., New York. 494 pp.

DAVIS, JOSEPH A., JR.

1961.   Red means go! Animal Kingdom, **64** (4):114–18.

1962.   Red light pays dividends. *Ibid.*, **65** (1):3–5.

DAVIS, MALCOLM.

1950.   Hybrids of the polar and Kodiak bear. Jour. Mammal., **31** (4):449–50.

DEARBORN, NED.

1915.   Silver fox farming in eastern North America. Bull. 301. U.S. Dept. ' Agriculture, Washington, D.C. 35 pp.

DEMMER, HEINI.

1958.   The first giant panda since the war has reached the western world. Internatl. Zoo News, **5** (4):99–101.

DE VOS, ANTOON, RICHARD MANVILLE, and RICHARD G. VAN GELDER.

1956.   Introduced mammals and their influence on native biota. Zoologica, **41** (4):163–94.

DITTOE, GEORGIE.

1944.   Lesser pandas. Zoonooz, **17** (12):4–5.

DOI, HIROYUKI.

1960.   Leopons were born for the first time in the world! Animals and Zoo (Tokyo), **12** (2):5.

DUETZ, GERTRUDE H.

1939.   Revised tables of maximum exhibition periods for animals in the Philadelphia collection as compared with available figures from other Zoos, together with some data on those now living in the Garden. Rept. Penrose Res. Lab., Zool. Soc. Philadelphia. 50 pp.

DUNCAN, MARTIN F.

1947.   Hand-rearing of a polar cub. Zoo Life, **2** (4):99–101.

ELLERMAN, J. R., and T. C. S. MORRISON-SCOTT.

1951.   Checklist of Palaearctic and Indian mammals. Trustees of the British Museum, London. 810 pp.

ELLERMAN, J. R., T. C. S. MORRISON-SCOTT, and R. W. HAYMAN.

1953.   Southern African mammals. Trustees of the British Museum, London. 363 pp.

ENDERS, ROBERT K., and ELEANOR M. PAXSON.

1946.   Ablation of the scent glands of skunks. Jour. Amer. Vet. Med. Assoc., **108** (827):84–86.

FINN, FRANK.

1907.   Pets and how to keep them. Hutchinson and Co., London. 219 pp.

1929.   Sterndale's mammalia of India. Thacker, Spink & Co. Calcutta and Simla. 347 pp.

FISHER, EDNA M.
  1939. Habits of the southern sea otter. Jour. Mammal., **20** (1):21–36.
FLOWER, S. S.
  1929. List of the vertebrated animals exhibited in the gardens of the Zoo-
         logical Society of London, 1828–1927. 1. Mammals. Zoological
         Society of London. 419 pp.
  1931. Contribution to our knowledge of the duration of life in vertebrate
         animals. 5. Mammals. Proc. Zool. Soc. London, pp. 145–234.
FOX, HERBERT.
  1936. Rept. Penrose Res. Lab., Zool. Soc. Philadelphia, 1936. 30 pp.
  1941. *Ibid.*, 1941. 37 pp.
FRIEDMANN, HERBERT.
  1955. The honey-guides. U.S. Nat. Mus., Bull. 208. Smithsonian Inst.,
         Washington, D.C. 292 pp.
FU-JEN, CHIN.
  1956. There are many rare animals in Peking Zoo. Zoo Life, **11** (3):93–94.
GANDER, FRANK FORREST.
  1928. Period of gestation in some American mammals. Jour. Mammal.,
         9 (1):75.
GEE, E. P.
  1956. The management of India's wild life sanctuaries and National Parks.
         Jour. Bombay Nat. Hist. Soc., **54** (1):1–21.
GOLDMAN, E. A.
  1912. New mammals from eastern Panama. Smithsonian Misc. Coll., **60**
         (2):14–15.
  1920. Mammals of Panama. *Ibid.*, **69** (5):1–309.
GOODWIN, GEORGE G.
  1946. Mammals of Costa Rica. Bull. Amer. Mus. Nat. Hist., **87** (5):275–473.
  1954. The animal kingdom. Vol. **1**. 680 pp. FREDERICK DRIMMER, Editor-in-
         chief. Greystone Press, New York.
GORHAM, JOHN R.
  1956. Diseases and parasites of foxes. In: Animal diseases. Year book,
         U.S. Dept. Agriculture, 1956. Washington, D.C.
GOSS, LEONARD J.
  1942. How are the giant pandas? Animal Kingdom, **45** (5):120–22.
  1944. Hospital and laboratory. In: 49th Ann. Rept., New York Zool. Soc.,
         for the year 1943.
  1945. Hospital and laboratory. In: 50th Ann. Rept., New York Zool. Soc.,
         for the year 1944.
  1951. Animal hospital. In: 56th Ann. Rept., New York Zool. Soc., for the
         year 1950.
  1956. Animal hospital. In: 61st Ann. Rept., New York Zool. Soc., for the
         year 1955.
GRAHAM, DAVID C.
  1942. How the baby pandas were captured. Animal Kingdom, **45** (1):19–23.

GRAY, ANNIE P.
   1954. Mammalian hybrids. Commonwealth Agricultural Bureaux, Farnham
          Royal, Bucks, England. 144 pp.
GREEN, R. G., C. A. EVANS, and W. E. CARLSON.
   1937. A summary of Chastek paralysis studies. Minnesota Wildlife Dis.
          Invest., 3:173.
GREEN, R. G., and J. E. SHILLINGER.
   1936. Chastek paralysis—a new disease of foxes. Minnesota Wildlife Dis
          Invest., 2:106.
GREENHALL, ARTHUR.
   1951. Something really rare. Your Detroit Zoo, 5 (3):2.
HAAGNER, ALWIN.
   1920. South African mammals. H. F. & G. Witherby, London. 248 pp.
HAGENBECK, CARL.
   1910. Beasts and men. Longmans, Green & Co., London. 299 pp.
HALL, E. RAYMOND.
   1951. American weasels. University of Kansas Publications, Vol. 4. Uni-
          versity of Kansas, Lawrence. 466 pp.
HALL, E. RAYMOND, and KEITH R. KELSON.
   1959. The mammals of North America. The Ronald Press Co., New York.
          2 vols.
HALLORAN, PATRICIA O'CONNOR.
   1955. A bibliography of references to diseases of wild mammals and birds.
          Amer. Jour. Vet. Res., 16 (61), Part 2:1–465.
HALTENORTH, T.
   1953. Die Wildkatzen der Alten Welt. Akademische Verlagsgesellschaft,
          Leipzig. 166 pp.
HAMILTON, W. J., JR.
   1933. The weasels of New York. Amer. Midland Nat., 14 (4):289–344.
   1943. The mammals of eastern United States. Comstock Publishing Co.,
          Ithaca, N.Y. 432 pp.
   1953. The black bear still hangs on. Animal Kingdom, 56 (1):22–26.
HARPER, FRANCIS.
   1945. Extinct and vanishing mammals of the Old World. Special Publication
          12, American Committee for International Wildlife Protection,
          New York. 850 pp.
HARRISON, R. J. and E. G. NEAL.
   1956. Ovulation during delayed implantation and other reproductive
          phenomena in the badger (*Meles meles* L.). Nature, 177 (4517):977–79.
HEDIGER, H.
   1950. Wild animals in captivity. Butterworths Scientific Publications,
          London. 207 pp.
   1952. Observations on reproduction behaviour in zoo animals. In: Ciba
          Foundation Colloquia on Endocrinology. 3. J. & A. Churchill Ltd.,
          London. 380 pp.

1955. Studies of the psychology and behaviour of captive animals in zoos and circuses. Butterworths Scientific Publications, London. 166 pp.

HELLER, EDMUND.
1930. Polar bears reared in Milwaukee. Bull. Washington Park Zool. Soc., 1 (2):1–5.

HERSHKOVITZ, PHILIP.
1961. On the South American small-eared zorro *Atelocynus microtis* Sclater (Canidae). Fieldiana: Zoology, 39 (44):505–23.

HILL, CRAVEN.
1946. The story of Lien-Ho. Zoo Life, 1 (3):72–75.

HILL, W. C. OSMAN.
1956. Longevity in the Ceylon ruddy mongoose *Herpestes smithii zeylanius* Thomas. Jour. Bombay Nat. Hist. Soc., 53 (4):687–88.

HILTY, REUBEN.
1932. Value of veterinary service in a zoological garden. Zoological Parks and Aquariums. 1. Amer. Assoc. Zool. Parks and Aquariums. 103 pp.

HINDLE, EDWARD.
1947–48. Notice. Proc. Zool. Soc. London, 117:606.

HORNADAY, WILLIAM T.
1907. Popular official guide to the New York Zoological Park. New York Zool. Soc. 172 pp.
1910. Two years in the jungle. Charles Scribner's Sons, New York. 512 pp.
1922. A remarkable black bear. Bull. New York Zool. Soc., 25 (1):32.

HUTZELSIDER, HUBERT B.
1940. Eine Malayenbärengeburt im Zoo Aarhus. Zool. Garten, Leipzig (N.F.), 12 (2/3):157–61.

JARVIS, CAROLINE, and DESMOND MORRIS, Eds.
1961. Species of animals bred in zoos and aquaria during 1960. In: Internatl. Zoo Yearbook, 1960, 2:252–79. Zool. Soc. London.

JENNISON, GEORGE.
N.d. Table of gestation periods and number of young. A. & C. Black, Ltd., London. 8 pp.

JOHNSON, EDWARD, and W. C. HALL.
1954. Seattle Woodland Park Zoo has new type of cage fronts. Parks and Recreation, 37 (6):17–18.

JONES, MARVIN L.
1958. Mammals in captivity. Mimeographed MSS (unpublished).

JONES, OLIVER G.
1952. Zoo babies. Zoo Life, 7 (4):112–18.

JORGENSEN, BENT.
1956. Note. Internatl. Zoo News, 3 (6):130.

KELHAM, MOIRA.
1954. Recent additions at London Zoo. Zoo Life, 9 (2):76–79.
1955. Report from Regent's Park. *Ibid.*, 10 (3):90.

KELLOGG, CHARLES E., CHARLES F. BASSETT, and ROBERT K. ENDERS.
    1948.   Mink raising. Circular 801. U.S. Dept. Agriculture, Washington, D.C.
            42 pp.
KEMNA, ALWIN.
    1953.   Über eine Ruckkreuzung eines Löwen-Tiger-Bastards mit einem
            Löwen in der zweiten Generation und tierärztliche Beobachtungen
            bei der Aufzucht der empfindlichen Jungtiere. Zool. Garten, Leipzig
            (N.F.), 20 (2/3):122–26.
KENNETH, J. H.
    1953.   Gestation periods. Technical Communication 5, Commonwealth
            Bureau of Animal Breeding and Genetics. Edinburgh. 39 pp.
LANG, E. M.
    1958.   Zur Haltung des Strandwolfes (Hyaena brunnea). Zool. Garten,
            Leipzig (N.F.), 24 (1/2):81–90.
LEYHAUSEN, P.
    1950.   Beobachtungen an Löwen-Tiger-Bastarden mit einigen Bemerkungen
            zur Systematik der Grosskatzen. Zeit. Tierpsychol., 7:46–83.
    1956a. Verhaltensstudien an Katzen. Zeit. Tierpsychol., Suppl. 2. Paul
            Parey, Berlin and Hamburg. 120 pp.
    1956b. Das Verhalten der Katzen (Felidae). Handbuch der Zoologie, 10
            (21):1–34.   Walter de Gruyter & Co., Berlin.
LIERS, EMIL E.
    1951.   Notes on the river otter (Lutra canadensis) Jour. Mammal., 32
            (1):1–9.
LOCKE, A.
    1954.   The tigers of Trengganu. Chas. Scribner's Sons, New York. 191 pp.
LOISEL, GUSTAVE.
    1912.   Histoire des ménageries de l'antiquité à nos jours. Octave Doin et Fils,
            Henri Laurens, Paris. 3 vols.
LORENZ, KONRAD Z.
    1952.   King Solomon's ring. Thomas Y. Crowell Co., N.Y. 202 pp.
LYDEKKER, RICHARD.
    1893–96. The royal natural history. Frederick Warne & Co., London & New
            York. 6 vols.
MANN, WM. M.
    1930.   Wild animals in and out of the zoo. Smithsonian Sci. Ser., Vol. 6.
            632 pp.
    1937.   Report on the National Zoological Park for the year ending June 30,
            1936. Smithsonian Inst. Report for 1936, pp. 57–59.
    1940.   Report on the National Zoological Park for the year ending June 30,
            1939. Smithsonian Inst. Report for 1939, pp. 76–105.
    1943.   Report on the National Zoological Park for the year ended June 30,
            1942. Smithsonian Inst. Report for 1942, pp. 65–74.
    1945.   Report on the National Zoological Park for the year ended June 30,
            1944. Smithsonian Inst. Report for 1944, pp. 67–93.

1950. Report on the National Zoological Park for the year ended June 30, 1949. Smithsonian Inst. Report for 1949, pp. 97–108.

1952. Report on the National Zoological Park for the year ended June 30, 1951. Smithsonian Inst. Report for 1951, pp. 104–16.

1953. Report on the National Zoological Park for the year ended June 30, 1952. Smithsonian Inst. Report for 1952, pp. 94–129.

1954. Report on the National Zoological Park for the year ended June 30, 1953. Smithsonian Inst. Report for 1953, pp. 102–20.

1955. Report on the National Zoological Park for the year ended June 30, 1954. Smithsonian Inst. Report for 1954, pp. 93–130.

1956. Report on the National Zoological Park for the year ended June 30, 1955. Smithsonian Inst. Report for 1955, pp. 104–28.

1957. Report on the National Zoological Park for the year ended June 30, 1956. Smithsonian Inst. Report for 1956, pp. 117–60.

MANVILLE, RICHARD H.
1953. Longevity of the coyote. Jour. Mammal., 34 (3):390.
1956. This "kinkajou" was really the very rare olingo. Animal Kingdom, 59 (4):109–11.

MARTINI, HELEN.
1955. My zoo family. Harper & Brothers, New York. 295 pp.

MATTHEWS, L. HARRISON.
1939. The bionomics of the spotted hyaena, Crocuta crocuta Erxl. Proc. Zool. Soc. London, 109, Ser. A: 43–56.
1949. Hyaenas. Zoo Life, 4 (3):67–69.

McCLURE, F. A.
1943. Bamboo as panda food. Jour. Mammal., 24 (2):267–68.

MEINERTZHAGEN, R.
1938. Some weights and measurements of large mammals. Proc. Zool. Soc. London, 108, Ser. A: 433–39.
1955. The speed and altitude of bird flight (with notes on other animals). Ibis, 97 (1):81–117.

MERRIAM, C. HART.
1918. Review of the grizzly and big brown bears of North America (genus Ursus) with description of a new genus, Vetularctos. N. Amer. Fauna, 41, 1–36. Bur. Biol. Survey, U.S. Dept. Agriculture, Washington, D.C.

MICHAELIS, [—].
1961. Note. Internatl. Zoo News, 8 (5):150.

MITCHELL, P. CHALMERS.
1911. On longevity and relative viability in mammals and birds; with a note on the theory of longevity. Proc. Zool. Soc. London, pp. 425–548.

MIVART, ST. GEORGE.
1890. A monograph of the Canidae. R. H. Porter, London. 216 pp.

MOHR, ERNA.
1938. Vom järv (Gulo gulo L.). Zool. Garten, Leipzig (N.F.), 10 (1/2):14–21.

1942. *Cryptoprocta ferox* im ehemaligen Hamburger Zoo. *Ibid.*, **14** (4): 210–11.

MORRISON-SCOTT, T. C. S.
1951–52. The mummified cats of ancient Egypt. Proc. Zool. Soc. London, **121**:861–67.

MURIE, OLAUS J.
1940. Notes on the sea otter. Jour. Mammal., **21** (2):119–31.

MUSGRAVE, M. E.
1926. Some habits of mountain lions in Arizona. Jour. Mammal., **7** (4): 282–85.

NAIR, KESAVAN R.
1957. Administration report of the museums and zoos and government gardens, for the year 1955–1956. Government Press, Ernakulam.

NEAL, ERNEST G.
1947. Badgers. Zoo Life, **2** (3):72–74.

NELSON, E. W., and E. A. GOLDMAN.
1933. Revision of the jaguars. Jour. Mammal., **14** (3):221–40.

NICKON, DONALD C.
1960. Note. Internatl. Zoo News, **7** (2):55.

NOBACK, CHARLES V.
1935. Observations on the seasonal hair moult in a New York State weasel (*Mustela noveboracensis*). Bull. New York Zool. Soc., **38** (1):25–27.

NOUVEL, J.
1952. La réproduction des mammifères au Parc Zoologique du Bois de Vincennes dans ses rapports avec l'alimentation. Mammalia, **16** (3):160–75.

OEMING, AL F.
1962. The friendly lynx. Zoonooz, **35** (4):3–7.

PALMER, RALPH S.
1954. The mammal guide. Doubleday & Co., Inc., N.Y. 384 pp.

PETZSCH, HANS.
1939. Nachrichten aus Zoologischen Garten. Zool. Garten, Leipzig (N.F.), **10** (5/6):234.

PHILLIPS, W. W. A.
1954. Longevity of the Ceylon ruddy mongoose (*Herpestes smithi zeylanicus*) in captivity. Jour. Bombay Nat. Hist. Soc., **52** (2–3):587.
1956. Longevity of the Ceylon ruddy mongoose (*Herpestes smithi zeylanicus*) in captivity. *Ibid.*, **53** (3):464.

POCOCK, R. I.
1907. Notes upon some of the African species of the genus *Felis*, based upon specimens recently exhibited in the Society's Gardens. Proc. Zool. Soc. London., pp. 656–77.
1912. On the moulting of an Arctic fox (*Vulpes lagopus*) in the Society's Gardens. *Ibid.*, pp. 55–60.

1927. Description of a new species of cheetah (*Acinonyx*). *Ibid.*, pp. 245–57.
1929. Tigers. Jour. Bombay Nat. Hist. Soc., **33** (3):505–41.
1930. The panthers and ounces of Asia. *Ibid.*, **34** (1):64–82; **34** (2):307–36.
1932. The leopards of Africa. Proc. Zool. Soc. London., pp. 543–91.
1935. Exhibition of the skull of a lion-tiger hybrid. *Ibid.*, pp. 736–40.
1936a. The Asiatic wild dog or dhole (*Cuon javanicus*). *Ibid.*, pp. 33–55.
1936b. The polecats of the genera *Putorius* and *Vormela* in the British Museum. *Ibid.*, pp. 691–723.

POURNELLE, GEORGE H.
1957. Animal old-timers: among the mammals. Zoonooz, **30** (9):10.
1960. Some longevity records of captive mammals. Jour. Mammal., **41** (1):114.

PRELL, H.
1930. Über die Fortpflanzungsbiologie der europäischen Bären. Zool. Garten, Leipzig (N.F.), **3** (4/8):168–72.

RAHM, U.
1962. L'élévage et la réproduction en captivité de l'*Atherurus africanus* (Rongeurs, Hystricidae). Mammalia, **26** (1):1–9.

RAINEY, PAUL J.
1911. The capture of "Silver King." Bull. New York Zool. Soc., No. 43, pp. 715–19.

RAND, A. L.
1935. On the habits of some Madagascar mammals. Jour. Mammal., **16** (2):89–104.

RATCLIFFE, HERBERT L.
1948–49. Rept. Penrose Res. Lab., Zool. Soc. Philadelphia, 1948 and 1949.
1953. *Ibid.*, 1953.

REED, THEODORE H.
1959. Report on the National Zoological Park for the year ended June 30, 1958. Smithsonian Inst. Report for 1958, pp. 140–79.
1961a. Report on the National Zoological Park for the year ended June 30, 1960. Smithsonian Inst. Report for 1960, pp. 131–71.
1961b. Enchantress! Natl. Geogr. Mag., **119** (5):628–41.

REUTHER, RONALD T.
1961. Breeding notes on mammals in captivity. Jour. Mammal., **42** (3): 427–28.

REVENTLOW, AXEL.
1953. Remarks on American black bears. Zool. Garten, Leipzig (N.F.), **20** (2/3):185–87.
1954. The Kodiak bear cub, "Ursula." Zool. Garten, Leipzig (N.F.), **20** (4/5):279–82.

ROBERTS, AUSTIN.
1951. The mammals of South Africa. Trustees of the "Mammals of South Africa" Book Fund, Johannesburg. 363 pp.

ROBINSON, F. B.
1928. White tigers. Jour. Bombay Nat. Hist. Soc., **32** (3):584–85.

RORIG, ADOLF.
1903. Über Säugetier-Bastarde. Zool. Garten, Leipzig, **44** (8):286–92.

SAGE, DEAN, JR.
1938. How "Pandora" came to the Zoological Park. Bull. New York Zool. Soc., **41** (4):115–18.

SÁNYÁL, RAM BRAMHA.
1892. A hand-book of the management of animals in captivity in Lower Bengal. Bengal Secretariat Press, Calcutta. 351 pp.

SAPORITI, ENRIQUE J.
1951. Observaciones biologicas en mamiferos autoctonos y foraneos de las colecciones del Jardin Zoologico de Buenos Aires. Diana (Buenos Aires), **135–40**:3–20.

SCHEFFER, VICTOR B.
1951. Measurements of sea otters from western Alaska. Jour. Mammal., **32** (1):10–14.
1953. Otters diving to a depth of sixty feet. Jour. Mammal., **34** (2):255.

SCHERREN, HENRY.
1907. Some notes on hybrid bears. Proc. Zool. Soc. London, pp. 431–35.

SCHEUNERT, A.
1933. Die Sternguckerkrankheit junger Löwen—eine Vitamin B_1 Avitaminose. Zool. Garten, Leipzig (N.F.), **6** (7/9):182–87.

SCHNEIDER, KARL MAX.
1933. Über das "Drehen" der Grosskatzen. Zool. Garten, Leipzig (N.F), **6** (7/9):173–81.
1937. Einige Bilder zur Aufzucht eines Schneeleoparden. *Ibid.*, **1** (1/2): 37–39.
1939. Einiges vom Grossen und Kleinen Panda. 1. Vom Grossen Panda. *Ibid.*, **11** (6):203–32.
1953. Von der Fleckung junger Löwen. *Ibid.*, **20** (2/3):127–50.

SCHOMBERG, GEOFFREY.
1957. British zoos. Allan Wingate, London. 194 pp.

SCLATER, P. L.
1882. Report of the secretary. Proc. Zool. Soc. London, pp. 631.

SETON, ERNEST THOMPSON.
1925–28. Lives of game animals. Doubleday, Page & Co., Garden City, New York. 4 vols.

SHELDON, W. G.
1937. Notes on the giant panda. Jour. Mammal., **18** (1):13–19.

SHORTRIDGE, G. C.
1934. The mammals of South West Africa. Wm. Heinemann Ltd., London. 2 vols.

SIMON, E. S.
1943. Life span of some wild animals in captivity. Jour. Bombay Nat. Hist. Soc., **44** (1):117–18.

SIMPSON, GEORGE GAYLORD.
   1945. The principles of classification and a classification of mammals.
          Bull. Amer. Mus. Nat. Hist., 85. 350 pp.
SLOAN, JOSEPH.
   1949. Life of a liger at Salt Lake City Zoo. Parks and Recreation, 32 (2):
          103-4.
SMITS, LEE J.
   1956. The illusive Michigan wolverine. Your Detroit Zoo, 11 (1):4.
SPEIDEL, GEORGE.
   1949. Milwaukee's polar bears. Parks and Recreation, 32 (4):235-37.
STEINMETZ, H.
   1940. Nachrichten aus Zoologischen Gärten. Zool. Garten, Leipzig (N.F.),
          12 (4/6):335-43.
STERNDALE, ROBERT A.
   1884. Natural history of the mammalia of India and Ceylon. Thacker,
          Spink & Co., Calcutta. 540 pp.
STEYN, T. J.
   1951. The breeding of lions in captivity. Fauna and Flora (Pretoria),
          2:37-55.
STOTT, KEN, JR.
   1954a. Baby food for thought. Zoonooz, 27 (6):5-6.
   1954b. Note. Ibid., 27 (3):2.
STULLKEN, DONALD E., and CHARLES M. KIRKPATRICK.
   1955. Physiological investigation of captivity mortality in the sea otter
          (Enhydra lutris). Transactions, 20th North American Wildlife Con-
          ference, 1955. Wildlife Management Institute, Washington, D.C.
TATE, G. H. H.
   1931. Random observations on habits of South American mammals. Jour.
          Mammal., 12 (3):248-56.
TAYLOR, WALTER P.
   1954. Food habits and notes on life history of the ring-tailed cat in Texas.
          Jour. Mammal., 35 (1):55-62.
TAYLOR, S., and CECIL S. WEBB.
   1955. Breeding dwarf mongooses. Zoo Life, 10 (3):70-72.
TEE-VAN, JOHN.
   1942. Two pandas—China's gift to America. Animal Kingdom, 45 (1):3-18.
TROUGHTON, ELLIS.
   1951. Furred animals of Australia. Angus & Robertson Ltd., Sydney.
          374 pp.
TYRWHITT-DRAKE, G.
   1914. Lions. Year Book, The Amateur Menagerie Club, 1914.
ULMER, FREDERICK A., JR.
   1951. Cats—great and small. America's First Zoo, 3 (2):4-6.
   1955. Fennec family affair. Ibid., 7 (4):6-7.
   1957. Cheetahs are born. Ibid., 9 (3):7.

VAN EE, C. E.
  1953. The ligers of the Bloemfontein Zoo. Parks and Recreation, **36** (5):16.
VEVERS, G. M.
  1948. The tiger. Zoo Life, **3** (2):35–36.
VIERHELLER, GEORGE.
  1957. Annual Report, St. Louis Zoological Garden, fiscal year April, 1956, to April, 1957.
VLASÁK, JAN.
  1950. Über künstliche Aufzucht eines Eisbären, *Thalarctos maritimus* Phipps. Zool. Garten, Leipzig (N.F.), **16** (5):159–79.
VOSSELER, J.
  1929. Beitrag zur Kenntnis der Fossa (*Cryptoprocta ferox* Benn.) und ihrer Fortpflanzung. Zool. Garten, Leipzig (N.F.), **2** (1/3):1–9.
WALL, F.
  1908. Birth of Himalayan cat-bears (*Aelurus fulgens*) in captivity. Jour. Bombay Nat. Hist. Soc., **18** (4):903–4.
WARD, ROWLAND.
  1922. Records of big game. Rowland Ward, Ltd., London. 526 pp.
WATSON, M.
  1877. On the female generative organs of *Hyaena crocuta*. Proc. Zool. Soc. London, pp. 369–79.
  1878. On the male generative organs of *Hyaena crocuta*. *Ibid.*, pp. 416–28.
  1881. Additional observations on the anatomy of the spotted hyaena. *Ibid.*, pp. 516–20.
WENDNAGEL, A.
  1938. Ein Schwarzling der Indischen Goldkatze (*Felis temminckii* Vig. & Horsf.) Zool. Garten, Leipzig (N.F.), **10** (3/4):114–15.
WHITEMAN, ELDON E.
  1940. Habits and pelage changes in captive coyotes. Jour. Mammal., **21** (4):435–38.
WIGHT, H. M.
  1931. Reproduction in the eastern skunk (*Mephitis mephitis nigra*). Jour. Mammal., **12** (1):42–47.
WINDECKER, W.
  1955. Breeding of hyena dogs. Minutes of meeting of International Union of Directors of Zoological Gardens, Basel, 1955.
WOLF, L. E.
  1942. Thiaminase in Atlantic herring. Fisheries Res. Bull., **2**, New York State Conservation Dept.
WOODS, GORDON T.
  1944. Longevity of captive wolverines. Amer. Midland Nat., **31** (2):505.
WRIGHT, BRUCE S.
  1961. The latest specimen of the eastern puma. Jour. Mammal., **42** (2): 278–79.

WRIGHT, P. L.
 1942. Delayed implantation in the long-tailed weasel (*Mustela frenata*), the short-tailed weasel (*Mustela cicognani*) and the marten (*Martes americana*). Anat. Rec., 83:341–53.
 1948. Breeding habits of long-tailed weasels (*Mustela frenata*). Amer. Midland Nat., **39** (2):338–44.
WRIGHT, PHILIP L. and ROBERT RAUSCH.
 1955. Reproduction in the wolverine, *Gulo gulo*. Jour. Mammal., **36** (3): 346–55.
WYNTER-BLYTH, M. A.
 1956. The lion census of 1955. Jour. Bombay Nat. Hist. Soc., **53** (4):527–36.
YOCUM, HAROLD A.
 1961. White bears, Ltd. Frontiers, **26** (2):35–38.
YOUNG, STANLEY P.
 1958. The bobcat of North America. The Stackpole Co., Harrisburg, Pa., and the Wildlife Management Institute, Washington, D.C. 193 pp.
YOUNG, STANLEY P., and EDWARD A. GOLDMAN.
 1944. The wolves of North America. American Wildlife Institute, Washington, D.C. 636 pp.
YUDKIN, WARREN H.
 1945. Occurrence of thiaminase in marine teleosts. Proc. Soc. Exper. Biol. and Med., 60:268–69.
ZUCKERMAN, S.
 1953. The breeding seasons of mammals in captivity. Proc. Zool. Soc. London, **122**:827–950.

ORDER PINNIPEDIA

.

Seals

Obviously closely related to the Carnivora and presumably having a primitive origin in common with that group, the seals have often been considered to form a suborder (Simpson, 1945). On the other hand, many recent authorities (Ellerman and Morrison-Scott, 1951; Frechkop, 1955; Scheffer, 1958; Hall and Kelson, 1959) have elevated the seals to ordinal rank and they are so treated here.

While the seals are especially adapted for an aquatic life, they are not so fully specialized as the whales and porpoises, for while they seek their food in the water and spend much of their lives in that element, they come ashore, or at least onto sea-ice, to breed and rear their young. The limbs have become modified as flippers so that they are of reduced value in progress out of water, the degree of usefulness varying in the families (Allen, 1880). Most of the species are marine, although a few are confined to fresh water. Their food in general consists of fishes, crustaceans, and mollusks, although the great leopard seal (*Hydrurga*), of Antarctica, is known to take warm-blooded prey.

Seals of some sort are found in every sea except for the northern Indian Ocean, with a concentration of both numbers and species toward the Poles. About thirty full species, many with a varying number of races, are usually recognized. These are assigned to three families: Otariidae, the eared seals; Odobenidae, the walruses; and Phocidae, the earless or true seals and the elephant seals.

FAMILY OTARIIDAE

Eared Seals: Sea Lions and Fur Seals

Characters common to the members of this family are long, sinuous bodies and extended necks, greatly thickened in adult males, small external ears and hind flippers capable of rotating forward under the body. Actually, the support given on land is sufficient to allow the animal to walk slowly in awkward quadrupedal fashion or to gallop clumsily for short distances when more speed is required. In the sea lions the hair is short and coarse, while in the fur seals there is a thick, soft undercoat, protected by longer guard hairs. The breeding habits of these animals are similar, in general, dominant males holding harems of more or less closely guarded females on the common breeding grounds, which usually are on rocky islands or promontories readily accessible from the sea.

The species most commonly seen in zoological gardens is the California sea lion (*Zalophus californianus*), found along the Pacific Coast of North America from British Columbia to Mexico. This animal not only ranks among the most attractive of zoo exhibits but is capable of being trained for the performance of tricks involving balancing or leaping skills. Adult males of this species develop a high, sagittal crest on the crown and may reach a weight of 600 pounds or even more. A male which had lived here for nearly 20 years weighed 590 pounds at death, while Townsend (1926) reports 620 pounds for an adult in the New York Aquarium. The greatest weight recorded here for an adult female is 190 pounds; the maximum weight is given by Scheffer (1958) as 200 pounds.

Accepted methods for the maintenance and exhibition of sea lions in zoological gardens vary widely but two general plans predominate. In Europe there is usually a rock background with varied crawl-outs, the pool at the front with a guard rail, so that the exhibit can be viewed from one side only. Detailed plans and photographs of an installation of this type in the Zoological Gardens of Leipzig are given by Schneider (1943). In America the open, elongated oval type seems more popular. In this style the rock work is usually reduced to an elevated structure containing a shelter, the roof being accessible to the animals and providing an eminence from which they readily learn to leap into the water. There may also be a rock or concrete island, its surface just above water level, which the animals use for basking. This provides a practically unobstructed view from all sides. Although this is in direct violation of the generally valid principle that captive wild animals dislike being surrounded by visitors, seals do not seem to be affected, perhaps because ready escape into the water is always available. Notable variations in the construction of seal pools are the magnificent arrangement of distant rocks seen across a long, narrow water area, used for gray seals at Skansen, and the deep grottos at San Diego, which are seen from a fairly high elevation, a great advantage when looking into water.

The Sea Lion Pool here is of the open type and measures 88 feet in length and 44 feet in average width. The depth of water ranges from 5 feet at one end to 7 feet at the other. It is furnished with the conventional stone-and-concrete shelter at one side and two small islands of similar construction. The pool is surrounded by a barrier of light steel rods, set on $2\frac{1}{2}$-inch centers, 4 feet high and strongly inturned at the top. This overhang is made necessary by the fact that immediately inside it there is a ledge $4\frac{1}{2}$ feet wide. This is frequently used by the animals, which are restrained from escaping only by the overhang. This rather unsightly construction is nicely avoided in an exhibit recently built in the Zoological Gardens at Kansas City, Missouri, details of which have been furnished by W. T. A. Cully, director (*in litt.*). This pool is circular, 90 feet in diameter, and has the usual shelter and islands. Its merit lies in the fact that the water level is $3\frac{1}{2}$ feet lower than the public walk, the surrounding barrier of wire mesh rising $3\frac{1}{2}$ feet above it. This barrier is set directly on the pool's edge and pitched outward, so that it is difficult for visitors to climb or sit upon it, while at the same time it gives an exceptionally clear view of the animals. A narrow keepers' walk circles the pool just above water level but is not used by the animals. The total clearance of 7 feet is probably beyond the leaping ability of a sea lion, although I once saw a female leap from a dry floor against a sheer wall 6 feet high, catch her flippers on its top, and draw herself up to the level above.

Fresh water only is used for our seals here, since the supplying of salt water presents many difficulties and seems to offer no advantages. Our Sea Lion Pool is drained and thoroughly scrubbed once weekly, and after it has been refilled, a reduced flow of water is allowed to run constantly. The lining is smoothly finished concrete which has been coated with light blue rubber-base paint. This gives improved visibility and avoids the unnatural appearance of tile. It also prevents strong adherence of algae during hot weather, a condition further inhibited by the use of copper sulfate. Since the water content of the pool is roughly 167,000 gallons, 9 pounds of powdered copper sulfate dissolved in advance and poured in slowly at the inlet provides, if evenly distributed, a solution of approximately 6.5 parts per million (Hale, 1954). At this strength there is no harm to the animals, and even though rapid dilution occurs, the growth of algae is considerably reduced.

While the California sea lion is reasonably cold-resistant at this latitude, it is not deeply hardy, and at more northerly institutions in this country is usually removed to heated quarters in winter. Here, the animals generally remain in the shelter during periods of severe cold, particularly if heavy ice forms on the pool. This is usually of short duration and so is not a serious problem. When it has been considered essential that open water be maintained, various means, such as compressed air pumped into perforated pipes and screened underwater propellers, have proved successful.

In the choice of food for sea lions, as well as for other seals, consideration must be given to the presence, in certain fishes, of thiaminase, an enzyme which adversely affects vitamin B_1. This condition has been discussed more fully under "Foxes" (p. 276). A detailed account of thiamine deficiency in captive sea lions is given by Rigdon and Drager (1955). Alan Best, curator of the Stanley Park Zoo, Vancouver, British Columbia, says (*in litt.*) that sea lions kept at his institution receive a daily supplement of vitamin B_1, in the hope that it will compensate for a possible deficiency. Sea lions and other seals here are fed butterfish (*Poronotus tricanthus*) and mackerel (*Scomber scombrus*), both of which are listed as being thiaminase-free (Lee, 1948). The supply is received here weekly in freshly frozen condition and carefully thawed in cold water before use. Butterfish is fed extensively in summer, but mackerel, because of its higher oil content, is the winter staple. The large male California sea lion referred to above as weighing 590 pounds took from 20 to 25 pounds of fish daily in winter and from 15 to 20 pounds in summer. An adult female now living here takes about 12 pounds daily in winter and 10 pounds in summer. These amounts are based, of course, on the animals' condition, for a sea lion's capacity for taking food, unless restricted, seems almost limitless. Fish up to 2 pounds in weight are readily gulped whole, but those of greater size are likely to be shaken and broken into bits, with resulting loss. Some skill on the part of the keeper is required to make certain that each individual in a mixed group receives its proper allotment.

It is well known, of course, that the stomachs of sea lions are often found to contain an accumulation of stones of various sizes. In captivity the habit of swallowing assorted inedible objects, such as metal bottle caps, rubber balls, etc., sometimes results in fatal impactions or internal injuries. On the other hand, while it appears that the presence of stones in the stomach is normal, this seems not to be essential, for captive animals kept in carefully cleaned pools do not usually have access to fresh supplies.

The California sea lion, when well established, frequently breeds in captivity, but while births have occurred in many zoological gardens, rearing of the young has not always been achieved. Our own early efforts to breed and rear sea lions were definitely fumbling. The first pup to be born here was found struggling in the deep water of the pool on June 26, 1905, and drowned before it could be rescued. As later experience showed, this disaster was most unusual, as no sea lion mother here has since allowed her offspring to drown. Another birth did not occur until June 1, 1935. On this occasion the pool was partly drained, and mother and baby were confined to shallow water at one end. Within a month the pup had learned to swim and, with its mother, was given the full liberty of the pool (Leister, 1935).

The first of a new series of births took place on June 16, 1944, when a female pup was born, this time in the rock shelter. With the catastrophe of 1905 in mind, we placed low barricades at the entrances, to prevent the youngster from falling into the pool. But after two days the mother took the cub by the nape and swam with it to one of the islands, on which she tossed it. Home life on the island then became routine, enlivened by the pup's frequent tumbles into the water. The resounding splashes drew the instant response of the mother and, rather surprisingly, of the father as well. Often the male was first to arrive but he never took the required action. His obvious anxiety, however, was always of short duration, for the mother never failed to arrive in a flash and toss the youngster to safety. This pup, known as "Benny," made no progress in learning to swim until she was about 6 weeks old. Her first experiences were gained by running up and down a series of stone steps that entered the water. Final success required a full 2 weeks, so that she was 8 weeks old before she was able to swim. At the age of 4 months, when confined in a crate, Benny would take, swallow, and digest small fish but would not do so after she was returned to her mother. She continued to nurse until November, 1945, when she began to take smelts, and soon was fully weaned (Crandall, 1946). This continuance of nursing for over 17 months certainly exceeds the normal expectation. Benny lived until May 26, 1947, when a small glass bottle that she had swallowed was somehow broken after ingestion, to her detriment.

Following the birth of Benny, in 1944, her mother, "Wendy," produced single pups annually from 1947 to 1953, missing only 1952. The 1950 pup was premature, but all of the others were safely reared, with much less anxiety, it must be said, on our part. Most of these youngsters were more precocious than Benny had been, and one was seen swimming and "porpoising" freely when only 13 days old. Under our pool conditions it was almost impossible for young sea lions to learn to eat, for at the tossing of a fish they could only flee in the opposite direction to avoid being crushed in the mad rush that followed. Therefore, when they reached an age of between 10 and 11 months, they were removed to a smaller pool where, in solitude, they were taught to feed. If another pup was expected, they were not returned until after its birth. The older pup usually would attempt to nurse but was invariably rebuffed by the mother.

All births of California sea lions here have occurred in late May or in June, as did twelve single births in the Zoological Gardens of London, as reported by Zuckerman (1953). The gestation period is usually given as 11½ months (Asdell, 1946). Harrison, Matthews, and Roberts (1952), in summarizing their investigation of the breeding habits of seals, say that the evidence "suggests that delayed implantation is universal in most, if not all, seals." The weights given in Table 9 are those of various animals born here, taken as opportunity offered but perhaps of interest because of known ages.

TABLE 9
WEIGHTS OF CALIFORNIA SEA LIONS

Birth,♀	13¾ lbs.
8 days,♀	14 lbs.
4½ months,♀	37 lbs.
6 months,♀	42 lbs.
1 year,♂	65 lbs.
1 year, 4 months,♀	85 lbs.
2 years, 4 months,♂	150 lbs.
6 years, 2 months,♂	301 lbs.
7 years, 5 months,♂	375 lbs.

Only one California sea lion is listed by Flower (1931) as having lived as long as 19 years. This was the old bull at the New York Aquarium referred to above as having weighed 620 pounds. Our bull already mentioned as having weighed 590 pounds lived from March 19, 1938, to June 18, 1957, a day short of 19 years, 3 months, and a female received here on April 26, 1941, lived until July 9, 1961, or 20 years, 2 months, 13 days. A specimen is reported to have lived at least 20 years in the San Diego Zoological Garden (Anon., 1956), Jones (1958) lists 20 years, 5 months, 6 days in the Philadelphia Zoological Garden, and Ehlers (1957) gives an account of a female kept at Bremerhaven for 28 years.

Steller's sea lion, sometimes known as the northern sea lion (*Eumetopias jubata*), is a very much larger animal than the California, males reaching a maximum weight of 2,000 pounds and females 600 (Palmer, 1954). The cranial crest developed by adult California males is lacking in this massive species. Steller's sea lion is found from Bering Strait and the Commander and Pribilof Islands in the Bering Sea, south along the coast of Alaska to southern California, where it overlaps the range of its smaller relative.

Presumably because of its great bulk and less amenable nature, Steller's sea lion is far less common in captivity than the California, and there is no regularly established source of supply. Early attempts to maintain chance specimens were not encouraging, and of six young animals received here in

1903, none survived longer than 18 months. Our next experience did not come until April 20, 1955, when a young pair was received from the Stanley Park Zoo at Vancouver, British Columbia. These animals, at first, ate only squids, taking 10–15 pounds daily and regurgitating the beaks. The female never really thrived and died some months after arrival. The male, however, soon abandoned his diet of squids in favor of mackerel and continued to increase in size. He lived until June 24, 1960, or 5 years, 2 months, 4 days, his weight at death being 730 pounds.

A Steller's sea lion received at the National Zoological Park on October 23, 1900, lived until January 22, 1918, or 17 years, 3 months (Hollister, 1919). An account of this animal is given by Mann (1930:122–23).

No other species of sea lion has been exhibited here, although the South American sea lion (*Otaria byronia*) is not uncommon in European collections. An animal of this species received at the Zoological Gardens of London in 1866 was, in fact, the first member of the group to reach that institution (Flower, 1929). The species has been kept in this country by the Zoological Garden of San Diego, where it has also bred (Stott, 1954). A South American sea lion is reported by Flower (1931) to have lived 17 years, 6 months, 4 days in the Zoological Gardens of London.

Persecuted for many years because of the value of their lovely pelts, the fur seals of the world have been greatly reduced in numbers, some to the verge of extinction. The recovery of the northern fur seal (*Callorhinus ursinus*), following an international agreement signed in 1911 by Great Britain (for Canada), Russia, Japan, and the United States, is too well known for detailed discussion here. Recent results of an international survey are given by Taylor, Fujinaga, and Wilke (1955).

The northern fur seal spends much of its life in the water, coming ashore on the Pribilofs and on islands in the Bering Sea off the eastern coast of Siberia only for the short summer breeding season. It winters along the western coast of North America as far south as Mexico, and on the Asiatic side, to Japan and Korea. Some authorities recognize three races (see Ellerman and Morrison-Scott, 1951; Hall and Kelson 1959), but Taylor *et al.* (1955) consider that these are not distinguishable.

The weight of "harem" bulls is given by Baker (1957) as from 450 to 600 pounds and of mature females as from 60 to 100 pounds. Taylor *et al.* (1955) report the weight of a pregnant female taken in the Gulf of Alaska as 67.1 kilograms.

Comparatively few specimens of the northern fur seal have been kept in captivity. It appears that the first were two pups received at the Aquarium of the Bureau of Fisheries in Washington in 1909 (Osburn, 1911*a*).

Strangely enough, these animals established a captivity record of 9 years, which seems not to have been equaled since (Flower, 1931). In 1910, six more were secured and were distributed, two each, to Golden Gate Park, San Francisco, the National Zoological Park, Washington, and the New York Aquarium. Neither of the New York pups lived for more than a few months, but useful accounts of their brief histories are given by Osburn (1911a, 1911b).

In more recent years, excellent results in maintaining the northern fur seal have been obtained in the San Diego Zoological Garden. One individual kept there was subjected to training and proved to be almost as receptive as the California sea lion (Bode, 1952). The species is reported by Stott (1954) as having been bred in the San Diego collection. Since females are bred within a few days of parturition, the gestation period is usually given as $11\frac{1}{2}$ months.

Of the southern fur seals, the nomenclature of which has been reviewed by Sivertsen (1954) and Scheffer (1958) without complete agreement, several forms have been exhibited by zoological gardens. The South African or Cape fur seal (*Arctocephalus pusillus*) inhabits South African waters, coming ashore to breed on rocky islands from Algoa Bay, Cape Province, to Cape Cross, South West Africa (Roberts, 1951). Four young animals of this species, a male and three females, received here in 1922, were fed mackerel and butterfish and otherwise treated as outlined for sea lions. The male, which lived here just short of 8 years, once climbed a 6-foot fence of wire netting and entered a pool occupied by penguins, which promptly left for the shelter of their rockery. This will give an idea of the height of the inclosing fence required for these seals.

A detailed account of the behavior and breeding of the South African fur seal at the Zoological Gardens of Leipzig is given by Schneider (1942). The species has also been bred at the Zoological Gardens of Berlin (Steinmetz, 1940). In an extensive study of the breeding biology of this species, Rand (1954–55) was able to demonstrate that while elapsed time from copulation to birth averages 359 days, implantation does not occur for 3–4 months, so that actual gestation requires only about 8 months. Flower (1931) reports a South African fur seal that lived for 20 years, 19 days in the Zoological Gardens of London.

The South American fur seal (*A. australis*) is found along the coasts of southern South America from Brazil to Peru and on islands of the area. Scheffer (1958) restricts the typical race to the Falklands, provisionally including those of South Georgia and nearby islands, and revives *gracilis* as a subspecific designation for the mainland animals. Fur seals of this species have been kept in various European zoological gardens, but in America, as far as I know, have been seen only at San Diego (Anon., 1951a) and New York. Of two young specimens received here in 1937, the female lived just over 2 years, the male 3 years, 2 months. Neither seemed to differ in requirements from other fur seals.

Two males of the Guadalupe fur seal, received at the Zoological Garden of San Diego in 1928 (Townsend, 1928), appear to be the only specimens of their kind to have been kept in captivity. Usually known as *A. townsendi* but recently designated as a race of *A. philippi* by Scheffer (1958), this animal apparently was once numerous not only on Guadalupe but on other islands off the coasts of southern California and Baja California. Recently considered as extinct or nearly so, Hubbs (1956) reports it to be still existing and apparently increasing on Guadalupe. Flower (1931) reports that an Australian fur seal (*A. doriferus*) lived for 16 years in the Taronga Zoological Park, Sydney.*

FAMILY ODOBENIDAE

WALRUSES

The walruses (*Odobenus*) are circumpolar in distribution and are practically confined within the Arctic Circle, although excursions southward have been recorded. Two races are presently recognized: the Atlantic walrus (*Odobenus r. rosmarus*) and the Pacific (*O. r. divergens*), the tusks in the latter being somewhat larger and differently set, besides other anatomical variations (Allen, 1880). The great tusks, present in both sexes but larger in the male, at once distinguish the walruses from other seals. Like the true seals, they have no external ears, but like the Otariidae, the walruses are able to rotate the hind legs forward in such a way that they can walk and gallop clumsily, as the eared seals do. The upper lips of young and adults of both sexes are armed with long, stiff bristles, which appear to serve a function in feeding.

The young are thinly clothed in coarse brownish hair, but adults are practically hairless, the skin being deeply wrinkled. Males greatly exceed females in size and have been reported to weigh as much as 3,000 pounds (Allen, 1880), and Dunbar (1949) suggests that "males weighing between two thousand and three thousand pounds when fully grown, appear to be the rule." The females are usually said to weigh one-third less than males. The famous female, "Thora," of the Copenhagen Zoological Gardens,

*See Addenda, p. 735.

weighed 520 kilograms or 1,144 pounds at the age of approximately 12 years (Reventlow, 1951).

The walruses are largely bottom-feeders, their food consisting principally of clams and mussels, presumably dug up with the tusks, and occasional fish. There are reports, too, of the remains of seals having been found in the stomachs of walruses. Breeding takes place largely on the ice, the animals seldom coming ashore. The gestation period is usually given as from 11 months to 1 year (Asdell, 1946), and nursing is believed to continue for 18 months to 2 years, so that young are presumably produced only in alternate years (Dunbar, 1949).

Efforts to establish the walrus in captivity have been long continued, but complete success appears still to be in the offing. In an extended account of early experiences, Allen (1880) mentions a living specimen that reached London in 1608 and a second exhibited in Holland in 1612. Neither of these young animals seems to have lived for more than a few weeks. The first specimen received by the Zoological Society of London came in 1853 and lived only a day; the second, which arrived in 1867, lived for 1 month, 18 days (Flower, 1929). A complete account of the external and internal anatomy of this animal has been given by Murie (1872). A most interesting account of walruses in captivity, embellished by observations made in nature by sealers, is given by Hagenbeck (1910). The first two specimens received at Stellingen soon died, but two others received later lived for nearly 2 years. The dates of arrival of these animals are not given, but in 1907 and 1908 there were further arrivals, so that Hagenbeck was then able to exhibit a total of eight at one time. They were fed on fish, cut into bits and with the bones removed. Actual longevities are not given, but the animals must have thrived, for Hagenbeck complains that three alone ate $2\frac{1}{2}$ tons of fish in a month, at a cost of £30!

Best results with the walrus in captivity have been obtained in the Zoological Gardens of Copenhagen, fortunately well documented by Reventlow (1938, 1951). Early experience comprised the survival of a young animal from 1906 to 1907, as well as the loss of others after only a few months. Renewal of these experiments began, under the direction of Mr. Reventlow, on June 15, 1937, when a female walrus named "Thora," judged to be about $1\frac{1}{2}$ months old, arrived at Rotterdam from the west coast of Greenland. Happily, she had been fed reconstituted powdered milk with cod-liver oil during her journey, so that apparently she was in good condition on arrival. She was fed from a nursing bottle provided with a strong rubber nipple. Soon after arrival cream was added to the milk, with ground herring, and when several months old, Thora was taking up to 7 liters daily, in six or seven meals. Fish was gradually substituted and the milk allowance reduced, but up to the age of 2 years she still received 1 liter of milk with her fish. At the age of 4–5 years, Thora was eating as much as 25 kilograms (55 pounds) of herring daily, given in four meals. Thora died on April 17, 1949, after 11 years, 10 months, 2 days in Copenhagen. This undoubtedly is the greatest longevity so far attained by a captive walrus. The cause of death is given as a cerebral infection originating from an abscess at the root of a badly worn tusk. Reventlow (1951) gives a table showing Thora's progressive weights, ending with 520 kilograms (1,144 pounds) at death. A young female named "Gine," received on September 18, 1937, lived until December 4, 1944, but a male that arrived with Gine died on November 1, 1938, and was found to have stomach and intestines heavily impacted by dead leaves, with some other foreign objects. Mr. Reventlow was keenly alert to the danger of leaf impactions in walruses and pointed this out to me on several occasions.

The first specimen to be received by an American zoological garden was probably a youngster presented to the New York Zoological Park by the Peary Arctic Club on September 21, 1902. This young animal lived for less than a month, the cause of death being reported as "enteritis." The best result here so far was obtained with a young male named "Flip," presented to us by Paul J. Rainey on September 17, 1910. Flip weighed 150 pounds on arrival and had been fed on a diet of cod and "shucked" clams, to which he was well accustomed. At first Flip took only 9 pounds of clams and boned fish in three meals daily. The clams were gradually increased and the fish reduced, so that by December, 1911, he was receiving 30 pounds of clams daily, with no fish. Later the clam allotment was increased to 40 pounds daily. Flip was kept in a small inclosure with a deep pool, about 15 feet across, the water in which was maintained at an approximation of ocean salinity by the addition of sea salt (Ditmars, 1914). A small hut was also available to him, and he slept in it winter and summer. Flip followed his keeper eagerly for a distance of 100 yards or more to the weighing platform, so that an accurate record of his progress was possible. This would have been disappointing had charts been available for comparison. On December 18, 1911, a year after arrival, Flip weighed only 220 pounds, on November 26, 1912, 325 pounds, and on February 4, 1914, 415 pounds, the greatest weight that appears on his record. Flip died on July 5, 1914, after 3 years, 9 months, 18 days here. The cause of death is not recorded.

A young walrus received here on September 4, 1935, and four more on

September 15, 1940, through the well-known Captain "Bob" Bartlett, had all been fed at first on a milk or milk-and-fish diet (Angel, 1935; Bartlett, 1940). However, by the time they reached us, all were being fed entirely on cut cod and could not be induced to revert to a presumably more suitable liquid formula. None survived for more than a few months.

Our most recent experience with the walrus here was certainly encouraging, if not entirely successful. This had to do with a young male named "Herbert," received from Copenhagen on October 18, 1951. On arrival by air, Herbert was in excellent health and condition, except for the usual skin lesions, and weighed 240 pounds, indicating birth in the spring of the same year. We were unable to learn the exact feeding schedule to which Herbert was accustomed. However, on the basis of the feeding method followed by Reventlow as described above and the analysis of the milk of the harp seal (*Phoca groenlandica*) reported by Sivertsen (1935), showing the fat content of a single sample to be 42.65 per cent, we improvised a formula consisting of 600 cc. of evaporated milk, undiluted with water, 350 cc. of Mazola oil, and 50 cc. of cod-liver oil. This thick, viscous mixture provided 1 liter or just over 1 quart of fluid containing approximately 40 per cent fat. Sivertsen's analysis of 1935, as well as those reported by him later (1941) for both harp and hooded seals (*Cystophora cristata*), show an entire absence of sugar, but the small amount in the evaporated milk appeared to be inconsequential. The cod-liver oil was kept at a low level not only because of the lower cost of the corn (maize) oil but also with due respect to the feeling of Reventlow (1951), often repeated verbally to me, to the effect that an excess of fish oil might be responsible for the skin lesions with which young captive walruses are almost invariably afflicted.

At first Herbert refused steadfastly to take the mixture, his first meal here consisting of the flesh of the mackerel, sucked cleanly from the bones, which were left intact. The lip bristles surely have a function here, for without their help the neat removal of the flesh could hardly be accomplished. Herbert's reluctance was readily overcome by adding comminuted mackerel to the formula with the help of a Waring Blendor and presenting the result to him in a large, deep pan, with a few floating pieces of whole fish. Herbert promptly reduced these bits to skeletons and having tasted the liquid inadvertently, proceeded to suck the pan clean. Twice daily thereafter, he consumed a quart of the milk mixture and, at first, 5 pounds of mackerel. As his size increased, the quantity of mixture remained static but gradual increases in the fish were made, so that when Herbert reached a final weight of 958 pounds he was receiving 40 pounds of mackerel, which he still drew from the bones, and the usual 2 quarts of mixture daily in two meals.

As Herbert grew, regular weight records became increasingly difficult to get. However, like all young walruses, he was extremely amenable and eventually learned to climb a ramp attached to a portable platform scales and to halt, on order, when a balance had been reached (Bridges, 1953). His progress is shown in Table 10.

TABLE 10
WEIGHTS OF MALE WALRUS, HERBERT

Date	Weight (pounds)
Oct. 18, 1951*	240
Feb. 7, 1952	385
Mar. 17, 1952	427
May 2, 1952	487
June 5, 1952	582
July 5, 1952	619
Aug. 12, 1952	633
Sept. 12, 1952	685
Oct. 10, 1952	725
Dec. 30, 1952	804
Mar. 17, 1953†	958

*Arrival
†Death

Herbert spent his entire time here in fresh water, the skin lesions present when he came soon healing without special treatment. During cold weather he slept in the water, usually with his head resting above it on the rock ledge. However, between naps he managed to agitate the water sufficiently to keep it from freezing solidly. We had thought that he might suffer from the direct rays of the sun during the summer and had erected an awning across one end of the inclosure to provide shade. This was never used, for when Herbert had sunned himself sufficiently on the bank, he simply slid into the water to cool off. A constant flow kept the temperature of the pool only slightly above 60°F., even during the hottest weather. Herbert's companions were two female harbor seals (*Phoca*). While friendly relations were maintained, these never reached the degree described by Reventlow (1951), for the wary seals skilfully avoided the walrus's constant efforts to clasp and hold them playfully in his front flippers. Herbert died on March 17, 1953, as the result of an impaction caused by his having swallowed a rubber ball, which lodged in the small intestine. He had lived here for 1 year, 4 months, 27 days.

A young male Atlantic walrus received at the San Diego Zoological Garden on October 19, 1951, is reported to have weighed only 100 pounds

1 day earlier. The San Diego walrus was fed on comminuted mackerel, red salmon, and shark liver, with cod-liver oil, and after 2 months his weight had increased to 250 pounds. He apparently was thriving but died unexpectedly on June 9, 1952. Mrs. Belle Benchley, then executive secretary at San Diego, informed me (*in litt.*) that no cause of death was found.

On October 9, 1956, a pair of young walruses was received at the New York Aquarium, (operated by the New York Zoological Society). These animals arrived in excellent condition, the male, "Olaf," weighing 240 pounds, the female, "Karen," 340 pounds, the latter weight, when compared with those given for Thora, noted above, suggesting birth in 1955. An account of the progress of these animals up to May, 1958, is given by Coates and Atz (1958). Feeding approximated the diet of Herbert, as already given, with the exceptions that Atlantic herring and "skimmer" clams (*Spisula* [*mactra*] *solidissima*) were used instead of mackerel. Because the Atlantic herring has been reported as containing thiaminase (Lee, 1948) while the "skimmer" appears not to have been investigated, empirical supplements of vitamin B_1 were added, in amounts varying from 150 to 300 mg. daily.

Some interesting notes on the water preferences of captive walruses developed from observations made on the behavior of Olaf and Karen. Kept at first in a small outdoor fresh-water pool, the young animals seemed quite content. However, when sea water was substituted, the animals managed to leave their inclosure and find their way to another basin filled with fresh water. A short time later, sea water was again run in and again the walruses made nuisances of themselves by wandering. By this time the large, permanent tank had been completed and filled with sea water and the animals were transferred to it. Soon, however, they showed signs of distress by refusing food, and it was not until they were seen trying to catch rain drops in their open mouths that the cause of the trouble was suspected. When a hose was hastily connected to a fresh-water inlet and run into the pool, both young walruses drank from it heavily and almost immediately resumed feeding.

Karen died suddenly in January, 1957, but Olaf continued to thrive. Unfortunately, no definite weights were obtainable, but in May, 1958, it was conservatively estimated that Olaf then had attained at least 1,000 pounds. At that time he was receiving, daily, 40 pounds of shelled "skimmers," 15 pounds of fish, with 200 mg. vitamin B_1 and some milk mixture, once or twice weekly (James W. Atz, *in litt.*). By the end of May the latter item had been omitted entirely.

Up to August, 1961, Olaf was kept in an open tank 60 feet long, 40 feet wide at one end and 20 at the other, its depth varying from 5 to 7½ feet. Glass on one side below water level permitted viewing the inmates under water, a most illuminating experience. Besides the walrus, the group included, from time to time, California sea lions and female gray (*Halichoerus*) and harbor seals (*Phoca*), all of which were amicable. In 1957 two young northern elephant seals (*Mirounga angustirostris*) were introduced but were found not only to persecute the comparatively clumsy Olaf but actually to bite him, so they were removed to the Zoological Park. Following the arrival of three white whales or belugas (*Delphinapterus leucas*) at the Aquarium in August, 1961 (Ray, 1961a), Olaf was removed to a smaller inclosure where he passed the winter. A new structure, known as Polar Bay, was ready for occupancy on May 9, 1962. On that day Olaf, by means of a derrick, was transferred to one of its pools measuring 70 by 40 feet and 8 feet deep, containing 100,000 gallons of salt water and with facilities for viewing from below or above. At that time Olaf's weight was found to be 1,880 pounds, presumably the greatest displacement so far attained by a captive walrus (Bridges, 1962). His daily food intake at that time was reported as 140 pounds of fish. His slender tusks had reached a length of 6–7 inches. Olaf's relations with three female gray seal companions appeared to be on a friendly basis.

All the captive walruses so far mentioned have been members of the Atlantic race (*O. r. rosmarus*). Benchley (1940) gives an account of a young female Pacific walrus (*O. r. divergens*) taken from an ice floe in the Bering Sea and presented to the San Diego Zoological Garden. Fed at first with milk from a rubber tube attached to a bottle, she later received a formula of milk, whole or canned, sardine oil, butter fat, limewater, and a trace of iodine. When skin lesions developed, milk poisoning (milk protein allergy) was blamed, and following the substitution of a mixture of ground fish, cod-liver oil, powdered clam shell, and water, her skin and coat returned to normal. Eventually this young walrus learned to eat handmade "clams" consisting of cubed fish treated with sardine oil, Viosterol, and a few drops of iodine, then rolled in powdered clam shell. George Pournelle, curator of mammals at San Diego, informs me (*in litt.*) that this animal was captured on July 10, 1932, and received at the Zoo on August 8. She died there on September 1, 1933, after 1 year, 24 days. Dr. Pournelle gives the cause of death as acute pneumonitis and her final weight as 216 pounds.

Later work with the Pacific walrus has produced more favorable results. Four specimens received at the New York Aquarium in 1958 were in poor condition, and none lived for more than a few weeks. In July, 1959, Carleton Ray, associate curator of the New York Aquarium, returned from

St. Lawrence Island, in the Bering Sea, with a young walrus named "Ookie" (Ray, 1960). Ookie was fed on a formula devised by Dr. Ray (1960, 1961b) consisting of minced clams, heavy cream containing 30 per cent butter fat, and a vitamin supplement. Ookie was successfully reared (Atz, 1961) and until her death on October 4, 1962, during an operation for the treatment of a worn and infected tusk, occupied a smaller pool, adjacent to Olaf's, in the company of two younger animals. The latter, collected by Dr. Ray off St. Lawrence Island, arrived at the Aquarium in 1961 (Ray, 1961b) and were thriving a year later.

Four Pacific walruses received at the San Diego Zoological Garden in 1961 were fed a comparable though more varied diet, but failed to survive (Pournelle, 1961) Four pups also collected in 1961, by David Brown of Marineland of the Pacific, at Palos Verdes Estates, California. were reported to be in good condition in 1962.

FAMILY PHOCIDAE

EARLESS, TRUE, OR HAIR SEALS; ELEPHANT SEALS

The earless seals are readily distinguished by two obvious characters. One, the absence of external ears, is shared by the walruses, but the fact that the hind legs, the principal propulsive force in swimming, cannot be rotated forward to support the body when out of water is typical of this group. In consequence, the earless seals are unable to raise the abdomen above a solid surface and can progress only by humping movements, with some pulling aid from the front flippers.

In the adult the pelage is short and coarse, with no heavy undercoat, protection against the cold being provided by the thick layer of blubber under the skin. The young of most species have a woolly coat, shed before birth or soon afterward. Monogamy or promiscuity are the usual rule, although polygamy is practised by the elephant seals (*Mirounga*) and, to a lesser extent, by the gray seal (*Halichoerus*). There are concentrations of species in cold or temperate seas of both Northern and Southern Hemispheres, the monk seals (*Monachus*) being the only tropical representatives. While most of the earless seals are marine, some have become landlocked in fresh-water lakes (Allen, 1880; Doutt, 1942, 1954).

The harbor or common seal (*Phoca vitulina*), while far from being a common zoo animal, is more likely to be kept than any other of the group. Found in five presently recognized races (Scheffer, 1958), in cold and temperate regions of the Northern Hemisphere, the rotund and attractive harbor seal seems to have a special appeal.

The infant harbor seal may shed its white baby coat before birth or certainly within a very few days after that event. Since it is usually born on a tidal flat or sand bank, it may be necessary for it to swim or at least to keep afloat within hours. The young seal is fed by its mother for from 4 to 6 weeks, after which, in company with others of its age, it must depend for food on such small fish and crustaceans as it can catch. If taken at this stage, harbor seals readily learn to eat dead fish and quickly become docile and friendly. On the other hand, animals which are still nursing must be given a milk formula approximating that already described for walruses. Sometimes, if great persistence is exercised, individuals may be induced to take this from a nursing bottle. If persuasion fails, as it too often does, then there is no resort but forceable feeding by tube. Harbor seals breed in some numbers along the coasts of Belgium, and nursing youngsters were frequently brought to the Zoological Gardens of Antwerp by well-meaning rescuers, in June and July. Force-feeding young seals five times daily is an onerous task, and in spite of the best efforts of the keepers, successful results were not always obtained. However, determined to save the lives of these waifs, they finally invented a lever-operated pump, by means of which feeding could be accomplished in much less time (Van den bergh, 1958). A photograph of three young harbor seals, safely reared to the fish-eating stage, attests the success of the device.

While harbor seals have been kept here, off and on, since 1899, they usually have been received in poor condition or suffering from injuries and seldom survived for long. However, in recent years better shipping facilities, especially through the use of air transport, have allowed specimens to reach us in a viable state. A female European harbor seal (*P. v. vitulina*), shipped by air from Copenhagen, traveled well and arrived here on November 30, 1950. She died at the New York Aquarium on August 7, 1959. For over 3 years she had as a companion a Pacific harbor seal (*P. v. richardii*) brought by air from California, where it is commonly known as "leopard seal." Two or three exceptionally cold winters occurred during this period, so that heavy ice formed on their pool. At such times the seals remained under water, making use of a blowhole for breathing. At first, this habit caused much distress to our visitors, who insisted that the lives of the animals were endangered, their fears being allayed only by the posting of large signs explaining the situation.

These two animals, as well as an Atlantic harbor seal (*P. v. concolor*), received in 1956 as a yearling, were fed an average of 4 pounds of mackerel and butterfish daily in two meals. At all times here, these seals were kept in fresh water. However, the European and the Atlantic, lent to the New York Aquarium in 1957, lived there in a large salt-water tank, with no apparent effect on health or condition.

The harbor seal is not commonly bred in captivity, and the only successes in this country known to me are those of the San Diego Zoological Garden (Stott, 1954), repeated in following years. Detailed accounts of the breeding of captive harbor seals at Bremerhaven are given by Stocker (1933) and Junker (1940), and of similar events in the Berlin Zoological Gardens by Heinroth (1958). Mohr (1955) says the gestation period is 11 months.

A harbor seal is reported by Hollister (1922) to have lived for 12 years, 1 month, 18 days in the National Zoological Park. Flower (1931) records 14 years, 4 months, 12 days for a specimen in the Zoological Gardens of London.*

The little ringed seal (*P. hispida*), in several races, is circumpolar in distribution. It is the common seal of the Arctic, seldom straying south of the regions of ice and snow. In gross appearance it closely resembles the harbor seal, but the adult is usually distinguishable by the irregular, yellowish rings on the upper surface. It feeds largely on crustaceans and other invertebrates, but fish are also included in the diet.

A ringed seal brought from St. Lawrence Island in the Bering Sea to the New York Aquarium by Carleton Ray in 1961 appears to be the first living specimen to be kept in this country (Ray, 1961*b*). The species was first received at the Zoological Gardens of London in 1905 (Flower, 1929), and Mohr (1952) presents photographs of specimens of several races living in the Zoological Gardens of Berlin and at Hagenbeck's Tierpark, Stellingen, Germany. On January 1, 1929, a female ringed seal kept at Skansen, Stockholm, give birth to a dead hybrid pup, sired by a gray seal (*Halichoerus grypus*). This appears to be the only instance of a ringed seal breeding in captivity. This female was received at Skansen in the autumn of 1914 and died in April, 1929, shortly after the birth of her pup. This span of nearly 15 years is the longest known to me for a captive ringed seal.

The harp or saddle-back seal (*P. groenlandica*) is found in North Atlantic and Arctic regions, from Newfoundland north to Hudson Bay and Ellesmere Island in the west and Severnaya Zemlya in the east. It is a gregarious species, spending its life in the water or on the ice and migrating southward or northward seasonally as the ice advances or retreats. Thousands are slaughtered annually for their pelts off the coasts of Newfoundland and

*See Addenda, p. 735.

Labrador. The young are born on the ice and do not begin to shed their white coats until just after the end of the nursing period of 10–12 days. The blubber-laden pups, having then been deserted by their mate-seeking mothers, do not take to the water to hunt food for themselves for 2 or 3 weeks, when the molt has been completed (Sivertsen, 1941). As already noted, this author has given a complete analysis of the fat-rich milk of both the harp and hooded seals.

Harp seals have occasionally been kept in European zoological gardens—four specimens were received by the Zoological Gardens of London in 1869 (Flower, 1929)—but no great success appears to have been obtained in maintaining them. Two yearlings received here in excellent condition in 1956 fed well on butterfish and mackerel, consuming 4 or 5 pounds daily in two meals, but the longer-lived of the pair survived, in a fresh-water pool, for only 4 months. Four newly molted pups were received at the New York Aquarium on April 5, 1958, and two more on April 24. Most of these young animals were in the pre-feeding stage, but within a few days of arrival, all were swimming freely in an outdoor salt-water tank and taking smelts from the fingers of their keepers. One died in July, apparently from an impaction caused by $4\frac{1}{2}$ pounds of small stones that it had swallowed. Of the remaining five, the survivor lived until August 2, 1961 (James W. Atz, *in litt.*).

The gray seal (*H. grypus*) is a large animal, adult males sometimes reaching a weight of 700 pounds. The long, doglike face, almost devoid of "stop," is a distinguishing character, though hardly a point of beauty. Unlike other members of the Phocidae, the gray seal may develop small external ears, as described by Pocock (1933).

Resident in the temperate North Atlantic, the gray seal population seems to have three principal points of concentration: the area of the Gulf of St. Lawrence, the British Isles, with extensions to Iceland and east to Novaya Zemlya, and the Baltic Sea. In the western Atlantic and in the Baltic the majority of pups are born on ice or on land, in February, while on the coasts of Britain pupping occurs, in various localities, from September to December and always on the rocky shores (Davies, 1957). In this species, territories on the breeding grounds are established by the adult males and loosely organized harems are formed, the females moving about practically at will. The pups wear white woolly coats at birth and are nursed by their fasting mothers for a period usually given as 2–3 weeks. The females, which have already remated, then abandon the young and leave them to shed their natal coverings unattended and finally take to the sea.

The gray seal is encountered fairly often in European zoological gardens, particularly those of the north. Spectacular groups are usually to be seen at Skansen and Copenhagen, as well as in Germany. In American collections, perhaps because of the remoteness of the western Atlantic breeding areas from the larger zoological institutions, the species is seldom seen. The first specimen to be received by the New York Zoological Park was a female, picked up in the Gulf of St. Lawrence in February, 1954, and reared at McGill University, Montreal (Myers, 1956). Presented to us by that institution, this animal arrived here on December 21, 1954. In 1963 she was still living in an outdoor fresh-water pool which, from time to time, she has shared peacefully with various other seals, including a young male northern elephant seal (*Mirounga angustirostris*). Her food consists of 5–7 pounds of whole mackerel up to $\frac{1}{2}$ pound in weight, given daily in two meals. Two young gray seals, also from the Gulf of St. Lawrence area, were received at the New York Aquarium on April 5, 1958, in company with the harp seals mentioned previously. The grays, too, had reached the feeding stage and took smelts and other small fishes readily. They seemed as contented in salt water as ours did in fresh.

There seem to be few records of breeding the gray seal in captivity, as with other members of this family. Mohr (1952) reports that the female of a pair received at Skansen in 1922 produced single young in 1931, 1932, and 1933, none of which lived. The male of this pair, incidentally, was also the sire of the pup produced by a female ringed seal, as already noted. Curry-Lindahl (1958) reports that a gray seal was born at Skansen on March 1, 1957, and fully reared, an event which he believes to be the "first successful birth of this species in captivity." Dr. Curry-Lindahl has informed me (*in litt.*) that the mother nursed the pup for about 3 weeks, at the end of which it took to the water and soon learned to eat small fish.*

The greatest longevity given by Flower (1931) for a gray seal in captivity is 18 years in the Berlin Aquarium. The *Annual Report* of the Royal Zoological Society of Scotland for 1957 (1958:8) mentions a gray seal that died on March 1, 1957, after 27 years in the Edinburgh Gardens, following 6 years in the hands of a showman, for a total of 33 years in captivity. Mohr (1952) gives an account of the well-known "Jacob" who, received at Skansen on October 28, 1901, at the estimated age of 2 years, lived there for 41 years. A series of photographs of this noteworthy animal at various stages is given by Mohr (1940).

The monk seals (*Monachus*) are tropical in distribution, the three known species being widely separated. The Mediterranean monk seal (*Monachus monachus*) is found in the area for which it is named, with Atlantic extensions to the Canary Islands and south to Río de Oro; the Caribbean monk

*See Addenda, p. 735.

seal (*Monachus tropicalis*), once apparently abundant in the Gulf of Mexico and the Caribbean area, is now close to extinction if, indeed, it has not already disappeared, while the Hawaiian species (*Monachus schauinslandi*) still persists in the northwestern islands of the Hawaiian Archipelago, where the present population is estimated as 1,000–1,500 animals (Scheffer, 1958).

The life history of the monk seals is still not thoroughly known, but an account of present knowledge is given by King (1956). Included are early captivity records, dating from 1777. In spite of this comparatively lengthy experience, the monk seals have seldom been kept in northern zoological gardens, possibly because of a presumed requirement for warm water. King (*loc. cit.*) records single specimens of the Mediterranean species as having been received at the Zoological Gardens of London in 1882, 1894, and 1910, but none survived for more than 4 months. A specimen from Madeira arrived at the Berlin Zoological Gardens in 1910 (Anon., 1910a), and photographs, presumably of this animal, have been reproduced by Mohr (1952).

No monk seal has ever been kept here, but specimens of both the Caribbean and the Hawaiian species have been received by other American institutions. Two Caribbean monk seals arrived at the National Zoological Park in the summer of 1897 but, unfortunately, they survived for only two months (Mann, 1930). At about the same time, the exact date now being indeterminable, two animals of this species were received at the New York Aquarium, where they were kept indoors in a large oval pool built in the floor. One lived for 2 years, while the other lived until January 6, 1903, after "a little over 5½ years" (Anon., 1903). Death was attributed to fatty degeneration of heart, liver, and kidneys, thought to have resulted from insufficient exercise. On June 14, 1909, an adult male and two young animals of the Caribbean species were received by the New York Aquarium and were kept together in the same floor pool. All seemed to adjust readily (Anon., 1910b) but Grant (1911) says that of the three animals, the adult died December 27, 1910, and one of the young pair on January 16, 1911. At the time of publication, which was March, 1911, the third seal was still living, but no further information concerning it is now available.

The captivity history of the Hawaiian monk seal is even scantier than those of the two other species. On May 17, 1951, a young specimen was received at the San Diego Zoological Garden as the gift of the Honolulu Zoo (Anon., 1951b). The death date of this animal has been given to me (*in litt.*) by George H. Pournelle, curator of mammals at San Diego, as August 7, 1951. Dr. Pournelle also informs me that a second specimen, again from the Honolulu Zoo, arrived at San Diego on September 20, 1957, and lived until March 8, 1958.

Of the four earless seals known from the Antarctic area, in addition to the southern elephant seal (*Mirounga leonina*), only one appears to have been kept in captivity successfully and that but briefly. This is the leopard seal (*Hydrurga leptonyx*), found here and there in the seas about Antarctica and moving northward in winter, its limits being about 30° S. lat. (Scheffer, 1958). It is a long, slender-bodied animal, adult males reaching a length of 12 feet. In addition to the usual seal diet of fish, squids, and crustaceans, the leopard seal also takes warm-blooded prey, including young seals of other species, penguins, other sea birds, and even carrion. Troughton (1951) says that a stranded male taken in 1870 near Sydney, Australia, had swallowed a full-grown platypus.*

My own experience with this species is limited to the viewing of a living specimen at Hagenbeck's Tierpark at Stellingen, Germany, in late November, 1912. This animal was appropriately shown at the front of a series of moated inclosures, with king penguins above and behind. As the leopard seal floated quietly in the water, it looked directly at me, giving a definite impression of sinister invitation, enhanced by the immense extent of its jaws. It was a chilling, unforgettable experience which I was never able to analyze fully until I read the lively description given by Matthews (1952), in which he ascribes to the leopard seal a reptilian appearance. That is exactly the point: no seal should suggest a crocodile!

The literature contains few references to the leopard seal in captivity. Troughton (1951) mentions a specimen kept in the Taronga Zoo, Sydney, which decimated a flock of ducks, to the mystification of attendants. A male leopard seal received at Stellingen on May 27, 1937, is described by Mohr (1939). This animal lived there until September 13, 1939, a survival of 2 years, 3 months, 17 days. It measured 320 centimeters (approximately 10 feet, 6 inches) and weighed 435 kilograms (957 pounds) at death.

Largest of all the pinnipeds are the elephant seals (*Mirounga*). Two species are currently recognized: the southern (*Mirounga leonina*), found at scattered points in the subantarctic area, and the northern (*Mirounga angustirostris*), now restricted, except for occasional wanderers, to small islands off the coasts of California and Baja California, with the largest concentration on Guadalupe Island. Both species have suffered heavily from the depredations of sealers, and while the southern still exists in some numbers, the northern was reduced almost to extinction in the early years of this century. Townsend (1912) considered the Guadalupe herd to number 150 animals in 1911. In that year the Mexican Government set

*See Addenda, p. 736.

up protective regulations, under which a gradual recovery was made, Scheffer (1958) estimating a total population of 8,000-10,000 individuals at that time.

Between the two species there appears to be little difference in potential size. The maximum lengths quoted by Scheffer (1958) for the northern elephant seal are 22 feet for males and 11 feet, 5 inches for females; for the southern, 21 feet, 4 inches for males and 11 feet, 6 inches for females. Maximum weights for males of the genus are given as 8,000 pounds and for females, 2,000 pounds. The principal superficial differences are found in the distensible trunk, which is shorter, narrower, and less pendulous in males of the southern species (Murphy, 1914).

The elephant seals are polygamous, large males gathering harems of females during the breeding season. This habit is contrary to the general custom of the earless seals, although the gray seal (*Halichoerus*) does form loosely held groups of females.

The thin, coarse hair of the elephant seals is shed annually, the epidermis stripping off in patches. This results in a most unsightly appearance in captive animals, since the bits of hair-covered skin are inclined to dry and curl at the edges, even though the animals have free access to water. Matthews (1952) describes the use of mud baths by molting elephant seals on South Georgia, a custom that certainly should be a great aid in the sloughing off of skin but unfortunately is not easily adaptable for use in the zoological garden.

The first elephant seals of which there is a captivity record appear to be six young specimens of the northern species that Osburn (1911c), quoting Townsend, says were taken to San Francisco in 1882, without being able to trace them farther. Osburn also reports that five young animals of the same species arrived on May 20, 1883, at the Philadelphia Zoological Garden, where they lived for "a short time." These may have been the five specimens referred to by Gronen (1884) as having been received in New York, presumably in 1883, by an animal dealer named Reiche. It seems perfectly possible, of course, that all three references are to the same animals.

The first elephant seals to be seen in Europe were members of the southern species, imported by the Hagenbecks. Lorenz Hagenbeck, second son of Carl, while in Buenos Aires on a mission for his father, secured two young specimens from South Georgia, which arrived safely at Stellingen in June, 1910 (Steinmetz, 1954). These animals are stated to have died in 1916, although Lorenz Hagenbeck (*in litt.*) says they lived until 1917, succumbing to a wartime shortage of fish. A southern elephant seal was received by the Zoological Society of London on March 23, 1911, and two more on April 6, 1914, all from private sources (Flower, 1929).

After the cessation of World War I the Hagenbecks resumed the importation of southern elephant seals and up to the outbreak of World War II had brought to Stellingen about twenty-four specimens (Steinmetz, 1954). The first adult male to arrive was the famous "Goliath," who came in February, 1926. He was then 16½ feet long and weighed 4,821 pounds. The maximum quantity of fish consumed in one day by Goliath was 385 pounds, given at intervals during "performances," but when he was in top condition, 80–100 pounds daily was sufficient for maintenance (Lorenz Hagenbeck, *in litt.*). Goliath was sold to Ringling Brothers in about 1928 and spent several years traveling with the circus, where his spectacular appearances are unlikely to be forgotten by anyone so fortunate as to have seen them.

The well-known "Roland," giant elephant seal of the Berlin Zoological Gardens, was received from Stellingen on March 10, 1930, and died suddenly on December 26, 1935 (Heck, 1936). Three southern elephant seals were received at the St. Louis Zoological Park from the Hagenbecks at about the same period, and for information concerning them I am indebted to Miss Hattie Ettinger, administrative assistant at St. Louis (*in litt.*). A large male and a female named "Freya" arrived on June 9, 1928. The male lived only until July 22, 1929, and was replaced on June 12, 1930, by another known as "Jonah." Jonah lived until January 11, 1934, and Freya until the summer of 1933. During her stay in St. Louis, Freya produced three single young, all of which were dead when found by keepers. These births are mentioned by Vierheller (1941) who further states that Jonah measured 13½ feet and weighed 3,600 pounds on arrival, and that he had increased 1 foot in length and "nearly a thousand pounds in weight" at death.

A female southern elephant seal named "Nixe," in the Stellingen collection, bore a single dead young on October 10, 1926, presumably the first to be born in captivity, and later produced another, also dead. A pup was also born to a female in the Berlin Zoological Gardens on March 4, 1938, but this, again, failed to live (Steinmetz, 1954).

Lorenz Hagenbeck (*in litt.*) says that the female, Nixe, lived at Stellingen from 1925 to 1940, about 15 years, although Steinmetz (1954) gives her longevity as 16 years. In any case, the figures closely approximate the span of a female which the same author reports as having lived with the Circus Krone for 15 years. These appear to be the best longevities so far recorded for elephant seals in captivity.

With the commencement of World War II, the importation of southern elephant seals ceased. Early in the fifties activities were renewed, and a few young specimens have since been obtained by various European and American zoological gardens.

Experience with the northern elephant seal in captivity has been much more extensive in this country than with the southern species. Following the arrivals of the early eighties, already reported, there appear to have been no further importations until 1911. In that year an expedition of the American Museum of Natural History and the New York Zoological Society, under the direction of C. H. Townsend, shipped six young animals from California to the New York Aquarium, where they arrived on March 13 (Osburn, 1911c). Two of these specimens were later presented to the U.S. Bureau of Fisheries and deposited in the National Zoological Park, where they arrived on October 2, 1911 (Mann, 1930). Unfortunately, they survived for only a little over 4 months. The four that remained in New York did little better, and none lived out the year.

There seem to have been no further importations of the northern elephant seal until 1923, when the first of a series of specimens arrived at the San Diego Zoological Garden on July 20 (George H. Pournelle, *in litt.*). An account of three further shipments received at San Diego is given by Benchley (1930): one between 1923 and 1926, another in June, 1926, and the third late in 1929. Some of the males, especially, caused the feeding difficulties common with large specimens when newly captured, and were forceably fed by wrapping them in canvas sheets. This continued for as long as 6 months, in one instance, before the animal began to accept fish voluntarily. One of the males in the 1929 group was very large, measuring $16\frac{1}{2}$ feet and weighing "nearly five thousand pounds" on arrival. Northern elephant seals have been received and kept at San Diego with some regularity since the arrival of the 1929 shipment, although there seems to have been a hiatus from 1938 to 1952, when two young specimens were received (Anon., 1952). Dr. Pournelle says (*in litt.*) that the best longevity at San Diego is that established by a female received November 25, 1953, and which died December 7, 1958, after 5 years, 12 days.

A male northern elephant seal received at the Chicago Zoological Park in the summer of 1936 weighed 2,640 pounds on arrival and thrived on a diet of 100 pounds of fish daily (Bean, 1937). This animal lived for "over 3 years" and had reached a weight of 3,800 pounds when he died of an intestinal impaction caused by swallowing peanuts thrown to him by visitors (Holabird, 1954).

From 1952 on, a number of northern elephant seals were brought to this country from Guadalupe, and specimens have been received by the

Zoological Gardens of Chicago and St. Louis, as well as San Diego, and by privately operated aquariums in California. In 1953 three specimens were sent in exchange to the Zoological Gardens of Copenhagen by the Chicago Zoological Park. Reventlow (1955) reports that these animals endured temperatures of from −10°C. to −12°C. (+14°F. to +10°F.), sleeping in the water during cold periods. This experience ended the controversy, long maintained among zoo people, about the ability of this species to resist freezing temperatures. San Diego, of course, could throw no light on the problem, and the male received at Chicago was kept indoors during the winter (Bean, 1937).

The first elephant seals to be kept here were a female received June 25, 1957, and a male received July 15, 1957, both of the northern species. These animals had arrived at the New York Aquarium a few weeks before and were transferred to us because of their persistent annoyance of a young walrus, as already noted. The male weighed only 320 pounds on arrival and the female 625 pounds. Although they had been kept in a tank of sea water at the Aquarium, they were placed here in a fresh-water pool, causing no apparent reaction. This pool was occupied by sea lions which so persecuted the male that he refused food and had to be removed to a smaller unit, where he quickly settled in the company of a female gray seal. The larger female elephant seal was soon able to establish herself in the sea lion colony and had no further trouble. This animal was found to weigh 930 pounds on September 3, 1958, but while the male appeared to have gained comparably, no actual weight was obtainable. During the winter of 1957–58, temperatures down to +5°F. (−15°C.) were experienced, and, as in the case of the Copenhagen animals, both seals remained in the water, usually below the surface, coming up at intervals to breathe through breaks in the ice made by themselves or other occupants of their pools. In 1958 the male was taking 22 pounds of whole mackerel and the female 35 pounds, given daily in two meals.

In accordance with the shedding procedure of elephant seals, already noted, these two young animals began showing cracks and breaks of the skin in April, 1958. Sloughing continued bit by bit, and by mid-June the molt had been completed and a new coat of hair, short but full, had appeared. Both animals fed erratically during the molting period, sometimes abstaining altogether for several days.

The male lived until June 5, 1960, the cause of death being determined as a liver neoplasm. His final weight was 1,200 pounds. The female died on August 12, 1959, when her weight was recorded as 1,100 pounds and her length 9 feet, 8 inches.

· *REFERENCES*

ALLEN, JOEL A.
  1880. History of North American pinnipeds. U.S. Geol. and Geogr. Surv.
         Terr., Misc. Pub. 12. 785 pp.
ANGEL, JACK.
  1935. How "Pee-uk" came to the Zoological Park. Bull. New York Zool.
         Soc., **38** (5):173–77.
ANON.
  1903. The West Indian seal. Bull. New York Zool. Soc., No. 9, p.83.
  1910*a*. Nachrichten aus Zoologischen Gärten. Zool. Beobachter, **51** (9):284.
  1910*b*. Rare tropical seals. Bull. New York Zool. Soc., No. 38, pp. 644–45.
  1951*a*. Pinniped hall of fame. Zoonooz, **24** (7):3.
  1951*b*. Hawaiian monk seal—marine rarity. Zoonooz, **24** (7):3.
  1952. Magnificent monsters. Zoonooz, **25** (8):2–3.
  1956. Note. Zoo Bell (San Diego Zoological Garden), **3** (9):5.
ASDELL, S. A.
  1946. Patterns of mammalian reproduction. Comstock Publishing Co.,
         Ithaca, N.Y. 437 pp.
ATZ, JAMES W.
  1961. Raising Ookie. Animal Kingdom, **64** (1):13–22.
BAKER, RALPH C.
  1957. Fur seals of the Pribilof Islands. Conservation in action. 12. Fish and
         Wildlife Service, U.S. Dept. of the Interior, Washington, D.C.
         23 pp.
BARTLETT, RUPERT W.
  1940. Walrus collecting with Captain Bob. Bull. New York Zool. Soc.,
         43 (5):139–43.
BEAN, ROBERT.
  1937. Mammals. In: Guide Book, Chicago Zoological Park. 104 pp.
BENCHLEY, BELLE J.
  1930. Experiences with elephant seals. Parks and Recreation, **13** (5):317–
         20.
  1940. My life in a man-made jungle. Little, Brown & Co., Boston. 294 pp.
BODE, NANCY.
  1952. Beautiful—but smart. Zoonooz., **25** (5):4–5.
BRIDGES, WILLIAM.
  1953. The weighing of Herbert. Animal Kingdom, **56** (1):19–21.
  1962. First project—the Polar Bay. *Ibid.*, **65** (3):66–69.
COATES, CHRISTOPHER, and JAMES W. ATZ.
  1958. Olaf: 1000 pounds of walrus charm. Animal Kingdom, **61** (3):66–72.
CRANDALL, LEE S.
  1946. Bringing up Benny. Animal Kingdom, **49** (2):61–65.
CROSBIE, GLEN G.
  1952. Bosco and the battle of the bulge. Zoonooz, **25** (6):4–5.

CURRY-LINDAHL, KAI.
  1958. [Birth of Gray Seal.] Internatl. Zoo News, **5** (2):59.
DARLING, F. FRASER.
  1952. The Atlantic gray seal. Animal Kingdom, **55** (4):122–26.
DAVIES, J. L.
  1957. The geography of the gray seal. Jour. Mammal., **38** (3):297–310.
D[ITMARS], R. L.
  1914. Items of interest: the walrus. Bull. New York Zool. Soc., **17** (1):1071.
DOUTT, J. KENNETH.
  1942. A review of the genus *Phoca*. Ann. Carnegie Mus., **29**:61–125.
  1954. Observations on mammals along the east coast of Hudson Bay and the interior of Ungava. *Ibid.*, **33**:235–49.
DUNBAR, M. J.
  1949. The pinnipedia of the Arctic and Subarctic. Bull. 85, Fisheries Research Board of Canada, Ottawa. 22 pp.
EHLERS, KURT.
  1957. Über die Seelöwin (*Eumetopias californianus*) "Inge" der Tiergrotten Bremerhaven. Zool. Garten, Leipzig (N.F.), **23** (1/3):189–94.
ELLERMAN, J. R., and T. C. S. MORRISON-SCOTT.
  1951. Checklist of Palaearctic and Indian mammals. British Museum (Natural History), London. 810 pp.
FLOWER, S. S.
  1929. List of the vertebrated animals exhibited in the gardens of the Zoological Society of London, 1828–1927. 1. Mammals. Zoological Society of London. 419 pp.
  1931. Contributions to our knowledge of life in vertebrate animals. 5. Mammals. Proc. Zool. Soc. London, pp. 145–243.
FRECHKOP, SERGE.
  1955. Ordre des pinnipèdes. In: Traité de Zoologie. Ed. PIERRE-P. GRASSÉ. 17. Mammifères. Masson et Cie, Paris. 1170 pp.
G[RANT], C[HAPMAN].
  1911. Aquarium notes. Bull. New York Zool. Soc., No. 44, p. 737.
G[RONEN], D[AMIAN].
  1884. Fünf See-Elefanten. Zool. Gart., Frankfurt a. M., **25** (1):27–28.
HAGENBECK, CARL.
  1910. Beasts and men. Translated into English by H. S. R. ELLIOT and A. G. THACKER. Longmans, Green & Co., London. 299 pp.
HALE, FRANK E.
  1954. The use of copper sulphate in control of microscopic organisms. Phelps Dodge Refining Corp., New York. 44 pp.
HALL, E. RAYMOND, and KEITH R. KELSON.
  1959. The mammals of North America. The Ronald Press Co., New York. 2 vols.
HARRISON, R. J., L. HARRISON MATTHEWS, and J. M. ROBERTS.
  1952. Reproduction in some Pinnipedia. Trans. Zool. Soc. London., **27** (5):437–540.

HECK, LUTZ.
  1936. Nachrichten aus Zoologischen Garten Berlin. Zool. Garten, Leipzig
          (N.F.), **8** (7/9):241.
HEINROTH, KATHARINA.
  1958. Über Seehundgeburten und eine Seehundaufzucht in Zoologischen
          Garten Berlin. Zool. Garten, Leipzig (N.F.), **22** (1/3):196–204.
HOLABIRD, CHRISTOPHER (Ed.)
  1954. The Brookfield Zoo, 1934–1954. Chicago Zoological Society, Brook-
          field, Ill. 79 pp.
HOLLISTER, N.
  1919. Report of the superintendent of the National Zoological Park, for the
          fiscal year ending June 30, 1918. Ann. Rept. Smithsonian Inst., for
          1918, pp. 66–81.
  1922. Report of the superintendent of the National Zoological Park, for the
          fiscal year ending June 30, 1922. Ann. Rept. Smithsonian Inst., for
          1922, pp. 88–103.
HUBBS, CARL L.
  1956. The Guadalupe fur seal still lives! Zoonooz, **29** (12):6–9.
JONES, MARVIN L.
  1958. Mammals in captivity. Mimeographed MSS (unpublished).
JUNKER, HERMANN.
  1940. Die Aufzucht der Seehunde in den Tiergrotten der Stadt Weser-
          münde. Zool. Garten, Leipzig (N.F.), **12** (4/6):306–15.
KING, JUDITH E.
  1956. The monk seals (Genus *Monachus*). Bull. Brit. Mus. (Nat. Hist.),
          3 (5):204–56.
LEE, CHARLES F.
  1948. Thiaminase in fishery products; a review. Comm. Fish. Rev., Fish
          and Wildlife Service, U.S. Dept. Interior, Separate 202.
L[EISTER], C. W.
  1935. Baby sea lion. Bull. New York Zool. Soc., **38** (5):182.
MANN, WM. M.
  1930. Wild animals in and out of the zoo. Smithsonian Sci. Ser., 6. 362 pp.
MATTHEWS, L. HARRISON
  1952. Sea elephant. Macgibbon and Kee, London. 185 pp.
MOHR, ERNA.
  1939. Vom seeleoparden, *Ogmorhinus leptonyx* Blainville. Zool. Garten,
          Leipzig (N.F.), **11** (6):238–46.
  1940. Bemerkungen über Seehund, Ringel- und Kegelrobbe. *Ibid.*, **12**
          (2/3):173–82.
  1952. Die robben der europäischen Gewässer. Monographien der Wild-
          säugetiere, 12. Paul Schops, Frankfurt am Main. 283 pp.
  1955. Der seehund. Neue Brehm-Bücherei, A. Ziemsen Verlag, Wittenberg
          Lutherstadt. 55 pp.

MURIE, JAMES.
    1872.   Researches upon the anatomy of the Pinnipedia. 1. On the walrus
            (*Trichechus rosmarus* Linn.). Trans. Zool. Soc. London, 7:411–64.

MURPHY, ROBERT CUSHMAN.
    1914.   Notes on the sea elephant *Mirounga leonina* (Linné). Bull. Amer. Mus.
            Nat. Hist., **33**:63–79.

MYERS, BETTY JANE.
    1956.   The rearing of a grey seal in captivity. Canadian Field Nat., **69** (4):
            151–53.

O[SBURN], R. C.
    1911*a*.   The fur seal. Bull. New York Zool. Soc., No. 44, pp. 732–34.
    1911*b*.   Notes on fur seal in captivity. *Ibid.*, No. 48, pp. 817–18.
    1911*c*.   California elephant seals at the New York Aquarium. *Ibid.*, No. 45,
             pp. 759–62.

PALMER, RALPH S.
    1954.   The mammal guide. Doubleday & Co., Inc., Garden City, N.Y.
            384 pp.

POCOCK, R. I.
    1933.   The presence of the external pinna in the grey seal (*Halichoerus
            grypus*). Proc. Zool. Soc. London, pp. 419–20.

POURNELLE, GEORGE H.
    1961.   Walrus—a delightful Arctic denizen. Zoonooz, **34** (9):3–7.

RAND, R. W.
    1954–55. Reproduction in the female Cape fur seal, *Arctocephalus pusillus*
            (Schreber). Proc. Zool. Soc. London, **124**:717–40.

RAY, CARLETON.
    1960.   Background for a baby walrus. Animal Kingdom, **63** (3):120–24.
    1961*a*.   White whales for the Aquarium. *Ibid.*, **64** (6):162–70.
    1961*b*.   Three baby walruses and the smallest seal. *Ibid.*, No. 4, pp. 98–105.

REVENTLOW, AXEL.
    1938.   Aufzucht dreier junger Walrosse im Kopenhagener Zoo. Zool.
            Garten, Leipzig (N.F.), **10** (1/2):50–53.
    1951.   Observations on the walrus (*Odobenus rosmarus*) in captivity. *Ibid.*,
            18 (5/6):227–34.
    1955.   Nordliche See-Elefanten (*Mirounga angustirostris*) im Zoologischen
            Garten Kopenhagen. *Ibid.*, **22** (1/3):73–76.

RIGDON, R. H., and GLENN A. DRAGER.
    1955.   Thiamine deficiency in sea lions (*Otaria californiana*) fed only frozen
            fish. Jour. Amer. Vet. Med. Assoc., **127** (944):453–55.

ROBERTS, AUSTIN.
    1951.   The mammals of South Africa. Trustees of the Mammals of South
            Africa Book Fund, Johannesburg. 700 pp.

SCHEFFER, VICTOR B.
    1958.   Seals, sea lions and walruses. Stanford University Press, Stanford,
            Calif. 179 pp.

SCHNEIDER, KARL MAX.
  1942. Von südafrikanischen Zwergseebären (*Arctocephalus pusillus* Schreb.). Zool. Garten, Leipzig (N.F.), **14** (1/2):69–95.
  1943. Die Robbenklippen im Leipziger Zoologischen Garten. *Ibid.*, **15** (1/2):68–80.
SIMPSON, GEORGE GAYLORD.
  1945. The principles of classification and a classification of mammals. Bull. Amer. Mus. Nat. Hist., 85. 350 pp.
SIVERTSEN, ERLING.
  1935. Über die chemische Zusammensetzung von Robbenmilch. Nytt Mag. Naturvidenskaberne, 75:183–85.
  1941. On the biology of the harp seal, *Phoca groenlandica* Erxl. Hvalradets Skrifter, 26. 166 pp.
  1954. A survey of the eared seals (Family Otariidae) with remarks on the Antarctic seals collected by M/K "Norvegica" in 1928–1929. Sci. Results Norwegian Antarctic Expedition, 1927–1928 et sqq. 36. Det Norske Videnskaps-Akademi i Oslo. 74 pp.
STEINMETZ, H.
  1940. Nachrichten aus Zoologischen Garten Berlin. Zool. Garten, Leipzig (N.F.), **12** (4/6):337.
  1954. Beiträge zur Geschichte unserer Kenntnisse vom See-Elefanten. *Ibid.*, **21** (1/2):24–43.
STOCKER, O.
  1933. Aufzucht eines in Gefangenschaft geborenen Seehundes. Zool. Garten, Leipzig (N.F.), **6** (10/12):237–38.
STOTT, KEN.
  1954. Baby food for thought. Zoonooz, **27** (6):5–6.
TAYLOR, F. H. C., M. FUJINAGA, and FORD WILKE.
  1955. Distribution and food habits of the fur seals of the North Pacific Ocean. Fish and Wildlife Service, U.S. Dept. of the Interior, Washington, D.C. 86 pp.
TOWNSEND, CHARLES H.
  1912. The northern elephant seal. Zoologica, **1** (8):159–73.
  1926. A long-lived sea lion. Bull. New York Zool. Soc., **29** (6):218.
  1928. Reappearance of the Lower California fur seal. *Ibid.*, **31** (5): 173–74.
TROUGHTON, ELLIS.
  1951. Furred animals of Australia. Angus and Robertson Ltd., Sydney. 374 pp.
VAN DEN BERGH, W.
  1958. Succes et échec d'ordre zootechnique. Zoo (Antwerp), **23** (4):130–33.
VIERHELLER, GEORGE P.
  1941. Mammals. Guide Book, St. Louis Zoological Gardens. p. 34.
ZUCKERMAN, S.
  1953. The breeding seasons of mammals in captivity. Proc. Zool. Soc. London, **122**:827–950.

ORDER TUBULIDENTATA

·

FAMILY ORYCTEROPODIDAE

AARDVARK

Like the pangolins, the aardvark was once considered to be an edentate but now is assigned to a separate order and family. In fact, only a single species (*Orycteropus afer*) is usually recognized, Allen (1939) listing seventeen races, which he considers to be subject to revision. The aardvark is found over much of Africa, from Senegal in the west and Ethiopia in the east, southward to the Cape. The name itself, applied by the early Dutch settlers in South Africa, is descriptive of the curious appearance of the animal. Measuring up to 6 feet in total length, the rounded, thinly haired body, huge ears, long snout, and disklike muzzle are all generally suggestive of the pig. Only the thick, cylindrical tail and stoutly clawed toes dim the illusion. Closer examination discloses that only cheek teeth are present in both jaws and that the rather broad tongue is fully extensile.

Ants and termites form the principal food, the short, chisel-like claws of the front feet being capable of breaking through the hard walls of termite nests. The burrows in which the aardvark passes the day in sleep are often dug in close proximity to the food source, usually visited by the animal only at night. Because of these nocturnal and burrowing habits, the aardvark is seldom seen in nature and has always been a rare animal in captivity. In many parts of Africa it is prized by the natives for its flesh and is usually captured, with great difficulty, by digging it from its burrows. It is in this way that most of the scattered specimens reaching zoological gardens are secured.

Aardvarks kept here have been provided with heated indoor quarters, to which they have been confined during the winter months. Metal or brick walls with fronts of stout wire mesh provide sufficient restraint. Both indoors and out, floors of concrete or asphalt prevent digging. A wooden platform covered with a bed of clean hay and placed in a far corner out of direct light seems to satisfy the animal's need for seclusion during its daytime sleeping hours. However, like the giant anteater, the aardvark is so large that even in sleep its huge bulk is always visible to visitors.

A proper diet for captive aardvarks, as for other ant- and termite-eating mammals, was a matter of great concern in earlier times, as it is today. A. D. Bartlett (1899) devotes some space to discussion of feeding methods for aardvarks in the Zoological Gardens of London. The book is a posthumous one, compiled and edited by his son, Edward Bartlett, so that the exact period to which his remarks apply is not clear. However, since Bartlett was superintendent of the Zoological Gardens from 1859 to his death in 1897, his experience would have included the first aardvark to be received in London, in 1869 (Flower, 1929). It is a little difficult, too, to divine just which schedule Bartlett favored, for he says that "the South African species not only eats raw flesh but a small quantity of grain. . . ." He advises that fresh meat be cut into thin strips and fed to the animal by hand and also suggests a mixture of minced raw meat, scalded bread, and milk, and the yolks only of hard-boiled eggs. He further remarks that the addition of honey and fowl entrails, well washed, should be helpful, ending with the admonition, "But if the feeding be entrusted to servants, who seldom take much interest in such things, I fear the result would be, as heretofore, useless."

Bartlett was a determined and inventive man, not easily defeated, and it is certain that he managed to develop a successful feeding system from these rather scattered suggestions, for the 1869 aardvark lived for 9 years, 8 months, 25 days, and another received at London in 1884, still in Bartlett's time, lived for 6 years, 3 months, 4 days (Flower, 1931).

Of the six aardvarks that have been exhibited here, none has equaled the early longevities established in London. In fact, our best result among earlier arrivals was obtained with a specimen of the Congo race (*O. a. erikssoni*) brought to us by Charles Cordier on June 15, 1949. This animal lived until August 17, 1951, or 2 years, 2 months, 2 days. Its diet consisted of the usual mixture of finely ground raw meat, coddled eggs, precooked cereal (Pablum), and reconstituted evaporated milk, with vitamin concentrate added. This was supplied in the evening, and the aardvark was always eager for it. Dried ants' "eggs" (pupae) and dried "flies" (aquatic insects) were invariably left behind. Some years ago we imported from South Africa a quantity of dried locusts to be added to an aardvark's diet, with no better acceptance.

An aardvark from eastern Africa, determined as *O. a. ruvanensis*, received here on December 11, 1957, was still living in October, 1963. It showed definite habit preferences, closely observed by a sympathetic keeper. It slept in a bare, metal-lined, shallow box, 3 by 4 feet, from which it ejected all bedding. A similar box in the opposite corner, filled with peat moss, was used meticulously as a latrine. Its food formula was as follows:

> 2 cans evaporated milk
> 4 cans water
> 3 lbs. finely chopped raw meat
> ½ tbsp. fine bone meal
> 1 handful dog meal
> 3 raw egg yolks (no white)
> 1 tsp. cod-liver oil

Robert Bean, director of the Chicago Zoological Park, has informed me that an aardvark received at his institution in 1949 and reported as still living 11 years later (Anon., 1960), died in late summer, 1961, after approximately 12 years. A specimen that arrived at the National Zoological Park, Washington, in February, 1950, was still living there in 1963.

An aardvark born in the Zoological Gardens of Frankfurt, Germany, on June 14, 1962, appears to have represented the first known instance of the breeding of this species in captivity, the mother having been received 2 years earlier (Anon., 1962). The youngster is reported to have survived for a few days only.

· REFERENCES

ALLEN, GLOVER M.
  1939. A checklist of African mammals. Bull. Mus. Comp. Zool. Harvard, 83.
ANON.
  1960. A is for aardvark. Brookfield Bandar-log, **23**:5–6.
  1962. Aardvark born at Frankfurt Zoo. Newsletter, Amer. Assoc. Zool. Parks and Aquariums, **3** (7):2.
BARTLETT, A. D.
  1899. Wild animals in captivity. Comp. and ed. EDWARD BARTLETT. Chapman and Hall, Ltd., London. 373 pp.
FLOWER, S. S.
  1929. List of the vertebrated animals exhibited in the gardens of the Zoological Society of London, 1828–1927. I. Mammals. Zoological Society of London. 419 pp.
  1931. Contributions to our knowledge of the duration of life in vertebrate animals. 5. Mammals. Proc. Zool. Soc. London, pp. 145–234.

ORDER PROBOSCIDEA

.

FAMILY ELEPHANTIDAE

ELEPHANTS

Largest of the living land mammals of the world, the elephants naturally have an important place in the zoological garden. Amenable in general to the restrictions of captivity, it is possible to keep and exhibit them under conditions in which their requirements can be satisfied and still permit them to be viewed freely. No matter how familiar one may become with their overpowering bulk, the marvel never ends. I once heard an old, very experienced keeper, working with one of his charges, say to it, "Move over, you wonderful, blasted lummox!" "Wonderful" in itself, "blasted" because its hugeness was an impediment to progress.

The living elephants are, in reality, a relict group, the present survivors of a great assemblage of related but now extinct forms once abundant throughout the Northern Hemisphere, even penetrating the polar region (Osborn, 1936–42). As we know them now, the elephants exist only in southern Asia (*Elephas*) and in Africa, south of the Sahara (*Loxodonta*).

Many races of the Asiatic elephant (*Elephas maximus*) have been described, Deraniyagala (1955) listing eight. However, Ellerman and Morrison-Scott (1951) simplify the matter by admitting only three on the mainland and Ceylon which, with the Sumatran subspecies (Chasen, 1940), make a total of four most generally accepted. These are *E. m. indicus*, the Indian elephant, found from India and Burma to Thailand and Indochina, and also in Borneo, where it is thought to have been introduced; *E. m. maximus* and *E. m. ceylanicus*, both from Ceylon, and *E. m. sumatranus*, the Sumatran race.

The situation regarding subspeciation in the African elephant (*Loxodonta africana*) is much the same as in the Asiatic species. Numerous races have been described, and while it is always possible that more will eventually be established as valid, only three are recognized by Allen (1939): *L. a. africana*, found from Angola and Rhodesia south; *L. a. knochenhaueri*, from East Africa, and *L. a. oxyotis*, which extends from the northeastern [Belgian] Congo across southern Sudan to Ethiopia. These three represent the large bush elephants as distinguished from the smaller forest elephant. The latter is treated by Allen (*loc. cit.*) as a full species, *L. cyclotis*, a designation accepted by many authorities. Others, however, including Ellerman, Morrison-Scott, and Hayman (1953) consider it merely a race of *africana*, thus raising the number of subspecies to four. The forest elephant inhabits the great rain forests of the west, extending from Sierra Leone south, possibly to northern Angola, and east across the basin of the Congo. Young specimens of the forest elephant have been imported into this country as "pygmy elephants"—in fact, a male named "Congo," received here on July 28, 1905, was made the type of a new "pygmy" race, *E. africana pumilio* (Noack, 1906). This designation is now usually synonymized with *L. a. cyclotis*, and while the possible occurrence of actual pygmy elephants is still in dispute, there seems no doubt that if chance dwarf individuals or groups do exist, they do not represent a separable race (Petter, 1958; Pfeffer, 1960).

Asiatic and African elephants are readily distinguished from each other by several external physical characters, even though the races of each are less easily separated. Body forms differ in that the high point of the back in the Asiatic is in the middle, while in the African shoulders and rump are elevated with an intervening hollow. The temples of the Asiatic are strongly bulbous, with a noticeable trough between the protrusions, and there is also a rounded "hump" at the base of the trunk between the eyes. In the African bush elephant the forehead is narrower and inclined to form a small, pointed eminence in the center. The forest elephant differs here, the forehead being broad, smooth, and flat.

Ears offer an even simpler distinction. Comparatively small and roughly triangular in shape in the Asiatic, they are huge in the bush elephant, with a long and rather narrow extension at the bottom. The ears of the forest elephant are smaller, smoother, and more rounded, with the lower extension less pronounced. A narrow flap at the upper margins of the ears falls backward in the bush elephant, forward in the Asiatic. The width of this flap is considered by Indian mahouts to be an indication of the age of the animal.

The skin is comparatively smooth and soft in the Asiatic elephant but rough and coarse in texture in the bush elephant. Rather curiously, the skin of the forest elephant resembles that of the Asiatic more than that of its larger African relative, a further point of distinction. Depigmentation, in the form of whitish or pinkish spots, is fairly common in the Asiatic elephant, and the frequency of its occurrence in certain districts has been used as a character in the designation of local races. Albino specimens sometimes occur and are regarded with reverence or even held sacred. No work is required of such animals, a situation giving rise to the opprobrious term "white elephant." These color deviations appear to be rare or even absent in African elephants.

Beyond their huge size and immense strength, the elephants' most remarkable character is the trunk. This unique organ, actually a prolongation of the nose and the upper lip, performs a variety of essential functions. It carries the nostrils at its tip, so that it serves basically in breathing and smelling. The trunk also acts as a prehensile hand in securing food and transferring it to the mouth; water is drawn part way up its length and then discharged into the throat. Capable of feats requiring both power and mobility, the trunk is still extremely delicate and sensitive; I once saw a great African bull place the tip of his trunk over a nest of young robins on the fence of his inclosure, test it cautiously, and gently withdraw, leaving the fledglings to be safely reared.

The tip of the trunk in the Asiatic elephant has a single "finger" on the anterior margin, while the posterior edge is flattened, usually with a faintly indicated division in the middle. In the African forms there is a "finger" on each margin, an unfailing point of distinction.

The Asiatic elephant is able to make a hollow, resonant sound by tapping "back-handed" on a hard surface with its trunk, the tip of which has been turned upward. This appears to be a warning or alarm signal, heeded at once by others of the species within hearing. I have never seen this device used by African elephants.

The teeth of elephants, also, are of special interest. Most prominent, of course, are the tusks, which are in reality a single pair of upper incisors, typically greatly elongated in males alone of the Asiatic elephant and in both sexes of the African forms. Actually, the female Asiatic does possess tusks but these usually are not sufficiently developed to protrude beyond the lips. On the other hand, tuskless males are not at all uncommon, especially in Ceylon where, according to Deraniyagala (1955) only 11 per cent of males of the typical race carry visible tusks. In the African elephants tusklessness is much more uncommon, but this condition, as well as the development of one tusk only, does occur in both sexes.

Elephant tusks, of course, have long been sought as the chief source of ivory, a quest that, continued through the centuries, has greatly reduced the elephant population in all parts of the range and in some areas has resulted in virtual extermination. While the tusks of Asiatic elephants do not equal the dimensions of those of African origin, they nevertheless may be very large, Rowland Ward (1928) recording a pair that measured 8 feet, 9 inches and 8 feet, 6 inches and weighed 162 and 160 pounds respectively. The longest African tusks listed by Ward are a pair in the National Collection of Heads and Horns, housed in the New York Zoological Park. These measure 11 feet, $5\frac{1}{2}$ inches and exactly 11 feet, respectively, and together weigh 293 pounds. A single tusk only 10 feet, $2\frac{1}{2}$ inches long but weighing $226\frac{1}{2}$ pounds is owned by the British Museum (Natural History). Tusks of female African Elephants are shorter and lighter than those of males.

Besides the tusks, the only teeth are molars, a total of twenty-four, six in each jaw, appearing during an elephant's lifetime. Only one in each series, perhaps with portions of its predecessor and successor, is functional at the same time, and as it wears down it is pushed out at the front by another moving forward from the rear (Lydekker, 1893–96; Allen, 1936; Morrison-Scott, 1947). The last tooth to come into use is usually the largest and may be as long as 300 millimeters, or nearly 12 inches (Morrison-Scott, *loc. cit.*). These immensely heavy teeth, strongly cross-ridged, provide a grinding apparatus of great crushing power, so that the toughest leaves and even tree branches of some thickness are readily reduced to pulp.

Each foot of all elephants has five toes, so deeply imbedded in strong, springy tissue that their presence is indicated, externally, only by the nails or hoofs. Not every toe has a nail, so that these vary in number, sometimes individually. In the Asiatic and forest elephants the usual number is five nails in front and four behind, although for the Asiatic, Deraniyagala (1955) says there may sometimes be five nails on each foot. The formula for the bush elephant is usually given as one less all around—that is, four in front and three behind. Specimens of all three types living in our collection are in accord with these figures, but variations, perhaps individual, somewhat confuse the picture, so that it is still not entirely clear (see Morrison-Scott, 1947, and Allen, 1936).

Maximum height measurements and weights of elephants are not firmly established, for obvious reasons. Measurements of animals killed in the field are useful for comparison but certainly do not represent true standing heights. Weights of such specimens cannot usually be obtained with any degree of accuracy and the many estimates recorded add to the confusion. Even where captive elephants are concerned, walk-on scales are not always available, and when they are, large animals usually cannot safely be led to them. Measurements taken from ground to ground across the shoulders do not give true heights when divided by 2, and computations of twice the circumference of a forefoot are equally inaccurate, as shown by Benedict (1936:98–99). An adjustable arm, attached at right angles to an upright, as devised and figured by Benedict (*loc. cit.*, pp. 96–97), applied across the shoulders of a standing elephant, does give the height accurately. Measurements of elephants here have been obtained by this method or were made by an engineer with proper instruments.

Regarding the Indian elephant, Blanford (1888–91:463) says, "Adult males do not as a rule exceed 9 feet, females 8 feet, in height," but goes on to mention a male reported by Sanderson as standing 10 feet, $7\frac{1}{2}$ inches and estimates of others up to "nearly 12 feet high." There can be no doubt of the authenticity of the statistics concerning "Bolivar," the large male Indian elephant kept in the Philadelphia Zoological Garden from 1888, when he was thought to be 27 years old, until his death in 1908. These data, furnished by Dr. Herbert L. Fox, pathologist at the Philadelphia Zoological Garden, and reported by Benedict (1936:108–9) show the shoulder height of Bolivar to have been 10 feet and his weight approximately 12,000 pounds (5,550 kilograms) at death. The carefully measured shoulder height of 8 feet, 1 inch and the scaled weight of 8,095 pounds (3,672 kilograms) given by Benedict (*loc. cit.*) for the female Indian elephant "Jap" represent typical figures for a large animal of this sex.

Accredited data concerning African elephants are even less readily available than those for the Asiatic. Shortridge (1934) says that while an exceptionally large male (bush elephant) may stand 11 feet, the average is about 10 feet, 6 inches, and he gives 12 feet, 2 inches as the greatest measured height. Few male bush elephants of great size have been kept in captivity, at least in modern times, so that actual measurements of living, standing specimens are few indeed. It is unfortunate that the famous "Jumbo," undoubtedly a very large animal, did not leave a really definite height record. Jumbo, while still quite young, was received in exchange from the Jardin des Plantes, Paris, by the Zoological Gardens of London, on June 26, 1865, and a few months later was found to stand 5 feet, 6 inches (Mitchell, 1929). Jumbo proved to be extremely tractable and was used for some years as a riding animal. However, he gradually became less reliable as he neared maturity and by 1881 could be approached only by his keeper, Mathew Scott, so he was sold to P. T. Barnum for the then great sum of £2,000. Bartlett (1899) recounts the final crating and shipping of the elephant, which arrived safely in America in March, 1882. He gives Jumbo's age at that time as "about 21 years" and his height as "nearly 11 feet." Under the care of Scott, who had accompanied the animal from

London, Jumbo achieved great fame with the Barnum and Bailey Circus until he was struck and killed by a railway engine at St. Thomas, Canada, on September 15, 1885 (Mann, 1930). Jumbo's weight at death is usually given as 6½ tons or 13,000 pounds, the 14,560 pounds given by Short-ridge (1934) having quite obviously been computed on the basis of the long ton of 2,240 pounds. His height, however, will never be accurately known, for his owner is said not to have allowed it to be measured. Hornaday (1911) gives an amusing account of his futile efforts to obtain permission to make the measurement. However, he later received a report of the determining of the height of Jumbo by a circus pole-jumper that showed him to be 10 feet, 9 inches at the shoulders. This was probably the most nearly accurate figure ever made known.

Jumbo's closest rival among captive bush elephants was "Khartoum," captured in the Blue Nile area by Captain S. S. Flower, then director of the Giza Zoological Gardens, and purchased by the New York Zoological Society through Carl Hagenbeck. Khartoum was received here on June 25, 1907, and lived until October 23, 1931, when he suddenly collapsed and died, death being attributed to myocardial degeneration (Noback, 1932). Noback gives Khartoum's weight, at death, as 10,390 pounds and his height as 10 feet, 10 inches. This measurement, however, was made while the animal was in a prone position and somewhat exceeds his greatest measured standing height, which was 10 feet, 8½ inches, on January 9, 1930, the last to be recorded. On June 28, 1907, 3 days after Khartoum's arrival here, he stood 4 feet, 9½ inches at the shoulder and weighed 1,235 pounds. He was estimated to have been born in 1903.

Probably the greatest true weight ever recorded for an elephant is the 14,641 pounds quoted by Benedict and Lee (1938) for a huge bull dis-membered and weighed in parts by Dr. George Crile, the endocrinologist, while on an expedition to Africa. Robertson-Bullock (1962) gives the total weights of four males, recorded in parts, in Northern Rhodesia as 9,662, 11,355, 11,413, and 13,242 pounds, respectively.

Roosevelt and Heller (1914) say that the female bush elephant averages 1½ feet less in shoulder height than the male and weighs approximately 2 tons less. The only adult female of which I have a standing shoulder measurement was "Sudana," captured in Tanganyika in 1929 and received here on November 9, 1931. Sudana was estimated to have been born in 1927 and died in 1962 at the presumed age of 35 years. On arrival she stood 5 feet, 7 inches at the shoulder and weighed 1,975 pounds. When these figures are compared with those given for Khartoum at the same presumed age (4 years), a discrepancy in birth-date estimates is obvious.

Sudana reached a shoulder height of 8 feet, 7 inches in 1947 and gave the same measurement on September 15, 1958.

While the forest elephant is certainly a smaller animal than the bush elephant, it cannot properly be called a "pygmy," as already noted. Allen (1936), quoting various sources, gives shoulder heights of six males, ranging from 6 feet, 4 inches to 9 feet, 7 inches. Allen also gives the shoulder height of "Josephine," a female forest elephant living in the Philadelphia Zoological Garden and thought to be aged about 15 years, as 6 feet, 11 inches. Ulmer (1953) says that Josephine was received in Philadelphia in 1925, when her height was 3 feet, $6\frac{1}{2}$ inches and her weight 530 pounds. In July, 1935, she had reached 6 feet, 11 inches, as given by Allen. However, Mr. Ulmer, who is curator of mammals at Philadelphia, has informed me (*in litt.*) that Josephine lived until March 12, 1943 (not 1942 as given in the article cited above) and that he has found records of two further measurements: 7 feet, 2 inches in 1936 and 7 feet, 8 inches in 1943, the latter measurement apparently made just prior to her death. While Mr. Ulmer is unable to vouch personally for the accuracy of these figures, they are well within the range given below. Her weight is given (Ulmer, 1953) as a "scant two tons" at death.

Commandant (later Colonel) Pierre Offermann, who was in charge of the elephant training stations at Api and Gangala-na-Bodio, Belgian Congo, is quoted by Morrison-Scott (1947) as giving the measured standing heights of living forest elephants at estimated ages of from 20 to 25 years, after growth had ceased, as averaging 2.35 meters (7 feet, $8\frac{1}{2}$ inches) for males and 2.10 meters (6 feet, $10\frac{1}{2}$ inches) for females. Maximum heights were 3 meters (9 feet, 10 inches) for males and 2.5 meters (8 feet, $2\frac{1}{2}$ inches) for females. Heights of young animals are given as from 2 feet, $7\frac{1}{2}$ inches to 2 feet, $9\frac{1}{2}$ inches at birth, 3 feet, $3\frac{1}{2}$ inches at one year, and 3 feet, 9 inches at two years.

Our first specimen of the forest elephant was a male, already referred to as having been received here on July 28, 1905. Congo's record card shows his height as 3 feet, 8 inches and his weight as 601 pounds on arrival. Congo's birth year was estimated as 1898, which would have made him 7 years old in 1905 and 17 at death on November 3, 1915. On the basis of Offermann's figures, it seems more likely that Congo was actually born in 1903 and that his age at death was only 12 years. This could account for his small size in 1915, for he then stood only 6 feet, 8 inches and weighed 2,700 pounds.

Congo was an ill-natured little creature, fully controllable only by "Alice," a steady Indian elephant cow who had adopted him. He once nearly succeeded in impaling me on his slender tusks, between which, at the last instant, I managed to slip. He always seemed to us to be afflicted with arthritis, which finally made necessary his death from a rifle bullet fired by Carl Akeley. Congo's remains now repose in the American Museum of Natural History, New York.

A second forest elephant, this time a female and again considered to be a "pygmy," was received here on December 6, 1922 (Hornaday, 1923). "Tiny" was believed to have been born in 1920, but since her height on arrival was 3 feet, 2 inches, Offermann's figures suggest birth in 1921. Tiny lived until March 2, 1933. Her weight at death was 2,045 pounds, as compared with 425 pounds on arrival. Her last recorded height, as of June 11, 1930, at the age of 9 or 10 years, was 5 feet, 10 inches.

On October 8, 1946, two forest elephants, male and female, along with a female of the bush type were received here from the training station at Gangala-na-Bodio as gifts of the Government of the Belgian Congo (Bridges, 1946; Carlisle, 1946). "Zangelima," the male, was considered by the authorities at the station to have been born in 1932. Measured in August, 1946, just before leaving for America, his shoulder height was 1 meter, 90 centimeters (6 feet, 3 inches). Zangelima later became "unmanageable and dangerous" and was destroyed on November 11, 1952. At the presumed age of 20 years his shoulder height, at death, appears on his record card as 7 feet, 4 inches and his weight 6,600 pounds.

The female of this pair, "Doruma," known to her keepers as "Pinky," was judged to have been born in 1938. Before leaving the Congo, Doruma's height in August, 1946, was 1 meter, 65 centimeters (5 feet, 5 inches). On September 15, 1958, at the presumed age of 20 years, she stood 6 feet, 8 inches at the shoulder. Doruma, still living in 1963, was recorded as standing 7 feet, 8½ inches on June 27 of that year.

The gait of the elephant is what is known as the amble or pace. In this action the feet of one side move forward together, alternating with those of the other, so that the trot or the gallop cannot be accomplished. This does not mean, of course, that the elephant is not able to move with speed, at least for short distances. Meinertzhagen (1955) reports that a frightened African elephant, timed with a stop-watch, covered 120 yards at the rate of 24 miles per hour.

The question of sleep in captive elephants has long been in dispute. Benedict (1936) and Hediger (1955a; 1955b) have shown that while elephants of all ages may sleep for short periods while standing, all but aged or infirm animals do lie down, usually flat on one side, often with a bundle of hay under head or body. This usually occurs after midnight, and sleep may continue for 2 or 3 hours in adult animals, longer in immature individuals. It was found that while this phenomenon was difficult to observe in zoo animals, unaccustomed to noise at night, it was readily studied, even photographed, in circus and working elephants. Elderly elephants appear to sleep while standing only, perhaps because of the difficulty of rising from a prone position. Even though elephants sleep so lightly that they may not easily be approached while lying down, flanks stained by dung will betray them in the morning.

Mature male Asiatic elephants in captivity are subject to periods of restless irritability, when they are likely to damage their surroundings and become dangerous even to keepers with whom they have long been on good terms. This condition is usually associated with enlargement of the temporal glands which lie between the ear and the eye, followed by discharge of a black, oily fluid. This state is known as "must" or "musth" and is said (Deraniyagala, 1955) to occur, rarely, in females also. Close observation over many centuries has made "must" well known wherever the Asiatic elephant is kept as a work animal. Since, of course, the daily work routine of males so affected is disrupted, many remedies for shortening the course of "must" have been devised (Evans, 1910). The most effective of these seems to be the limiting of food to reduced amounts of greens only and the usual precautions of restraint. According to Deraniyagala (*loc. cit.*), the first signs of "must" are likely to appear by the eighteenth year, the symptoms decreasing after middle age. Whether or not "must" has a sexual significance seems not to have been definitely determined.

While the male African elephant in captivity is likely to become obstreperous, even dangerous, when adult, it does not appear to have been demonstrated that it is subject to periods of "must," as is the Indian elephant. In fact, Colonel Pierre Offermann, who has had an extended experience at the Belgian Congo elephant training stations, says (*in litt.*, 1952), "most bulls are difficult or dangerous when they are full-grown, but I do not think it is musth, as with the Indian Elephant. We have never observed the symptoms of musth (swollen glands of the temples, discharge through the temple orifices, irritability, temporary hatred of the people the animal knows well). It seems that the African Elephant has no musth courses. He is simply very often ill-tempered. . . ."

It is significant that the two male African elephants that have been kept here followed closely Colonel Offermann's description. Khartoum, the bush elephant already mentioned, was high spirited and destructive but never showed animosity toward his keepers (Bridges, 1941), even though he lived to the presumed age of 27 years. On the other hand, little Zangelima, the forest elephant, became increasingly antagonistic and dangerous, so that it became necessary to destroy him, as already stated, at the probable age of 20 years. Neither of these animals showed evidence of periodic disturbance that could properly be described as "must."

The Asiatic elephant has been captured and trained by man for so long that the beginnings of the practice are lost in antiquity. Yet it has not become really domesticated and the supply is still drawn from the free herds, now usually carefully protected. It is unlikely that the methods of capture, whether by stealthy noosing of a hind leg or by the more ambitious drive into an inclosure of logs, as described by Deraniyagala (1955), have greatly changed since very early days. The elephant still takes an important part in the workaday economy of southern Asia and in its many ceremonials. Before the invention of firearms, it was often used in war. When Porus, an Indian prince, bitterly opposed the advance of Alexander the Great in the third century B.C., it was a troop of elephants trained in warfare that won the respect of the Macedonian. The elephants used by Hannibal in his great victory over the Romans in the battle of Cannae, late in the same century, had been marched into Italy by way of Spain and southern France. Whether these elephants, as well as others used in war by both the Carthaginians and the Egyptians, were of Asiatic or African origin has not been definitely established, but there is support for the belief that they were actually African, from areas in the north where the species no longer exists (Allen, 1945; Deraniyagala, 1955).

In any case, the training of elephants in Africa eventually became a lost art, probably because the elephant, as a working animal, never became an integral factor in the native economy of that continent, as it did in Asia. The efforts of the Government of the Belgian Congo to revive the capture and training of elephants, dating from 1900 and continuing at the station at Gangala-na-Bodio, constituted the first organized attempt since ancient times to make practical use of the African elephant. While this undertaking has been completely successful as far as the basic problems are concerned, it seems probable that increasing use of mechanized agricultural equipment will block the absorption of the working elephant into the African culture.

The elephant had its place in the processions and arenas of Rome and has been important as an exhibit in zoological gardens since their inception. The first elephant, an Asiatic, to be received by the Zoological Gardens of London arrived on May 11, 1831, its first African bush elephant—the famous Jumbo—on June 26, 1865, and a forest elephant on October 16, 1922 (Flower, 1929). America's first elephant was brought from

India aboard a sailing vessel and arrived in New York on April 13, 1796 (Goodwin, 1925). The same author has gathered reports of an African elephant said to have been brought to this country in 1824, although the record is not entirely clear. These importations continued, of course, in increasing numbers until, in the latter part of the nineteenth century, elephants had become commonplace in both circuses and zoos. The Philadelphia Zoological Garden exhibited an Asiatic elephant on its opening day, July 1, 1874, and acquired an African during the same year (Ulmer, 1953).

The New York Zoological Park's first elephant was "Gunda," a male Asiatic who came here on July 2, 1904. He was followed, in 1905, by Congo, the forest elephant, and in 1907 by Khartoum, the bush elephant, and a female of the same race known as "Sultana." Sultana was destroyed in 1919 because of an ulcer that developed on one of her feet, and the careers of Congo and Khartoum have already been outlined. Gunda, gentle and tractable in his early days, was used as a riding animal until, in 1912, he became unreliable, with the onset of "must" periods. Gunda soon became violently antagonistic toward everyone but his trusted keeper, Walter Thuman. However, in 1913 he attacked Mr. Thuman, injured him seriously, and would certainly have killed him but for the courageous intervention of another keeper, the redoubtable Dick Richards. Following this unfortunate episode, Gunda was kept in chains for a time but on June 21, 1915, the renowned Carl Akeley's rifle brought to Gunda the fate that so commonly befalls bull elephants kept to maturity in the accommodations usually provided by zoological gardens.

Consideration of housing arrangements for elephants in zoological gardens may well begin with a brief description of the Elephant House in the New York Zoological Park. This is a really imposing building, completed in 1908. Over-all, it is 141 feet long and 80 feet wide, constructed of white stone and topped by a lofty dome in Oriental style. Under large skylights and high arched ceilings there are seven compartments, each 24 feet square, four of which are for elephants, two for rhinoceroses, and one for hippopotamuses, the latter with an attached pool of equal size. Two cages at either end with bathing tanks provide smaller quarters for pygmy hippopotamuses and tapirs. Each indoor pen is adjoined by an outside yard of generous size, for summer use by the inmates.

Basically, these commodious rooms are very satisfactory. The walls are lined, for their lower 6 feet, with $\frac{1}{4}$-inch steel plate, followed above by mat-surfaced tile of warm, light brown. Floors are of steel-troweled concrete and provided with grill-protected drains. As originally built, fronts were of 2-inch round steel bars, 10 feet high, set in concrete at the base on 20-inch centers and joined at the top by two heavy steel cross-members. However, since the guard rails are only $4\frac{1}{2}$ feet distant, it was soon found that the elephants could too easily extend their trunks across it. This dangerous activity was finally checked by the addition of light cross-bars, 10 inches apart. Since keeper access to the rooms was between the bars only, a space, protected by an angled bar, was left at each end. This arrangement has worked perfectly well for 50 years, but there is still the ever-present problem of the general unsightliness of bars.

The alternative to bars, of course, is the indoor moat, used at Leipzig as long ago as 1926 (Gebbings, 1928) and later at Detroit, Berlin, and elsewhere. An elephant will not ordinarily attempt to cross a moat 6 feet wide and 5 feet deep and might very well be restrained by one of lesser dimensions; the minimum safety span of 10 feet between the animal and the public can be maintained by moving back the guard rail at the expense of the public space. This brings up the basic difficulty of the plan, for such a moat must have its sides perpendicular or sloped at a sharp angle, which means that if an elephant should get into it by accident or design, it can be extricated only with great difficulty and is likely to be injured in the process. To avoid this risk, both indoors and out, rows of spikes set along the moat rim to prevent the animal from reaching it were once the usual practice. However, too frequent injuries to elephants' feet, to say nothing of the implications obvious to the public, have brought this method into disrepute. It is for this reason that in some recent buildings, such as that in the Philadelphia Zoological Garden, where moats are used for rhinoceroses and hippopotamuses, bars are still used for elephants.

The outer doors of our elephant compartments are 10 feet high, built of wood, and open manually in two sections. As originally constructed, both inner and outer surfaces were reinforced with bands and bolts of steel, which from time to time required extensive repair to remedy damage by the animals. Nowadays these doors are firmly covered with impervious sheets of steel but still must be opened by hand. No trouble has so far resulted from this practice, but in more modern structures, doors are operated electrically by remote control, as complete safety requires. While a spare stall cannot always be provided for use as a shift-cage, there should be some means for removing an elephant from its regular quarters while they are serviced. It may never be necessary to put such provision to use, it is true, but its value as a safety factor should not be overlooked.

Elephants are capable of withstanding fairly low temperatures for short periods, as demonstrated by Benedict (1936), but cannot be expected to maintain condition if so exposed for long. Our Elephant House is heated, in winter, to about 70°F. (approximately 21°C.), which seems to be satisfactory.

Outside yards for the summer use of elephants again present the conflict of bars or fences versus moats, with the latter having the better of it. When first built, our elephant yards were surrounded by two fences, an outer one of light bars, 7 feet high, as a visitors' guard and an inner one of heavy steel beams, the cross-members 2 feet apart, to restrain the animals. Even this, however, could not resist the great strength of the African bull, Khartoum, in an exploratory mood, and eventually he managed to reduce the barrier to splinters. Reconstruction with steel rails of double strength studded, it must be admitted, with stout, blunt spikes, ended Khartoum's destructive efforts.

In 1951 the inner barriers of the elephant yards were removed entirely and the outer fence replaced by a regulation guardrail filled in with wire mesh. The two principal inclosures, as well as a smaller one for emergency use, were surrounded by stone walls to whose bases the yard surfaces sloped down at a well-graduated angle, leaving the central part at a level slightly higher than the public viewing area. One yard was smoothly paved with asphalt, with a much-used, shallow pool. The other inclosure was left with its natural covering of well-packed earth, drainage problems precluding the installation of a pool.

These half-moats or "ha-has" have the effect of increasing the safety margin between elephant and public, because when extending the trunk in begging, a prerogative of all zoo elephants, the animal is either standing downhill in forward presentation or sideways. Even Sudana could not fully span the space of 8 feet to the guard rail, although her open trunk-tip could come within receiving distance. Even more important is the avoidance of the hazard to the animals inherent in the deep moat with perpendicular sides, still too often used. But final solutions of exhibition problems are difficult to evolve and some curious results have followed the installation of our "ha-has."

The wall of the yard for small elephants extends upward only 4½ feet from the bottom of the "ha-ha." As soon as construction had been completed, two female Asiatic elephants, estimated to be about 15 years old and standing approximately 7 feet, 10 inches at the shoulder, were liberated in the inclosure. For a time all went well, but one morning I was electrified by a telephone call from a keeper, who said that one of the elephants had jumped over the wall and, while she had allowed herself to be led back, she was still greatly excited. Needless to say, I ran for the Elephant House,

which was close at hand, and arrived just in time to witness an extraordinary spectacle: an elephant jumping over a wall! When I reached the
front of the inclosure, the animal, known as "Cutie," was standing in the
doorway of the inner stall, facing outward, with ears extended and trunk
waving. Suddenly, with a loud trumpet, she charged directly at us at full
speed. Without checking, she ran into the corner of the moat, turned
sideways, and threw her right feet over the wall, so that her momentum,
probably aided by a push against the slope with her left legs, carried her
completely over. Once across, she stood trembling in the space between
the outer face of the wall and the guardrail, obviously not knowing what
to do once the primary obstacle had been cleared. For the second time
she walked quietly back to the gate leading to the inclosure, a keeper
holding to one of her ears. Cutie had no opportunity for further development of her project, for she and her companion, "Dolly," were promptly
transferred to the opposite inclosure, occupied by the African, Sudana.
Sudana lost no time, butting and trunk-slapping, in convincing the Asiatics
that she was mistress, a situation that continued for some years.

After the transfer, Dolly remained calm enough, but Cutie was still
bent on exploration. In this yard the wall extends 6 feet, 6 inches upward
from the moat bottom, and Cutie soon found that she could increase the
reaching distance of her trunk by putting her front feet on the wall. She
could then reach farther than we liked, so electrically charged cattle
guard wires were installed near the top of the inner face of the wall.
Exploring trunk-tips soon found the wires and received mild shocks,
sending the recipients running off with loud shrieks and much trunk-
tapping on the part of the Asiatics. For a matter of 2 or 3 weeks, wires and
walls were shunned with caution, but gradually the shocks came to be
avoided or ignored and finally the wires were ripped out altogether.

With this slight impediment removed, Cutie renewed her activities and
proceeded to develop the possibilities of climbing the wall, the outer face
of which extended 2 feet above the grass plot between it and the guardrail.
By getting her front feet over the wall and pressing them against the exposed
outer surface, she was able to draw herself upward. When she had reached
the point where only the toes of one hind foot remained on the ground and
it was obvious that she might very well succeed in getting over, we reluctantly resorted to a light cross-chain—right rear to left front—which
ended the matter.

While it seems hardly reasonable to expect that an elephant might be able
to scale a 6-foot, 6-inch wall or to propel itself over one 4 feet, 6 inches high,
these examples establish both possibilities. As far as climbing goes, it

appears that the chances for success may be reduced by bringing the outside surface flush with the wall top, thus leaving no pulling purchase. This
has been done successfully, in the Philadelphia Zoological Garden. A
narrow apron of concrete adjoining the wall would increase the safety
factor.

Elephants in nature, as well as captive animals, consume great quantities
of leafy and grassy foods where hay is not available, perhaps as much as
600–700 pounds daily (Blanford, 1888–91). For zoo animals, fed largely on
dried materials, the actual weight consumed is naturally much less. Sudana,
the female bush elephant, standing 8 feet, 7 inches at the shoulder,
required approximately 300 pounds of timothy hay daily, given at intervals.
The frequency of feeding periods was determined by the animal herself,
for she trumpeted loudly when the supply was low, "purring" softly
when it was renewed. Two or three times weekly, 75–80 pounds of dried
alfalfa was substituted for an equal amount of timothy. In addition to hay,
Sudana received 16 quarts of mixed ground grains, containing minerals
and salt, so that the latter were not given separately. She was also given
four or five loaves of bread, three or four cabbages, and raw white potatoes,
apples, and carrots as treats. In summer, green stalks of corn (maize),
grass, and leafy branches were supplied as available. All this was in addition
to the tidbits constantly solicited from visitors.

The two Asiatics, Cutie and Dolly, receive between them 250–300
pounds of timothy daily, with the substitution of approximately 75 pounds
of alfalfa two or three times weekly. Each has 16 quarts of ground feed
with three or four loaves of bread, with the same allowance of other items
as given to Sudana. Pinky, the forest elephant, eats only about 100 pounds
of timothy daily, with the same substitution of alfalfa and proportionate
allowances of the other items.

Elephants consume water in great quantities, of course, an animal of
average size requiring somewhere between 35 and 50 gallons, as stated
by Benedict (1936). Here we follow the usual custom of watering the
animals twice daily, morning and night, bringing it to air temperature.
No water is allowed to stand in the stalls, as it then serves only as a play-
thing. In summer some of our animals have access to an outdoor pool,
so that the amount of water taken is not entirely controllable. However,
the routine indoor watering is continued the year around.

Care of the skin of zoo elephants has always been a matter of some
concern, since it may become dry and thickened, especially when the
animals are confined indoors. At one time we followed the then usual
practice of applying neat's-foot oil in liberal quantities, followed by a brisk

scrubbing. Nowadays, however, we rely entirely on the hose, each animal receiving a thorough wash-down with warm water daily, accompanied by a thorough massage with a stiff broom. This treatment keeps the animals' skin in good condition and is well received by them, even big Sudana rolling about on the floor of her compartment from which, because of its slipperiness, she often had some difficulty in rising. In summer hosing is less important, for the gentle rains to which the elephants are exposed serve the purpose well. Rubbing against any available surface, the rougher the better, helps remove the softened outer skin layers.

While fairly extensive studies of the reproductive habits of Asiatic elephants have been made, much less is known concerning those of the African forms. Shortridge (1934) expresses the opinion that in the gestation period, at least, there is little difference between the African and the Indian. Flower (1943) has summarized accumulated data concerning the latter in several categories. He gives the age at which males are usually sexually mature as 14–15 years, with a report of a 9-year-old becoming a father. Females are reported as usually being 15–16 years old when the first calf is born, although one was produced by a mother of 13 years, and there are reports of others of $10\frac{1}{2}$ years, 9 years and 1 month, and 8 years. The gestation period, established from the figures of Burne (1943) and others, is usually 19–21 months, with a minimum of 17 months and a maximum of 24. Heights of newborn young range from 2 feet, 6 inches to 3 feet, and weights from 175 to $213\frac{1}{2}$ pounds.

Burne (1943) and Hundley (1934) have recorded growth increments, summarized by Flower (1943), giving height increases in captive elephants of known ages. Extracts from Hundley's list give the following average heights: for males, first year, 3 feet; fifth year, 5–6 feet; tenth year, 6 feet, 5 inches; fifteenth year, 6 feet, 11 inches; twentieth year, 7 feet, 5 inches; twenty-fifth year, 7 feet, 10 inches; for females, first year, 3 feet; fifth year, 5 feet, 1 inch; tenth year, 5 feet, 10 inches; fifteenth year, 6 feet, 7 inches; twentieth year, 7 feet, 6 inches; twenty-fifth year, 7 feet (one individual). The natural variation of individuals, as well as that due to sex, make these figures difficult to apply in determining the age of a newly acquired animal, except in the most general way.

For the African elephant, gestation periods quoted by Shortridge (1934) range from 19 to 23 months. Gowers (1931) reports that for three births at the Belgian Congo elephant farms at Wando and Api, the period in each case was 22 months. Perry (1953) examined the bodies of 150 elephants made available through control measures of the Uganda Game Department. Of these, 69 were males and 81 were females, 67 of the latter being adult and 31 pregnant. Studies of this extensive material led him to the conclusion that both sexes mature at from 8 to 12 years, that the gestation period is about 2 years, and that approximately 2 years elapse between parturition and the next conception. It would thus be possible for a female to produce two young within a period of 4 years.

Asdell (1946) gives the Indian elephant as polyestrous, estrus lasting 3–4 days in captivity. Evans (1910) says that the only indication of estrus is the uttering of low sounds by the female. Benedict (1936) bears this out, in general, although he notes that sexual activity is more marked in some females than in others. We have never been able to note positive indication of estrus in female elephants here.

During the summer of 1948, when the elephants were out of doors, the male forest elephant, Zangelima, then presumed to be 16 years old, engaged in frequent sexual play, consisting largely of trunk-entwining and exploration, with a female bush elephant named "Bamangwa," presumed to be aged 12 years. This procedure was repeated during the following summer, but while coitus was frequently attempted, achievement was never observed. There seemed to be no periodicity in these activities beyond the seasonal one, for they were practically continuous. Presumably they were not successful, for after her death in 1950 from a paratyphoid infection, Bamangwa was found not to be pregnant.

The facts that the testicles of male elephants are inguinal and not externally visible and that the vaginal opening of the female is carried very low, with the well-developed clitoris sometimes conspicuous, have led to exaggerated and fanciful accounts of copulatory methods. Actually, the position is the usual ventro-dorsal one of quadrupeds, and while much time may be occupied with foreplay, the act itself is quickly accomplished. Schneider (1930) has given a complete account, well illustrated with photographs, of the mating of Indian elephants in the Zoological Gardens of Leipzig.

Births are usually of single young, although twins have been recorded (Blanford, 1888–91; Deraniyagala, 1955). The newborn young are heavily coated with hair which gradually becomes reduced, although varying amounts persist throughout life. While the paired mammary glands are located well forward on the mother's chest, between the forelegs, the infant is nevertheless able to apply its mouth directly to the nipple, although it was once thought to use its trunk for the purpose. After several months it begins to eat green foliage and grass, although it is thought that nursing continues for about 2 years. Parental supervision continues for some years after the young animal is entirely able to feed itself.

While births are not unusual among trained and working Asiatic elephants, particularly in Burma and Thailand (Evans, 1910), and have occurred in the captive herds of African elephants at the Belgian Congo training stations, breeding is often discouraged as unprofitable, since well-grown animals can be acquired at less cost than that required for rearing young (Evans, *loc. cit.*).

In zoological gardens such events are rare, although by no means unknown. The basic reason for the infrequency of zoo births is the difficulty of maintaining and controlling mature bulls under exhibition conditions without constant risk of injury of keepers or even the public. Reluctance to undertake the keeping of bull elephants is almost universal in American zoological gardens, not only because of the danger involved but also from dread of the usually necessary destruction of such animals. Of the five bull elephants, both Asiatic and African, that have been kept here, all but Khartoum, the giant bush elephant, have had to be destroyed because they had become dangerous. In quarters constructed primarily for breeding purposes with exhibition a secondary consideration and with remote controls and convenient shifting areas, so arranged that neither keepers nor public need ever be in contact with the animals, a breeding pair could live and rear young in peace and safety.

The zoological gardens of continental Europe appear to have been less reluctant to become involved with male elephants, and a number of breeding successes have been achieved. Two births of Asiatic elephants occurred in Europe in 1906, one at Vienna and one at Berlin (Schiött, 1908), with another at Buenos Aires in the same year (Strassberger, 1907).

On December 9, 1907, the first of three calves was born at the Zoological Gardens of Copenhagen (Schiött, 1908), followed by two others to the same parents on April 6, 1912, and April 3, 1916 (Hvass, 1932). The latter author says that, up to 1932, nine elephant births had been reported in European zoological gardens, including, of course, the three in Copenhagen.

Several births of Asiatic elephants have occurred in Europe since Hvass's enumeration, including one in 1948 and another in 1952 at the Zoological Gardens of Moscow (Sosnovsky, 1958). The birth of a calf at the Zoological Gardens of Budapest in 1961, listed as the fifth to be born at that institution, is reported by Anghi (1961). Of special interest are accounts of the hand-rearing of calves born in the Zoological Gardens of Rome on August 6, 1948, and September 2, 1950, respectively. In each case the calf was rejected by the mother and rearing was successfully accomplished by hand. A full account of the first experience, based on a report by Lamberto Crudi, director at Rome, is given by Hindle (1950).

The basic food, fed from a bottle, was whole cow's milk, fortified with cream to increase the fat to 6.7 per cent, lactose to raise the sugar to 6.4 per cent, and vitamin B_1 to equal two and one-half times the amount in cow's milk. Separately, the calf received a daily allowance of tomato juice sufficient to provide a supply of vitamin C four times that of cow's milk. These requirements were established by Professor Ensalmi of the Institute of Public Health, Rome, from an analysis of the milk of the mother elephant. The calf progressed well at first, but on the one hundred and sixteenth day, a drop in body temperature occurred, followed by evidences of indigestion and a rapid loss of weight. Finally, the young animal was put on a diet of cooked rice and barley, with yogurt. This seemed to agree with it well, and a month later a return was made to whole cow's milk, this time with no additions of cream or lactose. The calf had now completely recovered, and by June, when it was 10 months old, it was receiving a daily ration of 21 pints of cow's milk, 15 pounds of fruit, 9 pounds each of carrots and tomatoes, $4\frac{1}{2}$ pounds of bread, and $6\frac{1}{2}$ pounds of cooked rice. At the age of 1 year, the calf, a female, weighed 807 pounds and stood 48 inches at the shoulder.

When the second calf, a male, was born at Rome on September 2, 1950, a firm effort was made to profit by the earlier experience. The sequence of events was reported by Dr. Crudi at the meeting of the International Union of Directors of Zoological Gardens held at Amsterdam, June 4–7, 1951, and recorded in detail in the minutes of that meeting. Because of the difficulty in the digestion of the fat of cow's milk suspected in the first calf, the second was started on fat-free milk reinforced with lactose and magnesia. This was continued until the eighth day, after which whole milk was gradually introduced and the fat finally increased to 4.25 per cent, vitamins A, C, and D being added at the same time. However, by the seventy-fifth day, increasing saponification in the feces was noted, and after receiving only water for 24 hours, a diet of one part water to three parts whole milk was tried. Gradually, the water was increased to one part to one and one-half parts milk, reducing the fat content to about 2 per cent. Lactose and maltose were added to raise the sugar to approximately 9 per cent, and vitamins of the B group and $\frac{1}{4}$ liter of yogurt were also given. This formula proved to be entirely suitable, and the calf progressed well to the age of 6 months, when bran and corn meal were mixed with the milk. Fruit juices and fresh fruits were given, and on May 30, 1951, at the age of 9 months, the calf weighed 345 kilograms (758 pounds). While Dr. Crudi's report does not carry beyond that point, it may be added that this calf was fully and successfully reared.

Published reports of analyses of elephant's milk show wide variation in the percentage of fat, ranging from 3.8 per cent (Benedict, 1936:83) to 22.07 per cent (Frade, 1955:722). It seems possible that this difference is related to the lactation stage of the donor, but in any case, as Dr. Crudi points out in concluding his report, it appears that the fat of cow's milk is not readily digested by elephant calves and that a content of approximately 2 per cent is most suitable for artificial rearing.

While American zoological gardens have been slow in establishing breeding elephants, several births have occurred in this country among circus animals. Early accounts of these have been gathered by Heller (1933), all, of course, referring to Asiatic elephants.

The first elephant birth in this country appears to have been one that occurred on March 10, 1880, the mother being a cow named "Hebe" belonging to the Cooper and Bailey Circus, then wintering in Philadelphia. This calf is said to have reached the age of 25 years, when it was destroyed as a "killer." Two years later, on February 2, 1882, a calf was born to an elephant cow named "Queen," of the Barnum and Bailey Circus, at Bridgeport, Connecticut. This young animal died in the same city 5 years later, in a fire that took place while the circus was in winter quarters.

Most remarkable of these elephant births are those of four successive young born to a cow known as "Alice" and a bull called "Snyder," both belonging to the Sells-Floto Circus. They are recorded by Heller (1933) as follows: April 25, 1912, at Salinas, California; March, 1914, at Denver, Colorado; March, 1916, at Denver, Colorado; April, 1918, at Liberty Park Zoo, Salt Lake City, Utah.

In each of the first three cases Alice rejected her offspring, and rearing was attempted by hand, the longest survival being 6 months. Regarding the fourth birth, Fred G. Alispaw, writing in a circus magazine, *White Tops* (June, 1932), says that Alice was sold to the Liberty Park Zoo in August, 1916, and that she was pregnant at that time. This birth seems to be the only one recorded up to 1962 as having occurred in an American zoo, although, of course, the calf was not bred there. Perhaps because of more settled conditions, Alice nursed this last calf, but in spite of parental care, it died in March, 1919.

A calf stillborn to a cow named "Old Mom" or "Mama Mary" and sired by Snyder is mentioned by both Heller and Alispaw. This birth appears to have occurred at Sheboygan, Wisconsin, on June 20, 1917, while the Sells-Floto Circus was en route to Milwaukee.

On April 14, 1962, a male calf was born to "Belle" at the Washington Park Zoo at Portland, Oregon, as reported and figured by Alexander (1962).

The parents, then the property of Morgan Berry, had alternated for several seasons between the zoological gardens of Portland and Seattle, Washington. The calf was reported as weighing 225 pounds at birth, which occurred after a gestation period of 20 months, 26 days. On June 19, 1962, Jack Marks, director at Portland, told me that the mother was nursing the calf naturally and that its weight on June 16 was 424 pounds. The family was subsequently purchased for the Portland Zoo. A second calf, this time a female, was born to the female, "Rosie," at Portland on October 3, 1962. In 1963 two further elephant calves were born at Portland: a male to "Pet" on September 15, and a female to "Tuy Wah" on September 24. Thus four Indian elephant cows have produced calves at Portland within 2 years, all sired by the bull "Thonglaw." Mr. Marks informs me that all doors in his Elephant House are operated by hydraulic-electric control and that shifting of animals is done with complete safety. Thonglaw is dangerous during his "must" periods but can always be brought back under control when this subsides.

The only birth of an African elephant outside its natural habitat appears to have been that of a calf born at the Hellabrunn Zoological Gardens near Munich on April 11, 1943 (Hediger, 1950:144). Photographs of this calf and its parents are shown in the Hellabrunn guidebooks, at least as late as 1958.

As with most other phases of interest in elephants, the age to which they may live has long been subject to misunderstanding and exaggeration, tales of individuals having lived well over 100 years being abundant in the literature (Flower, 1947–48). While Deraniyagala (1955:74) thinks that elephants in the wild state may live as long as 120 years under good foraging conditions, though only 70 under less generous ones, there seems to be no practical way in which this can be determined. Authentic records of captive elephants, especially in zoological gardens, under presumably optimum conditions, indicate a maximum life span of far less than 100 years.

Our best record for an Asiatic elephant here is that of Alice, received on September 3, 1908, and destroyed on August 27, 1943, a span of 34 years, 11 months, 24 days. Estimated to have been aged 15 years on arrival, Alice is presumed to have been almost exactly 50 at death. For several of her later years, Alice had been showing signs of senility and no longer lay down to sleep. Four times in her last 3 years she had gone down while out of doors and, being unable to rise, was set on her feet by a derrick. On the fifth occasion, her plight was deemed hopeless and she was quietly euthanized.

No other African bush elephant has lived as long here as Sudana, received on November 9, 1931. Sudana became practically immobilized by arthritis in 1962 and was euthanized on August 11. Her span here was therefore 30 years, 9 months, 2 days, and her presumed age was approximately 35 years. When loaded on a huge truck and drawn to our platform scales, her weight at death was found to be 9,670 pounds.

Of forest elephants, Congo lived here for only a little beyond 10 years. Doruma, or Pinky, already noted as having arrived here on October 8, 1946, is still living in 1963, after approximately 17 years, and is in excellent condition. There are few records of longevity in forest elephants, and of these the longest seems to be that of Josephine, who lived at the Philadelphia Zoological Garden from April 24, 1925, to March 12, 1943, or 17 years, 10 months, 16 days.

The best longevity given by Flower (1931) for an Asiatic elephant is 47 years, 11 months, 1 day for an animal in the Dresden Zoological Gardens, although he mentions a female known as "Jessie," then living in the Taronga Zoological Park, Sydney, after more than 46 years. In a final summary of his continued researches, Flower (1947–48) gives records that exceed his earlier findings. Most important is the remarkable second report of Jessie, who lived at Taronga from 1882 to September 26, 1939, or approximately 57 years. A full account of the career of Jessie, with photographs, is given by Patten (1940). Patten estimates her age on arrival as 20 years, so that she would have been about 77 at death. However, A. S. Le Souef, quoted by Flower, guessed her age when received as 12, making her 69 at death, a figure accepted by Flower. It is unfortunate that, as is too often the case with zoo animals, the exact age of Jessie will never be known. Nevertheless, whether 69 or 77, Jessie was certainly the oldest elephant of which there is an acceptable record.

The greatest longevity known to Flower for African elephants, as of 1931, is 35 years, 4 months, 16 days in the Berlin Zoological Gardens. In his 1947–48 résumé Flower reports 38 years, 6 months, 1 day for an animal known as "Karkoj," in the Giza Zoological Gardens. Karkoj was "probably under 1 year old," and stood 3 feet, 6 inches at the shoulder when purchased, so would have been not more than 40 at death. An African elephant called "Jumbina," received at the National Zoological Park on August 8, 1913, lived until June 30, 1952, or 38 years, 10 months, 22 days (Mann, 1953). Since Jumbina's height on arrival in Washington is given as 4 feet, 3 inches, her actual age at death could have exceeded that of Karkoj by only a year or two. As stated by Maj. Flower in his 1947–48 summary, there is still no properly documented record of any elephant having reached the age of 70.

· REFERENCES

ALEXANDER, SHANA.
  1962. Belle's baby—225 pounds and all elephant. Life, **52** (19):104–20.
ALLEN, GLOVER M.
  1936. Zoological results of the George Vanderbilt African expedition of 1934. 2. The forest elephant of Africa. Proc. Acad. Nat. Sci. Philadelphia, **88**:15–44.
  1939. A checklist of African mammals. Bull. Mus. Comp. Zool. Harvard, **83**.
  1945. South African bush elephant. In: FRANCIS HARPER, Extinct and vanishing mammals of the Old World. Spec. Pub. 12, American Committee for International Wildlife Protection, New York. 850 pp.
ANGHI, CS. G.
  1961. Quinba, the fifth elephant calf. Internatl. Zoo News, **8** (3):78–79.
ASDELL, S. A.
  1946. Patterns of mammalian reproduction. Comstock Publishing Co., Inc., Ithaca, N.Y. 437 pp.
BARTLETT, A. R.
  1899. Wild animals in captivity. Ed. EDWARD BARTLETT. Chapman & Hall, Ltd., London. 373 pp.
BENEDICT, FRANCIS G.
  1936. The physiology of the elephant. Carnegie Institution of Washington. 302 pp.
BENEDICT, FRANCIS G., and ROBERT C. LEE.
  1938. Further observations on the physiology of the elephant. Jour. Mammal., **19** (2):175–94.
BLANFORD, W. T.
  1888–91. The fauna of British India. Mammalia. Taylor and Francis, London. 617 pp.
BRIDGES, WILLIAM.
  1941. Twelve elephants. Bull. New York Zool. Soc., **44** (5):137–52.
  1946. The Belgian Congo's gift to the New York Zoological Society. Animal Kingdom, **49** (5):158–64.
  1948. Elephants in the Belgian Congo. Ibid., **51** (1):20–28.
BURNE, E. C.
  1943. A record of gestation periods and growth of trained elephant calves in the Southern Shan States, Burma. Proc. Zool. Soc. London, **113**, Ser. A:27.
CARLISLE, DONALD T.
  1946. Trustees of friendship. Animal Kingdom, **49** (6):191–92; 214.
CHASEN, FREDERICK NUTTER.
  1940. A handlist of Malaysian mammals. Bull. Raffles Mus., Singapore. **15**:1–209.

DERANIYAGALA, P. E. P.
1955. Some extinct elephants, their relatives and the two living species. Colombo Nature Museum, Ceylon. 161 pp.

ELLERMAN, J. R., and T. C. S. MORRISON-SCOTT.
1951. Checklist of Palaearctic and Indian mammals, 1758–1946. British Museum (Natural History), London. 809 pp.

ELLERMAN, J. R., T. C. S. MORRISON-SCOTT, and R. W. HAYMAN.
1953. Southern African mammals. Trustees of the British Museum (Natural History), London. 363 pp.

EVANS, G. H.
1910. Elephants and their diseases. Superintendent, Government Printing, Rangoon, Burma. 343 pp.

FLOWER, S. S.
1929. List of the vertebrated animals exhibited in the gardens of the Zoological Society of London, 1828–1927. 1. Mammals. Zoological Society of London. 419 pp.
1931. Contributions to our knowledge of the duration of life in vertebrate animals. 5. Mammals. Proc. Zool. Soc. London, pp. 145–234.
1943. Notes on age at sexual maturity, gestation period and growth of the Indian elephant. Proc. Zool. Soc. London, 113, Ser. A:21–26.
1947–48. Further notes on the duration of life in mammals. 5. The alleged and actual ages to which elephants live. Ed. L. HARRISON MATTHEWS. Proc. Zool. Soc. London, 117:680–88.

FRADE, F.
1955. Ordre des Proboscidiens. In: Traité de Zoologie. Ed. P.-P. GRASSÉ. 1 (1):715–83. Masson et Cie, Paris.

GEBBINGS, JOHANNES.
1928. Das neue Dickhauterhaus des Leipziger Zoologischen Gartens. Zool. Garten, Leipzig (N.F.), 1 (1/2):13–18.

GOODWIN, G. G.
1925. The first living elephant in America. Jour. Mammal., 6 (4):256–63.

GOWERS, SIR WM. F.
1931. Letter. Proc. Zool. Soc. London, pp. 77–78.

GRZIMEK, BERNHARD.
1957. No room for wild animals. W. W. Norton & Co., New York. 271 pp.

HEDIGER, H.
1950. Wild animals in captivity. Butterworths Scientific Publications, London. 207 pp.
1955a. How elephants sleep. Animals asleep. Vol. 4. J. R. Geigy S. A., Basel.
1955b. Studies of the psychology and behaviour of captive animals in zoos and circuses. Butterworths Scientific Publications, London. 166 pp.

HELLER, EDMUND.
1933. Elephants in and out of the Zoo. Bull. Washington Park Zool. Soc., Milwaukee, 4 (1):2–18.

HINDLE, ELLEN M.
1950. Birth of an elephant in the Rome Zoo. Zoo Life, 5 (1):7–9.

H[ORNADAY] W[M]. T.
1911. The real height of Jumbo. Bull. New York Zool. Soc., No. 48, pp. 821–22.
1923. Our second pygmy elephant. *Ibid.*, 26 (1):3–4.

HUNDLEY, GORDON.
1934. Statistics of height increments of Indian calf elephants. Proc. Zool. Soc. London, pp. 697–98.

HVASS, HANS.
1932. Von der indischen Elefantin Ellen und ihren drei in Gefangenschaft geborenen Jungen. Zool. Garten, Leipzig (N.F.), 5 (7/9):191–99.

LYDEKKER, RICHARD.
1893–96. The royal natural history. Frederick Warne & Co., London and New York. 6 vols. 583 pp.

MANN, WM. M.
1930. Wild animals in and out of the zoo. Smithsonian Sci. Ser., 6. Washington, D.C. 362 pp.
1953. Report on the National Zoological Park for the year ended June 30, 1952. Smithsonian Inst. Report, 1952, pp. 94–129.

MEINERTZHAGEN, R.
1955. The speed and altitude of bird flight (with notes on other animals). Ibis, 97 (1):81–117.

MITCHELL, P. CHALMERS.
1929. Centenary history of the Zoological Society of London. By the Society, London. 307 pp.

MORRISON-SCOTT, T. C. S.
1947. A revision of our knowledge of African elephants' teeth, with notes on forest and "pygmy" elephants. Proc. Zool. Soc. London, 117:505–27.

NOACK, T.
1906. Eine Zwergform des afrikanischen Elefanten. Zool. Anz., Leipzig, 29:631–33.

NOBACK, CHARLES V.
1932. Report of the veterinarian. In: 36th Annual Report, New York Zoological Society, pp. 40–42.

OSBORN, HENRY FAIRFIELD.
1936–42. Proboscidea. A monograph of the discovery, evolution, migration and extinction of the mastodonts and elephants of the world. American Museum of Natural History, New York. 2 vols. 1675 pp.

PATTEN, ROBERT A.
1940. "Jessie" joins her ancestors. Parks and Recreation, 23 (5):200–202.

PERRY, J. S.
1953. The reproduction of the African elephant. Phil. Trans. Roy. Soc. London. Ser. B., Biol. Sci., 237 (643):93–149.

PETTER, GERMAINE.
  1958. À propos de quelques petits éléphants de forêt attribués à *Loxodonta cyclotis* Matschie. Mammalia, **22** (4):575–90.

PFEFFER, PIERRE.
  1960. Sur la validité de formes naines de l'éléphant d'Afrique. Mammalia, **24** (4):556–76.

ROBERTSON-BULLOCK, W.
  1962. The weight of the African elephant, *Loxodonta africana* Proc. Zool. Soc. London, **138**:133–35.

ROOSEVELT, THEODORE, and EDMUND HELLER.
  1914. Life histories of African game animals. Chas. Scribner's Sons, New York. 2 vols.

SCHIÖTT, J.
  1908. Geburt eines Elefanten im Zoologischen Garten zu Kopenhagen. Zool. Beobachter, **49** (5):133–36.

SCHNEIDER, KARL MAX.
  1930. Einige Beobachtungen über das Geschlechtsleben des indischen Elefanten. Zool. Garten, Leipzig (N.F.), **3** (11/12):305–14.

SHORTRIDGE, G. C.
  1934. The mammals of South West Africa. Wm. Heinemann, Ltd., London. 2 vols. 779 pp.

SOSNOVSKY, I.
  1958. Moscow garden—oldest Zoo in the Soviet Union. Animal Kingdom, **61** (5):147–52.

STRASSBERGER, O.
  1907. Note. Zool. Beobachter, **48** (1):58.

ULMER, FREDERICK J., JR.
  1953. The greatest beast on earth. America's First Zoo, **5** (3):3–6.

WARD, ROWLAND.
  1928. Records of big game. Ed. J. G. DOLLMAN and J. B. BURLACE. Rowland Ward, Ltd., London. 523 pp.

ORDER HYRACOIDEA

·

FAMILY PROCAVIIDAE

HYRAXES

Variously known as conies, dassies, rock rabbits, etc., the hyraxes are small, furry creatures, brownish or grayish in coloration. In Bible references to the "cony," a name properly applied to the rabbit, it is thought that the Syrian hyrax (*Procavia capensis syriaca*) was really intended.

Often described as resembling short-eared rabbits, the hyraxes might equally well be compared with tail-less marmots, although, of course, they are entirely unrelated to either. Four of the five front toes carry broad, hooflike nails, the fifth being rudimentary, while the three hind toes are similarly equipped. In the upper jaw there are only two lengthened incisor teeth, but in the lower there are four, the general dental arrangement suggesting that of the rhinoceroses. The tail is almost non-existent.

Hyraxes are found from Syria and Arabia to north Africa, thence southward in suitable localities to the Cape. Most commonly seen in captivity are the rock hyraxes of the widely distributed species *P. capensis*, found, in many races, throughout the range of the family. They live in colonies, preferring the shelter of rocky ledges, and are diurnal or at least crepuscular in habit. Being entirely herbivorous, food preferences are for low-growing foliage, grasses, and such other vegetable material as may be available.

Rock hyraxes seem to accept captivity readily enough, quickly becoming quiet and docile. However, this docility seldom carries to the point where the animals can be handled with impunity. They are not particularly active and have appeared content here in cages no more than 3 by 4 feet, with shallow rock work at the back containing crevices for retiring. Some of the races may very well be capable of living without heat in winter, but we seldom have been certain of the origin of specimens received here and have always kept their quarters warm. Hyraxes here are fed raw vegetables, such as potatoes and carrots, apples, any available greens, bread, and rolled oats. Some specimens will take hay, especially clover and alfalfa. Fresh drinking water, of course, is always before them.

Asdell (1946) gives the gestation period for *P. capensis* as $7\frac{1}{2}$ months and the number of young as ranging from 1 to 6, the mean being 2.6. Three births have occurred here, one of 2 young, the others of 1 only. The young are born fully furred, with the eyes open, and are actively ambulatory. Zuckerman (1953) reports six births of South African animals in the Zoological Gardens of London, with from 1 to 3 per litter, as well as a single birth of 2 young of the Syrian hyrax. The latter race was bred in the Giza Zoological Gardens for four generations (Flower, 1932). Fourteen litters produced averaged 2.57 young, with a maximum of 5. All these were born in March or April, while the births in London occurred from June to November. Shortridge (1934) says that in South West Africa "there seems to be no particular breeding season." In a species of such very wide distribution, local breeding seasons must vary greatly.

Rock hyraxes do not appear to be particularly long-lived, the greatest longevity here being 3 years, 11 months, 7 days. Flower (1931) gives 6 years, 2 months, 20 days for a specimen in the Zoological Gardens of London and 7 years, 4 months, 21 days for a Syrian hyrax at Giza.

The tree hyraxes (*Dendrohyrax*) are found, in several forms, in forested areas of Africa from at least as far west as Liberia, eastward across the [Belgian] Congo, and south to the Cape. As the name implies, they are essentially arboreal, although Shortridge (1934) says they sometimes come to the ground to feed. The tree hyraxes are nocturnal in habit, spending the days hidden in foliage or in hollow trunks. The coat is longer and softer than in *Procavia* and there is some variegation with white.

For some reason not readily understood, tree hyraxes are much more uncommon in captivity than their terrestrial relatives and have been represented in our collection only by four specimens of Emin's tree hyrax (*D. dorsalis emini*) brought to us from the Belgian Congo by Charles Cordier on June 15, 1949. Two of these animals survived for only a few months, but one lived for just over 2 years, and the fourth for 3 years, 3 months, 13 days. Feeding and housing were essentially the same as for rock hyraxes, except for the provision of branches for climbing. The tree hyraxes used these freely but did not hesitate to descend to the floor for their food.

Incidentally, while the hyraxes in general are said to be extremely vociferous in the bush, I cannot recall ever having heard a vocal sound of any sort made by these or other captive specimens.

Our tree hyraxes produced no young during their brief time with us.

The female of a pair of *D. arboreus crawshayi* that had been kept in semi-captivity in Kenya and had bred there gave birth to a single young on December 1, 1945, after having been brought to the Zoological Gardens of London (Webb, 1946). Shortridge (1934) says the young per litter in *Dendrohyrax* may vary from one to three and that "there may be no particular breeding season."

· REFERENCES

ASDELL, S. A.
  1946. Patterns of mammalian reproduction. Comstock Publishing Co., Inc., Ithaca, N.Y. 437 pp.
FLOWER, S. S.
  1931. Contributions to our knowledge of the duration of life in vertebrate animals. 5. Mammals. Proc. Zool. Soc. London, pp. 145–234.
  1932. Notes on the recent mammals of Egypt, with a list of the species recorded from that Kingdom. *Ibid.*, 369–450.
SHORTRIDGE, G. C.
  1934. The mammals of South West Africa. Wm. Heinemann, Ltd., London. 437 pp.
WEBB, C. S.
  1946. An interesting birth at the Zoo. Zoo Life, 1 (1):9.
ZUCKERMAN, S.
  1953. The breeding seasons of mammals in captivity. Proc. Zool. Soc. London, 122:827–950.

ORDER SIRENIA

•

Manatees and Dugong

The grotesque animals of this order are entirely aquatic in habit, never leaving the water. Members of two of the four recognized species frequent shallow marine bays and coastal areas, often ascending rivers for considerable distances, so that they may live in salt, brackish, or fresh water, while those of one are confined entirely to rivers and of another, to the sea. They feed chiefly on aquatic vegetation, although occasionally, as I once saw a manatee do in the Botanical Gardens of Georgetown, British Guiana, they may project head and shoulders above the water to browse on plants growing along the margins.

In the sirenians the tail is broadened horizontally, serving as the principal propellant force in swimming. The rear limbs are missing entirely, while in the forelimbs the five digits are inclosed in a common skin to form a flipper, with traces of nails sometimes remaining. The eyes are very small and the ears are tiny openings with no external shells. The nostrils, two in number, are provided with valves which close when the animal submerges. The thick, muscular upper lip is divided in such a way that the two sections are movable laterally and so are useful in drawing food into the mouth. In the manatees (*Trichechus*) there are but six cervical vertebrae and no incisors, but in the dugong (*Dugong*) there are two incisors in the upper jaws of males which project downward in the form of tusks. In both groups the molars drop out in front as they wear down and are replaced from the rear, as they are in the elephants. The thick, wrinkled skin of the body carries only occasional scattered hairs, but the muzzle is furnished with bristles which may have some function in feeding. In females of both manatees and dugong the paired mammary glands are on the chest. Living members of this order are assigned to two families: Trichechidae, the manatees, and Dugongidae, the dugong.

FAMILY TRICHECHIDAE

MANATEES

This family contains a single genus (*Trichechus*), the most obvious distinguishing character of which is the rounded, paddle-like form of the tail. Three species are usually recognized: *Trichechus manatus*, the American manatee, which ranges, in two races, in coastal areas from North Carolina to Florida, the Gulf of Mexico, the West Indies, and northeastern South America, frequently ascending slow-flowing rivers (Miller and Kellogg, 1955); *T. inunguis*, the Amazonian manatee, a somewhat smaller animal with no vestige of claws remaining on the flippers, found only in the fresh waters of the Amazon basin of northern South America (Cabrera and Yepes, 1940), and *T. senegalensis*, the African manatee, which lives along the western coast of Africa from Senegal to Angola, sometimes entering the larger rivers (Ellerman, Morrison-Scott, and Hayman, 1953).

No manatee has ever been kept here, so that my only experience with the group in captivity has been in the capacity of spectator and I can contribute little at first hand. All the species have been exhibited by various zoological gardens and aquariums, including our sister institution, the New York Aquarium, so that a considerable amount of information has been amassed. Much of this has been recorded by Vosseler (1924), who has chronologically tabulated specimens kept up to 1913. Essentially, Vosseler's paper has to do with a pair of Amazonian manatees received at the Hamburg Zoological Gardens in 1912 and still living there in 1924, after $12\frac{1}{2}$ years, probably the greatest authentic longevity for any sirenian in captivity.

Following early experiences in or near the areas of origin, American manatees were received by the zoological gardens of Philadelphia and London in 1875 (Ulmer, 1959), with further arrivals of all three species recorded at intervals. Specimens of the American manatee reached the New York Aquarium in 1903, 1904, and 1906 (Townsend, 1904, 1905, 1907). The latter animal lived for at least 19 months, which was stated to have "broken the captivity record for a manatee by 1 month" (Anon., 1908). On July 3, 1916, an Amazonian manatee, said to be the first to be seen alive in this country, was received at the New York Aquarium (Anon., 1916). This animal's habit of lying on its back when the pool was drained is well shown in a photograph. It lived until July 9, 1918, just over 2 years (Anon., 1919).

In a comprehensive article Coates (1939) describes experiences with a young Amazonian manatee which arrived at the New York Aquarium in 1939. Presumably not yet fully weaned, this creature could be induced to eat only lettuce leaves and lived for but 22 days. However, it served a definite purpose, for when given a choice between water temperatures of 68°F. and 78°F., it chose the latter, which was thereafter maintained, a point of some significance.

Our Aquarium's latest experience had to do with two further Amazonian manatees received in 1940 (Coates, 1940). These animals refused to take any of the several kinds of greens offered but finally accepted clover and alfalfa hay, placed in a rack at water level. They appeared to be thriving, but Mr. Coates, now director of the Aquarium, informs me that they lived for only a few months.

In general, European results in the keeping of manatees seem to have been better than those so far obtained in this country. In 1948 A. L. J. Sunier, then director of "Artis," the Amsterdam Zoological Gardens, told me that he had kept a manatee for over 8 years in his Gardens and that it ate approximately 20 pounds of lettuce and chicory thrown into the water daily. Specimens of the Amazonian manatee at the zoological gardens of both London and Frankfurt have somewhat exceeded the longevity of the Amsterdam animal, whose specific identity I failed to note.

The African manatee is less well known in captivity than its congeners but has been kept successfully in the Zoological Gardens of Antwerp. A specimen seen there in 1950 and 1951 was living in a pool surrounded by an open pergola which could be inclosed with glass in winter. The animal could best be seen when its tile pool had been drained. It was then inclined to lie on its back, as described for an Amazonian manatee at the New York Aquarium. Received in 1948, "Zooke" lived for just over 4 years, to December, 1952 (Gijzen, 1953). A replacement, named "Goliath," was received on August 26, 1953. At first, Goliath would eat only the stems of water lilies but later took, daily, approximately 7 kilograms (15.4 pounds) of cabbage, endives, and chicory (Anon., 1954). In spite of apparent recovery from extensive wounds acquired in capture, this animal lived for only a few months. Through continued efforts of friends at the Zoo in Leopoldville, a third African manatee was received at Antwerp on October 29, 1954. "Hukunga" proved to be particularly docile, soon learning to respond when his name was called and to take food offered by hand. This amounted to 15 kilograms (33 pounds) of chicory, endive, lettuce, and cabbage daily, supplemented in summer with available aquatic plants, principally *Elodea* (Gijzen, 1958).

Numerous experiences have shown that manatees will take a great variety of herbaceous food, including aquatic plants, many leafy and fleshy vegetables, fruits, bread, and even hay. Concerning temperatures best suited to their needs, Vosseler (1924) thinks that, at least for Amazonian manatees, the water should range from 25° C. to 30° C. (77° F. to 86° F.) and especially emphasizes the need for air temperatures between 20°C. and 25°C. (68°F. to 77°F.). The latter point, which might be overlooked, probably is of especial importance, not only because of the shock of cold air intake in breathing but also because of the risk of total exposure when the pool is drained. The preference of the young Amazonian manatee in the New York Aquarium for a water temperature of 78° F., already noted, gives support to Vosseler's theory. It seems probable that American manatees, at least those of the northern race (*T. m. latirostris*), are somewhat less sensitive to cold, but Moore (1951, 1956) gives accounts of the gathering of manatees at warm-water outlets entering the Miami River, within the city of Miami, Florida, during cold periods.

While there appear to be no records of the actual breeding of any manatee in captivity, at least three births to female American manatees, pregnant when captured, have been recorded (Moore, 1957). All these births have occurred in Florida commercial exhibits. In at least two of these cases the young animal was nursed by the mother while she was in a horizontal position, entirely under water (Moore, 1956, 1957). The gestation of the manatee is given by Jennison (n.d.) as 365 days but confirmation appears to be lacking. Births are usually of single young, though twins may sometimes occur. With the increasing popularity of the manatee as an exhibition animal in Florida, it may be hoped that more complete information on its breeding habits will become available.

FAMILY DUGONGIDAE

DUGONG

In the dugong (*Dugong dugon*) the end of the tail is crescentic or concave, rather than rounded or convex, as in the manatee, no remnants of nails remain on the flippers, and in the males, as already noted, two upper incisors project downward in tusklike fashion. The dugong is found in the Red Sea and along the shores of the Indian Ocean as far south as Madagascar and east at least to the Marshall Islands in the Pacific. Several races have been named but are of doubtful status. Beyond the points that it appears to be confined to salt water and is thought to be entirely herbivorous, little is known of the life history of the dugong, although Asdell (1946) gives the gestation period as 1 year.

It has been thought that the reported habit of the female dugong of holding her young above the water to nurse may have given rise to the ancient fables of mermaids. However, since the belief that this custom prevailed also in manatees has only recently been discounted by the observations of Moore (1956, 1957), it may be that further study is required in the case of the dugong.

Captivity records for the dugong appear to consist entirely of injured or accidentally netted specimens. In November, 1955, an animal speared in the Palau Islands of the Caroline group was taken to the Steinhart Aquarium in San Francisco, where it lived for a short time. An excellent series of photographs of this specimen was published (Anon., 1955). News stories of October, 1958, reported the netting of two dugongs off the coast of Kenya, East Africa. The animals were stated to be thriving in the swimming pool of a local hotel.

· REFERENCES

ANON.
    1908. Manatee. Bull. New York Zool. Soc., No. 29, p. 427.
    1916. A manatee from the Amazon. *Ibid.*, **19** (6):1419–21.
    1919. Amazon manatee. *Ibid.*, **22** (2):46.
    1954. Notre lamantin "Goliath." Zoo, Anvers, **19**:78.
    1955. A pip of a stiff upper lip. Life, **39** (24):73–74.

ASDELL, S. A.
    1946. Patterns of mammalian reproduction. Comstock Publishing Co., Inc., Ithaca, N.Y. 437 pp.

CABRERA, ANGEL, and JOSÉ YEPES.
    1940. Historia natural ediar. Mamiferos Sud-Americanos. Campañia Argentina de Editores, Buenos Aires. 370 pp.

COATES, C. W.
    1939. Baby mermaid—a manatee at the Aquarium. Bull. New York Zool. Soc., **42** (5):140–48.
    1940. Manatees at the Aquarium. *Ibid.*, **43** (3):99–100.

ELLERMAN, J. R., T. C. S. MORRISON-SCOTT, and R. W. HAYMAN.
    1953. Southern African mammals. British Museum (Natural History), London. 363 pp.

GIJZEN, A.
  1953.   Une perte sensible. Zoo, Anvers, **18**:89.
  1958.   Palmares de nos raretés zoologiques. *Ibid.*, **24** (1):6–38.
JENNISON, GEORGE.
  N.d.   Table of gestation periods and number of young. A. & C. Black, Ltd.,
          London. 8 pp.
MILLER, GERRIT S., JR., and REMINGTON KELLOGG.
  1955.   List of North American recent mammals. Bull. 205, U.S. National
          Museum, Smithsonian Institution, Washington, D.C. 954 pp.
MOORE, JOSEPH CURTIS.
  1951.   The status of the manatee in the Everglades National Park, with notes
          on its natural history. Jour. Mammal., **32** (1):22–36.
  1956.   Observations of manatees in aggregations. Amer. Mus. Novitates,
          1811:1–24.
  1957.   Newborn young of a captive manatee. Jour. Mammal., **38** (1):137–38.
TOWNSEND, C. H.
  1904.   Notes on the manatee or sea-cow. Eighth Annual Report of the New
          York Zoological Society, for 1903, pp. 85–87.
  1905.   Report of the Director of the Aquarium to the Board of Managers.
          Ninth Annual Report of the New York Zoological Society, for 1904,
          p. 97.
  1907.   Report of the Director of the Aquarium to the Board of Managers.
          Eleventh Annual Report of the New York Zoological Society, for 1906,
          p. 86.
ULMER, FREDERICK A., JR.
  1959.   The golden age of zoo exhibits. America's First Zoo, **11** (1):5–9.
VOSSELER, J.
  1924.   Pflege und Haltung der Seekühe (*Trichechus*) nebst Beiträgen zu
          ihrer Biologie. Pallasia, **2** (1):58–67; 114–33; 167–80; 213–30.

ORDER PERISSODACTYLA

.

HORSES, TAPIRS, AND RHINOCEROSES

The members of this group, the odd-toed hoofed mammals, have a common factor in the method of support of the body weight, for in all it rests chiefly upon the third toe of each foot. The tapirs still retain four toes on the front feet but have only three behind, while the rhinoceroses have three all round. In the horses the functional toes have been reduced to one on each foot. In this group the stomach is simple, so that there is no rumination or chewing of the cud. Incisors are usually present in both jaws—the African rhinoceroses are exceptions—while horns and antlers, as true bony outgrowths, are absent. The tapirs are the sole existing representatives in the New World, while Africa has both horses and rhinoceroses, and all three groups persist in Asia.

FAMILY EQUIDAE

HORSES, ASSES, AND ZEBRAS

The most familiar member of this family is, of course, the domestic horse (*Equus caballus*). The origin of this animal is far from clear, but it is presumed to have resulted from the domestication of one or more of the wild forms that existed in Europe and Asia almost to historical times and may have persisted nearly to the present, presumably with some admixture of the blood of feral horses. It seems unlikely that this problem will ever be fully solved, but the basic facts, as far as known, are well covered by Lydekker (1893–96, 2), Antonius (1937a), and Harper (1945). In any case, domesticated horses have been known since the second or possibly even the third millennium B.C. and have played an important part in human progress, a status that increasing mechanization has greatly reduced in this century.

At the present time the only truly wild horse known to be surviving is the Przewalski or Mongolian horse (*E. przewalskii*), now apparently confined to a small area in southwestern Mongolia and northeastern Sinkiang Province, China. While it is thought by some that the present survivors may have been affected by contact with feral domestic horses (Harper, 1945), Bannikov (1958) repudiates this possibility and presents a photograph of three specimens made in Mongolia in 1954 that show no evidence of feral influence.

Przewalski's horse, as we know it, is a small, chunky animal, light bay or "yellow dun" in color, with a narrow dark stripe down the back and occasionally with faint leg stripes. Lower legs, mane, and tail are black and the muzzle and abdomen are usually pale or even whitish. The head is proportionately large, with Roman nose, while the ears are small and neat. The mane is short, stiff, and upright, there is no forelock, and the tail is fairly full except at the base, which is thinly haired. In winter the coat becomes long, thick, and heavy, with cheek tufts prominent, while in summer the hair is short and sleek.

A skin and skull brought from central Asia by N. M. Przewalski were the basis of the first description of this horse, by I. S. Poliakov, in 1881. Apparently, the first living specimens to be obtained were three young animals kept by F. A. Falz-Fein on his estate in Russia in 1900. An account of this and other scattered early arrivals is given by Salensky (1907) as incidental to a well-illustrated treatise on the history and anatomical characters of Przewalski's horse

Acting on an order from the Duke of Bedford for several pairs of Przewalski's horses, the resourceful and enterprising Carl Hagenbeck sent a special expedition to Mongolia to attempt to secure them. After overcoming seemingly insurmountable difficulties, the collectors returned to Hamburg in October of 1901 with twenty-eight survivors of a total of fifty-two young wild horses captured. These animals were distributed to various collections, including that of the Duke of Bedford, and from them the present captive stock has descended. Hagenbeck (1910) has given a full account of this important undertaking, in which he says that the foals were captured by mounted Mongolians, who pursued the herds until the young were exhausted and thus easily secured. They were then taken back to camp and given into the care of domestic brood mares. This is the commonly accepted version, but in November, 1912, while in Germany, I met William Greiger, who was in charge of the expedition. Greiger said that it had been found that many of the driven foals had died as the result of overexertion. To avoid these losses, teams of Mongolian horsemen were assigned to cutting out the wild mares that were heavy with foal, keeping them under surveillance until the young were born and picking up the latter before they were steady enough to run. According to Greiger, most of the animals brought safely back to Hamburg had been captured in this way.

The first Przewalski horses to reach this country were two received at the New York Zoological Park from Carl Hagenbeck on December 30, 1902. These animals, however, were not considered to be acceptable, and while we have no record of their disposal, Mohr (1959) says they were transferred to the Cincinnati Zoological Gardens, presumably on instructions from Mr. Hagenbeck. A replacement pair, sent from Mr. Hagenbeck, reached us on March 4, 1905. The male lived until June 19, 1919, the female until November 29, 1923. They became the parents of six foals, while three more were sired by the male when mated to daughters and three were produced by a pair of the young. In all a total of twelve were born here, the last on June 16, 1929. For lack of space, the surplus animals were sent to various institutions, and when breeding ceased, we were left with only two aged mares. One of these, born July 29, 1918, died on February 18, 1948, aged 29 years, 6 months, 20 days; the other, born June 27, 1925, lived until July 23, 1951, or 26 years, 26 days.

The history of this small herd is paralleled by most zoological-garden experience. However, complete disappearance of the descendants of the Hagenbeck importation was avoided by the maintenance of thriving stocks in the Zoological Gardens of Munich (Hellabrunn) and Prague. As an aid to the continuance of the Przewalski horse in captivity, Volf (1958) proposed the establishment of a stud book by means of which the status of existing animals and their progeny could be kept under continuing surveillance. As a first step, he developed a list of the wild horses, numbering fifty, known to be living in the world's collections on January 1, 1958, together with the background data of the twelve specimens comprising the herd at Prague. As the result of a symposium held at Prague in September, 1959, it was decided that an international organization for the preservation of the Przewalski horse should be formed and that a stud book, in continuation of the compilation of Mohr (1959), should be established. Under the editorship of Jiří Volf (1960, 1961) of the Zoological Gardens of Prague, the first issue of the *Pedigree Book* lists a total of fifty-nine horses of approved origin known to be living in captivity as of January 1, 1960, while the second records an increase to seventy-three as of January 1, 1961.*

Aside from a single specimen in the National Zoological Park, the only

*See Addenda, p. 736.

Przewalski horses living in this country in 1963 were the thriving herd at the Catskill Game Farm, New York. Based on seven animals imported from the Munich Zoological Gardens in 1957, with two more received in 1959, this group had produced a total of eighteen foals up to 1963.

Quarters for Przewalski's horses here consisted of several grassy, wire-inclosed runs, each from $\frac{1}{3}$ to $\frac{1}{2}$ acre in extent. Unheated shelters were provided but seldom used, for the animals appeared to be indifferent to cold. While no attempt was made to accustom them to handling, they were quiet and reasonably gentle in disposition, and even adult stallions never exhibited the savage natures so frequent in male wild asses and zebras. They were fed timothy hay and crushed oats as staples, with occasional potatoes, apples, and carrots. A block of rock salt was always available. They grazed freely on the grass of their inclosures but never sufficiently to damage it seriously. They seemed always to maintain good condition, an adult stallion weighing 550 pounds at death and two mares 560 and 580 pounds, respectively.

The twelve births that occurred here were all of single foals. Of these, one was in April, one in May, four in June, two in July, and four in September. The twenty-seven birth dates given by Volf (1958) for the foundation animals of the Prague herd and their descendants fall in 8 months of the year and exclude only January, August, October, and November, the preponderance being in April and May. It is presumable that the gestation period is approximately 330 days, as in the domestic horse (Asdell, 1946), but it appears not to have been recorded accurately. As listed by Gray (1954), Przewalski's horse interbreeds freely with the domestic horse and has produced hybrids, probably sterile, with zebras but failed to do so when mated with donkeys.

Basing his estimate on the excellent longevities established by Przewalski horses in the Jardin des Plantes, Paris, where probable ages of 27 years, 10 months, and 28 years were recorded, Flower (1931) concluded that the latter figure approximated the normal maximum for the species. Since that time, however, at least three specimens have lived in captivity for periods beyond Flower's estimate. The span of 29 years, 6 months, 20 days in the New York Zoological Park has already been noted, while Ratcliffe (1948–49) records 364 months or 30 years, 4 months in the Philadelphia Zoological Garden. A mare born in the Philadelphia Zoological Garden on July 13, 1926, and later transferred to the National Zoological Park, died at that institution on June 6, 1959, after 32 years, 10 months, 24 days.

Close relatives of the horse are the asses, of which two wild species still persist. The wild ass of Asia (*Equus hemionus*) is a comparatively large animal, more or less reddish in color, with dark vertebral stripe and usually no shoulder bar, although this seems to be present in some male onagers (*E. h. onager*) (Harper, 1945:360). The rather long tail is short-haired for half its length, ending in a brushlike tassel, and the ears are small. The following four living races, in the indicated ranges, are usually recognized: the Mongolian wild ass or kulan (*E. h. hemionus*), central Mongolia; the onager (*E. h. onager*), northeastern Iran, northwestern Afghanistan, Russian Turkestan; the Indian wild ass (*E. h. khur*), northwestern India to southeastern Iran; and the kiang (*E. h. kiang*), Nepal, Sikkim, Tibet, and southeastern Kashmir (Ellerman and Morrison-Scott, 1951). The little Syrian wild ass (*E. h. hemippus*), smallest of the recent Equidae, is now presumed to be extinct. Both the onager and the Indian wild ass have been so seriously reduced in numbers that they may soon follow their smaller relative, but both the kiang and the kulan are presumed to be holding their own in the remote fastnesses in which they live.

The wild ass of Africa (*E. asinus*) is a smaller animal than its relatives of Asia. It is typically light gray in color, with a narrow dark vertebral stripe and usually a shoulder bar. The ears are proportionately larger than those of Asiatic wild asses. Originally known from northern and northeastern Africa, this species gave rise to the domestic donkey, which is designated as the nominate race (*E. a. asinus*). Several other subspecies have been described, but most have either become extinct or so interbred with feral donkeys that their identities have become uncertain. The Somali wild ass (*E. a. somalicus*), a pale reddish animal with dark cross-bars on the lower legs and usually lacking a shoulder bar (Antonius, 1937a), apparently still exists, in small numbers, under governmental protection. A herd of five representatives of this race was seen at the Catskill Game Farm, New York, in September, 1961. Heinz Heck offered the information that they were the descendants of animals captured in Somaliland in the thirties, sent first to the Rome Zoological Gardens and finally to Munich. They were pale fawn in color, with short, very narrow chevrons and well-marked leg bars.

All of the living forms of both Asiatic and African wild asses, as well as the now presumably vanished Syrian, have been kept in European zoological gardens and most of them have been bred. For some reason, they have never been widely kept in America, although there was a breeding stock of onagers in the Philadelphia Zoological Garden in the early years of this century. Our own collections have included only four kiangs, all single animals, the first having been received in 1909 as the gift of the Duke of Bedford, three onagers, one of which emanated from the Philadelphia herd in 1905, and one African male, identified in our records as *E. asinus taeniopus*, the Abyssinian wild ass.

The latter animal was secured by an expedition sent out from Khartoum by the late Ellis Joseph and was received here on June 30, 1925. It was a male, pale gray in color, with typical dorsal and shoulder stripes as well as leg bars. Slenderly built, he suggested a domestic donkey only in his color. He lived until October 31, 1949, or for 24 years, 4 months, 1 day in a large, grassy inclosure confined by a wire stock fence, with an unheated shelter. He remained savage, nervous, and unapproachable but behaved well when not disturbed. Although he seemed indifferent to cold, his winter coat was only slightly heavier than that of summer, showing no tendency toward rufous, and not approaching the bearlike coverings often assumed by domestic donkeys similarly exposed. His weight at death was 384 pounds. Whether or not this was a truly wild animal with no infusion of feral blood or whether, for that matter, *taeniopus* is a tenable race are matters still open to question (see Harper, 1940:201).

The kiang, largest and darkest of the races of *E. hemionus* and a native of high country, is as hardy in captivity as such an animal might be expected to be. In winter its coat is long and shaggy, in contrast to its sleek condition in summer. The only adult male kept here was ill-natured and dangerous. Obtained from the Zoological Gardens of London, he arrived on September 11, 1914, and lived until October 18, 1930, his final weight being 495 pounds. The best longevity recorded for the kiang here was that of a female which was received on August 20, 1929, and died on November 25, 1952, after 23 years, 3 months, 5 days in captivity. Her weight at death was 475 pounds.

Onagers living here have proved to be quite as resistant to cold as the kiang, both having been kept in large inclosures with unheated shelters, although the winter coats of onagers appeared less dense than those of kiangs. Onagers, in general, have been more docile than kiangs, and none of our specimens was actually dangerous. The only wild asses bred here were two foals produced by a female onager, sired by a kiang. Dates of birth were June 29 and July 19. Our best longevity for an onager is 17 years, 4 months, 11 days and the greatest recorded weight, that of a male, is 480 pounds. The feeding of wild asses here has been as described for Przewalski's horses.

Maximum longevities for wild asses in other institutions, as recorded by Flower (1931) are: kiang, Jardin des Plantes, Paris, 24 years, 11 months, 19 days; onager, Philadelphia, 24 years, 5 months, 22 days; Indian, London, 15 years, 7 months, 9 days; Syrian, Vienna, "over 22 years" and 22 years, 10 months, 20 days; Nubian (*E. asinus africanus*), Vienna, at least 22 years, 2 months. Jones (1958) gives the following later records: kiang, London, 25 years, 10 months, 20 days and onager, Washington, 28 years, 11 months, 18 days. Hill (1957) reports 22 years and $22\frac{1}{2}$ years for two specimens of the Indian wild ass in the Zoological Gardens of London. A kiang received at the National Zoological Park on October 14, 1934, lived until August 16, 1960, or 25 years, 10 months, 2 days (Reed, 1962).

For births of wild asses in the Zoological Gardens of London, Zuckerman (1953) gives the following data: kiang, fourteen of single young, all in June and July; Indian, four of single young, two in June, one each in October and December; Syrian, one birth only, in May, 1869. Fourteen births of African wild asses, all of single foals, occurring from April to November, are also given, although there appears to be some question about the races involved (Flower, 1929:252–53). The female of a pair of onagers in the Lincoln Park Zoological Gardens, Chicago, produced a foal in July, 1961. In the same year two young were born in the small but thriving herd at the Catskill Game Farm, New York.

Kenneth (1953) gives the average gestation period of the Indian as 330 days and that of the Somali and the kiang as 365 days, the latter figure also being given by Asdell (1946) for the domestic ass. Numerous hybrids between wild asses and horses, zebras and donkeys, as well as interracial crosses, are listed by Gray (1954).

Most spectacular of the Equidae, at least as far as coloration goes, are the zebras. Once abundant on the plains and in lightly wooded areas of Africa, east and south of the Sahara and the great forests of the west, from Ethiopia and Angola to the Cape, the zebras are rapidly losing ground. Some forms have disappeared entirely within recent times, while others are perilously close to extinction. At the present time it is generally agreed that the living zebras fall into three species: *E. grevyi*, Grevy's zebra, of southern Ethiopia and northern Kenya; *E. burchelli*, the Burchell's group, of eastern, central, and western Africa, as far north as Angola; and *E. zebra*, the mountain zebras, from the south. Grevy's zebra, the largest and most handsome species, is characterized by its sharp and narrow striping extending to the hoofs, its white belly and large ears. Largely because of wide local or even individual variations in markings, many subspecific names have been assigned within the Burchell's group, so that until the revision by Cabrera (1936), the taxonomy was greatly confused. Cabrera's realignment, now generally accepted, resolves these animals into three living races: *E. b. antiquorum*, Chapman's zebra, found across south central Africa from southern Angola to the Transvaal; *E. b. bohmi,* Grant's zebra, from southern Sudan and Ethiopia to northern Rhodesia; and *E. b. selousi,* Selous's zebra, in Mozambique, southern Rhodesia, and Nyasaland.

Probably the widest variations are found in Chapman's zebra, in which the ground color may be more yellow than white. Strong "shadow" stripes are usually present and leg markings do not continue to the hoofs. In Grant's zebra shadow-striping is usually absent but may sometimes be faintly indicated, while the legs are strongly banded to the hoofs. Selous's zebra closely resembles Grant's, but neck and body stripes are more tightly spaced.

Burchell's zebra (*E. b. burchelli*), much like Chapman's except for the almost complete absence of leg markings below the elbow and knee or stifle joints, was once abundant in Orange Free State and Bechuanaland but is now considered to be extinct. According to Antonius (1937*a*), the last living specimen died in the Schönbrunn Zoo, Vienna, in 1908.

The quagga (*E. quagga*), now totally extinct, once roamed the plains of Cape Colony. Striped in brown and white on the head, neck, and forepart of the body, the remainder of the upper parts were solid brown, while the belly, legs, and tail were white. An excellent series of photographs of a living quagga in the Zoological Gardens of London, as well as of other zebras, is given by Antonius (1951). Quaggas were kept in the nineteenth and possibly even the late eighteenth centuries (Loisel, 1912, 3:42, 127) by various European zoological gardens, several apparently outliving their congeners in nature. Statements about which was the actual final survivor are not entirely in accord: of three specimens exhibited by the Zoological Gardens of London, one which arrived on March 15, 1851, and died on July 7, 1872 (Flower, 1929), is often quoted as the last living quagga; Harper (1945) thinks the honor belongs to an animal that died in the Berlin Zoological Gardens in 1875, while Antonius (1937*a*) says "the true Quagga became totally extinct in 1883, in which year the last mare died in the Amsterdam Zoo." The quagga is assigned by some authorites to the Burchell group, the members of which are then treated as races of *E. quagga.* However, anatomical differences, especially in skull structure, seem to justify separation of the quagga from the Burchell group (see Harper, 1945:335) and we here follow Ellerman, Morrison-Scott, and Hayman (1953) in the use of *burchelli* for the latter.

The mountain zebras (*E. zebra*), native to South Africa, are smaller than their more northerly relatives. They are strongly striped to the hoofs, with no shadow markings, the body stripes not reaching the longitudinal band on the abdomen. Short cross-bars on the rump and tail base join the upper flank stripes to the spinal stripe, forming a distinctive pattern known as the "gridiron." A small fold of skin on the throat forms a dewlap or "bell" not seen in other zebras. The Cape race (*E. z. zebra*), once apparently common in the mountainous areas of Cape Province, is now reduced to a mere remnant. Very recently on the verge of extinction, it appears that the race may be preserved. Knobel (1958) reports an estimated eighty-two animals living in official reservations and adjacent protected areas in the Cape region, where they are slowly increasing. Once well known in zoological gardens, the only living specimens outside Africa at the present time are said to be small groups in the Zoological Gardens of Perth, Australia, and Giza, Egypt (Marvin Jones, *in litt.*). In Hartmann's mountain zebra (*E. z. hartmannae*), which is somewhat larger than the Cape race, the background color is inclined to buffy and the dark stripes are narrower and more widely spaced, so that the general effect is much lighter. Bigalke (1958) says this form is holding its own within a restricted range in the mountains of South West Africa northward from the Orange River and extending into Angola. Recent importations have placed Hartmann's mountain zebras in various zoological gardens in Europe and in this country. A herd of fifteen young representatives of this race was imported from South West Africa in 1960 by the Catskill Game Farm, New York, to form a breeding stock.

In captivity, at the latitude of New York zebras cause borderline problems. Almost hardy but not completely so, there is constant temptation to treat them as cold-resistant, usually with unhappy results. Where a number of animals can be kept together in fairly snug indoor quarters, so that their body heat can be confined, the probability of survival increases. But even then, prolonged periods of deep cold are too likely to result in disaster. An attempt to acclimatize Grant's zebras in a large run with an unheated shelter, made here in earlier years (Hornaday, 1911), was abandoned after 3 years as impractical. Under zoological-garden conditions, where animals are shown or at least maintained on a year-round basis, heated quarters in winter appear to be essential.

The Zebra House in the New York Zoological Park, opened in November, 1912 (Ditmars, 1913), is a low building, 180 feet long, with a visitor's corridor 12 feet wide. It contains twelve stalls, along one side only, eight of which are 12 by 15 feet and four 11 by 17 feet, with a guardrail 4 feet from the cage fronts. The latter are fashioned of light steel bars, 7 feet high, while partitions have 3-foot solid steel panels at the bottom, topped by bars for 4 additional feet. Floors are of concrete cut into 3-inch squares, providing a suitably non-slip surface, at least for equines. Each stall has a permanent installation 2 feet high containing a water basin with spigot and drain and another receptacle for grain. Originally, hay racks were installed on the walls but these were soon removed because of the risk of injury to a skittish animal by any projection. Each pair of stalls connects directly with an outdoor run 30 feet wide and 75 feet long, extending to a visitors' walk. This arrangement permits alternate use of the runs by pairs of animals that, for one reason or another, must be temporarily separated. The run divisions, 7 feet high, are of light metal bars, but where these barriers front on public walks they carry a cover of 2-inch mesh wire netting. Some such provision is essential for the protection of visitors, who find it difficult to believe that a creature as beautiful as a zebra could be so ready to bite and even maim the hand that offers it a tidbit. This brings up the point that zebra stallions and even the occasional mare, of any species, may be savagely aggressive and dangerous. In this category I recall a Grevy and a Grant that would attack man or beast at any oppor-tunity. On the other hand, we have in the collection now stallions of both sorts that appear to be perfectly docile, although no keeper would risk a real test.

The 7-foot height in all our restraining elements for zebras has so far proved adequate, as zebras are not famed as high jumpers. However, a note in *Zoo News*, the organ of the Royal Zoological Society of South Australia, for March-April, 1958, describes an incident in which a male zebra, startled by a falling branch, cleared a fence 4 feet, 10 inches high from a standing start.

The temperature in our Zebra House is maintained at about 60°F. (approximately 15.5°C.) during the winter months. The animals are turned out into their runs daily, unless the weather is very severe or temperatures are below the freezing point—zebras are not clever on icy footing. They are always in their indoor stalls overnight.

The outdoor yards are paved with a mixture of asphalt and crushed stone which provides a resilient base and sufficient abrasive effect to prevent excessive growth of the hoofs. On surfaces either too smooth or too soft, "snowshoes" are likely to develop. This is a condition difficult to reduce by paring, as zebras are particularly resistant to restraint.

Each yard supports a small growing tree, set in a stoned earth circle, for shade purposes. The trunks of these trees are covered with slat-and-wire protectors from nibbling teeth, and these, at the same time, provide the much-used rubbing posts which Hediger (1955) has mentioned as essential for coat condition. A rolling pit 12 feet across, its perimeter flush with the yard floor, is filled with sand, to meet another requirement of zebra wellbeing.

Zebras are not infrequently used in mixed groups kept in large inclosures during the summer months. This may be done effectively and successfully if due precautions are taken in selecting individual animals as well as the species with which they are to be associated. At the Detroit Zoological Park I have seen zebra mares living quietly in summer with elands, lechwe, and ostriches on an "African Veldt," although the stallion could not be so privileged and for much of the time was confined to winter quarters. In our own experience, we have found zebra mares to live quietly with elands of both sexes, but when, of necessity, aoudads were added to the group, the experiment assumed a different aspect. The zebras hunted the small aoudads so persistently that only the superior agility of the latter saved them from destruction. The zebras were removed and later returned, one at a time, in the hope that at least one less aggressive individual might be found but in this we were not successful. Even an elderly animal, so afflicted with "heaves" that any movement seemed difficult, promptly proved herself more able than we had thought her.

At another time we tried a zebra stallion, aged barely 2 years, with a mixed group of antelopes and birds on our "African Plains." For a time all went well, but eventually the stallion's interest became focused on a pair of wart hogs which he soon confined to a burrow they had dug in a bank above a pool. When the zebra finally managed to crash through the roof of the burrow, the experiment came to an end.

Zebras here are allowed a ration of about 20 pounds of timothy hay and from 3 to 4 quarts of crushed oats daily, the amounts varying, of course, with form, age, sex, and condition. In addition, carrots, potatoes, and apples as well as fresh greens are given in small quantities. Salt blocks, sometimes impregnated with iodine, are always available.

Zebras breed well in captivity, and while it is true that not all the foals produced reach maturity, certainly a fair percentage succeed in doing so. In zebras here, heat periods of females begin in spring, usually ending in late summer but sometimes continuing well into autumn, unless bred. Males appear to have no definite rutting season. The gestation period is usually considered as approximately 12 months; Kenneth (1953), from various sources, gives 336–75 days for Burchell's zebra, 390 for Grevy's, and 300–75 for the mountain zebra. Brown (1936) has reported observed periods of 11 months, 6 days and 11 months, 20 days for Burchell's. The only definite contributions I can make from our own records are 11 months, 20 days and 11 months, 25 days for Grant's.

Births of single young have occurred here as follows. Grevy's: May, one, and August, one. Chapman's: May, four; July, two; August, one; and November, two. Grant's: May, one, and August, one. Mountain: May, one; June, two; and July, one. The latter were foaled by a Hartmann's mare and sired by a Cape stallion between 1924 and 1931. One of these racial intergrades was sent to the Zoological Gardens of London and is figured by Antonius (1951:196). These dates are in general accord with those given by Zuckerman (1953) for births in the Zoological Gardens of London, although the latter's more extensive records for Grevy's zebra show occurrences in every month excepting only February, May, and September. Many crosses between zebras and both horses and asses, wild and domestic, are listed by Gray (1954). In most cases it is believed that male hybrids are sterile, but there is some evidence indicating that females may sometimes be fertile. Several such hybrids are figured by Antonius (1951).

In spite of some difficulties of temperament, zebras live well in captivity when their requirements are at all fairly met. Longevities of up to 20 years are frequently attained—at least four animals here have reached that age or better—and several well in excess of that figure are known. A mountain zebra, reported by Bourdelle and Mouquet (1930) as having lived for 25 years, 8 months in the Jardin des Plantes, Paris, is listed by Flower (1931) as the longest-lived specimen of this species known to him. The best given by Flower (loc. cit.) for Grevy's zebra is 15 years, 10 days in the National Zoological Park. However, two Grevy's have lived here in excess of 16 years, and Jones (1958) reports a specimen as having lived in the Zoological Gardens of London from June 3, 1925, to July 1, 1947, or 22 years, 28 days. A female Grant's zebra received at the New York Zoological Park on May 21, 1914, as an adult died on October 16, 1935, after 21 years, 4 months, 25 days. While it seems probable that there are better records for this race, I have failed to come across one. The best longevity established in captivity by the now extinct quagga is given by Flower (1931) as 21 years, 4 months, 10 days. This applies to the animal already mentioned as having died in the Zoological Gardens of London in 1872. Chapman's zebra, a commonly kept form, seems to have outdone its congeners in longevity. The longest-lived zebra in our records is a Chapman's mare that was born here May 1, 1936, and died February 17, 1959, after 22 years, 9 months, 16 days. A Chapman's stallion, received at the Prospect Park Zoo, Brooklyn, New York, on May 19, 1929, lived until April 4, 1954, or 24 years, 10 months, 16 days, a very long record for a zebra of that sex (Crandall, 1954). However, Miss Hattie Ettinger, administrative assistant in the St. Louis Zoological Park, informs me (in litt.) that a male Chapman's received by that institution on April 24, 1925, died on March 20, 1953, after 27 years, 10 months, 24 days. The 28 years, 1 month, 24 days for a Chapman's mare in the Zoological Gardens of Basel, as given by Flower (1931) is probably the greatest authentic span so far reported for any captive zebra.

FAMILY TAPIRIDAE

TAPIRS

The tapirs are characterized by heavy bodies supported by stout legs, the front feet having four toes, the back ones only three, each terminating in a small hoof. The nose and upper lip are prolonged to form a short, mobile proboscis; the tail is rudimentary. The typical habitat is heavy jungle, often swampy or close to streams or lakes, either in tropical lowlands or high in mountainous regions. Tapirs swim well and take freely to water when pressed by enemies. The natural food consists of aquatic or low-growing forest vegetation and various fallen fruits. Mainly nocturnal, tapirs, whether in nature or in captivity, pass much of the day in sleep, although they quickly become alert, even in bright sunlight, if disturbed. Usually described as harmless, defenseless, and slow moving, tapirs, once aroused, may become serious antagonists, able to use their teeth with devastating effect and to exhibit surprising speed and agility. While hand-reared specimens usually remain tame and gentle and are often kept as pets about native villages, they are still subject to occasional moods best described as "tantrums," when their usually quiet habits may be reversed.

Present-day tapirs are found only in Central and South America and in southern Asia, four species usually being recognized. Most commonly seen in zoological gardens is the Brazilian tapir (*Tapirus terrestris*), found in tropical South America from northern Argentina and Paraguay to north-western Colombia, where *T. terrestris colombianus* occurs, the only race, besides the typical one, considered presently tenable by Hershkovitz (1954). The prevailing coloration is in shades of brown, with cheeks and throat paler, and the ears, as in all tapirs, usually but not invariably edged with white. The Brazilian tapir carries a well-marked crest rising between the ears and extending onto the neck. This elevation emphasizes the concave profile of the head, completing a distinguishing character in the living animal.

Baird's tapir (*T. bairdii*), which still remains something of a rarity as far as zoological gardens are concerned, is known from southern Mexico to western Colombia and western Ecuador, ranging from sea level to high elevations in the mountains. Absence of the sagittal crest, which is represented by a thin mane, and the strongly convex head profile are ready means for identification in the flesh.

The mountain or woolly tapir (*T. pinchaque*), the third American species, has been recorded sparingly from the Andes of Colombia and Ecuador, at elevations of from 2,000 to 4,400 meters (Hershkovitz, 1954). In this little-known species the inch-long, crinkled hair is black or blackish brown over the body, with the sides of the head paler, white ear fringes and lips being made more conspicuous by the dark coloration and dense coat. In all three living specimens that have been kept here, the thinly haired or even bare areas on each side of the rump, frequently noted in the literature, have been evident. While there is a slightly developed crest, there is no mane and the head profile is convex. The mountain tapir has commonly been known as *T. roulini*, but we here follow Hershkovitz (1954) in the use of *T. pinchaque* for this species.

The sole Old World representative of this family is the Malay or saddle-backed tapir (*T. indicus*), ranging from Sumatra northward through the Malay Peninsula to the borders of Burma and Thailand (Ellerman and Morrison-Scott, 1951). Strikingly different from the American forms in coloration, the Malay tapir is black or blackish brown in general but has a blanket of white or grayish white extending over the back from shoulders to hips. White ear fringes are usually present. Although apparently becoming reduced in most parts of its range, this handsome species is still sometimes imported and is represented in many European and American zoological gardens.

In the matter of size, Hershkovitz (1954) gives measurements that establish Baird's as the largest of the American species, with the Brazilian next and the mountain tapir the smallest. He considers, also, that the Malay is somewhat larger than Baird's. This arrangement is in accord with visual judgment, but actual weights are seldom recorded and even then vary greatly with age and condition. When supposedly aged 2½ years, "Panchita," a female mountain tapir kept here, weighed 223 pounds; a male Brazilian tapir that had lived here for 8 years weighed 375 pounds at death; we have no actual weights for Baird's, but a male Malay weighed 520 pounds after 10 years here and a female of the same species, at the presumed age of 5 years, weighed 690 pounds. Bode (1952) gives 750 pounds as the death-weight of an adult female in the San Diego Zoological Garden.

Tapirs of all sorts are usually considered as requiring heated quarters in winter and are ordinarily so treated in zoological gardens where really cold weather is experienced. However, Mann (1930:229) gives an account of a Brazilian tapir that lived out of doors with only an unheated shelter for several years in the National Zoological Park, indicating the desirability of further experimentation. Indoor quarters for tapirs here are in the Elephant House, each pen providing floor space about 10 feet square with a tank at the front. These tanks were once fronted with stout wire netting which later was replaced with $\frac{1}{2}$-inch plate glass, for better visibility. However, a male Brazilian tapir, much given to "tantrums," broke this glass as well as a replacement by flinging himself against it. As a final resort, shock-resistant laminated Herculite glass was installed, which proved able to repel the animal's charges.

The tapir stalls connect with large, grassy outdoor runs, used only in summer. They are inclosed by light steel-bar fences, 6 feet high, that will sometime be replaced by moats and walls. These need be no more than 5 feet high, if provided with overhangs, for tapirs are not leapers. However, they are skilled climbers and are also able to squeeze through spaces that appear much too small for their bulk, so that internal surfaces of barriers must be free from chinks or footholds.

The question of the need for pools for tapirs is debatable. Commonly provided, the animals use them freely, both for bathing and for defecation. However, they do perfectly well, at least for considerable periods, without pools, usually defecating when sprayed with water from a hose. The late Axel Reventlow, while director of the Copenhagen Zoological Gardens, always insisted that bathing is unnecessary for tapirs, and the animals in his care were maintained in excellent condition without such facilities. However, water plays such an important part in the natural lives of tapirs that pools certainly appear to be desirable if not actually essential.

Tapirs here are fed from 7 to 8 pounds of alfalfa hay and from 2 to 3 pounds of commercial meal mixture containing vitamin and mineral supplements, with bread, carrots, apples, and potatoes as available. In winter, greens in the form of lettuce and cabbage are provided, while in summer the animals graze freely on the ample grass of their inclosures. Tapirs seem especially subject to rectal prolapsus, which may be caused by ingestion of coarse or indigestible food. Robert Bean, director of the Chicago Zoological Park, tells me that for this reason all tapirs in his collection receive only finely chopped food, including alfalfa hay, fruits, and vegetables. Mr. Bean credits this practice for freedom from digestive troubles in his tapirs. We have felt here that first-grade alfalfa, free from heavy stalks and fed in the whole state, is quite safe for use, but certainly where this is not available Mr. Bean's procedure should be followed.

A young mountain tapir received here in 1953, weighing 72 pounds, was put on the following diet: morning: 2 cans of evaporated milk, diluted with an equal quantity of water, with 2 cups of Pablum, 1 pound of diced bananas, and 1 tablespoonful each of fine bone meal and cod-liver oil added; evening: 1 can of evaporated milk with water and 2 cups of Pablum. During the day she received diced carrots and sweet and white potatoes and had access to as much alfalfa hay as she cared to eat. As the animal grew, the milk was gradually reduced, so that her diet eventually became that of the normal adult.

Births of tapirs are usually of single young and apparently may occur at any season. The gestation period is roughly 13 months or 400 days. Baker (1920) suggests the latter as a fair average for the Brazilian, his records for eight of ten births in the National Zoological Park running from 392 to 405 days. Brown (1936) gives 13 months for the Malay tapir and Schneider (1936) reports 392 days for the same species. The young of all tapirs are handsomely marked with white or yellowish stripes and spots, which gradually give way to adult coloration. This change in young Malay tapirs born in the zoological gardens of Leipzig and Dresden has been described and figured by Schneider (1936) and Krumbiegel (1936). A youngster 145 days old with only faint markings remaining on the flanks, as shown by the latter author, is almost indistinguishable from an adult. The change in the young of American species is virtually complete at the age of 6 months, although, as pointed out by Hershkovitz (1954:468) some markings may persist past the first year or even longer.

The Brazilian tapir breeds well in captivity, and births, both in Europe and in this country, have been frequent. Records for the other species are fewer or altogether lacking, in direct relation to their abundance in captivity. Zuckerman (1953) has tabulated seven births of Brazilian tapirs up to 1937 in the Zoological Gardens of London, and in this country the successes of the National Zoological Park, the Detroit Zoological Park, and the Highland Park Zoological Gardens of Pittsburgh with this species are especially notable. In the Washington series, as reported by Baker (1920), seven of nine young born to a single pair between 1903 and 1918 were successfully reared. Scattered births of Malay tapirs have occurred in various European zoological gardens, and for this country there are the records of Brown (1936) for the Philadelphia Zoological Garden and of Mann (1945) for the National Zoological Park. Neither the mountain tapir nor Baird's appears to have been bred in captivity up to 1963. Carey Baldwin, director of the

Zoological Gardens of San Francisco, California, informs me (*in litt.*) that in both 1959 and 1960 single young were produced by a female Baird's when paired with a male Brazilian tapir. Both young were fully reared.

The best longevity for a Malay tapir given by Flower (1931) is 11 years, 2 months, 16 days in the Zoological Gardens of London. A female of this species lived in the New York Zoological Park from September 11, 1908, to February 20, 1932, or 23 years, 5 months, 9 days. This record is surpassed by that of an animal which, as I am informed (*in litt.*) by Pierre A. Fontaine, director of the Dallas (Texas) Zoo and Aquarium, lived in that institution from May, 1929, to October 4, 1958, at least 29 years, 4 months.

Brazilian tapirs have not done particularly well here, our best record being just over 11 years. For this species Flower (1931) records 24 years, 2 months, 5 days and 24 years, 3 months, 14 days in the zoological gardens of Frankfurt and Basel, respectively, and 30 years, 5 months, 3 days, again in Frankfurt. The unusually prolific female of the National Zoological Park lived for 20 years, 10 days (Hollister, 1922), while an even better record was established by a specimen that was received by the same institution on November 5, 1911, and died February 20, 1939, after 27 years, 3 months, 15 days (Theodore H. Reed, director, *in litt.*).

The few records that are available for Baird's tapir are fairly comparable to the preceding. A male received here on May 29, 1947, died on September 3, 1961, after 14 years, 3 months, 5 days, while a specimen received at the National Zoological Park in May, 1924, died in 1941, after approximately 17 years (Mann, 1943). I am informed by Robert Bean, director of the Chicago Zoological Park, that a female Baird's tapir received there in 1932 was still living in 1959, after approximately 27 years, certainly the best longevity so far recorded for this species in captivity.

Life-spans of the three specimens of the mountain tapir kept here were too short for useful comparison. The first of these, a female named "Panchita," received from Ecuador on November 26, 1950, through the efforts of Charles Cordier and Rolf Blomberg (Crandall, 1951), died of tuberculosis on October 8, 1952, after only 1 year, 10 months, 12 days. A young male, "Panchito," obtained for us by Charles Cordier, arrived here on June 12, 1952, and lived only to November of the same year, never having fully accepted any diet we could devise. An illustrated account of this animal, while still in the possession of the Cordiers in Quito, Ecuador, has been published by Naundorff (1953), the accompanying photographs showing the juvenile markings well. The third specimen, a female, was obtained from Rolf Blomberg and arrived from Quito on September 3,

1953. She died on December 20, 1955, after 2 years, 3 months, 17 days, our best record for the species but certainly not a promising one. The cause of death in this case, as in that of Panchita, was tuberculosis. The skins and skeletons of all these animals have been preserved in the American Museum of Natural History, where they make an important addition to the scanty existing study material.

FAMILY RHINOCEROTIDAE

RHINOCEROSES

The rhinoceroses, of course, are much the largest of the members of this order, being rivaled only by the hippopotamus as second to the elephants among the greatest of the living land animals of the world. Their heavy, thick-skinned bodies are usually hairless, except for ear fringes and tail-tips, only the small two-horned Asiatic species, *Didermocerus sumatrensis*, being lightly haired. Each foot has three toes carrying hoof-like nails, while the sole is tough and horny. Canine teeth are absent but a reduced number of incisors are present in the Asiatic species, two forming well-developed tusks in the lower jaw. Adult African rhinoceroses have no front teeth, so that the jaws are noticeably shortened. Characteristic are one or two horns borne on the median line of the forepart of the head; when two are present, the forward one is usually the longer. These horns are products of the skin, composed of closely compressed fibers often compared to hairs. There is no bony core, and while the horn is loosely attached to a roughened supporting area at its base, it is easily separated when the animal is skinned (Mochi and Carter, 1953). The horn grows continuously and may be replaced if lost. Jacobi (1957) gives an illustrated account of an instance in which a horn torn almost completely loose at its base and later removed entirely, was regrown to nearly its former length within 2 years, in the Zoological Gardens of Amsterdam (Artis). Belief in the value of rhinoceros horn in various medical capacities, especially as an aphrodisiac, widespread in Oriental countries, has been largely responsible over the years for the continuous slaughter that has reduced most of the forms almost to extinction.

All the rhinoceroses are entirely vegetarian, some feeding largely on grass, others relying chiefly on leafy vegetation. There is variation, too, in preferred habitat, some species living on open or broken plains, while others frequent marshy areas or tall growths of reeds and grass. All swim well and bathe freely as well as rolling in mud or dust.

Actually the relicts of a once numerous and widely distributed group, the rhinoceroses of the present day are found only in southern Asia and in Africa. Five species, in three genera, are usually recognized. A key to the species is given by Pocock (1944–45). For the use here of *Diceros* for *Ceratotherium* for the white rhinoceros, see Ellerman, Morrison-Scott, and Hayman, 1953:163.

In all three species of rhinoceroses found in Asia, the thick skin is arranged in folds with thinner and more pliable areas lying between them, giving an armor-plated effect. This armature depends on its thickness for its defensive value and is far from being bullet-proof, as was once believed.

Largest and best known of this group is the Indian rhinoceros (*Rhinoceros unicornis*). Once apparently widely distributed from Kashmir to Indochina, the remnants of this fine species are now found chiefly in government reserves in Assam and Bengal, with a further number living under protection in the Kingdom of Nepal. Gee (1958) estimates a total of 400 animals in India and perhaps 35 in Nepal, while Stracey (1957) quotes the official figure for the latter area as 500–600. In a report of a more recent personal investigation of the situation in Nepal, Gee (1959) raises to 300 his previous estimate of the rhinoceroses present in that country.

The plates of the skin reach their greatest development in the Indian rhinoceros, and small rounded excrescences, often compared to rivet heads, add to the impression of impenetrability. Both sexes carry a single horn; Rowland Ward (1928) gives a length of 24 inches, measured on the front curve, for a record specimen in the British Museum. Blanford (1888–91) gives the shoulder height as from 5 feet to 5 feet, 9 inches, and the estimated weight is frequently quoted as about 4,000 pounds. An adult female recently living here measured 4 feet, 10 inches at the shoulder. A male which had lived here for 11 years had a standing shoulder height of 5 feet, 2 inches a month before his death, when his weight was found to be 2,620 pounds. In the *Annual Report* of the Zoological Gardens of Basel for 1959 (1960) the weight of the breeding male living in the collection is given as 2,070 kilograms (approximately 4,554 pounds) and that of the female as 1,680 kilograms (approximately 3,696 pounds).

The Javan or lesser one-horned rhinoceros (*R. sondaicus*), once found from Burma, Thailand, and Indochina south to Sumatra and Java, appears now to be represented only by from thirty to forty animals living in the Udjung Kulon reservation in western Java (Boyle, 1959). There are occasional reports of supposed representatives of the species from other parts of its former range (Anon., 1958), and it seems possible that some may survive in remote areas. Lighter in build than the Indian rhinoceros, the Javan appears to be practically as tall, for Blanford (1888–91) gives the height of a female as 5 feet, 6 inches. The surface of the skin shows a mosaic pattern and does not have the rounded "rivets" seen in the larger species. The male carries a rather short single horn, the greatest length given by Ward (1928) being $10\frac{3}{4}$ inches; the female is usually hornless.

Smallest of the rhinoceroses is the two-horned *Didermocerus sumatrensis*, of which two subspecies are known: the Sumatran rhinoceros, *D. s. sumatrensis*, from Sumatra and Borneo, and the hairy-eared, *D. s. lasiotis*, found in Burma, Thailand, and the Malay States. Both are thinly clothed in short, stiff hair, somewhat longer in the hairy-eared, which is further distinguished by its greater size and the development of the ear fringes. A colored plate of the type of *lasiotis* is given by Sclater (1872*a*), and one of *sumatrensis*, with drawings of the heads of both races, appeared subsequently (Sclater, 1872*b*). In both the young are rather heavily coated with hair which becomes much reduced as the animals mature. Photographs of a calf captured in Sumatra at the presumed age of 1 month are given by Ullrich (1955), and others of older examples are included by Antonius (1937*b*) in an extended coverage of the rhinoceroses. The latter reference quotes measurements made by Bartlett of animals living in the Zoological Gardens of London showing the shoulder height of an adult female *sumatrensis* as 3 feet, 8 inches and that of a female, the type of *lasiotis*, as 4 feet, 4 inches. Anderson (1872), in an account of the latter animal, seen in Calcutta before shipment, estimates her weight as "nearly 2,000 pounds." Both front and rear horns appear to be short, particularly in females. However, Ward (1928) records a horn measuring $32\frac{1}{8}$ inches on the curve, in the British Museum, attributed to this species. While both races of the Asiatic two-horned rhinoceros still exist in scattered parts of their range and seem less in danger of complete extermination than the lesser one-horned, they nevertheless are in need of more stringent protection (see Harper, 1945; Talbot, 1960).

In the rhinoceroses of Africa, of which there are two species, the skin is comparatively smooth and unplated, although a deep fold between thighs and ribs and a transverse one at the elbows undoubtedly aid in the free movement of the limbs. There are two horns in each sex, often reaching great lengths. In adults, as already noted, there are no front teeth and, of course, no tusks such as those found in the Asiatic species.

Best known and most abundant of the African forms is the black rhinoceros (*Diceros bicornis*). Once common enough in East Africa, from

Ethiopia to the Cape and extending westward, avoiding the Sahara and the great rain forests, to the Cameroons and Angola, the black rhinoceros has been eliminated from much of its former range and is now found in greatest numbers in Kenya and Tanganyika. A race, *Diceros b. somaliensis*, said to be slightly smaller than the typical one, has been described. The black rhinoceros is not actually black but dark brownish gray, although the true color is usually obscured by such mud and dust as may overlie it. The upper lip is extended in a point which has some prehensile ability. The front horn, usually the longer, may reach a considerable length, the record given by Ward (1928) being 53½ inches for a female taken in Kenya. Shoulder heights given by Shortridge (1934) run from 4 feet, 9 inches to 6 feet and weight "about 2 tons." For a series of sixteen animals shot, weighed, and measured by Meinertzhagen (1938), shoulder heights ran from 58½ inches to 65 inches and weights from 2,199 to 2,896 pounds. A male that had lived here for nearly 13 years weighed 2,200 pounds at death, and a male now living here at the presumed age of 7 years has a standing height of 4 feet, 9 inches.

The black rhinoceros feeds largely on browse, including both leaves and small branches, and on leafy plants. It seems to prefer brush-covered hilly country, although it may at times be found on open plains. While the senses of smell and hearing are certainly sufficiently keen, eyesight is reputed to be weak, which may account for the unpredictable charges attributed to this animal. Such rushes may be made at surprising speeds: Meinertzhagen (1955) reports 32–35 miles per hour at the gallop and 27.2 at the trot.

The white rhinoceros (*Diceros simus*) occurs in two races, geographically widely separated. The southern form (*D. s. simus*), once rather widely but spottily distributed in South Africa, is now confined to reserves in Zululand, Natal, where "not more than 300" were living in 1958 (Knobel, 1958). The northern subspecies (*D. s. cottoni*) still exists in some numbers in a restricted area including northwestern Uganda, southern Sudan, and northeastern Belgian Congo (Dorst, 1958). An excellent account of the white rhinoceros in Uganda is given by Heppes (1958).

While not really white, of course, the white rhinoceros is a lighter and clearer gray in color than the black, at least when the skin is free from discoloration. The long head, terminating in a broad, shovel-like muzzle, and a great hump on the nape are characteristic. The latter has been found by Cave and Allbrook (1959) to be formed simply by a specialized thickening of the dermis. This is a considerably larger animal than its congener, its dimensions, in fact, exceeding those of any other rhinoceros. Its shoulder height as quoted by Shortridge (1934), presumably based on measurements of dead animals, runs from 6 feet, 6 inches, to 6 feet, 9 inches and weight from 3 to 4 tons. The longest horns listed by Ward (1928) are $62\frac{1}{4}$ inches for the southern race and $45\frac{3}{4}$ inches for the northern. The white rhinoceros subsists chiefly by grazing, a purpose for which the wide lips are well adapted, and is usually found in open, grassy areas. It is more social than the black, small groups sometimes forming, and it seems less given to the violent charges that characterize its relative (Shortridge, 1934).

Along with other large or savage beasts known to the ancient world, rhinoceroses were not infrequently kept in menageries or shown in the arenas popular in early days. Many accounts of such captives have been gathered by Loisel (1912), and while it is seldom possible to distinguish the species involved, it is evident that both Asiatic and African animals were included. Occasional records continued through the Middle Ages and the Renaissance. Beddard (1905:58) quotes an account of a rhinoceros or "unicorn," presumably an Indian, that East Indian merchants brought to England in 1684 and thought to be the first seen in that country. An Indian rhinoceros was received by the Zoological Society of London on May 24, 1834 (Flower, 1929), and a black that arrived on September 11, 1868 (Flower, *loc. cit.*), is said by Peel (1903) to be the first seen alive in Europe since the days of the Romans. Flower (*loc. cit.*) also gives February 14, 1872, as the date of arrival at the London Gardens of a hairy-eared rhinoceros which became the type of *lasiotis*; August 2, 1872, for a Sumatran; and March 17, 1874, for a Javan.

At the present time rhinoceroses of one sort or another are kept by most of the world's larger zoological gardens. By far the greater number, of course, are blacks, since more specimens of this species than of any other still exist in nature. However, the Indian was fairly well represented in this country in 1963 by pairs at the zoological gardens of Chicago, Philadelphia, and Milwaukee and a single male at Washington. In Europe there are the breeding pairs at Whipsnade and Basel, as well as scattered individuals elsewhere. As far as known, there is no specimen of the Javan rhinoceros presently in captivity, but a single female of the Sumatran, unique in modern collections, was received at the Basel Zoological Gardens in July, 1959 (Anon., 1959a). Unfortunately, this animal failed to survive. A second female, received at the Zoological Gardens of Copenhagen in November, 1959, was still living in 1963. An account of this arrival, with a figure, is given in the *Annual Report* of the Zoological Gardens of Copenhagen for 1959 (1960). The first record of a white rhinoceros in captivity appears to be that of a female calf of the southern race received at the National Zoological Gardens of South Africa, Pretoria, on July 29, 1946, and safely reared on whole cow's milk and corn (maize) porridge (R. Bigalke, 1947; Bigalke, Steyn, de Vos, and de Waard, 1950–51). On January 16, 1949, a bull thought to be 1 year old was received at Pretoria and was followed on August 23, 1952, by a cow, also considered to be a yearling. These three animals came from the Umfolosi Game Preserve in Natal, where they had been orphaned or abandoned (R. Bigalke, 1957). All were in good condition at the time of the cited report. The white rhinoceros was not represented in collections outside Africa until April 7, 1950, when a young pair of the northern race, captured in the Sudan, arrived at the Zoological Gardens of Antwerp. Complete and well-illustrated accounts of these animals have been given by Van den bergh (1952, 1955) and Micha (1958). In 1955 a pair of the same race was received by the Zoological Gardens of London, followed, in quick succession, by young pairs at the National Zoological Park in 1956 and at the St. Louis Zoological Park in 1957. In August and September, 1962, eleven white rhinoceroses of the southern race were brought to the United States from the Umfolosi Game Preserve in Zululand, Natal, through the co-operation of the Natal Parks, Game and Fish Preservation Board. All arrived in good condition and were distributed among the zoological parks of Chicago, Milwaukee, New York, and San Diego, and also the Catskill Game Farm. Several pairs from the same area were also received by various European gardens.

Accommodations for rhinoceroses here are provided, traditionally, in the Elephant House, where required winter heat is available. There are only two stalls, already described in general (p. 461). Each is fronted with $2\frac{1}{2}$-inch steel bars, on 20-inch centers, making an intervening space of $17\frac{1}{2}$ inches. A concrete basin at one side is used for grain while a similar installation at the other provides running water. Walls and floors are as described for elephants (p. 462). As originally constructed, arrangements were far from convenient and also lacked provision for safety, since no shifting areas were provided and doors were manually operated. As a first step toward the improvement of this condition, a concrete wall 38 inches high was built from front to back across a stall occupied by a particularly obstreperous black rhinoceros bull. Spaces 5 feet wide were left at front and back, so that the animal could circulate freely. A heavy chain was so arranged that it could be drawn across the forward gap, hanging loosely about 12 inches above the floor. For 10 winters the rhinoceros struggled daily with this apparently slight obstruction, never succeeding in crossing it, so that servicing could be carried out on one side after the other in complete safety. Nowadays hydraulically operated doors under remote control and a former storeroom doing duty as a shifting cage insure complete safety of operation.

The outer yards are floored with hard-packed earth and gravel and are surrounded by concrete walls, which originally rose 40 inches above the bottom of a shallow "ha-ha" moat. While it seems unlikely that a rhinoceros could surmount such a barrier, a black bull did actually place his front feet upon its top in order to reach the leaves of an overhanging shrub. As a precaution, the wall was raised 14 inches to a total of 54 inches, which certainly is adequate. One of the yards, lately occupied by an aged Indian female, has a pool about 10 by 12 feet with a sloping approach on one side. It is in almost constant use during the summer months. There are no pools indoors, but liberal use of the hose during the winter keeps the animals' skin in good condition.

More recent indoor exhibition areas for rhinoceroses have made use of the moat instead of bars for restraint. This can be done with little loss of space, the fully successful moats in the newly completed building in the Cleveland Zoological Park being only 5 feet, 10 inches across and 3 feet, 4 inches high at the front, with a gentle slope, heavily crosshatched, downward from the cage floor.

In any indoor construction for rhinoceroses a shifting cage should always be provided, and all doors should operate by remote control. No keeper, of course, should ever enter an inclosure occupied by an adult animal of any species or of either sex. That any black rhinoceros, however quiet it may appear to be, is likely to charge at any time is well understood. In this species the horns are the usual offensive weapons, but while the Indian may use its horn on occasion, it has a real predilection for biting. I once saw a supposedly gentle female of this species savage a steel cage-bar with her teeth after just missing the rapidly departing rear of a too-trusting keeper. The use of horns by both black and white rhinoceroses and of teeth as the principal weapons by the Asiatic species is discussed by Pitman (1956), while instances of the latter are given by Glover (1956) and Talbot (1957).

Since the horns of rhinoceroses are constantly growing, it follows that the animals must abrade them to keep them in order. This is accomplished by rubbing against solid objects and probably to a lesser extent by digging in the earth. In consequence, it is important to avoid sharp-edged members in bar construction or other projections within the animals' reach, for serious damage to horns may result from too frequent contact with cutting surfaces, a point which has been discussed by Hediger (1950:103). We had thought that a tree stump set in the yard used by our black rhinoceros might serve as a gentle abrasive, but a succession of animals have ignored it.

The use of chosen spots for defecation by rhinoceroses in nature as well as scraping of the deposits with the hind feet are mentioned by Shortridge (1934:418). The scraping action, commonly seen in captive animals, is treated in some detail by Bigalke, Steyn, de Vos, and de Waard (1950–51), as observed in a young white rhinoceros in the Pretoria Zoological Gardens; its function is obscure. Deposition of feces in special places is a common habit of rhinoceroses in captivity and, as pointed out by Hediger (1950:137), is advantageous in the maintenance of sanitation. An Indian recently in our collection made use of two such depositories, an African of only one. Male rhinoceroses normally eject urine toward the rear, often with such force that it may carry several feet. There seems to be some selectivity in the locale for such action, perhaps for marking purposes, and here we have had to erect a high glass barrier in front of one of the stalls to protect the public from unwelcome showers.

An adult female Indian rhinoceros recently living here received a daily allowance of about 60 pounds of hay, usually alfalfa, with clover or fine timothy sometimes substituted, and 10 pounds of commercial feeding pellets containing mineral and vitamin supplements. In addition she was given during the day raw white potatoes, carrots, cabbage, or other greens and two or three loaves of bread. A male black rhinoceros is supplied with the same items but in somewhat smaller quantity. Captive rhinoceroses seem as much subject to rectal prolapse as do tapirs, and as a possible preventive we are careful to provide only fine hay, of whichever sort, free from coarse or heavy stalks. Salt blocks are sometimes supplied to rhinoceroses, but we feel that the feeding pellets used contain an amount sufficient for the animals' needs. Fresh water is always available in the basins provided for that purpose.

Until comparatively recently, births of rhinoceroses in captivity were rare indeed. For one thing, the animals were so costly that few zoological gardens, in older days, were able to own pairs. For another, even when male and female of the same species were maintained simultaneously, the violent battles that took place were so alarming that the combatants were promptly separated to save them from serious injury. It appears that the numerous births that have occurred in recent years have been due largely to the determination of those in charge to allow the animals to fight it out, sometimes with horns carefully blunted. Accounts of such brawls, often less serious than they appear to be, have been given by Ulmer (1958) and Jacobi (1959). The frequent happy results attest success in many cases, but often the continuing antagonism of the animals involved has brought the experiment to an end, so that many potential breeding pairs remain irreconcilable.

The first recorded birth of a captivity-bred rhinoceros appears to be that of a racial intergrade between a male Sumatran and a female hairy-eared, born in the Zoological Gardens of Calcutta on January 30, 1889 (Sányál, 1892). This calf was fully reared by the mother and had reached the age of 2 years, 7 months at the time of Sányál's writing. It is presumable that Sányál's reference to a previous birth is to a calf born in 1872 to a wild-caught Sumatran rhinoceros on arrival in London (Bartlett, 1873), an incident which led to Bartlett's frequently quoted but questionable estimate of 7 months as the gestation period.

On October 9, 1925, an Indian rhinoceros was born, also in the Zoological Gardens of Calcutta (Ali, 1927). This birth was thought to have been somewhat premature, and the calf lived for only a few hours. Its weight is given as 74 pounds and the gestation period estimated as about 19 months.

No further births of captive rhinoceroses were recorded until October 7, 1941, when a black rhinoceros calf was born at the Chicago Zoological Park (Edward H. Bean, 1941), followed by a second, to the same parents, on September 19, 1944 (Robert Bean, in litt.). Both young animals were successfully reared. Another hiatus of nearly 10 years was ended on February 14, 1954, with the birth of a black rhinoceros calf in the Zoological Gardens of Rio de Janeiro (Ulmer, 1958), a second birth occurring in 1956. In that year and the two following breeding successes were numerous. Saporiti (1957) reports the birth of a black rhinoceros in the Zoological Gardens of Buenos Aires in April, 1956. This calf lived for only a few days, but a second, born on January 2, 1958, is figured at the age of 20 days. apparently in excellent condition. The first birth of a black rhinoceros in Europe occurred at the Zoological Gardens of Frankfurt on December 24, 1956 (*Internatl. Zoo News*, **4** (3):74), followed by another on December 10, 1958 (*Internatl. Zoo News*, **6** (1):24), and one at Bristol, England, in the same year (Ulmer, 1958). The list continues, in America, with births in three zoological gardens: Pittsburgh, October 27, 1960, Cincinnati, July 27, 1961, and Detroit, April 19, 1962; in Europe, Rotterdam, August 29, 1960, and a second at Bristol, December 28, 1961. When visiting here in May, 1962, Sir Edward Hallstrom reported a total of three births in the large herd maintained at Taronga Park, Sydney, the first in August, 1958. These mounting successes indicate that the black rhinoceros, at least, is definitely established as a breeding species in the zoological garden.

Following the premature birth in the Calcutta Zoological Gardens in

1925, no further breeding successes with the Indian rhinoceros occurred until 1956, when on September 14 a male calf was born in the Zoological Gardens of Basel (Lang, 1957). This was the first rhinoceros to be bred in Europe and naturally caused a great sensation. During the night of October 29–30, 1957, a female Indian calf was born at Whipsnade and was quietly nursing when discovered by the keeper in the morning (Tong, 1958). On August 17, 1958, a second calf, this time a female, was born to the Indian pair at Basel (Geigy, 1959:12) and the Whipsnade pair produced another female calf in August, 1960. All these Indian calves were fully reared by their mothers. The 1956 male at Basel and the 1957 female at Whipsnade were transferred to the Milwaukee Zoological Park in 1959, making the first pair of captivity-bred rhinoceroses in zoological-garden history.*

No white rhinoceros calf has yet (1963) been born in captivity, but since both races of this species are now represented by mature or maturing pairs, there is an excellent possibility that breeding may occur.*

In general, female rhinoceroses have proved to be excellent mothers in captivity, and most of the calves born have been reared. The greatest obstacle to successful breeding continues to be the difficulty in persuading potential parents to tolerate each other long enough for the purposes of procreation.

Rhinoceroses appear to have no well-defined breeding seasons. Single young per birth are the rule (Asdell, 1946). From reports of breeding in captivity, the gestation period for the black rhinoceros seems to be between 15 and 16 months (Ulmer, 1958). For the Indian, 474 and 477 days were recorded at Basel and 488 days at Whipsnade, the average of approximately 16 months being in the area of that established for the black.

Recorded weights of newborn captive black rhinoceroses, either actual or estimated, average 63.2 pounds (Ulmer, 1958). An accurate birth weight of the male Indian calf born at Basel in 1956 is given by Lang (1957) as 60.5 kilograms or approximately 133 pounds. At the age of 2 years, 9 months its weight was 1,300 kilograms or 2,860 pounds (Anon., 1959b).

As pointed out by Flower (1931), the average longevity of captive rhinoceroses is comparatively short, although the greater spans achieved by some individuals indicate that the potential maximum is much greater than the age usually reached. This supposition is well supported by Flower's (loc. cit.) figures for the Indian rhinoceros: about 40 years in the Antwerp Zoological Gardens and 40 years, 4 months, 11 days in the Zoological Gardens of London and the less definite span of about 47 years in

*See Addenda, p. 736.

the Zoological Gardens of Calcutta given by Sányál (1892). A female of this species received here on May 24, 1923, died on January 25, 1962, after 38 years, 8 months, 1 day. Her weight at death was 3,065 pounds.

Longevities recorded for other species are less favorable. Flower (1931) gives 10 years, 10 months, 16 days for a Javan rhinoceros in the Zoological Gardens of London, while Sányál (1892) says a female of this species received at the Zoological Gardens of Calcutta in 1887 and still living in 1892 had previously lived "for about 10 years" in the menagerie of the king of Oudh, making a total of over 14 years. The hairy-eared that was the type of *lasiotis* lived in the Zoological Gardens of London for 28 years, 6 months, 16 days; since she had been captured just over 4 years before her arrival in London, her actual captivity span was about 32 years, 7 months (Flower, *loc. cit.*).

Flower's best record for a black rhinoceros is 22 years, 7 months, 1 day for a female in the Zoological Gardens of London. A male received here on May 25, 1906, lived until November 5, 1931, or 25 years, 5 months, 11 days, and Jones (1958) reports that a specimen received at the National Zoological Gardens of South Africa at Pretoria on December 31, 1914, died on November 15, 1942, after 27 years, 10 months, 15 days. The breeding pair of black rhinoceroses at the Chicago Zoological Park, received on May 19, 1935, were still living there in 1963.*

As already noted, the first white rhinoceros known to have been kept in captivity, a female of the southern race, was received at the National Zoological Gardens of South Africa at Pretoria on July 29, 1946, and was still living there in 1963. Its present span must be taken as the greatest longevity so far established for this species.

· REFERENCES

ALI, SALIM A.
   1927. The breeding of the Indian rhinoceros (*Rhinoceros unicornis*) in captivity. Jour. Bombay Nat. Hist. Soc., **31** (4):1031.
ANDERSON, JOHN.
   1872. Notes on *Rhinoceros sumatrensis*, Cuvier. Proc. Zool. Soc. London, pp. 129–32.
ANON.
   1958. Misc. Notes. 4. Rediscovery of the smaller onehorned rhinoceros (*Rhinoceros sondaicus* Demarest) in Malaya. Jour. Bombay Nat. Hist. Soc., **55** (3):554–6.
   1959a. Note. Zolli—Bull. 137. Zoologischer Garten, Basel.
   1959b. Note. *Ibid.* 130.

*See Addenda, p. 736.

ANTONIUS, OTTO.
 1937a. On the geographical distribution, in former times and today, of the recent Equidae. Proc. Zool. Soc. London, 107, Ser. B:557–64.
 1937b. Bilder aus dem Früheren und jetzigen Schönbrunner Tierbestand. 1. Nashörner. Zool. Garten, Leipzig (N.F.), 9 (1/2):18–26.
 1951. Die Tigerpferde. Monographien der Wildsäugetiere, 11. Paul Schops, Frankfurt. 148 pp.

ASDELL, S. A.
 1946. Patterns of mammalian reproduction. Comstock Publishing Co., Ithaca, N.Y. 437 pp.

BAKER, A. B.
 1920. Breeding of the Brazilian tapir. Jour. Mammal., 1 (3):143–44.

BANNIKOV, A. G.
 1958. Distribution géographique et biologie du cheval sauvage et chameau de Mongolie (Equus przewalskii et Camelus bactrianus). Mammalia, 22 (1):152–60.

BARTLETT, A. D.
 1873. On the birth of a Sumatran rhinoceros. Proc. Zool. Soc. London, pp. 104–6.

BEAN, EDWARD H.
 1941. Baby rhinoceros at Chicago Zoological Park. Parks and Recreation, 25 (3):119–20.

BEDDARD, FRANK E.
 1905. Natural history in zoological gardens. Archibald Constable & Co., Ltd., London. 310 pp.

BIGALKE, R.
 1947. Pretoria Zoo has a baby white rhinoceros. Animal Kingdom, 50 (2):48–55.
 1957. Notes on the square-lipped rhinoceros in the National Zoological Gardens of Pretoria. Mimeographed minutes of meeting of International Union of Directors of Zoological Gardens, Rotterdam, 1957.

BIGALKE, R., T. STEYN, D. DE VOS, and K. DE WAARD.
 1950–51. Observations on a juvenile female square-lipped or white rhinoceros (Ceratotherium simum simum [Burch.]) in the National Zoological Gardens of South Africa. Proc. Zool. Soc. London, 120:519–28.

BIGALKE, R. C.
 1958. On the present status of ungulate mammals in South West Africa. Mammalia, 22 (3):478–97.

BLANFORD, W. T.
 1888–91. Fauna of British India. Mammalia. Taylor and Francis, London. 617 pp.

BODE, NANCY C.
 1952. The antique tapir. Zoonooz, 25 (12):2–3.

BOURDELLE, E., and A. MOUQUET.
 1930. La longévité des mammifères à la ménagerie du Muséum National

d'Histoire Naturelle. Bull. Mus. Hist. Nat., Paris. 2d ser., **2** (5): 488–97.

BOYLE, C. L.
1959.   The Survival Service Commission. Oryx, **5** (1):30–35.

BROWN, C. EMERSON.
1936.   Rearing wild animals in captivity, and gestation periods. Jour. Mammal., **17** (1):10–13.

CABRERA, ANGEL.
1936.   Subspecific and individual variation in the Burchell zebras. Jour. Mammal., **17** (2):89–112.

CAVE, A. J. E., and M. B. ALLBROOK.
1959.   The skin and nuchal eminence of the white rhinoceros. Proc. Zool. Soc. London, **132** (1):99–107.

CRANDALL, LEE S.
1951.   The mountain tapir in the Bronx Zoo. Animal Kingdom, **54** (1):2–8.
1954.   A good longevity record for a Chapman's zebra. *Ibid.*, **57** (3):94.

D[ITMARS], R. L.
1913.   The new zebra house. Bull. New York Zool. Soc., **16** (55):958.

DORST, J.
1958.   Enquête sur le statut des ongules dans l'Afrique au sud du Sahara. Introduction. Mammalia, **22** (3):357–70.

ELLERMAN, J. R., and T. C. S. MORRISON-SCOTT.
1951.   Checklist of Palaearctic and Indian mammals, 1758 to 1946. British Museum (Natural History), London. 810 pp.

ELLERMAN, J. R., T. C. S. MORRISON-SCOTT, and R. W. HAYMAN.
1953.   Southern African mammals. British Museum (Natural History), London. 363 pp.

FLOWER, S. S.
1929.   List of the vertebrated animals exhibited in the gardens of the Zoological Society of London, 1828–1927. 1. Mammals. Zoological Society of London. 419 pp.
1931.   Contributions to our knowledge of the duration of life in vertebrate animals. 5. Mammals. Proc. Zool. Soc. London, pp. 145–234.

GEE, E. P.
1958.   Four rare Indian animals. Oryx, **4** (6):353–58.
1959.   Report on a survey of the rhinoceros area of Nepal. *Ibid.*, **5** (2):57–85.

GEIGY, R.
1959.   Note. 86 Jahresbericht 1958. Zoologischer Garten, Basel. 42 pp.

GLOVER, RICHARD.
1956.   Weapons of the great Indian rhinoceros. Oryx, **3** (4):197.

GRAY, ANNIE P.
1954.   Mammalian hybrids. Commonwealth Agricultural Bureaux, Farnham Royal, Slough, Bucks, England. 144 pp.

HAGENBECK, CARL.
   1910. Beasts and men. Translated into English by H. S. R. ELLIOT and
         A. G. THACKER. Longmans, Green & Co., London. 299 pp.
HARPER, FRANCIS.
   1940. The nomenclature and type localities of certain Old World mammals.
         Jour. Mammal., 21 (2):191–203; 21 (3):322–32.
   1945. Extinct and vanishing mammals of the Old World. Spec. pub. 12.
         American Committee for International Wildlife Protection, New
         York. 849 pp.
HEDIGER, H.
   1950. Wild animals in captivity. Butterworths Scientific Publications,
         London. 207 pp.
   1955. Studies of the psychology and behaviour of captive animals in zoos
         and circuses. Butterworths Scientific Publications, London. 166 pp.
HEPPES, J. B.
   1958. The white rhinoceros in Uganda. African Wild Life, 12 (4):273–80.
HERSHKOVITZ, PHILIP.
   1954. Mammals of northern Colombia, preliminary report No. 7: Tapirs
         (Genus *Tapirus*), with a systematic review of American species.
         Proc. U.S. Nat. Mus., 103 (3329):465–96.
HILL, W. C. OSMAN.
   1957. Report of the Society's prosector for the years 1955 and 1956. Proc.
         Zool. Soc. London, 129:431–46.
HOLLISTER, N.
   1922. Report of the superintendent of the National Zoological Park for the
         fiscal year ending June 30, 1922. Ann. Rept., Smithsonian Inst. for
         1922, pp. 88–103.
H[ORNADAY], W. T.
   1911. An experiment in acclimatization. Bull. New York Zool. Soc.,
         No. 47, p. 802.
JACOBI, E. F.
   1957. Recuperative power of the horn of the black rhinoceros (*Rhinoceros
         bicornis* L.). Zool. Garten, Leipzig (N.F.), 23 (1/3): 223–27.
   1959. Neushoorn-kennismaking. Artis, 4 (6):184–91.
JONES, MARVIN L.
   1958. Mammals in captivity. Mimeographed MSS (unpublished).
KENNETH, J. H.
   1953. Gestation periods. Commonwealth Agricultural Bureaux, Farnham
         Royal, Slough, Bucks, England. 39 pp.
KNOBEL, R.
   1958. Present day status of certain ungulates in the Union of South Africa.
         Mammalia, 22 (3):498–503.
KRUMBIEGEL, INGO.
   1936. Beitrage zur Jugendentwicklung des Schabrackentapirs (*Rhinochoerus
         indicus* [Cuv.]) Zool. Garten, Leipzig (N.F.), 8 (4/6):96–99.

LANG, E. M.
   1957. Geburt eines Panzerhorns. 84. Jahresbericht, 1956. Zoologischer
           Garten, Basel. 39 pp.
LOISEL, GUSTAVE.
   1912. Histoire des ménageries de l'antiquité à nos jours. Octave Doin et fils,
           Henri Laurens, Paris. 3 vols.
LYDEKKER, RICHARD.
   1893–96. The royal natural history. Frederick Warne & Co., New York and
           London. 6 vols.
MANN, WM. M.
   1930. Wild animals in and out of the zoo. Smithsonian Sci. Ser., 6.
           362 pp.
   1943. Report on the National Zoological Park for the year ended June 30,
           1942. Smithsonian Inst. Report for 1942, pp. 77–85.
   1945. Report on the National Zoological Park for the year ended June 30,
           1944. Smithsonian Inst. Report for 1944, pp. 67–93.
MEINERTZHAGEN, R.
   1938. Some weights and measurements of large mammals. Proc. Zool. Soc.
           London, 108, Ser. A:433–39.
   1955. The speed and altitude of bird flight (with notes on other animals).
           Ibis, 97 (1):81–117.
MICHA, M.
   1958. Le rhinoceros blanc (Ceratotherium simum cottoni [Lydekker]). Zoo,
           Anvers, 23 (4):111–15.
MOCHI, UGO, and T. DONALD CARTER.
   1953. Hoofed mammals of the world. Chas. Scribner's Sons, New York and
           London.
MOHR, ERNA.
   1959. Das urwildpferd. Die Neue Brehm-Bucherei. 249. A. Ziemsen,
           Wittenberg Lutherstadt. 144 pp.
NAUNDORFF, ELIZABETH.
   1953. Meine Begegnung mit einem Bergtapir (Tapirus pinchaque Roulin).
           Zool. Garten, Leipzig (N.F.), 20 (1):51–52.
PEEL, C. V. A.
   1903. The zoological gardens of Europe. F. E. Robinson & Co., London.
           256 pp.
PITMAN, CHARLES R. S.
   1956. Weapons of the two African rhinoceroses. Oryx, 3 (4):195–96.
POCOCK, R. I.
   1944–45. Some cranial and dental characters of the existing species of Asiatic
           rhinoceroses. Proc. Zool. Soc. London, 114:437–50.
RATCLIFFE, HERBERT L.
   1948–49. Report of the Penrose Research Laboratory, Zoological Society of
           Philadelphia, 1948 and 1949.

REED, THEODORE H.
1962. Report on the National Zoological Park for the year ended June 30, 1961. Smithsonian Inst. Report for 1961, pp. 133–77.

SALENSKY, W.
1907. Prjevalsky's horse. English translation by M. H. HAYES and O. C. BRADLEY. Introd. by J. C. EWART. Hurst and Blackett Ltd., London. 65 pp.

SÁNYÁL, RAM BRAMHA.
1892. A hand-book of the management of animals in captivity in Lower Bengal. Bengal Secretariat Press, Calcutta. 351 pp.

SAPORITI, ENRIQUE J.
1957. Nacimiento del Rhinoceronte en el Jardin Zoologico. Diana, **19** (216):10–11.

SCHNEIDER, KARL MAX.
1936. Zur Fortpflanzung, Aufzucht und Jugendentwicklung des Scha-brackentapirs. Zool. Garten, Leipzig (N.F.), **8** (4/6):83–96.

SCLATER, P. L.
1872a. Report on the additions to the Society's menagerie during the month of February, 1872. Proc. Zool. Soc. London, pp. 493–96.
1872b. Report on the additions to the Society's menagerie during the months of June, July, August and September, 1872. *Ibid.*, pp. 789–95.

SHORTRIDGE, G. C.
1934. The mammals of South West Africa. Wm. Heinemann Ltd., London. 2 vols. 779 pp.

STRACEY, P. D.
1957. On the status of the great Indian rhinoceros (*R. unicornis*) in Nepal. Jour. Bombay Nat. Hist. Soc., **54** (3):763–66.

TALBOT, LEE MERRIAM.
1957. Stalking the great Indian rhino. Natl. Geogr. Mag., **61** (3):388–98.
1960. A look at threatened species. Oryx, **5** (4/5):169–293.

TONG, E. H.
1958. Notes on the breeding of Indian rhinoceros, *Rhinoceros unicornis*, at Whipsnade Park. Proc. Zool. Soc. London, **130**:296–99.

ULLRICH, WOLFGANG.
1955. Bemerkenswerte Aufnahmen eines jungen Sumatra-Nashorns (*Dicero-rhinus sumatrensis* Cuv.). Zool. Garten, Leipzig (N.F.), **22** (1/3): 29–33.

ULMER, FREDERICK A., JR.
1958. On breeding rhinoceroses. America's First Zoo, **10** (3):3–6.

VAN DEN BERGH, W.
1952. Nos rhinoceros blancs. Zoo, Anvers, **18**:6–26.
1955. Nos rhinoceros blancs (*Ceratotherium simum cottoni* Lydekker). Zool. Garten, Leipzig (N.F.), **21** (3):129–51.

VOLF, JIŘÍ.
 1958. Pour le sauvetage des chevaux de Przewalski. Mammalia, **22** (4):
        598–600.
 1960, 1961. Pedigree book of the Przewalski horse. Zoological Gardens,
        Prague.
WARD, ROLAND.
 1928. Records of big game. Rowland Ward, Ltd., London. 523 pp.
ZUCKERMAN, S.
 1953. The breeding seasons of mammals in captivity. Proc. Zool. Soc.
        London, **122**:827–950.

ORDER ARTIODACTYLA

.

Pigs, Peccaries, Hippopotamuses, Camels, Deer, Giraffes, Wild Cattle, Antelopes, Goats, and Sheep

The even-toed hoofed mammals comprising this order usually have on each foot two functional toes, the third and fourth, each encased in a horny hoof and carrying the body weight equally between them. The second and fifth toes are often absent, or if present, are carried behind at a higher level, so that they ordinarily do not touch the ground. An exception, of course, is found in the hippopotamuses, in which all four toes are used in walking. Horns or antlers, supported by bony structures, are borne by some, the dentition is frequently reduced, and complex stomachs, which permit the function of rumination or cud-chewing, are characteristic of many species. With the exception of the hippopotamuses, which are amphibious, all the Artiodactyla are terrestrial and are almost entirely herbivorous, only the pigs and the peccaries being omnivorous. This vast assemblage of species seems to fall naturally into three suborders, as defined by Simpson (1945), and this arrangement is followed here.

SUBORDER SUIFORMES

Pigs, Peccaries, and Hippopotamuses

In this suborder, incisor teeth are present in both jaws, while canines are enlarged and elongated as tusks. There are no antlers or horns of any type, and while the stomach may be simple or complex, there is no rumination. Three families are included.

FAMILY SUIDAE

Pigs

In spite of wide variation in size, color, and tusk form, all pigs are readily known by the flat, rounded disk in which the flexible muzzle terminates.

This structure, in which the nostrils are located, is of great service in rooting for food and is duplicated only in the peccaries, which have other points of distinction. The upper canines turn upward as tusks and sometimes are kept in order by attrition with the lower pair. In some species the tusks may achieve great size and bizarre form, particularly in males. Hair covering is usually coarse and scanty or sometimes almost wanting. There are four toes on each foot, only the forward pair, the third and fourth, being functional. The stomach is simple. While vegetable material forms the bulk of the food, most pigs will eat such small animals or even carrion as they may come across. The family is confined to the Old World and is represented in Europe, Asia, and adjacent islands, Africa and Madagascar. An illustrated account of the group, both in nature and in captivity, is given by Mohr (1960).

Most important of the pigs, both historically and economically, is the Eurasian wild boar (*Sus scrofa*). The species is widely distributed in forested areas of continental Europe, northern Africa, and Asia, with southward extensions through the Malay Peninsula to Java, Sumatra, and numerous other islands, many races having been described. Domestic swine, carried from island to island in the East Indies by natives, have interbred with wild pigs, if these were present, to such extent that relationships are now often confused. Wild boar hunting has been a dangerous but popular sport from very early times, but more important is the derivation of our many breeds of domestic swine from this fierce but obviously pliant ancestor. Wild boars have been introduced in various places and in the southern United States appear to have become well established. Feral domestic swine, the descendants of purposely or accidentally liberated animals, have proved to be destructive to both wild life and crops (de Vos, Manville, and Van Gelder, 1956). A history of feral swine in the southeastern United States is given by Hanson and Karstad (1959).

The European wild boar (*Sus scrofa scrofa*) no longer exists in the British Isles, where it was once common. It is still found, however, in suitable localities, from France and Spain eastward to Russia. This is a large animal, males sometimes reaching a weight of 350 pounds (Goodwin, 1954). The grayish brown outer hair is long and coarse, while a thick woolly undercoat provides ample protection from cold. The tusks, particularly in males, are well developed and make formidable weapons. Many races have been described from other areas of the range of the species, perhaps the best known of which are the Indian wild boar (*Sus scrofa cristatus*) and the white-whiskered boar or pig (*Sus scrofa leucomystax*) of Japan. The former is somewhat smaller than the typical race, with lengthened bristles on neck and shoulders, while the Japanese animal is distinguished by a streak of white on the jaws.

All these pigs, as well as numerous relatives, have been kept by zoological gardens and may still be seen in many European collections. However, because of the rigors of importation restrictions and the high cost of transportation, wild pigs of any sort are present zoo rarities in this country.

The wild boars have been represented here only by several specimens of the European, two males from North Africa, presumably but not certainly *barbarus*, and a single white-whiskered. The latter was received in 1902 and was sent, two years later, to the National Zoological Park, so that its stay here was short. All were kept out of doors, in large runs floored with concrete or asphalt and stone, leaving a small area filled with earth or sand to provide a much used wallow. A small, open-fronted shed, well bedded with straw, provided year-round shelter sufficient for even the North African animals. All were fed any available greens, with potatoes, carrots, and apples, mixed with meal, bread, chopped horse meat, either cooked or raw, and some alfalfa hay. This regimen was by no means adhered to with regularity, of course, for little that is edible comes amiss to a wild boar, and the diet was varied accordingly.

The rooting ability of the wild boar was demonstrated in spectacular fashion by the two North Africans during their stay here. Starting from some small crevice in the hard flooring of their yard, these animals slowly but inexorably demolished the paving, three to four inches thick, reducing it and the crushed stone beneath it to rubble. The destruction was complete, but a strategically placed descriptive label converted a seeming catastrophe into an exhibit of great interest to our visitors.

Many of the forms of *Sus scrofa* have been bred in zoological gardens, principally in Europe. The wild boar has been bred in the San Diego Zoological Garden (Stott, 1954), but I have been unable to find any other zoo records for this country. Zuckerman (1953) lists nine births, also of the typical race, in the Zoological Gardens of London, running from one to four young per litter and occurring in most months of the year. The same author also reports five births of the Indian wild boar, varying from four to seven young per litter, as well as scattered births of other races. Kenneth (1953) quotes figures ranging from 101 to 130 days for the gestation period of *Sus scrofa*, an average of 115.5 days, as compared with 112–15 days for domestic pigs of various breeds, as given by Asdell (1946).

Young wild boars are marked with longitudinal stripes of light and dark gray. Domestic piglets obtained from large pig farms in the New York area for our Children's Zoo have occasionally been similarly striped, although recent introduction of the blood of the wild boar seems unlikely.

A male European wild boar received here on August 29, 1920, lived 14 years, 7 months, 7 days; a companion male that died after just over 12 years weighed 275 pounds at death. Mann (1930) records 15 years, 3 months for an animal presumably of the same race in the National Zoological Park. A female received in the Zoological Gardens of London on March 5, 1880, died on September 11, 1899, after 19 years, 6 months, 6 days (Flower, 1931), apparently the greatest longevity so far recorded for the species.

The bush pigs (*Potamochoerus*) of Africa are found in forested or scrub country over much of that continent, south of the Sahara. In these animals the body hair is long and the ears are tipped in varying degree with tapering tassels. A large protuberance is found, especially in males, on each side of the rather slender nose between nostril and eye, with a smaller one below the latter. Some of these animals may attain a considerable size, males reaching weights in excess of 200 pounds (Shortridge, 1934). A number of races have been described, ranging in color from rich reddish chestnut to gray or black. The red river hog (*Potamochoerus porcus porcus*), usually considered to be the most nearly handsome of the pigs, is a native of Guinea. Bright reddish in general, it is sharply marked with black and white, the ear tufts being particularly well developed. The South African bush pig (*Potamochoerus porcus koiropotamus*) may be taken as typical of the grayish races, although gray, brown, black, and white may appear in varying extent.

While the red river hog and several of the gray-to-black bush pigs have been kept here as well as in other American zoological gardens, it is doubtful that any of the races are now represented in this country, although they may be seen in various European institutions. In general, their care does not differ from that outlined for the wild boar, with the exception that for most heated quarters in winter are required.

Bush pigs of several races have been bred in zoological gardens, principally in Europe. The only birth in our collection here was that of a litter of two born on May 8, 1927, to parents of an East African race, *Potamochoerus porcus maschona*. Both piglets were fully reared. I know of no other American records for the species. Zuckerman (1953) lists six births of the red river hog in the Zoological Gardens of London between 1857 and 1902, young per litter ranging from one to four. Bush pigs are striped in brown and buff at birth.

Although the average longevity of bush pigs in captivity is probably rather low, some examples have achieved satisfactory spans. A red river hog lived here for an even 12 years, while Flower (1931) gives 14 years, 7 months, 29 days for an animal born in 1858 in the Zoological Gardens of London. Jones (1958) reports that an Abyssinian bush pig (*Potamochoerus porcus hassama*) lived in the Zoological Gardens of London for 13 years, 1 month, 15 days.

Because of its grotesque appearance, the wart hog (*Phacochoerus aethiopicus*) is among the most popular of zoo animals. Grayish in color, it is almost devoid of hair, save for a long, thin mane on neck and back and a tuft at the tip of the tail. Two pairs of protuberances or "warts" on the sides of the face give the animal its name. The upper canines curve up, out and then inward, in a great sweep, sometimes, in males, reaching a length of more than 2 feet. The lower tusks, seldom exceeding 6 inches, are sharpened by abrasion with a small section of the upper ones, making them formidable weapons. A female that had lived here for just over 15 years weighed 180 pounds, and a male, after 7 years, weighed 195 pounds, both at death. Eighteen adult males killed and weighed in the field in Kenya varied from 155 to 234 pounds; six females, from 123 to 149 pounds (Meinertzhagen, 1938).

Wart hogs are found in open or scrub country, from Ethiopia west to Senegal, thence to South Africa. Numerous subspecies, differing in size and skull characters, have been described. The typical race, from the Cape area, is now considered to be extinct.

Like other pigs, the wart hog feeds chiefly on roots, grass, and other vegetable material, as well as on carrion. In feeding it usually kneels on the forelegs, an action made simpler by thick pads on the wrists or "knees." It dens in holes in the earth, either digging them itself or taking over from aardvarks or other burrowing animals. A pair kept out of doors here in summer excavated a snug burrow for themselves in a bank near a pool. In entering, the animal usually goes backward in order to defend the entrance against possible intruders. If alarmed when afield, the wart hog makes for its burrow, usually moving at a smart trot, tail stiffly erect and flag waving.

The wart hog accommodates well to captivity and soon loses any tendency to timidity. Many individuals become gentle and a long series of males—or even odd females—kept here and traditionally known as "Clarence" have endeared themselves to keepers and public (Cully, 1940). They have been fed as suggested for wild boars, heated quarters being required in winter.

The wart hog has been bred in captivity perhaps more often than have most other wild pigs, although successes certainly have not been frequent. The male of the only potential breeding pair kept here invariably was seized with convulsions so alarming when he even approached the female that the animals had to be kept apart. At other American institutions, however, better results have been obtained, and the wart hog has been bred at least twice in both the National Zoological Park (Mann, 1930) and the Philadelphia Zoological Garden (Brown, 1936), as well as in the San Diego Zoological Garden (Stott, 1954). Reproduction has occurred in various zoological gardens in continental Europe, while the birth of two young at Whipsnade in 1957 appears to have been the first in England (Tong, 1957a). Brown (1936) gives the gestation periods for two Philadelphia births as 171 and 175 days. The piglets, lacking either stripes or spots, usually number from two to four.

Possibly because of its comparatively placid nature, the wart hog sometimes lives in captivity for extended periods. A female received here on November 15, 1940, lived until January 30, 1956, or 15 years, 2 months, 15 days, while Flower (1931) reports 16 years, 6 months for a female in the Zoological Gardens of Giza. Jones (1958) says that an animal of this species received at the Philadelphia Zoological Garden on July 17, 1875, died on June 5, 1892, after 16 years, 10 months, 19 days.

The giant forest hog (*Hylochoerus meinertzhageni*) is a tall, rangy animal, clothed in coarse, blackish-brown hair. The muzzle is noticeably broad and there is a large protuberance on each side of the face below the eye. The tusks bear some resemblance to those of the wart hog but do not reach the same degree of development. This pig is a giant indeed, for Meinertzhagen (1938) gives the weight of a single male collected in Kenya as 329 pounds, while Cotton (1936) reports a freshly killed female, minus blood as well as fat eaten raw by skinners, as having scaled 423 pounds; he estimates that her total weight approximated 450 pounds.

In several forms, the giant forest hog inhabits the great tropical forests of equatorial Africa, often at considerable altitudes, from Kenya to the Cameroons. First described in 1904, its habits still are imperfectly known. Mohr (1942) gives an illustrated résumé of available information.

The limited experience with this fine species in captivity has generally been unsatisfactory, the few animals so far received by zoological gardens having failed to become firmly established. A female that arrived here in 1939 and another from the same shipment, assigned to the National Zoological Park, each lived for only a few months. Ours at least received the diet followed for other wild pigs but never seemed to accept it freely. Results with this species in Europe have generally been of the same order.

However, a forest hog received at the Zoological Gardens of Frankfurt on May 14, 1954, lived until April 5, 1957, or 2 years, 10 months, 22 days, which is more encouraging (Jones, 1958).

The babirusa (*Babyrousa babyrussa*) is a slender, almost hairless pig, especially notable for the development of the tusks in the male. In this sex the canines of the upper jaw grow directly upward, piercing the skin between eyes and muzzle, close to the middle line. They then describe an almost perfect circle, so that the tips may eventually approach the skin before the eyes. The lower tusks take a similar but shorter course, the two pairs being so far removed from each other that there is no attrition between them. The center of distribution of the species is Celebes, where the race *B. b. celebensis* is found, while the typical subspecies, *B. b. babyrussa*, first described, inhabits Buru, a small island lying eastward of Celebes. The babirusa is known as an excellent swimmer and has reached other small islands nearby. Several of these populations have been designated as races, as listed by Laurie and Hill (1954).

In captivity the babirusa is usually gentle and responsive (Leister, 1939), in contrast to animals of some other species, perhaps because specimens reaching zoological gardens may have been reared as pets in their native islands, as is reportedly customary. The single animal kept here was fed the usual wild-pig diet, which it always took well. It was sensitive to cold but spent much time out of doors in summer.

The babirusa has never been common in zoological gardens but has been bred on several occasions. The only successful rearing in this country, as far as I know, is that of a single piglet born in the summer of 1938 in the Chicago Zoological Park (Robert Bean, *in litt.*). A single birth occurred in the San Diego Zoological Garden in September, 1941, followed by another of two young in 1942, but none was reared (Dittoe, 1945). Three births in the Zoological Gardens of London between 1884 and 1933 are recorded by Zuckerman (1953), while Heck (1936) reports and figures two young born in the Zoological Gardens of Berlin in 1935. The usual number of young per birth is one or two, the piglets being without spots or stripes. Gestation periods given by Kenneth (1953) are 125 and 150 days.

Our single babirusa lived here for 10 years, 10 months, 29 days, but several much better records have been established. Jones (1958) reports a specimen as having lived from May 11, 1932, to July 6, 1951, or 19 years, 1 month, 25 days in the National Zoological Park, while the animal born in the Chicago Zoological Park in the summer of 1938 died on April 27, 1959, after more than 20 years (Robert Bean, *in litt.*). The greatest recorded longevity appears to have been that of a female reported by Flower (1931) to have been in his care for 9 years, 6 months, 20 days when, on April 4, 1908, it was sent to Hamburg. There, according to Jones (1958), it died in February, 1920. This rather complicated history works out to approximately 4 months over 21 years, a remarkable span.

FAMILY TAYASSUIDAE

PECCARIES

While in general the peccaries are definitely piglike, they differ from the true pigs in several important characters. The short but sharp upper tusks grow downward, instead of up as in the Suidae, the tail is vestigial, and there are but three digits, only two of which are functional, on the hind feet. A large scent gland on the lower back produces a viscid secretion with an unpleasant musky odor which may be effective in both courtship and recognition (Neal, 1959). The stomach is complex, approaching that of the ruminants.

The peccaries are found only in the New World, extending from the southwestern border of the United States to Patagonia. Usually frequenting forested areas, they may invade more open brush country where this is available. Omnivorous in feeding habits, the diet includes roots, fruits, nuts, and such animal life as may be obtainable. Peccaries usually live in herds and are said to be dangerous if attacked, although this does not appear to have been fully confirmed.

Two species are recognized, each with several races: the collared peccary, *Tayassu tajacu*, found from southern Arizona, New Mexico, and Texas to Patagonia, and the white-lipped peccary, *T. pecari*, the range of which extends from southern Mexico to Paraguay.

Most commonly seen in zoological gardens is the collared peccary. This is the smaller of the two species, its maximum weight being given by Palmer (1954) as 65 pounds. The long, coarse hair is black mixed with white or pale tawny, so that the general effect is grayish, with some variation between the races. A narrow, semicircular collar of lighter hairs rings the shoulder on either side.

Collared peccaries thrive in captivity and are easily maintained in good condition on the diet followed for the Suidae (p. 523). We have always kept them indoors in winter, although animals from the colder parts of their range are sometimes provided only with unheated shelters, even at northern latitudes. While there is still some question concerning the reputed ferocity of peccaries in the wild, there can be no doubt that captive animals, especially males, may sometimes be aggressive. Such individuals usually give warning of impending attack by raising the hair over the rump gland and loudly snapping the teeth.

Births of the collared peccary in zoological gardens have been frequent, the mothers usually rearing their offspring well. Litters number one or two young; Palmer (1954) gives the gestation period as 112–16 days. Births have occurred here in May, June, July, and November.

The greatest longevity given by Flower (1931) for the collared peccary in captivity is 15 years, 9 months, 23 days in the Jardin des Plantes, Paris, while Urbain, Nouvel, Bullier, and Rinjard (1955) report a specimen of this species as having lived from 1935 to 1953, or 18 years, in that institution. A female born in the New York Zoological Park on July 12, 1908, died on December 13, 1929, after 21 years, 5 months, 1 day, and a male born here on June 6, 1909, lived until February 14, 1934, or 24 years, 8 months, 8 days.

The white-lipped peccary is a somewhat larger animal than the collared, Hall and Kelson (1959) giving 940 millimeters (approximately 37 inches) as maximum total length for the latter species and 1,040 millimeters (approximately 41 inches) for a female white-lipped from Costa Rica. The nearly black pelage is more or less variegated with dark tawny, so that it gives the impression of brownish rather than gray. The area of the lips and sometimes adjacent areas is white and there is no encircling band on the shoulders.

This species is far less common in captivity than the collared, perhaps because of its marked preference for inaccessible deep tropical forests. However, once received and established, it has done reasonably well here on the same diet as that provided for the collared, even though it is a "softer" and somewhat less adaptable animal. The white-lipped is also more sensitive to cold than the collared and presumably is unable to withstand low temperatures without heat. As to temperament, the most irascible peccary I can recall was a male white-lipped, an animal of really savage inclination, at least as far as I was concerned.

No births of the white-lipped peccary have occurred here or, as far as I am aware, elsewhere in this country. Among scattered births in Europe, noteworthy are successive births of twins, in 1953 and 1954, in the Zoological Gardens of Antwerp (Anon., 1954, 1955a). Births of several hybrids between the white-lipped and the collared in the Zoological Gardens of London are recorded by Zuckerman (1953). The number of young per litter appears to be one or two, as in the collared, but the gestation period of the white-lipped seems not to have been determined.

As already pointed out, longevities recorded for the white-lipped peccary in captivity are less extended than those for the collared. Flower (1931) reports only a span of 9 years, 4 months, 11 days for a male in the Zoological Gardens of London, while Jones (1958) lists a specimen that was received at the National Zoological Park on July 11, 1933, and died on June 11, 1945, after 11 years, 11 months. A female transferred to our collection from the Central Park Menagerie, New York, on November 16, 1943, died here on February 7, 1957, 13 years, 2 months, 22 days later.

FAMILY HIPPOPOTAMIDAE

Hippopotamuses

Much the largest and heaviest members of this suborder, the hippopotamuses rate with the elephants and the rhinoceroses as the world's greatest living land mammals. Huge, bulging bodies supported by short legs that seem hardly capable of performing their function give a misleading impression of clumsy ineptitude. The smooth skin is almost hairless, save for tufts at the tail-tip and about the lips and ears. Incisors and canine teeth are present in both jaws, the canines developed as formidable tusks, although they do not protrude beyond the lips. The stomach is complex, as illustrated by Verheyen (1954) and Frechkop (1955), but rumination does not occur. The structure of the foot is unique among the Artiodactyla in that all four toes, encased in hoofs and joined by membranes, share in supporting the body weight.

The two living species of this family, the hippopotamus (*Hippopotamus amphibius*) and the pygmy hippopotamus (*Choeropsis liberiensis*), are confined to Africa. The hippopotamus, once found, in several races, in most of Africa's great lakes and rivers, has been extirpated from the northern and southern extremes of its former range, so that it is now practically confined to the equatorial region, with the greatest concentration in the east. Here, in fact, it has thrived so well under protection that conservationists are faced with an apparent necessity for reducing their numbers to prevent dangerous overgrazing (Bere, 1958, 1959).

The great, soft body, comparatively large head, and short legs of the hippopotamus would seem better adapted to life in the water than on land, as indeed they are. Both eyes and nostrils, the latter provided with valves, are raised above the general level of the face, so that the animal may float submerged with these organs and the ears projecting above the surface. In the adult there are four incisors in each jaw, those of the lower projecting forward. As already noted, the canines take the form of large tusks, the edges of upper and lower bearing upon each other.

The skin is provided with glands that secrete a thick, oily exudate, reddish in color. This is produced profusely during periods of excitement and has given rise to the belief that the hippopotamus actually "sweats blood."

The hippopotamus is capable of remaining under water for considerable periods, although it appears that the length of time it is able to do so without coming to the surface to breathe has sometimes been exaggerated. Numerous careful observations, as gathered by Verheyen (1954:39–40), indicate that the normal maximum is about 4 minutes.

As with most large mammals, properly determined weights of hippopotamuses are seldom recorded. The figures usually quoted are from $2\frac{1}{2}$ to 4 tons, the latter having been given by W. L. Sclater (1900–1901, 1:269) for a male in the Zoological Gardens of London. Figures for hippopotamuses killed and weighed in the field in Kenya, as given by Meinertzhagen (1938), run from 5,267 to 5,872 pounds for four males and from 3,994 to 5,174 pounds for three females. Weights obtained from a larger number of animals destroyed during a population reduction project in Uganda between Lake George and Lake Edward gave an average of 3,256 pounds for males and 3,002 pounds for females, with respective maxima of 4,184 and 4,454 pounds (Bere, 1959). Accurate weights of three adult animals living in the San Diego Zoological Garden in 1960 are reported in *Zoonooz* (**33** [6]:12) as follows: male, 4,190 pounds; female, 3,400 pounds, and female, 2,690 pounds.

While the hippopotamus is a social animal, often found in groups of forty or fifty individuals, such gatherings are usually composed of females and young, the males largely keeping to themselves (Verheyen, 1954). Amphibious in habit, swimming freely in lakes and the deep reaches of rivers or even going to sea on occasion, the hippopotamus spends much of the day sleeping on the banks or in shallow water. Aquatic plants form a large part of the diet, but inland excursions of some distance are undertaken, usually at night. These seem to be principally for the purpose of grazing where grass is available and browsing on low-growing foliage. At such times the animals show surprising ability to surmount obstacles, Mochi and Carter (1953) relating an instance in which hippopotamuses were accustomed to climbing an escarpment some 200 feet high to reach a valley beyond. Individual inland territories, their limits marked by the claimant's voidings, are frequently established (Hediger, 1951; Verheyen, 1954).

As a zoo animal of particular interest, the hippopotamus has had a long career in captivity. According to Loisel (1912, 1:103), the first living specimen to reach Europe was an animal kept in the menagerie of the Roman Emperor Augustus between the years 29 B.C. and A.D. 14. In 1850 the Zoological Gardens of London received a hippopotamus named "Obasch," believed to be the first to arrive in Europe since the days of ancient Rome (Mitchell, 1929), and another was obtained by the Jardin des Plantes, Paris, in 1853 (Loisel, 1912, 3:41), both as gifts of the viceroy of Egypt. Since that time the hippopotamus has become thoroughly well known as a zoological-garden resident.

Accommodations for hippopotamuses here are in the Elephant House and consist simply of a single compartment 24 feet square with an attached pool of equal size. Frontal barriers are of 2-inch round steel bars, 6 feet high and set on 20-inch centers, as already described for other compartments in the building. Access to the pool is by means of a rather steep concrete stairway, 5 feet wide, with 18-inch treads and 7-inch risers. This stairway is placed against the back wall of the inclosure, a precaution made necessary by the animal's habit of rapidly switching the tail as it emerges from the water, widely dispersing water, feces, and urine, the latter ability being facilitated, at least in males, by the backward direction of the penis. A light rail along the free side of the stairway serves to keep the climbing beast on the proper course.

The pool is able to hold water to a depth of only 3 feet, which rises a few inches, of course, when an animal enters. Depths of 5–6 feet are customary, but ours seems to serve very well. The building temperature is maintained at about 70° F. (approximately 21° C.) in winter, but to hold the water at this point is another matter. About 70° F. water temperature is desirable, but to keep this in spite of constant loss through the overflow requires a heating plant of very considerable capacity. Banks of heating pipes line the walls of our pool and play an important part, but even then the temperature of the pool may sometimes drop to as low as 60° F. (approximately 16° C.). This is acceptable to most hippopotamuses, but many will refuse to enter water colder than this. The problem of water temperature is involved with another of aesthetic if not practical importance. Hippopotamuses frequently defecate in the water, much of the waste material quickly rising and floating thickly on the surface. A scum-gutter will serve to remove much of this flotsam, especially when the water level is raised by an entering animal. A slow, constant inflow of water would keep the surface fairly clean, but during the winter months, at least, flow cannot be maintained without excessive heat loss. At a meeting of the American Association of Zoological Parks and Aquariums, held in Philadelphia in September, 1959, George Speidel, director of the Milwaukee Zoological Park, reported that a thorough investigation of filters, scum-gutters, etc., incidental to the planning of new hippopotamus quarters under construction in his Park had brought him to the conclusion that there is now no practical solution for this problem.

Two outside yards of generous proportions adjoin the inside room and are used alternately in summer. These are floored with sod, so that while one is in use, the other is able to prepare for rather scanty grazing.

Our present hippopotamus quarters provide well for basic needs but offer little in the way of aesthetic attraction. From this point of view, much can be done by the shaping of pools, by the use of moats to replace bars, and with background planting protected from the animals, as in the Zoological Gardens of Rotterdam (Kuiper, 1943).

Food for an adult hippopotamus here includes 80–100 pounds of alfalfa hay, about 12 pounds of grain mixture in pellet form fortified with vitamin and mineral supplements, and approximately 8 quarts of cut potatoes, apples, carrots, and cabbage, with a loaf or two of stale bread. Kinds and amounts of food will vary, of course, with sex, age, condition, and individual preference of the animal concerned. When growing grass is available, hippopotamuses will crop it almost as closely as would sheep.

Until fairly recently our experience with the hippopotamus in the New York Zoological Park had to do with only a single specimen, the renowned "Peter the Great." Pete was born in the Central Park Menagerie, New York, on July 13, 1903, transferred to us on July 14, 1906, and lived here until his death on February 1, 1953. This span of 49 years, 6 months, 19 days is the greatest recorded for a captive hippopotamus up to 1963 (Anon., 1953a). Pete was the seventh offspring of "Caliph" and "Mrs. Murphy," prolific sources of hippopotamuses for American zoological gardens of earlier days. For the history of these animals I am indebted to John Galm, supervisor of menageries for New York City, who has extracted it from the records. Mrs. Murphy was received at Central Park "from Africa," on October 16, 1886, and her mate, Caliph, was obtained on April 20, 1888, from the Zoological Gardens of Cincinnati, where he had been deposited by the Hagenbecks. A total of ten young were born to this pair, the first on December 2, 1889, the last on May 14, 1914. Of these, seven were fully reared. Mrs. Murphy died on April 28, 1929, after 42 years, 6 months, 12 days, while Caliph lived until January 8, 1935, or 46 years, 8 months, 19 days.

While captive hippopotamuses may sometimes become dangerously savage, as was the case with Obasch, London's first specimen (Bartlett, 1899), Pete remained completely gentle during his long stay here. Toward the end arthritis hampered his movements, but more serious was a condition presumably caused by attrition of the molars combined with reduction of tone in the cheek muscles that resulted in loss through the corners of his mouth of most of his food intake. However, this was remedied by grinding his rations and mixing them in a watery gruel, which he readily swallowed. This sustained Pete well until final immobilization caused by arthritis made his painless destruction necessary. His weight at death was 3,102 pounds.

After Pete's death, a young male was obtained, arriving on July 2, 1953. He weighed 259 pounds and was estimated to be about 12 months old. A female received soon afterward died from an obscure infection after 3 years and was replaced with another. This second female arrived on August 30, 1956, and weighed 690 pounds. She was considered to be aged 3 years or perhaps a little more. These two lived quietly together, no mating behavior being noted, but on the morning of December 23, 1958, a hippopotamus calf was found floating dead in the pool. Its weight was 53.9 pounds; no sign of injury was evident. Reported birth weights of hippopotamus calves are quoted by Verheyen (1954) as varying from 34 to 40 kilograms (74.8 to 88 pounds). Allowing for a gestation period of about 240 days, the male would have been approximately 6 years old and the female between 5 and 6 years at the time of conception, if our age estimates were correct. These data suggest sexual maturity at ages earlier than those given by Brown (1924), whose animals were considered to have been just under 7 years old when conception occurred.

More accurate information is offered by the following instances in which the exact age of the female is known. John Galm's search of the records of the Central Park Menagerie, New York, shows that the second offspring of Caliph and Mrs. Murphy was a female called Fatima, born on September 4, 1890. On April 6, 1896, Fatima gave birth to a male calf, sired by Caliph. Fatima was thus 5 years, 7 months, 2 days old at the time of parturition and would have been about 1 month under 5 years old at conception. Raymond F. Gray, superintendent of the Overton Park Zoo at Memphis, Tennessee, informs me (*in litt.*) that a female hippopotamus born in his Gardens in June, 1940, produced her first calf on March 24, 1949. In this instance the animal would have been aged just over 8 years at conception. Reuther (1961) estimates that a pair of hippopotamuses in the Cleveland Zoological Park reached sexual maturity at the age of 3 years. Frechkop (1955:519) says that sexual maturity in the hippopotamus is attained at the age of $7\frac{1}{2}$ years. These data, however, suggest a considerable variation, and more extensive exact information would seem desirable.

On December 27, 1958, following the birth of a hippopotamus calf here on December 23 as noted above, the female appeared to be receptive, and copulation was observed. This took place in the water, the usual habit, although this apparently is not invariable (Verheyen, 1954). Acceptance of the male 4 days after the loss of a calf immediately after birth has also been noted in the Cleveland Zoological Park (L. J. Goss, *in litt.*).

No further sexual activity was observed until March 18, 1959, when copulation occurred, with some activity late in the preceding afternoon and on the following morning. This was repeated on April 22, 35 days later, in general confirmation of a monthly interval, as given by Asdell (1946). As the months passed without recurrence of estrus, we became assured that another birth was in prospect. Since only the single stall and pool were available, a temporary partition of heavy aluminum posts and bars was erected across the stall, so that we might conform with the established custom of removing the male when a birth is impending. However, by pushing with muzzle and shoulders and finally by rearing on his hind legs and applying his weight, he soon so weakened this structure that it had to be removed. The male promptly rejoined his mate in the pool. Restlessness of the female increased, and on the afternoon of December 15, 1959, she drove the male up the steps and into the stall, the door of which was then closed. On the morning of December 16 enlargement of the vulva indicated that birth was imminent. The pool was quickly drained, sketchily hosed out, and the valves set for refilling. This had progressed to a depth of about 18 inches when at 10:05 A.M., while the female was in a standing position, a watching keeper saw the calf unceremoniously dropped into the water with none of the explosive force sometimes reported. The calf swam at once. At 10:35 A.M. it scrambled onto a step, just awash, where it was barely able to stand and was quickly pushed back into the water by a nudge of the mother's muzzle. The calf continued to swim about the pool, apparently agitated, but at 12:30 P.M., when the water had reached its maximum depth of 3 feet, the female was seen to be lying on her side, the calf nursing quietly under water. This situation continued for the next 2 days, the calf nursing regularly, rising to the surface to breathe at intervals of up to 40 seconds.

On December 18, when the calf was 2 days old, the female was admitted to the stall occupied by the male, the calf following somewhat shakily up the steps. The female was strongly antagonistic toward the male, roaring loudly and finally attacking him by striking upward to bring the heavy lower tusks into play, thus inflicting several superficial cuts in his skin. He defended himself as best he could with open jaws but made no effort to strike back and appeared only to seek escape. The mother and calf finally returned to the pool, and when introduction was again tried several days later, the female seemed somewhat less violent, although still strongly defensive. This situation continued daily until January 20, the animals being separated at night. The female guarded the entrance to the pool vigilantly, and on only a single occasion was the male able to enter. The female, with calf trailing, then rushed after him and launched an attack which confined him to a single corner. It was some hours before he could be extricated, uninjured and presumably greatly benefited by his soaking. On the evening of January 19, after the separation gate had been closed for the night, the animals called to each other in low, muffled tones. When the gate was opened on the morning of January 20, the female left the pool and approached the male on the floor of the cage. As soon as he rose, she returned to the pool, the male following. Copulation occurred almost immediately and was repeated at least once during the day. The gate was left open and pairing was again observed, for the last time, on the morning of the twenty-first. Following this interlude, the animals continued to associate on a peaceful basis, although the female continued, with gradually decreasing effort, to keep herself between the calf and its father.

This detailed account is given as an example of successful rearing under difficult conditions; it varies in many particulars from the experiences recorded by Brown (1924) and Vevers (1926). Yet basically, it is in accord with now well-established facts. The observed gestation period in this instance was 238 days; the figures given by Asdell (1946) are 237.4 ± 1.2 days. The single estrus interval obtained was 35 days, as already noted; the same period elapsed between the birth of the living calf and the first following estrus. Nursing under water appears to be usual but has sometimes been seen to take place out of water (Verheyen, 1954:47). Both copulation and birth usually take place in the water, but there have been observations of the latter, at least, occurring in dry areas (Verheyen, *loc. cit.*, pp. 45–46).

The difficulties experienced with our first successful hippopotamus birth here, as fully reported by Bridges (1960), might suggest that in spite of the great number of calves that have been reared in captivity, an approved method of handling has not yet been devised. This is far from true, for there is a generally accepted system, subject to some variation, depending on the temperaments of the animals involved. In general, it is customary to provide adjoining compartments, each with its own pool, so that the male and female can be kept separately except for mating periods or at least can be separated when a birth is impending While it is now evident that the depth of the water in which the calf is born is not of great consequence, the general practice in this country is to lower the water in the maternity tank to 12–18 inches, raising it as the calf grows. In Europe it seems to be more usual to allow the calf to be born in deeper water. At Rotterdam in 1951 a male and two females were kept, each in its own pen and pool, the latter filled to a depth said to be 6 feet. The male was introduced to each female as required, performed his function, and was removed. This small group was reported to be producing young regularly and with a minimum of loss or upset.

This certainly is a sound and dependable system for general use, but occasional steady pairs can sometimes be operated on a simpler basis. At the Prospect Park Zoo, Brooklyn, New York, in the winter of 1957, the female of a pair kept in a rather small compartment with a pool 5–6 feet deep gave birth to an unexpected calf. It was impossible to remove or separate the male, but the calf was reared without difficulty. Frederick H. Ulmer, Jr., curator of mammals at the Philadelphia Zoological Garden, reports (*in litt.*) a similar incident at that institution which was so successful that the method has been continued for the pair involved.

Too often, when the parents have remained together during a birth, the calf has been lost, a misfortune usually attributed to the father. He may actually have been at fault in some instances, but injury to the calf is more likely to occur accidentally during the turmoil caused by the efforts of the female to expel the male from the pool. There seems to be no doubt of the usual insistence of the female on sole occupancy of this domain by herself and her calf, at least for the first few weeks of its life, and when the male yields readily to her roars and threats, the risk of damage to the calf diminishes. Some females are so defensive of their calves that their quarters cannot be approached even by their keepers without the greatest caution, a point that must be kept in mind until the temperament of the mother has been fully determined.

In our first experience here the male showed no inclination to injure the calf purposely. On one occasion, when mother and young were on the platform and the male had retreated to a corner, the calf escaped the mother's notice and approached the father. It actually managed to touch the great muzzle with its own, the contact causing the male to back away.

This display of caution was quickly justified, for the female became aware of the activity, rushed between her mate and the calf, and forced the former into another corner.

In April, 1963, twin hippopotamuses, male and female, were born in the St. Louis Zoological Park. Both calves thrived until they had reached the age of 5 weeks, when it was noted that the young male was lagging. Separated from the group with some difficulty, he fed readily on reconstituted evaporated milk and Pablum, diced vegetables and greens. As reported on June 25, 1963, by Moody Lentz, general curator at St. Louis, he was then growing as well as his still nursing sister.

The hippopotamus is notable for its ready acceptance of captivity and for the excellent longevity records it has established. "Guy Fawkes," a female born in the Zoological Gardens of London on November 5, 1872, and said by Street (1956:61) to be the first hippopotamus to have been born and reared in captivity, lived until March 20, 1908, or 35 years, 4 months, 15 days (Flower, 1931). The greatest longevity listed by Flower (*loc. cit.*) is that of a female that was received at the Jardin des Plantes, Paris, on June 4, 1855, and which died on February 3, 1897, after 41 years, 7 months, 30 days. Since the publication of Flower's classic work, several even longer spans have been recorded.

A male known as "Bongo," received at the National Zoological Park on April 7, 1914, was retired to Zoorama, a commercial establishment at New Market, Virginia, on July 7, 1959, and died there on December 4, 1959, after 45 years, 7 months, 27 days, within the knowledge of the Washington authorities (Theodore H. Reed, director, *in litt.*).

"Adonis" and "Venus," a remarkable pair, arrived at the Memphis Zoological Garden and Aquarium, Memphis, Tennessee, on April 4, 1914. Venus died in 1957, approximately 43 years later, but Adonis was still living in July, 1963, after roughly 49 years, 3 months. During her lifetime Venus gave birth to sixteen young fathered by Adonis, fourteen being fully reared. Adonis has also sired nine young by other females, the latest having been born on July 8, 1961, bringing his total to twenty-five (Gray, 1956, 1959, and *in litt.*).

The established captivity spans of Bongo, Caliph, and Adonis suffer in comparison with Pete's 49 years, 6 months, 19 days, since their ages, when received at the respective institutions in which they lived, were unknown. Adonis, of course, may still go on to greater achievement.

The pygmy hippopotamus (*Choeropsis liberiensis*) is known only from a restricted area in West Africa centering in the hinterland of Liberia, with reported border extensions into Sierra Leone on the north and the Ivory

Coast on the south. As compared to its larger relative, the appellation "pygmy" is amply justified, yet it is a more than substantial beast in its own right, attaining a weight in excess of 500 pounds. In appearance the pygmy hippopotamus is strongly suggestive of a young hippopotamus, for in both the head is comparatively smaller than in the adult of the larger species and eyes and nostrils are not noticeably raised above the level of the face. There are but two incisors in the lower jaw of the pygmy hippopotamus, although the canines are well developed as tusks. The skin exudate is clear instead of reddish.

The pygmy hippopotamus appears not to be a social animal but lives in solitary fashion in swampy forests, rather than in lakes and rivers, although it may sometimes resort to the larger bodies of water, in which it swims with complete ease. The nostrils are equipped with valves, as in the larger species. First described by Morton (1844) from prepared material, there seems to be no record of a living specimen having been seen outside Africa until the arrival of a young animal at the Dublin Zoological Gardens, where it lived for a short time only, was noted by P. L. Sclater (1873). It was not until 1912, when Hans Schomburgk delivered to Carl Hagenbeck five living pygmy hippopotamuses, that the establishment of the species in captivity became possible. Schomburgk (1912, 1913) has reported his extraordinary experiences in the capture of these animals in Liberia, together with notes on their habits and distribution. Three of Schomburgk's specimens, purchased from Hagenbeck, were received at the New York Zoological Park on July 9, 1912, as recorded by Hornaday (1920).

Schomburgk's (1913) description of the pygmy hippopotamus as a "dear sensible little beast" will hardly be supported by most of those who have dealt with the animal in captivity, for most specimens are irascible, some even savage. On the other hand, Schomburgk's feeling that "animals that feed so readily when caught should thrive in captivity if properly cared for" has been amply justified, for the first captives received here lived and bred well, as have the scattered later arrivals.

Our three pygmy hippopotamuses consisted of a male, considered to be adult, and a younger pair. The older male remained here until November 21, 1925, when he was sold to Chapman, the English dealer. Of the young pair, the male lived until February 17, 1952, or 39 years, 7 months, 8 days, the female until October 2, 1950—38 years, 2 months, 23 days. The latter's weight at death was 350 pounds.

Accommodation for these animals was found in the Elephant House in the small compartments already described for tapirs. There are four of these installations, two at either end of the building, all provided with small, glass-fronted tanks. Tapirs and pygmy hippopotamuses have alternated in occupancy as conditions required. Each of these compartments connects with large outside runs, one set of two being inclosed by stone walls 4 feet high. While these are sufficiently high for restraint, the two runs are separated internally by a wall of only 2 feet, 6 inches. Very occasionally, when each yard has been occupied by a single animal, one or the other has managed to surmount this obstacle. This has called for prompt separation, for even in this roomy area serious quarreling might result. The reported solitary habit of the pygmy hippopotamus is fully substantiated by the behavior of the animals here. We never have had two adults that, regardless of sex, would live peaceably together, except for a pair during the brief estrus periods of the female.

Daily food for an adult pygmy hippopotamus here consists of approximately 15 pounds of alfalfa hay, sometimes alternated with clover, and a mixture of feeding pellets, bread, cabbage, white potatoes, and carrots, totalling about 5 pounds. Other vegetables and greens are used, of course, in season. The animals graze in summer, just as their larger relatives do.

The young pair received from Hagenbeck on July 9, 1912, lived quietly together, with some indefinite indications of mating, until December 23, 1919, when an unexpected calf was born (Hornaday, 1920), constituting what appears to have been the first captivity birth for the species. This calf was unable to stand or nurse and died on the following day. Its weight was but $9\frac{1}{2}$ pounds, the range given by Steinmetz (1937) for five calves born in the Zoological Gardens of Berlin being from 5,000 to 7,000 grams (11–15.4 pounds). Following this event, which had caused the separation of the parents, they would no longer live together without quarreling and were reunited only when the muffled calls of the female indicated the onset of estrus. In following years young were born to this female on January 23, 1921, March 24, 1923, December 9, 1925, and February 1, 1929, three of the four calves being successfully reared.

No further young were born to this female, but in 1936 a daughter, born on March 24, 1923, produced a calf on January 16, fathered by the old bull (Bridges, 1936). This was followed by three more, born on March 17, 1939, June 12, 1940, and October 1, 1944. Of these four, two were reared. The mother of these calves died on March 2, 1953, after 29 years, 11 months, 6 days, her weight at death being 400 pounds. A sister of this animal presented to the Zoological Society of London in April, 1929, at the age of 8 years, weighed 510 pounds at shipment, the greatest weight recorded here for the species.

Following the loss of our last representative of the original importation, we were not long without pygmy hippopotamuses, for a young pair bred in the National Zoological Park was obtained from the Catskill Game Farm on October 13, 1953. The Washington stock was based on a male acquired in 1927 and a female received in 1929, reinforced by a female brought from Liberia in 1940 by the Smithsonian-Firestone Expedition, headed by William M. Mann. A brief history of these animals, together with their remarkable breeding record, is given by Reed (1960). From 1931 to 1954 the first two animals, known as "Billy" and "Hannah," produced fifteen calves, of which seven were reared or at least lived for more than 1 year. During the later years Billy was also paired with the 1940 female, "Matilda," who gave birth to eight young between 1943 and 1956, six being reared. These twenty-three births were distributed as follows: January, one; February, three; March, three; April, three; May, two; June, three; July, one; August, two; October, two; December, three. Billy died on October 11, 1955, and Hannah on March 6, 1958, each after approximately 28 years. Matilda and two of her daughters were still living in Washington at the time of Dr. Reed's report.

The pair received here on October 13, 1953, were the offspring of Billy and Hannah, the male having been born on June 13, 1951, the female on March 12, 1950. Although only 2 and 3 years old when they arrived, they refused to live together and were assigned to separate but adjoining quarters. On the evening of July 1, 1958, the female indicated estrus for the first time, her known age being 8 years, 3 months, 19 days. The male was given access on the following morning, and several apparently unsuccessful attempts at copulation were observed, usually in the dry area but sometimes in the shallow pool. The animals were left together overnight and separated in the morning, the female then showing mild antagonism toward the male. These events were repeated on October 27 and again on December 5, estrus in each instance appearing to extend over one full day, with some indications on the preceding afternoon and the following morning. While successful copulation was not observed in any of this series, there was no indication of further recurrence of estrus, and this fact, coupled with a gradual increase in the girth of the female, convinced us that conception had occurred. However, the established gestation period of approximately 7 months as given by Steinmetz (1937) expired in July, 1959, without a birth, although we did not give up hope entirely until the female signaled renewal of estrus on August 28, after a lapse of nearly 9 months. This time copulation was definitely observed and the ability of the male was fully established. He had then reached the age of 8 years, 2 months, 15 days, which so closely approximates the age of the female at the first onset of estrus as to appear to confirm for both sexes the statement of Frechkop (1955:520) that the female achieves puberty at 8 years.

In any case, there was no doubt this time of conception. There were no further signals from the female and her girth noticeably increased. At 1:00 P.M. on March 15, 1960, she was lying on a bed of straw in a corner of her pen, the unbroken amniotic sac slightly protruding. At 1:10 she moved into the pool, which was filled to a depth of 4 inches, and at 1:20, while the mother was in a squatting position, the calf was dropped into the water. This occurrence is not in accord with the general understanding that birth in this species occurs on land: Steinmetz (1937) reports that a female in the Zoological Gardens of Berlin left her outdoor pool to give birth in the dry indoor stall. The gestation period in this instance was 200 days; Steinmetz (*loc. cit.*) gives seven instances in which this varied from 201–10 days.

The calf received no attention from the mother but walked at once, in wobbly fashion, its head and back above water. At 1:40 the umbilical cord broke at a point approximately 6 inches from the umbilicus. Mother and young remained in the water, the mother lying on her side. The calf began exploring, apparently searching for the nipples. These, however, are very small, and the calf was unable to reach them without putting its head under water, which it appeared unwilling to do. At 2:30 the pool was drained and by 2:45, the mother lying on her side with the left hind leg raised, the calf had found the nipples and was nursing strongly. The bottom of the dry pool measured only 6 by 4 feet, but both animals remained in these cramped quarters, the calf nursing frequently, until March 17. The female then went to the pen platform, where she drank water from a basin and fed lightly, the calf not following. On the next day, however, when the female left the empty pool, the calf accompanied her. They then remained for 3 days on the dry platform, and as the mother was only mildly excitable or defensive, both animals were sprayed lightly with tepid water, with obvious benefit to their drying skins. The calf now had gained noticeably in strength, and on March 21 tepid water to a depth of 3 inches was run into the pool. Both animals entered at once and were in and out during the day, remaining on the platform only when the pool was drained at night. On a single occasion the calf was seen to nurse in the water, the female lying so far over on her side that the nipples were at or above the surface. It soon developed that the female was spending most of the day in the water to the evident discomfort of the calf, which stood or walked constantly and appeared unwilling to lie down in it, once leaving the water and sleeping for an hour on the platform, unattended. The plan of providing a shallow bath for 1 hour only, twice daily, was then adopted and proved to be a satisfactory solution. At the age of 15 days the calf was seen to swallow a small piece of bread as well as a substantial mouthful of alfalfa hay. Further births followed on May 13, 1961, and on June 4, 1963, the young being successfully reared.

At the present time (1963) the pygmy hippopotamus is at rather low ebb in captivity. In this country the once fecund stock in the National Zoological Park was reduced to the three females already noted, but a young male received from Liberia early in 1960 brought about revival, one calf being born in July, 1963. Most of the few specimens living at other institutions are either aged or immature, so that our own beginners and Washington's are the only breeding animals in America. In Europe, in addition to scattered specimens, the center of activity is in the Basel Zoological Gardens, where two males and five females were living in 1959 (Anon., 1959a). This is a production herd, in which twenty young had been born up to 1959 (Langer, 1959).

Perhaps because of the comparatively small number of specimens that have been kept in captivity as well as the more recent introduction of the species, longevities so far attained by the pygmy hippopotamus have not equaled those recorded for its larger relative. The greatest spans known to me up to 1963 have already been noted: Billy and Hannah, at Washington, approximately 28 years each; 29 years, 11 months, 6 days for a female born in New York in 1923; 38 years, 2 months, 23 days for our female imported in 1912 and 39 years, 7 months, 8 days for her mate.

SUBORDER TYLOPODA

FAMILY CAMELIDAE

Camels, Guanaco, Vicuña, Llama, and Alpaca

Practically a relict group, the presently existing members of this suborder, comprising a single family, are few in number and widely separated geographically. All are adapted to walking on rough mountain terrain or on sandy deserts, the two toes of each foot, ending in broad nails, being provided with a tough, leathery pad. Incisor and canine teeth are present in both jaws, while horns and antlers, of course, are absent. The stomach is separated into three specialized compartments, permitting the rumination practiced by all species. The upper lip is divided into two sections, greatly increasing its mobility and prehensile usefulness. The common gait is the "pace," the legs of each side moving in unison. Only three living genera, *Camelus* of the Old World and *Lama* and *Vicugna* of South America, are known.

Of the camels, *Camelus*, there are two species: the Bactrian or two-humped (*Camelus bactrianus*) and the dromedary or one-humped (*C. dromedarius*). Both are now known certainly as domesticated beasts of burden only, the Bactrian being used largely in central Asia, from Afghanistan to China, while the dromedary is a common means of transportation in southern Asia and northern Africa. Untamed herds of animals of both species are sometimes found and are usually considered as merely feral, living in much the same way as the "wild" horses of the plains of the western United States. However, Harper (1945) produces much evidence in support of the belief that really wild Bactrians (*C. b. ferus*) may exist in the Gobi Desert area of Mongolia and northern China, a possibility strongly supported by Montagu (1957) and Bannikov (1958a).

The humps of camels, whether the pair of the Bactrian or the single one of the dromedary, are probably their most characteristic feature. The backbone does not deviate from its normal course to support these structures, which are merely masses of fleshy tissue, large and full when the animal is healthy and well fed, presumably providing a store that may be drawn upon in times of need. When this occurs, the humps may decrease greatly in size or, especially in aged animals, fall to one side.

While it has long been considered that the small cells lining the first two compartments of the stomach serve as receptacles for the storage of water, accounting for the well-known ability of the cameloids to go for some time without drinking, Bohlken (1960) presents evidence to show that this is not the case and that the cells have a digestive rather than a storage function. While camels certainly have been known to go without water for as long as 10 or 12 days, such deprivation is not conducive to well-being. Leonard (1894) says that working animals should be watered every third day at least, and daily if possible. In the zoological garden, of course, camels usually have constant access to water, which seems in no way to disturb their economy.

The points of the body and limbs on which the animal's weight bears in the resting position are protected by bare, leathery pads or callosities. These are seven in number, one on the chest and one on each elbow, wrist or "knee," and true knee. These pads are so appropriately placed that they may appear to have been caused by abrasion during the animal's lifetime but actually they are present at birth.

Inoffensive though the camels may seem to be, they nevertheless can be very disagreeable, even dangerous, on occasion. The well-known habit of "spitting," which consists of the forcible ejection of saliva and even regurgitated stomach contents, is unpleasant enough, but kicking and biting may be really serious. A single outer incisor tooth, a canine, and an advanced premolar at each side of the upper jaw, all well separated, with three normal incisors, a canine, and again an advanced premolar in each side of the lower provide a formidable armature, able to inflict great damage on an adversary. Camels are not noted for good nature, as their moans and groans under any sort of pressure or urging testify. At such times they are only too willing to exercise any or all of their offensive abilities.

The Bactrian camel is stoutly built, with comparatively short legs, well suited for heavy work on difficult terrain. Typically, it is dark brown in color, although there may be variations in shade and white individuals are sometimes seen. In winter the coat is heavy and dense, with longer growth on the head, neck, and humps and about the shoulders. In spring much of the hair is shed, leaving the skin almost bare, with longer wisps on the humps, neck, elbows, and tail. The coat is gradually renewed as cold weather approaches. The weight at death of a male that had lived here for 11 years was 1,175 pounds; an adult female weighed 1,580 pounds at death. A fully grown male measured 7 feet from the ground to the top of the forward hump.

While in general the dromedary is more lightly built than the Bactrian and with longer legs, it has been bred through the centuries with such care that definite breeds have been developed, differing greatly in size and build. These fall into two groups: the light but swift riding camel and the heavy, plodding "baggager." Each of these is found in many local varieties. Leonard (1894) gives the weight of the common working dromedary in the field as from 1,000 to 1,150 pounds. In the zoological garden, where better food and less work would be anticipated, greater weights are to be expected. Three ordinary females, in daily use on our Riding Track here, registered 1,380, 1,570, and 1,990 pounds, respectively. However, two tremendous "baggagers," obtained in 1940 and engaged during following years in stolidly plodding around our Riding Track loaded with children, were surprisingly heavy. The male, which had been castrated, gave weights of 1,975, 2,150, and 2,230 pounds at various periods, while the female was recorded at 2,040, 2,065, and 2,255 pounds. No measurements of these huge animals were made, but a reasonably large female, the greatest weight of which was 1,610 pounds, stood 7 feet from ground to top of hump, exactly the height noted above for a Bactrian. In color the dromedary varies from almost black through shades of brown to pure white. The pelage in winter is soft and thick but never approaches that of the Bactrian in length. It goes through the same process of shedding in spring, when the animal presents an extremely moth-eaten appearance.

Camels of both species have been shown by menageries since very early times (Loisel, 1912) and of course are seen in most zoological gardens today. The Zoological Gardens of London received its first dromedary in 1829, its first Bactrian in 1842 (Flower, 1929). Two "camels from Arabia" are reported as having been seen in Salem, Massachusetts, in 1789 (Goodwin, 1925) and may have been the first to reach this country.

The Bactrian camel is perfectly hardy, of course, at the latitude of New York, and while the dromedary is somewhat less resistant to cold, it requires only an unheated shelter even in the most severe winter weather. In consequence, quarters for camels in cold climates may range from formal buildings to the sketchiest of barns. Barriers of light wire netting, which the animals are not likely to damage, or moats, dry or water-filled, serve equally well for restraint. The latter are both attractive and effective, since camels are reluctant to enter water and are ineffective as swimmers. They seem especially subject to internal parasites, which are more easily held in check when the animals are kept on sand or hard bottoms rather than in poorly drained earth-floored runs.*

In their native lands camels are prized for their ability to eat and thrive on the roughest of fodder, and there seems to be a general belief that such fare is well suited to their needs. However, better food seems to satisfy the animals well enough, once they have become accustomed to it. Camels here receive about 4 pounds of alfalfa hay and 4 pounds of mixed grain pellets with mineral and vitamin supplements, twice daily. This flexible regimen is varied, of course, according to the size and condition of the individual receiving it. Water is available at all times or, in the case of riding animals, at least twice daily.

Camels of both species are bred fairly frequently by zoological gardens, but there is wide divergence in recorded gestation periods, which Hediger (1952) suggests may be due to the state of lactation of the mother. Kenneth (1953) quotes averages ranging from 389.3 days to 406 days for the Bactrian and from 315 to 360 days for the dromedary. Asdell (1946) says that the female Bactrian is polyestrous, heats occurring at varying intervals the year around. However, six births of the species in the Zoological Gardens of London are reported by Zuckerman (1953) as having occurred in March

*See Addenda, pp. 736–37.

or April and the same number of young born here appeared during these two months, supporting the statements by Pocock (1910) and Heape (1901) that rut in males occurs in spring. Only two births of dromedaries have occurred here and those in the months of February and April, but Zuckerman (1953) reports births in the Zoological Gardens of London in February, April, September, and December, indicating a wider periodicity than that of the Bactrian. Leonard (1894) says, in regard to rut in the dromedary, that "I have not noticed that it was confined to any particular season of the year."

In both sexes of the two species paired glands lying at the back of the head appear to be of sexual significance, becoming enlarged during mating periods, particularly in males, and producing an odorous secretion (Pocock, 1910:973; Frechkop, 1955:582–83). During the rut, the uvula or soft palate of the male dromedary may become enlarged and protrude from the mouth as a membranous sac (Leonard, 1894:30–31). The function of this manifestation appears not to be fully understood. In copulation the female crouches with her legs folded beneath her in the usual resting position, which the male forces her to assume by pressing upon her back with head and neck.

Hybrids between the two species are said to be in frequent use in areas of Asia where they meet. Gray (1954) says that while hybrid males are sterile, females are usually fertile when bred to males of either species. A male hybrid bred in the St. Louis Zoological Park was received here in 1941 and remained until he was sold in 1957. This animal had a single hump with a slight indication of division at the top, well concealed by hair. His weight in 1947 was 1,190 pounds.

Flower (1931) says that "definite records of Camels over 16 years old are rare." He quotes for the Bactrian, however, several longevities in excess of this figure, including 24 years, 16 days at the Jardin des Plantes, Paris, 24 years, 6 months, 25 days at Berlin, and 25 years, 5 months, 1 day at Basel, the latter the greatest known to me. For the dromedary, Flower's best record is 24 years, 9 months, at the Jardin des Plantes, and Duetz (1939) reports an Arabian camel (dromedary) as having been for 299 months (24 years, 11 months) in the Philadelphia Zoological Garden and still living. Jones (1958) lists a dromedary, presumably the same animal, that was received at Philadelphia on April 4, 1914, and died on September 5, 1942, after 28 years, 5 months, 1 day. This span, probably the greatest properly authenticated longevity so far recorded for any camel, is confirmed on page 12 of the Centennial Celebration booklet published in 1959 by the Zoological Society of Philadelphia.

The South American representatives of this order are four in number.

Of these, only two are known as wild animals: the guanaco (*Lama guanicoe*) and the vicuña (*Vicugna vicugna*). The llama (*L. glama*), and the alpaca (*L. pacos*) exist only in domestication. The general distribution of the group is in western South America, ranging to altitudes of 15,000 feet or more in the Andes and in the case of the guanaco to much lower levels in the southern extensions of its habitat.

All species are slender in build, with noticeably long necks and legs. Backs are flat and straight, with no indication of humps, and size, of course, is much smaller than that of their Old World relatives. The unpleasant habit of "spitting" is even more readily employed by the llama-like species than by the camels. Biting may be a serious form of offense, for in adults the well-separated single incisor and the canine of each side of the upper jaw and the canine of the lower are both long and sharp, particularly in males. In the guanaco, the llama, and the alpaca, there is a bare, glandular space on both inner and outer sides of the metatarsal region; this hairless area is not found in the vicuña.

The guanaco ranges from southern Peru and Bolivia southward through the Cordillera of Chile and the high pampas of western Argentina to Tierra del Fuego and to even smaller islands off the southern tip of South America. Its comparatively short coat is thick, almost woolly, and its coloration is a uniform grayish brown, with blackish face and white underparts. The height at the shoulder is given by Cabrera and Yepes (1940) as approximately 1.10 meters or about 43 inches. The weight of a male born here was 147 pounds at 15 months; a fully adult animal would certainly exceed this. A smaller race, *L. g. cacsilensis*, has been described from Peru. A social animal, small groups of females and young are gathered and controlled by a single male, young males and those unable to secure females living together in separate herds. After the breeding season these groups may join to form bands of some size (Cabrera and Yepes, 1940). The skins of adults are not in great demand, but the young are so much sought for their lovely, soft coats that the species is seriously persecuted in some areas (de la Tour, 1954).

The vicuña, smallest and most graceful of the lamoids, lives on the high *puna* of the Andes, at elevations of from 12,000 to 16,000 feet (Koford, 1957). Because of the difficulties of travel in this rugged terrain, exact limitations of the distribution of the vicuña are not easily determined, but the range is usually given as extending from northeastern Chile and northwestern Argentina to Bolivia and Peru. Specimens from the latter two areas have been described as a darker race, *V. v. mensalis*. In color the typical vicuña is light brown above, of varying intensity, with lighter areas about the face, the underparts and inner surfaces of the legs approaching white. In nature a long bib of off-white hair hangs from the chest, a feature seldom seen, for some reason, in zoo animals. A character unique among the living members of the Artiodactyla is the condition of the lower incisors of the vicuña, the roots remaining open, so that growth may continue throughout the animal's lifetime (Miller, 1924). Cabrera and Yepes (1940) give the height as varying from 70 to 90 centimeters or approximately 28–35 inches. A male born here weighed 116 pounds when just over 3 years old. In much the same fashion as the guanaco, the vicuña lives in family groups, composed of a dominant male and a number of females and young, with immature or unsuccessful males associating in separate herds (Koford, 1957). Group territories are well established and usually respected, serious battles resulting when invasions occur. The wool of the vicuña is the finest known and has caused persecution of both adults and young for centuries, naturally bringing about gradual reduction of the herds. Some effort, apparently not too successful, has been made to cultivate the species under controlled conditions (Koford, *loc. cit.*).

The llama and the alpaca, known only in the domesticated state, were developed by the Incas of Peru, where large numbers of both were found by the Spanish conquistadors of the sixteenth century. The llama as a beast of burden, the alpaca as a producer of wool, and both as sources of food were of the greatest importance and value to the ancient dwellers in the inhospitable mountains. The origin of these animals is a matter of some doubt. It has generally been considered that both the llama and the alpaca are simply domesticated descendants of the guanaco, both carrying the naked areas of the hind legs as seen in the parent species (Lydekker, 1893–96, 2:416; Allen, 1942:406). However, Frechkop (1955), while agreeing on the ancestry of the llama, considers that the alpaca was derived from the vicuña or from hybrids of the latter and the llama. A third possibility expressed by Cabrera and Yepes (1940) is that both the llama and the alpaca are the domesticated survivors of distinct species once living in the Andean area but now extinct.

The llama is the largest of the group, Cabrera and Yepes (1940) giving 1.15 meters or about 45 inches as the average shoulder height. However, there is great variation in this respect, and particularly fine males would certainly be taller. A male born here weighed 280 pounds when 2 years old and a female, also born here, weighed 170 pounds at death after 19 years. Llamas range in color from black through shades of brown to pure white, with many spotted or pied variations. The coat is short and rather coarse, with little commercial value. Once maintained in great numbers for use in transportation by the inhabitants of the Andes, the llama has largely been displaced, first by horses and mules and more recently by motor vehicles. In the more difficult areas of northern Chile, Peru, and Bolivia, however, it is still in general use.

The alpaca is a much smaller animal than the llama, the standing height being given by Cabrera and Yepes (1940) as 90 centimeters or about 35 inches. An adult male kept here weighed 140 pounds. The most common color is dark brown, although both white and black individuals occur. The alpaca appears to have been developed by the Incas purely for the production of wool, the coats in the finer breed being so long as often to drag on the ground. Alpacas are still kept in numbers in the highlands of Bolivia and Peru, the product of the annual shearing being an important factor in national incomes.

According to Cabrera and Yepes (1940), hybrids between the llama and the alpaca are frequently bred for the production of wool of intermediate quality, various other crosses also being made for the same purpose. Gray (1954) lists reports indicating general fertility of hybrids within the group, use of the vicuña appearing to be somewhat restricted.

The llama and the guanaco are commonly seen in the zoological garden, the alpaca and the vicuña probably less frequently. All are excellent subjects, easily maintained and entirely indifferent to cold when provided with simple unheated shelters. They seem less subject to the invasion of internal parasites than are the camels, and while the latter always impress me as safer in bare inclosures, grassed runs suit the lamoids well enough, at least if regular checks for parasites are made. All species are kept here in large runs, each with an open shelter, surrounded by fences of wire netting 7 feet high, certainly more than adequate for restraint. A male with several females and young, as llamas and guanacos are kept here at present, make excellent exhibits, although as young males grow large enough to come to the attention of the herd leader they must be removed for their own protection. Alpacas, if available, can be treated in the same way, but the vicuña offers problems. We never have owned an adult male that could be trusted at liberty with a herd, at least in limited quarters. When this has been attempted, the result has invariably been a female with badly lacerated legs.

Llamas here receive 1 pound of alfalfa hay and 1 pound of mixed grain pellets with mineral and vitamin supplements, twice daily, the smaller species being given proportional quantities of the same items. In summer the animals graze freely, and during the winter receive small allowances of greens and vegetables in addition to the regular diet.

With the exception of the vicuña, the lamoids breed freely in captivity, single births being the rule. In South America there seems to be a more or less restricted season of births (Cabrera and Yepes, 1940), but in northern zoological gardens it appears to be less sharply defined. Of thirty-eight llamas born here, births have taken place in every month except February, the largest number (eleven) in September. Births of guanacos to a total of thirty-three have occurred in every month but March, the largest number (seven) in July. Five alpacas have been born between March and December, while nine young vicuñas have appeared between April and December, with no emphasis on any month. The reports of Zuckerman (1953) concerning births in the Zoological Gardens of London indicate a similar distribution. Gestation periods for the llama, the guanaco, and the alpaca are given as 11 months, 10 for the vicuña (Cabrera and Yepes, 1940; Brown, 1936). The copulatory position for all is the same as that of the camels, the male forcing the female to crouch with her legs folded beneath her and abdomen resting on the ground.

As already noted, the vicuña is usually difficult to breed in the zoological garden because of the savagery of the male in attempting to force the female down, whether or not she is receptive. Here, our males have been kept in quarters adjacent to those of the females and have been admitted to their run only when one has indicated receptivity by approaching the male with only the wire partition separating them. After admission, the male has been kept under close observation and successful or not, removed after a few hours. Fred Stark, director of the San Antonio Zoological Park, Texas, where some success in breeding vicuñas has been attained, tells me that he restrains and muzzles the male before giving him brief access to the females.

Considering the great altitudes at which the lamoids live in South America, it is somewhat surprising to find that they are able to adapt perfectly well to lower levels. Flower (1931) says for the four species that they "all appear to have an ordinary life span of about 12 years." The greatest zoo longevities he was then able to list for each are: llama, Dublin Zoological Gardens, 20 years, 3 months, 4 days; guanaco, Zoological Gardens of London, 19 years, 24 days; alpaca, Cologne Zoological Gardens, 17 years, 6 months; vicuña, Zoological Gardens of London, 16 years, 10 months, 21 days, still living. Considerably longer spans are now known for all of the species. A llama born here on November 17, 1904, lived until April 7, 1926, or 21 years, 4 months, 21 days; Jones (1958) says a specimen received at the National Zoological Park on April 26, 1916, died on March 15, 1938, after 21 years, 10 months, 17 days. A guanaco received at the

Philadelphia Zoological Garden on April 29, 1909, is said by Jones (1958) to have lived until February 13, 1933, or 23 years, 9 months, 15 days. A white alpaca, received here as an adult on October 17, 1903, was destroyed on January 4, 1922, 18 years, 2 months, 18 days later; Rabb (1960) records 20 years for an alpaca in the Chicago Zoological Park. The vicuña listed by Flower (1931) as having been received at the Zoological Gardens of London on December 20, 1913, and still living is reported by Jones (1958) as having died on February 17, 1933, its final span being 19 years, 1 month, 28 days; a vicuña born here on October 27, 1904, lived until September 23, 1928, or 23 years, 10 months, 27 days.

SUBORDER RUMINANTIA

CHEVROTAINS, DEER, GIRAFFES, PRONGHORN, ANTELOPES, WILD CATTLE, GOATS, AND SHEEP

An immense number of species, forming five distinct families, make up this diversified, widely distributed, and highly successful suborder. Varying widely in size and general appearance, they nevertheless share a number of common characters. There are no incisor teeth in the upper jaw, although upper canines are present in some species and may sometimes be developed as tusks. The canines of the lower jaw are incisor-like in form and are closely aligned with the three incisors of each side. Hollow horns with bony cores or solid, deciduous antlers on permanent pedicels of bone, are frequent. Except in the chevrotains, the stomach has four compartments, allowing full powers of rumination.

FAMILY TRAGULIDAE

CHEVROTAINS OR MOUSE DEER

Strongly suggestive of tiny deer in general appearance, the chevrotains differ in several particulars. Among these are the well-developed bony support of the two small outer toes, lacking in other members of the subfamily, and the complete or partial separation of the main metacarpal and metatarsal elements that in others are fused to form the cannon bones (Lydekker, 1893–96, 2:399). The stomach is comparatively simple and is usually said to have three instead of four compartments, as in the camels, although rumination takes place. No antlers are borne by either sex, but the upper canines of males are lengthened as tusks which extend outside the lips to below the line of the lower jaw.

The chevrotains are small, furtive creatures, keeping to dense jungle and depending upon concealment for protection. In walking they seem to move on tiptoe, giving them a stiff and stilted appearance. There are two genera: *Tragulus*, confined to Asia and nearby islands, and *Hyemoschus*, of Africa.

Three species are included in *Tragulus*: *T. meminna*, the Indian chevrotain or mouse deer, from southern India and Ceylon; *T. napu*, the larger Malayan chevrotain or mouse deer, found in southeastern Asia, Sumatra, Borneo, and nearby islands, and *T. javanicus*, the lesser Malayan, of similar distribution but including Java (Ellerman and Morrison-Scott, 1951). More than fifty races of the latter two have been described. All three species are brownish in color, with white underparts. The Indian is spotted and striped with white on body and sides; the two others have no white markings on the body, but there are usually five white stripes on the fore-neck of the larger Malayan, while in the lesser Malayan there are but three bands, with a blackish area on the nape. Blanford (1888–91) gives the shoulder height of the Indian as 10–12 inches and of the larger Malayan as 13 inches; the more diminutive lesser Malayan is among the smallest of the hoofed mammals of the world.

In spite of the fact that most of the Asiatic chevrotains that reach zoological gardens are hand-reared, perfectly tame animals, they never have become firmly established. Perhaps the extreme delicacy generally imputed to them is somewhat exaggerated, but in any case they are invariably regarded as difficult and are treated on that basis. From 1904 to 1926 six specimens of *Tragulus*, one identified as the Indian, were received here. All were shown in small, glass-fronted compartments in our Monkey House, where the best longevity achieved was 2 years, 10 months, 18 days. These animals were fed browse, chiefly Russian mulberry, lettuce, fruits, vegetables, and bread, finely diced. In spite of maintenance difficulties, Asiatic chevrotains have occasionally been bred, Zuckerman (1953) recording nine births of two races of *T. napu* in the Zoological Gardens of London between 1836 and 1922. The breeding habits are not well known; for *T. meminna*, Blanford (1888–91) gives the rutting season in India as "about June or July," while the gestation period of 120 days usually quoted for this species appears to stem from Jennison (n.d.). Flower (1931) gives no longevities for chevrotains. Jones (1958) says specimens of *T. napu stanleyanus* lived in the Philadelphia Zoological Garden from June 6, 1899, to December 14, 1903, or 4 years, 6 months, 8 days, and in the Zoological Gardens of London from September 26, 1910, to September 1, 1915, or 4 years, 11 months, 6 days. He adds that an Indian chevrotain was kept at London from April 13, 1905, to December 31, 1909, or 4 years, 8 months, 18 days.

A pair of lesser Malayan mouse deer received here on September 13, 1961, was placed in a glass-fronted compartment, approximately 6 by 8 feet, in our Small Mammal House, with a low rock structure at the back. Periods of natural and red light alternated without appearing to affect the animals. Food consisted of diced apples, bananas, carrots, and raw sweet potatoes, with feeding pellets of mixed grain, crushed monkey pellets, rolled oats, and alfalfa hay, little of the latter being eaten. On January 8, 1962, the female gave birth to a single young which, on the next day, was found to weigh 371 grams. The parents remained on friendly terms with each other and the male was several times seen to lick the young. The latter was observed nibbling alfalfa on January 26. It grew rapidly and appeared to be thriving but died unexpectedly on March 31. The female was receptive and was bred on the day following the birth, producing a second young on June 10, 1962. Receptivity again occurred on the following day. At intervals of approximately 5 months, further young were born on November 10, 1962, and on April 14, 1963. The latter three were fully reared by the mother.

The water chevrotain (*Hyemoschus aquaticus*), of which three races have been described, is found in the dense forests of equatorial Africa, from the eastern [Belgian] Congo to the west coast. This is a considerably larger animal than its Asiatic relatives, Lydekker (1913–16, 4:296) giving its height as about 13–14 inches. Color varies from bright chestnut to olive, handsomely spotted and striped with white on the body, throat, and chest. As its name implies, the water chevrotain haunts rivers and swampy bush areas, seeking water for escape and safety when in danger.

Perhaps because of the general inaccessibility of its habitat, the water chevrotain seems to have been kept in captivity less frequently than the Asiatic species, although the Knowsley Menagerie is said to have possessed it as early as 1841 (Flower, 1929). Seven specimens were received at the New York Zoological Park on June 15, 1949, these having been collected for us in the eastern [Belgian] Congo by Charles Cordier. Two were sent almost immediately to the Chicago Zoological Park but the others were retained here. Because of their comparatively large size, they were treated like small duikers and were kept in fairly large compartments in our

Kangaroo House, with access to roomy outside runs in summer. Although wild-caught, they settled down well, and while they never became really tame, were reasonably steady. While there was some difficulty, at first, in persuading them to take dried food items, they eventually became conditioned to accepting small amounts of alfalfa hay and rolled oats or grain pellets, with fresh leaves of the Russian mulberry, when available, lettuce and other greens, dried fruits and vegetables, and bread. There was no breeding activity, the only recorded captivity birth appearing to be one in the Zoological Gardens of London in 1883 (Zuckerman, 1953). The survivor of this group, a male, lived until December 31, 1952, a span of 3 years, 6 months, 16 days, apparently the greatest so far recorded for the species.

FAMILY CERVIDAE

DEER

The most striking characteristic of the deer, of course, is found in the antlers, often of impressive size and intricately branched, borne by the males of many species. These antlers are deciduous and composed of solid, bony tissue, supported by permanent bases or pedicels that extend from the frontal bones. They are usually dropped at least once annually, following the breeding season. As they rise again from the pedicels, they are covered with a highly vascular, finely haired coating known as velvet. When growth has been completed, the velvet dries and is rubbed off by friction against any convenient projection, leaving the antlers clean and hard, a condition usually coinciding with the onset of the rutting period. Antlers are tender and subject to injury during their growth, serious damage being likely to result in malformation. At this time the animal's only defense is his hoofs. These proved inadequate in the case of a Malay sambar (*Cervus unicolor equinus*) that was killed here by a previously persecuted female, soon after dropping his antlers.

In the reindeer and caribou (*Rangifer*), females as well as males bear antlers, while in the Chinese water deer (*Hydropotes*) and the musk deer (*Moschus*) they are lacking in both sexes. In males of antlered species these usually appear at the age of one year and take the form of a single spike. Branching then continues, year by year, until the maximum development and number of points have been achieved and the owner has reached his full size. As his vigor begins to wane, the antlers retrogress, year by year, so that eventually they may hardly exceed the original spikes. A series of antlers dropped by a male axis deer (*Axis axis*) born here on April 15, 1901, preserved up to the time of his death in 1914, showed steady increase in size up to the seventh year, a leveling off in the eighth and ninth years, and gradual retrogression thereafter (Ditmars, 1919). In Europe the great economic importance of deer, particularly the red (*Cervus elaphus*) and the roe (*Capreolus*), as well as the ancient traditions of hunting for sport, have developed an almost legendary nomenclature for the antlers and their parts. These are fully set forth by Lydekker (1898*a*) and Frechkop (1955). Damage to the testicles or complete loss results in curious deformities of the antlers (Wislocki, Aub, and Waldo, 1947). Antlers, usually small or often single spikes, sometimes occur in females of species in which they normally do not appear. Such animals may be apparently sexually normal, diseased, senescent, or hermaphroditic (Wislocki, 1954, 1956). A female Père David's deer born here in June, 1954, grew a single spike in 1955 and was still living, in apparent good health, in 1963. Up to that time the spike had not been shed nor had the animal borne a fawn.

In antlered species upper canines are often present, though usually poorly developed. In those species lacking antlers, the Chinese water deer and the musk deer, the upper canines of males are greatly lengthened as tusks, while the muntjacs (*Muntiacus*) and the tufted deer (*Elaphodus*) are doubly armed. Lateral toes are usually present, though not functional. Facial or preorbital glands, situated before and below the eyes, are found in all but the musk deer and the roe deer (*Capreolus*) (Lydekker, 1913–16:4), and there may also be glands between the hoofs and on the lower extremities of the hind legs. As suggested by Lydekker (1898*a*), these scent glands presumably have both recognition and sexual functions. Only the musk deer has a gall bladder (Lydekker, 1913–16:4).

The deer are widely distributed, being found over most of Europe, Asia, and both North and South America. Even Africa is represented, for the Barbary deer (*Cervus elaphus barbarus*), once fairly abundant on the northern fringe in Tunis and Algeria though now greatly reduced, is said by Salez (1959) to have still existed in 1953, to the number of from three to four hundred animals living under protection in the latter country. There are no native deer in Australia, New Zealand, or New Guinea, although various species have been introduced by man into all these areas (de Vos, Manville, and Van Gelder, 1956). Specific habitats vary from the treeless tundra of the Arctic to the dense jungles of the tropics and forbidding mountainous heights.

All the deer are herbivorous, some species being largely grazers, while others feed chiefly on browse, including leaves, twigs, and tender bark or even on lichens or "reindeer moss." Annual migrations covering considerable distances to and from seasonal feeding grounds are made by some species, notably the American wapiti (*Cervus*) and the caribou and reindeer (*Rangifer*). For the most part, deer are social animals, often living in herds that break up into smaller groups or harems during the mating season. Some, however, such as the moose (*Alces*), live solitary lives, pairs coming together only during the period of rut.

Coloration of adults is principally in shades of brown or gray, usually lighter or more reddish in summer pelage. Fawns are commonly spotted with white, although such markings are sometimes wanting, as in the moose and the Indian sambar. When spots are present in fawns, they usually have disappeared by the age of $3\frac{1}{2}$ or 4 months, although they persist throughout life in some species, such as the axis deer (*Axis axis*), and to a lesser extent in the fallow (*Dama*) and in the races of the sika (*Cervus nippon*), when they are more conspicuous in summer than in winter coats.

Variations in size among the members of the Cervidae are great, ranging from the tiny pudu (*Pudu pudu*) of Chile, with a shoulder height of approximately 13 inches and maximum weight of 24 pounds (Goodwin, 1954), to the great Alaska moose (*Alces gigas*), for which Seton (1927, **3**:155–56) estimates a live weight of 1,700 or 1,800 pounds, with a shoulder height of 7 feet, 8 inches.

While deer of some sort, most commonly the fallow, are included in most collections, few zoological gardens maintain extensive series. This results, presumably, from lack of space, for while deer are easily maintained in large inclosures, they are much more difficult in smaller quarters. Bucks are very likely to injure or even kill does if closely confined during the rutting season. For this reason it has become common practice in some institutions where deer are so kept to de-antler bucks as soon as these appendages have hardened, destroying their most attractive feature.

Deer have always been of major importance in our collection here. The principal area devoted to these animals consists of a series of inclosures varying in size from $\frac{1}{2}$ acre to as much as 2 acres or more. These are situated on rather high ground so that, while they are well grassed, there is excellent drainage. Shade is provided by scattered trees that must have their trunks wire-covered to protect them from nibbling and the rubbing of antlers. Low, rustic buildings are internally divided into compartments that provide heatless protection for the inmates of adjoining corrals. Shelters to which the animals may be confined are essential for the operation of deer herds, not only for the comfort of the animals but to facilitate the almost annually necessary removals. Fencing now in use consists of wire netting of oblong mesh, 4 by 6 inches, American Standard 9 gauge, 7 feet high, strung on stout steel posts set at intervals of 10 feet. As originally constructed, these barriers were of somewhat heavier gauge and all dividing partitions were double, the sections being about 1 foot apart to prevent adjoining bucks from injuring each other in fighting. The single partitions now used are reinforced by an extra panel of wire for the lower 4 feet, and this, coupled with separating the more aggressive bucks by keeping a placid one between them, has kept fighting at a minimum. While of course almost any deer can clear a 7-foot fence with no difficulty, they seldom attempt to do so unless unduly disturbed, and I cannot recall a single actual escape here by this means. Most of our deer fences are set over shallow, sunken walls of stone that prevent the animals from digging under, a project in which many of the smaller species are proficient. Diamond-mesh wire, often useful for inclosing animals of some other groups, is not suitable for deer, since it is subject to damage by antlers or, for that matter, may entangle them.

Each of our herds consists of an adult male with up to six females and their young. While several males of some species, such as axis and fallow, will live with a herd without too much bickering except by occasional cantankerous individuals, bucks of most kinds will not tolerate rivals at anything like close quarters. Consequently, each autumn, as antlers begin to harden, young males of the previous year's crop are removed, usually by means of the convenient shelter house. In order to make the continuity of the herd certain, at least one young buck of each of the more uncommon kinds is held in reserve in a series of smaller inclosures, out of the public view. Males of most if not all species are capable of breeding in their second autumn, although in nature they may not have the opportunity to do so.

Feeding schedules for deer here are on a fairly simple basis. For the grazing species, such as wapiti, abundant grass is available during the summer months in practically all inclosures. The needs of browsers, such as whitetails (*Odocoileus*) and moose (*Alces*), cannot be supplied by natural growth and must be furnished in cut form. As pointed out by Hastings, Duke of Bedford (1949), captive deer will not thrive on natural food alone, and even in summer this diet must be supplemented. In general, deer prefer clover or alfalfa hay, and in former days we used clover almost exclusively. This was not entirely satisfactory, however, since the animals ate only the tender tips and left the tougher stalks, with resultant waste. In recent years we have turned to alfalfa, which is now fed almost exclusively. Since smaller amounts are required and all parts are eaten, this hay has proved more economical than clover and we believe that our deer herds keep in better condition. Hay is fed in racks, placed high enough so that antlered bucks cannot damage them but still can reach the contents. In addition to hay, all deer receive an allowance of feeding pellets. These are specially mixed and pressed for us, from the following formula:

200	lbs.	cane molasses
200		linseed-oil meal
200		wheat bran
400		hominy feed and corn meal
419.5		crushed oats
200		beet pulp
240		chopped alfalfa
60		wheat-germ meal
40		brewer's yeast
0.5		irradiated yeast
20		salt
15		dicalcium phosphate
5		ground limestone
2,000	lbs.	

This mixture is loosely pressed into pellets about $\frac{1}{2}$ inch long by $\frac{1}{2}$ inch wide. They bind together well, are eaten freely, and are superior to meal in that there is no danger of inhalation and no wastage, since everything is eaten cleanly. Close supervision of feeding is maintained and quantities reduced or increased as required to maintain condition without waste.

When browse is provided, it should be freshly cut, tied into bunches, and hung tips down, well above the ground. This avoids loss by trampling, as well as the unsightly tangle resulting if browse is thrown on the ground. Birch, maple, and willow are all suitable, but wild cherry should be avoided because of the risk of possible poisoning. Browse is a problem here, since there is little available for many miles, but of course it is abundant in greater variety in many other localities. Salt and mineral blocks impregnated with phenothiazine, as a deterrent to gastrointestinal parasites, are available in each inclosure. Running water in concrete troughs is maintained at all times.

Fawns of all species with which we have had experience here are easily reared on whole cow's milk or reconstituted evaporated milk, warmed and fed from a rubber-nippled nursing bottle. We usually allow the young animal to nurse naturally for 24 hours before it is picked up, to give it the advantage of whatever virtue the mother's first milk or colostrum may possess. However, fawns orphaned at birth seem to thrive as well, and if there should be any difficulty in evacuation, wiping the anus with warm, moist cotton wool or, if necessary, administering a light enema will usually bring the desired result. If there should be diarrhea, this generally can be checked by diluting the milk with water or by the addition of limewater. Small quantities at intervals of from 3 to 4 hours should be given at first, with increases commensurate with growth. Fawns will begin nibbling solid food at 2 or 3 weeks, and care must then be taken that only readily digestible foods are available. Calf-meal moistened with milk is an excellent starter. Feeding experiments reported by Silver (1961) suggest that undiluted evaporated milk may produce better results than whole cow's milk for white-tailed deer fawns.

These general notes will apply to most of the hardy species; exceptions will be noted in the following. However, it should be pointed out here that, with the exception of occasional quiet individuals, rutting bucks are almost uniformly dangerous and inclosures containing them must be entered with caution, if at all. Our first old deer-keeper went on his daily rounds in autumn with a grain bucket in one hand and in the other a pick-ax handle, with which he banged sharply on such rocks or other solid objects as he chanced to pass. Whether or not because of this precaution, I cannot recall that he was ever seriously attacked. Nowadays, we find means to confine dangerous animals when inclosures must be entered, but cautious and experienced keepers in any case are unlikely to expose themselves to obvious danger.

Of the well over one hundred and fifty forms of deer generally recognized, certainly more than half have been exhibited by the world's zoological gardens and all seventeen genera of Simpson (1945) have been represented. Up to 1953 we had shown here forty-two forms, as listed by McClung (1953), and one added since (the Roosevelt wapiti, *Cervus canadensis roosevelti*) brings our total to forty-three forms of fourteen genera, with only *Moschus*, the musk deer, *Elaphodus*, the tufted deer, and *Pudu*, the pudu, missing. In 1963 our collection consisted of fourteen kinds, of seven genera. An attempt to cover all the many known members of this family would obviously be beyond our present scope, but some notes on the groups should be in order.

The genus *Moschus* contains a single species, the musk deer (*Moschus moschiferus*), ranging in the mountains of central and eastern Asia from Kashmir to Siberia, Sakhalin Island in the Sea of Okhotsk, Manchuria, Mongolia, China, and Korea. Seven races are listed by Ellerman and

Morrison-Scott (1951). The musk deer is a small, brownish creature, more or less marked with gray and white. Blanford (1888–91) gives the shoulder height of a male as about 20 inches, the weight of a female as about 20 pounds. Some of the characters of the musk deer have already been noted: the absence of antlers and facial glands, the presence of a gall bladder, and, in males, the great development of the movable canines (Aitchison, 1946–47). The lateral hoofs are said to be functional (Lydekker, 1913–16:4). A large abdominal gland in males contains the musk for which the animal is named; the high commercial value of this material has led to persecution of this species throughout its range.

In spite of its wide distribution, the musk deer has always been rare in collections of living animals. Flower (1929) says that the first specimen received alive in Europe arrived at the Zoological Gardens of London on March 31, 1869, and died on October 27 of the same year. Scattered specimens received at various European zoological gardens appear to have fared no better. No specimen has been kept here, and I find no record of arrival elsewhere in this country. Hastings, Duke of Bedford (1949), writing of the great collection of ungulates at Woburn Abbey, Bedford, England, in the early part of the present century, says that a number of musk deer were liberated in wooded sections of the estate, but that while several young were born, the species failed to become established. Lydekker (1898a) presents a photograph of one of these animals. Blanford (1888–91) gives the rutting season in a captive pair as January and the gestation period as about 160 days, a single spotted fawn being born in June. He adds that two young are sometimes produced and that they procreate when less than 1 year old. A musk deer fawn was born in the Zoological Gardens of Frankfurt in 1962 (*Internatl. Zoo News*, 9 [4]:103).

The Chinese water deer (*Hydropotes inermis*) is light yellowish brown in general, while the underparts and a narrow perpendicular band on the muzzle are whitish. Shoulder heights of eleven specimens as given by Allen (1938–40, 2:1139) range from 450 to 550 millimeters (approximately 17.7 inches to 21.6 inches) and weight from 20 to 24 pounds. There is little if any difference in size between the sexes. There are no antlers, and the upper canines of males are strongly developed, extending well below the line of the lower jaw. The typical race is best known from the marshy borders of the Yangtze River in eastern China, although Allen (1938–40, 2:1141) says it may sometimes be found on mountainsides or in cultivated areas. A somewhat darker form (*H. i. argyropus*) has been described from Korea.

The water deer was first described in 1870, and in 1873 a living specimen was received at the Zoological Gardens of London (Flower, 1929). Occasional arrivals followed, but it was not until animals were received and liberated in the park at Woburn Abbey that the species really became established in captivity. Young were sent to various estates in both France and England, where they continued to thrive under conditions of semi-liberty (Hastings, Duke of Bedford, 1949).

A single water deer was received here in 1901. This animal lived for just over four years. Two pairs, received from Woburn Abbey on December 27, 1946, were liberated in an inclosure of perhaps 1½ acres, along with four young Père David's deer (*Elaphurus davidianus*) that had arrived at the same time. Here the water deer have continued to thrive and breed, proving themselves completely hardy and indifferent to cold. No water for bathing or wading is provided, but this appears not to violate a basic requirement—in fact, the little animals keep mostly to the higher ground. Water deer are inveterate grazers but require supplemental rations, provided in the form of alfalfa hay and the feeding pellets already described, which they take well. In order to make certain that the Père David's do not prevent free access to food, a feeding pen (creep), with openings small enough to exclude the larger animals, was provided. The water deer, shy at first, soon learned to make use of this refuge.

At the breeding season, which occurs in late autumn and early winter, some fighting may occur between rival males, but while the long canines can inflict serious wounds, results are seldom fatal. Of the forty-five fawns that have been born here, ten appeared in late May, the remainder in June. An inclosure of 4 by 6-inch mesh, of course, offers no obstruction to the tiny youngsters, so that to prevent their loss, the entire circumference of the paddock had to be covered at the bottom with a run of fine netting. Water deer are often said to produce litters of from five to seven young, and in fact Allen (1938–40, 2:1141) reports several instances of six and seven fetuses recovered from collected specimens. However, most births here have been of twins, with occasional singles and two or three sets of triplets, but no more. In spite of the narrow flight threshold of the water deer, several young hand-reared on reconstituted evaporated milk or fresh whole milk fed from a nursing bottle have remained steady and completely tame. However, we have never been able to return one of these pets to the group because of the antagonism of established members.

Few records of the longevity of the Chinese water deer in captivity have been kept. One of our original males, received December 27, 1946, lived until March 8, 1952, or 5 years, 2 months, 9 days; a male born here on June 5, 1948, died November 18, 1955, after 7 years, 5 months, 13 days; a female born on June 7, 1948, died June 18, 1959, or 11 years, 11 days. Jones (1958) lists a specimen received at the Zoological Gardens of London on January 1, 1874, as having lived until October 9, 1884, or 10 years, 9 months, 8 days.

The muntjacs (*Muntiacus*) are small, furtive creatures, widely distributed in the southern Asiatic region. The males bear short, incurved antlers with a single small brow tine, rising from slender pedicels almost as long. The pedicels are supported by downward extensions along the frontal bone, so prominent that the name "rib-faced deer" is sometimes applied. The upper canines of males are developed as tusks and have been shown to be slightly movable (Blanford, 1888–91; Aitchison, 1946–47). Adults of all the numerous forms are brownish or blackish in general, with some variation in tone, while the young are lightly spotted with white. The lateral hoofs are weakly developed or even entirely missing.

Five species are recognized by Ellerman and Morrison-Scott (1951), but only two are sufficiently well known to be of importance to the zoological garden. These are the Indian muntjac (*Muntiacus muntjak*) and Reeves's muntjac (*Muntiacus reevesi*). The Indian muntjac is found, in a great number of races, from southeastern China and India to the Sunda Islands and Borneo, the typical locality being Java. In general this is a dark-brown animal, with white underparts, for which Blanford (1888–91) gives a shoulder height of 20–22 inches and the weight of a male as 38 pounds. It is solitary in habit, keeping mostly to heavy forest or seeking grazing spots along the edges.

In this country the Indian muntjac has been kept sparingly by most of the larger zoological gardens and has been bred at San Diego (Stott, 1954) and perhaps elsewhere. Twelve representatives of this species, of undetermined race, were received at the New York Zoological Park between 1900 and 1937. The greatest longevity achieved was 5 years, 6 months, and no young were born. In Europe the species has been more widely kept and freely bred. Blanford (1888–91) says that rut occurs in northern India in January and February, that the gestation period is 6 months, and that the young are usually born in June or July, though some may be produced throughout the year. However, since captive animals may have come from widely separated areas, much variation in breeding periods is to be expected. Zuckerman (1953) shows that thirty births of Indian muntjacs in the Zoological Gardens of London were distributed through every month except January, single young being the rule.

Hastings, Duke of Bedford (1949), says that Indian muntjacs proved perfectly hardy at liberty at Woburn and that they increased well. However, because males proved dangerous to small dogs, they were eventually eliminated in favor of the supposedly less aggressive Reeves's muntjac. Here the Indian muntjac was considered to be non-hardy, as might well be the case with specimens from southern parts of the range, and were kept indoors in cold weather. Our specimens received alfalfa hay, a mixture of ground grains, greens, and diced vegetables.

Jones (1958) lists an Indian muntjac that arrived at the National Zoological Park on October 13, 1937, and died on May 26, 1946, after 8 years, 7 months, 13 days and a specimen received at the Zoological Gardens of London on October 20, 1926, that lived until October 19, 1941, or 14 years, 11 months, 29 days.

Reeves's muntjac is a native of southern China, with a possibly separable race (*micrurus*) in Formosa. It is a smaller animal than the Indian, Allen (1938–40, 2:1156) giving the shoulder height of a male as 445 millimeters (approximately 17.5 inches) and the weight as 15 kilograms (approximately 33 pounds). It is brown above, with the underparts white. A black streak runs up each side of the face, the intervening area being bright yellowish brown in adult males and duller in females, providing a ready distinction when antlers are not easily distinguished.

Reeves's muntjac was described from a living pair received at the Zoological Gardens of London on May 26, 1838, the male becoming the type (Flower, 1929). Since that time the species has been seen with some frequency in European collections, though it is less commonly kept in this country. Our first representatives were a male and two females received on June 30, 1938, reinforced by two females obtained in 1941 from the Zoological Gardens of London. These animals were liberated in a grassy, wired inclosure of about 1½ acres, which they shared with a small herd of Indian blackbuck (*Antilope cervicapra*). A small concrete pool provided drinking facilities, and an unheated shelter with an entrance too small for the blackbuck furnished a retreat for feeding and was often used by females during parturition. Here the muntjacs proved perfectly hardy at all seasons. There never has been any conflict between the two species, which ignore each other completely. However, adult male muntjacs may be aggressive toward each other, and we have always had to keep the members of this sex at a minimum. In pursuing a defeated rival or even when driving a female, males will sometimes strike downward with their antlers on the hips of the hunted animal with such force as to drive it to the ground. Very occasionally both males and females may be found to have suffered severe cuts, suggesting use of the canine teeth, but these have seldom resulted in loss.

Muntjacs seem to be primarily browsers rather than grazers, but when leaves and bark are not available they eat grass readily enough. They also take alfalfa hay and feeding pellets freely, so that there is no dietary difficulty.

Allen (1938–40, 2:1158) gives the breeding season as late January and February and the time of birth as early June. The gestation period appears not to have been determined, although presumably it approximates that of the Indian muntjac. Zuckerman (1953) reports the births of seventeen Reeves's muntjacs in the Zoological Gardens of London as having occurred in each month of the year except January, February, March, and October, all being of single young. Of one hundred young of this species born here, some have appeared in every month, with a preponderance in April, May, June, and July. No multiple birth was recorded. The tiny young are extremely secretive and hide themselves so successfully in tufts of grass or behind any small obstruction that they are not easily found. Like fawns of the water deer, they have no difficulty in passing through or under the wire mesh of their inclosure, concealing themselves in the surrounding shrubbery. This caused us some concern until we found that, unlike the water deer that simply wandered away and became lost, the young muntjacs returned regularly to their mothers and appeared to be perfectly oriented.

The greatest longevity recorded for a Reeves's muntjac here is for a female born July 13, 1949, that died on February 16, 1960, after 10 years, 7 months, 3 days. Jones (1958) lists a specimen born in the Philadelphia Zoological Garden on July 18, 1941, that died on October 4, 1956, after 15 years, 2 months, 16 days, and another that lived at the same institution from April 10, 1937, to August 22, 1953, or 16 years, 4 months, 12 days.

The tufted deer (*Elaphodus cephalophus*) is found, in three usually recognized races, in southern China and northern Burma. Strongly suggestive of the muntjacs in general appearance, the tufted deer differs in the tiny antlers, almost hidden by the long blackish hair of the forehead, and the absence of supporting bases of the pedicels. The upper canines of males are tusklike. The color is dark brown or grayish, with some variation between the races, and there are white markings on ears and tail. The fawns are faintly spotted. The shoulder height is given by Tate (1947) as 22–23 inches and weight as about 40 pounds. The species is rare in living collections and there seem to be no records of its importation into this country. It has been seen sparsely in Europe, the Zoological Gardens of London, according to Lydekker (1898a:215), having received ten examples of Michie's tufted deer (*Elaphodus c. michianus*) between 1876 and 1884.

Jones (1958) lists a specimen of *Elaphodus c. ichangensis* as having lived at London from December 15, 1932, to November 1, 1939, or 6 years, 10 months, 17 days.

Best known of all the deer and certainly most commonly kept in captivity, is the fallow (*Dama dama*). While the original home of the species is thought to have been southern Europe and Asia Minor, it has been so widely introduced by man that it now occurs as a wild animal in many areas. The typical summer color is given by Lydekker (1913–16:4) as bright fawn, spotted over back and sides with white, a black line down the back and buttocks, and underparts white. The winter coat is grayish brown, with spotting very faint or entirely lacking. In captive herds a number of color variations occur, including a lighter, more strongly spotted phase, brown with faint spotting, and both black and white. Several other less common varieties, including blue, are described by Whitehead (1950). Antlers of males are broadly palmated at the tip, and a small dewlap or "bell," just below the throat in both sexes, is characteristic. Height at the shoulders is given by Lydekker (1913–16:4) as from 3 feet to 3 feet, 2 inches, and the weight of a five-year-old buck is reported by Whitehead (1950) as 182 pounds, 13 ounces.

The fallow deer is perfectly hardy, seldom seeking the protection of a shelter. Bucks are fairly tolerant of rivals, and if space is adequate, several will usually live with the herd with a minimum of fighting, although an occasional truculent individual may require removal. Fallows will take browse when it is available but otherwise keep in good condition on the general diet outlined, supplemented in summer by grazing.

Antlers are commonly dropped in May, and the new ones have hardened by the onset of the rutting season in September and October. Average gestation periods as given by Kenneth (1953) range from 230 to 246 days. Of 200 fawns born here, including one set of twins, 158 were recorded in June, 34 in July, 5 in August, and 1 each in September, November, and December.

The best longevity established by a fallow deer here was that of a doe born on June 17, 1906, and killed by a buck—an unusual occurrence—on January 2, 1918, after 11 years, 6 months, 16 days. Flower (1931) gives 15 years, 3 months, 16 days in the Basel Zoological Gardens and 15 years, 6 months, 14 days at Frankfurt. Jones (1958) lists an example of an animal having lived at the Philadelphia Zoological Garden from July 1, 1884, to April 2, 1900, or 15 years, 9 months, 1 day.*

The Persian fallow deer (*D. mesopotamica*), first named in 1875, was believed until recently to have become extinct. It is described by Lydekker

*See Addenda, p. 737.

(1913–16:4) as larger than *D. dama* and brighter in color. The antlers are broadened in the middle area but are not palmated at the tip, where they break into points. According to Lydekker (1898a), a male of this species was received by the Zoological Gardens of London in 1877 and a female was obtained in 1878, followed by another in 1881. Zuckerman (1953) reports six young born to these animals between 1880 and 1887 as well as eight hybrids between this species and *D. dama* from 1878 to 1885. In 1957 a male believed to represent *mesopotamica* was captured alive in Iran and taken to the von Opel Freigehege für Tierforschung, at Kronberg, Germany (Haltenorth, 1958). Later it was reported that a female had been obtained from the same area and breeding results were anticipated.*

The axis deer or chital (*Axis axis*) is found from the foothills of the Himalayas through most of India to Ceylon, where a small race (*A. a. ceylonensis*) is known. The axis is a strikingly beautiful animal, the bright reddish coat being marked with large white spots, present at all seasons. There is a dark dorsal stripe, and the underparts are white. Blanford (1888–91) gives the shoulder height of males as from 36–38 inches and, quoting Hornaday, the weight of a 36-inch male as 145 pounds. The antlers are simple, with only three points, consisting of a brow tine and forked tip. The greatest length on the outside curve given by Ward (1922) is 39 inches.

Adult axis deer are perfectly hardy in the New York area but require a shelter in severe winter weather. Fawns born in winter are less resistant and often fail to survive unless they remain well bedded in the shelter for at least a few days. Axis bucks, like fallows, are more peaceable than most, and usually several will live quietly with the herd. However, they have the peculiarity of dropping their antlers without regard to season, so that at any given time bucks with antlers at various stages may be seen. This results, of course, in constant changes in the order of dominance, which may occasionally have serious consequences. In one instance here it happened that the only hard-antlered male in the herd was a spike buck that previously had been kept in order by older animals. Released from restraint, his persecution of now defenseless superiors resulted in extensive damage before he could be removed. This almost random shedding of antlers may cause the production of two sets in the same year, as has often been reported. Axis deer are notoriously difficult to restrain and can be successfully crated for shipment only by the exercise of the greatest caution. They are predominantly grazers and are especially attractive when seen on closely clipped grass. The feeding regimen already outlined (pp. 558–59) suits them well.

*See Addenda, p. 737.

Fawns may be born at any season. A total of 225 births here were recorded as follows: January, 8; February, 15; March, 30; April, 21; May, 30; June, 25; July, 27; August, 16; September, 18; October, 17; November, 17; and December, 1. Only one pair of twins was noted. The gestation period is given by Asdell (1946) as from 7 to $7\frac{1}{2}$ months, while the averages listed by Kenneth (1953) run from 210 to 238 days.

The greatest longevity reported by Flower (1931) for a captive axis deer is that of a specimen born in the Jardin des Plantes, Paris, on July 25, 1885, which died March 22, 1904, after 18 years, 7 months, 25 days. A female born here on July 7, 1915, lived until April 28, 1936, or 20 years, 9 months, 21 days, while Simon (1943) reports 22 years for a male in the Trivandrum Zoo, India.

The hog deer (*Axis porcinus*) is a small, stout-bodied animal with comparatively short legs that enhance the appearance of solidity. The typical race, found across northern India to Burma, is brownish in general and rather darker in winter, with most individuals showing faint spotting in summer pelage. An eastern subspecies, *A. p. annamiticus*, from Thailand and Indochina, is described by Lydekker (1913–16:4) as being slightly larger with uniformly unspotted coat. Shoulder height of the typical form is given as 25–29 inches. Whitehead (1950) says an average stag weighs 100 pounds; a male aged $3\frac{1}{2}$ years and a female of $2\frac{1}{2}$ years, both born here, weighed 60 pounds each when being boxed for shipment. The antler pattern is similar to that of *A. axis*, with three points only. The greatest length on the outside curve listed by Ward (1922) is $21\frac{5}{8}$ inches.

Like the axis deer, the adult hog deer is perfectly hardy at this latitude, if provided with an unheated shelter for winter use. Males are somewhat less tolerant of each other than axis, at least at close quarters. Hog deer are also said to be more conventional in breeding habits, but dates here do not confirm this, a total of thirty-two single births having occurred as follows: January, four; February, two; March, three; April, eight; May, four; June, three; July, three; September, three; October, one; November, one. A similar distribution is shown by Zuckerman (1953) for seventy-eight births in the Zoological Gardens of London. A hybrid between axis and hog deer was born here on November 3, 1908—a not uncommon event.

A hog deer received at the Rotterdam Zoological Gardens on May 20, 1913, is said by Flower (1931) to have been still living June 1, 1930, after 17 years, 12 days, while a female born here on September 28, 1910, died on June 23, 1928, after 17 years, 8 months, 26 days.

The genus *Cervus* is a very large one, its members being found in North America, Europe, Asia, and even northwestern Africa. Variation in size is also great, ranging from species standing barely over 2 feet at the shoulder to others in which this measurement may exceed 5 feet.

The sambar group extends, in numerous forms, over much of southern Asia and the neighboring islands. While many of these deer have been kept in captivity on occasion, only two are of major importance to the present-day zoological garden. These are the Indian sambar (*Cervus unicolor niger*), found from Nepal through peninsular India, and the Malayan sambar (*Cervus u. equinus*), which ranges from southwestern China, Assam, Burma, Thailand and Indochina southward through the Malay Peninsula to Sumatra.

The Indian sambar is a large, heavily built animal, for which Blanford (1888–91) gives the shoulder height of males as 48–56 inches and the weight as 700 pounds. Two males born here weighed 410 and 445 pounds, respectively, at death as adults; a mature female weighed 360 pounds. The antlers in both Indian and Malayan races have three points only on each side but are roughened and heavy. The greatest length on the outside curve given by Ward (1922) for the Indian is 50$\frac{1}{8}$ inches. Coloration is dark grayish brown, somewhat paler in females than in males. The rather coarse hair, which is longer on the neck and throat, is thin on the body in summer but dense and long in winter. Fawns are unspotted.

Adult sambar are hardy here but will make use of an unheated shelter in cold weather. As in the two preceding species, fawns may be born at any time and do not always survive if births occur in winter. Does with newborn fawns are likely to be savage, and their weight and strength command respect. Sambar are inclined to become overly fat in confinement, and while food requirements seem to offer no special deviations, quantities should be commensurate with the condition of the animals.

According to Blanford (1888–91), the rutting season of the sambar in the Indian peninsula occurs in October and November and in the Himalayas in spring, the antlers having dropped a few months previously. Perhaps because of diverse origins, sambar males in captivity may shed their antlers at any season. This irregularity may result in two such occurrences or none at all within a calendar year, perhaps giving rise to reports of antlers remaining unshed for several years (Lydekker, 1898a), a condition which has not been observed here.

As already noted, births in captivity may occur at any season, forty-one fawns having been born here as follows: January, two; March, one; April, four; May, six; June, five; July, four; August, two; September, five; October, seven; November, five. One pair of twins was included. This experience is in accord with that of the Zoological Society of London, as reported by Zuckerman (1953). The gestation period is given by Asdell (1946) as about 8 months.

The greatest longevity given by Flower (1931) for an Indian sambar in captivity is 17 years, 4 months and still living, for a female in the Belle Vue Gardens, Manchester. Three females kept in the New York Zoological Park lived for periods in excess of 20 years. One born here on October 26, 1906, was destroyed on November 26, 1928, 22 years, 1 month later; of two received from Carl Hagenbeck on September 23, 1903, one died on February 22, 1928, after 24 years, 5 months.

The Malayan sambar is slightly smaller than the Indian and considerably darker, sometimes approaching black. The rather long tail is heavily and coarsely haired, so that the name "horse-tailed sambar" is sometimes used. Fawns may be faintly spotted at birth, markings not always easily discernible. A male born here in 1907 weighed 575 pounds at death 20 years later.

In general the Malayan sambar has seemed to us somewhat less hardy than the Indian and is often reluctant to leave the protection of its unheated shelter in cold weather. At that season it grows a particularly heavy coat, some individuals becoming almost shaggy. The usual feeding regimen in effect here has seemed suitable.

The same irregularity in the shedding of antlers and the birth of young is seen in this race as in the Indian. Twenty-four births of single young have occurred here, as follows: January, three; February, one; March, two; April, three; May, four; June, two; August, one; September, three; October, one; November, two; December, two.

Jones (1958) reports a Malayan sambar as having lived in the Philadelphia Zoological Garden from April 14, 1916, to September 30, 1935, or 19 years, 5 months, 16 days. A female born in the New York Zoological Park on April 29, 1912, died on April 17, 1936, after 23 years, 11 months, 19 days. A young pair received here on July 5, 1929, lived together for several years, in the course of which no young were produced, and the male, when in hard antler, persecuted the female with increasing severity. On December 8, 1936, when the male had just dropped his antlers, he was killed by the sharp hoofs of his mate. The female then continued to live alone, becoming a great favorite with visitors and keepers, until December 11, 1955, when she died after 26 years, 5 months, 6 days.

A number of other closely related deer have been sparingly kept by various zoological gardens. A male of the small Timor deer (*Cervus t. timorensis*) was received here in 1904 but lived for only just over 1 year. Of a pair of the very similar Molucca deer (*Cervus t. moluccensis*) that arrived here on March 24, 1904, the female lived until October 1, 1917, or 13 years, 6 months, 7 days, the male until October 14, 1917, or 13 years, 6 months, 20 days. All these animals were treated as non-hardy and were housed in heated quarters during the winter months. Our Molucca deer produced no offspring, but the form bred freely in the Zoological Gardens of London between 1863 and 1893, as reported by Zuckerman (1953). The Molucca deer has been introduced into New Guinea and the Aru Islands (de Vos, Manville, and Van Gelder, 1956).

Another species of this group that has been shown infrequently is the small, beautifully marked Philippine spotted or Prince Alfred's deer (*Cervus alfredi*). This handsome little animal has been kept by the Philadelphia Zoological Garden, and four breeding records in the Zoological Gardens of London are given by Zuckerman (1953).

The barasingha or swamp deer (*Cervus duvauceli*) ranges through the Himalayan foothills from Assam in the east to Sind in the west, as well as in the Central Provinces of the Indian peninsula. The typical race occupies the area north of the Ganges, while animals south of that river have been designated as *C. d. branderi* (see Ellerman and Morrison-Scott, 1951). This is a slenderly built and graceful species, seeming to prefer open woodlands and grassy plains to heavy jungle. Blanford (1888–91) gives the shoulder height as 44–46 inches and the weight of males as 460–570 pounds. An aged female here weighed 305 pounds at death, while a much younger female gave a living weight of 320 pounds. The antlers have no points between the brow tine and the tip, which divides into two, each division producing several points. The greatest length on the outside curve listed by Ward (1922) is 41 inches. The winter coat is rather heavy, especially about the neck and throat, uniformly brown in color, and somewhat darker in males than in females. In summer the short, fine hair is a lovely bright yellowish-brown, almost golden, with faint white spotting in both sexes along the sides and flanks. The orange velvet of developing antlers enhances the effect. Fawns are prettily spotted with white.

The barasingha is thoroughly hardy here, making little use of a shelter and thriving on the usual diet, with abundant grazing in summer. Does with young are strongly defensive, although perhaps less so than sambar. Males are not markedly aggressive, although the only instance here in which a man was seriously injured by a deer was a savage attack by a barasingha buck.

Blanford (1888–91) says that in Mandla, central India, herds collect in September and October, the rutting season occurring soon afterward, and suggests that antlers would be shed not later than February. These dates must, of course, be subject to some variation according to locality, but they approximate our experience here. Our bucks drop their antlers in February and March (specific dates are February 19, 1949, and March 14, 1950, for the same animal), and the main rut takes place from August to October. Eight births of barasinghas in the Zoological Gardens of London as plotted by Zuckerman (1953) occurred in June, July, and August. The dates of 109 births here are much more widely spread, as follows: March, 7; April, 18; May, 30; June, 29; July, 13; August, 7; September, 2; October, 2; November, 1. Since the gestation period is given by Asdell (1946) as 250 days and by Kenneth (1953) as 240 and 250 days, these birth dates indicate that the breeding season is not rigidly defined. This matter has been discussed at some length by Whitehead (1950).

A female barasingha born here on March 31, 1920, died on July 10, 1941, after 21 years, 3 months, 10 days, while a female purchased from William Jamrach, London, on April 28, 1904, was destroyed on September 14, 1925, 21 years, 4 months, 17 days later. Flower (1931) reports that a female received at the Zoological Gardens of London on June 9, 1906, lived until June 24, 1929, or 23 years, 15 days.

The thamin or Eld's deer (*Cervus eldi*) is native to southeastern Asia. The typical race is found in Manipur; *Cervus e. siamensis* is known from Thailand, Indochina, and Hainan, while *Cervus e. thamin* designates animals from Burma, Tenasserim, and part of Thailand (Ellerman and Morrison-Scott, 1951).

Eld's deer is a smaller animal than the barasingha, Blanford (1888–91) giving the shoulder height of males as about 45 inches and of females as 42 inches, the weight of males from 210 to 245 pounds, of females about 140 pounds. An aged female weighed 135 pounds at death here. Both sexes are light brown in summer coat, the males becoming darker in winter. Fawns are lightly spotted with white. The antlers are unique in that the long brow tine forms a continuous curve with that of the main beam. As in the barasingha, there are no other branches except at the bifurcated tip, which may produce several points. The greatest length given by Ward (1922) is $38\frac{1}{4}$ inches measured on the outside curve, without the brow tine.

Eld's deer frequents open country on plains or in swampy areas, seldom entering forests. The Manipur race (*Cervus e. eldi*) was reported as extinct in 1951. However, a small group was found in 1952–53 and a restricted area was established to protect it (Gee, 1958; Talbot, 1960). The Burmese form (*Cervus e. thamin*) was thought to be in an equally precarious position, but Talbot (1960) reports an estimated population of from twenty-five hundred to three thousand animals, living under the protection of the Burmese Government. No recent information appears to be available concerning the eastern subspecies, *Cervus e. siamensis.*

Eld's deer has been shown in zoological gardens sparingly but rather widely over a considerable number of years, the Zoological Society of London having received its first specimen in 1867 (Flower, 1929). The only captive stock of consequence at the present time is the small herd in the Parc Zoologique du Bois de Vincennes, Paris. The original animals were brought from French Indochina just before World War II and presumably represent the eastern race, *Cervus e. siamensis.*

Our first specimens of Eld's deer, a male and two females of unknown origin, were obtained from William Jamrach, in London, and came to us in 1905 as the gift of William Rockefeller. A second pair, again of undetermined race, was purchased in 1928. A female offspring of the latter pair, born in 1930, lived until 1950 and was the survivor of the group, so that the species is no longer represented in our collection.

Eld's deer, in our experience, were more sensitive to cold than other members of *Cervus* and were provided with mildly heated shelters during the winter months, although they had free access to their runs at all times. They presented no feeding problems but were flighty and easily alarmed. I recall a young male that, startled by some unusual sight or sound, hurled himself completely through two wire fences—perhaps not as stout as they might have been—and was killed by impact against a third.

Blanford (1888–91) says that antlers are shed in June in Manipur but not until September in Lower Burma. The breeding season in Burma is from March to May, the young being born in October and November. Unfortunately, I have no notes on these periods here, though a rather extended rut is suggested by the distribution of twenty-five births here: September, four; October, two; December, four; January, nine; February, two; March, four. One pair of twins was included. Although most of these dates fall within the cold months, the rather delicate young survived well, since they usually were born in the heated shelters. One youngster, less fortunate, succumbed to a December reading of $-2°$F. $(-18.8°$C.). A terse note on its record card reads: "Carcass fed to thylacine"—a most unusual sequence, not likely to be repeated. The very short gestation period of 183 days given by both Asdell (1946) and Kenneth (1953) stems from Jennison (n.d.) and requires verification.

A female received by the Zoological Gardens of London on April 21, 1900, lived until October 19, 1913, or 13 years, 5 months, 28 days (Flower, 1931), while a specimen born at the Philadelphia Zoological Garden on July 7, 1918, and transferred to the National Zoological Park, lived there until

October 21, 1936, or 18 years, 3 months, 14 days (Jones, 1958). A female received here on August 16, 1928, died on November 19, 1948, after 20 years, 3 months, 3 days, while a daughter of this animal, born here on January 7, 1930, lived until April 24, 1950, or 20 years, 3 months, 17 days.

The sika deer (*Cervus nippon*) range through eastern Asia from Siberia and Japan to Manchuria, Korea, southern China, and Formosa. Numerous races have been described and the validity of many is still not clear; seven are listed as acceptable by Ellerman and Morrison-Scott (1951). While there is rather wide variation in size and coloration, all have points of agreement. These include a conspicuous white, black-margined erectile rump patch, a rather heavy mane on neck and throat in winter pelage, and antlers consisting of a brow tine, another above it, and a bifurcated tip, usually resulting in four points on each side. All the races are more or less spotted with white in summer, and some retain a trace of these markings in the darker winter coat. Fawns are spotted.

The sikas are forest deer, seldom venturing out of cover. In captivity, however, they thrive in open, grassy inclosures provided with some shade. All that have been kept here are fully hardy, seldom making use of the unheated shelters provided. The usual feeding schedule seems entirely suitable. The three races living here are the Japanese sika (*Cervus nippon nippon*), Dybowski's sika (*Cervus n. hortulorum*), and the Formosan sika (*Cervus n. taiouanus*).

The Japanese sika, hailing from Japan and Korea, is widely kept in zoological gardens, probably ranking second only to the fallow in abundance in captivity. It is the smallest of the group, Lydekker (1913–16:4) giving the shoulder height as 32–34 inches. In summer the typical color is reddish brown spotted with white in both sexes; the heavy winter coat is dark brown, sometimes with a vestige of spotting. A darker variant, blackish brown at all seasons and practically free from spots, is frequently seen, at least in this country. Due to escapes from captivity and intentional liberations, the Japanese sika has become established in the wild in many parts of England, as well as elsewhere.

The Japanese sika is thoroughly well adapted to captivity and is able to thrive under conditions most deer will not endure. In spite of their diminutive size, bucks are inclined to be bold or even savage and usually will not tolerate rivals. This, however, is subject to variation, and individuals are occasionally found that do not trouble younger males. Both sexes, but more particularly females, are inclined to accumulate fat, so that diets must be carefully controlled.

The greatest antler length recorded by Ward (1922) is $28\frac{3}{8}$ inches.

Antlers are shed in early spring, and the main rut occurs in September and October. Of 102 births here, 51 were in May, 31 in June, 8 each in July and August, 3 in September, and 1 in October. We have no records of twins, although Zuckerman (1953) reports five sets in 108 births in the Zoological Gardens of London. Average gestation periods given by Kenneth (1953) run from 222 to 246 days.

Bourdelle and Mouquet (1930) report that a Japanese sika born in the Jardin des Plantes, Paris, on July 24, 1911, lived until January 2, 1930, or 18 years, 5 months, 9 days. Our best longevity here is for a male received on September 22, 1905, which died August 22, 1924, after 18 years, 11 months. Jones (1958) lists a specimen born in the National Zoological Park on July 9, 1911, which died there on December 9, 1936, 25 years, 5 months later.

Dybowski's sika ranges from Korea through Manchuria and southeastern Siberia. This is the largest of the group, its shoulder height being given by Lydekker (1913–16:4) as 3 feet, 7 inches. The summer coat is light brown on the body, well spotted with white, the head and neck bluish gray. In winter the shaggy hair is dark brown, sometimes with faint indication of spotting. Mature bucks produce really fine antlers, the greatest length recorded by Ward (1922) being $34\frac{1}{4}$ inches.

As might be expected, this handsome sika is quite hardy and apparently indifferent to wide variations of temperature. If bucks are somewhat less aggressive than those of the diminutive Japanese sika, their greater size commands respect. Antlers are shed in early spring, April 6 and April 8 being specific dates here, the rut taking place in September and October. Of thirty-eight births recorded here, nine occurred in May, twenty-one in June, seven in July, and one in August. There were no cases of twinning. The average gestation period is given by Kenneth (1953) as 225 days.

A female is reported by Flower (1931) to have lived in the Zoological Gardens of London from August 20, 1872, to October 28, 1886, or 14 years, 2 months, 8 days. An adult male received here on September 26, 1928, died on August 22, 1945, after 16 years, 10 months, 27 days, while a female born here on June 19, 1929, lived until September 26, 1946, or 17 years, 3 months, 7 days.

The Formosan sika, found in the mountainous interior of that island, is intermediate in size between the two preceding forms, Lydekker (1913–16:4) giving the shoulder height as about 35 inches. The ground color is slightly lighter and brighter than that of the Dybowski and is carried over the head and neck, which do not show the gray of that race. The white spots are large and sharp and even in the heavier and darker pelage of winter are at least partially discernible. Heads of males are likely to be less impressive than those of the Dybowski, the longest antler measurement given by Ward (1922) being 19¾ inches. A female born here weighed 105 pounds when she died at the age of 15 years.

The first Formosan sikas received here were a male and two females of unknown origin purchased in 1940. The sudden death of the male in 1943 left us with females only, with no replacement available in this country. However, through the kindness of the Duke of Bedford, a male fawn born at Woburn Abbey on July 16, 1946, was picked up and hand-reared for us at Whipsnade, through the co-operation of the Zoological Society of London. Soon after his arrival here on December 27, 1946, we attempted to introduce this young male to the herd, but the females were so antagonistic that he had to be removed. Further efforts were then postponed until September of 1947, when the young buck's spikes had hardened. He did not hesitate to use them in establishing himself, and the introduction was entirely successful, the first of his offspring being born on July 11, 1948. The future conduct of this buck was typical of that of most males of the sika group, for he was intolerant of rivals, which had to be removed to save their lives. However, a son that replaced the old buck after his death in 1958 was far less aggressive toward younger males.

Formosan bucks here are likely to drop their antlers a little later than Dybowski's, a specific date being May 4. The mating season extends from mid-September into early November, and a total of forty-seven single fawns have been born here as follows: June, thirty-one; July, ten; August, five; September, one. The gestation period appears not to have been recorded but presumably it approximates the 225 days given for Dybowski's sika.

A female Formosan born here on June 5, 1943, lived until February 17, 1959, or 15 years, 8 months, 12 days. Another female, born here on August 6, 1942, died on August 15, 1958, after 16 years, 9 days.

The controversial *pseudaxis* of Eydoux and Souleyet still remains something of an enigma. A single male obtained in Java during a voyage in 1841–52 and described as the type lived for several years in the Jardin des Plantes, Paris, where it produced fertile hybrids when paired to a female axis deer (Lydekker, 1913–16, 4:116). Delacour (1931) gives an account of living sikas that he brought to Paris from Indochina and which he considers to be identical with the type preserved in the Museum d'Histoire Naturelle. He gives the range in Indochina as Tonkin and northern Annam, where the animals were well known to sportsmen as "axis deer." The question of *pseudaxis* has been discussed by Lydekker (1913–16, 4:116) and later by Glover (1956). In a list of ungulates living in the Paris collections, Nouvel, Pasquier, Rinjard, and Chauvier (1958) refer the descendants of Delacour's importations to *hortulorum*. It is well known, of course, that deer of many sorts have been transported freely since very early times in the Asiatic area, resulting in much later confusion. But whatever the final disposition of *pseudaxis* may be, the small but vigorous herds at the Jardin des Plantes and the Parc Zoologique de Vincennes continue to impress visitors with their beauty.

The European red deer (*Cervus elaphus*) is the traditional native deer of that region, while the species, in many races, extends from the British Isles across Europe and Asia to the Sea of Japan and even, as already mentioned, to the northwestern fringe of Africa. The typical form (*Cervus e. elaphus*), described from Sweden, is said by Lydekker (1913–16:4) to have become greatly reduced in numbers even then, but the British race (*Cervus e. scoticus*) still persists in the wild state in parts of Ireland, England, and Scotland, while the red deer of Continental Europe (*Cervus e. hippelaphus*) is abundant in suitably wooded localities. Red deer have been kept in the hunting preserves and in the great private parks of Europe for centuries, and while herds presumably are largely of local origin, introductions from other areas have often been made. For this reason and also because specimens reaching zoological gardens are usually of unknown origin, exact designations are usually impossible.

The red deer is a large animal, Lydekker (1898a) giving the shoulder height as 4–4½ feet. Whitehead (1950) gives a table of the weights of parts of an adult male, totaling 422 pounds, 7 ounces. A fine stag destroyed here at the age of 17 years weighed 350 pounds. General color is reddish brown in summer, darker in winter, when the lengthened mane becomes conspicuous; there is a yellowish-white rump patch. Fawns are spotted, the markings sometimes persisting faintly in adults.

The antlers are long and well branched, typically showing a brow tine, followed by a second or "bez," a third or "trez," and a fourth, just below the divided tip. The latter, in mature animals, may become elaborated to form a "crown" or "cup." The bez tine is missing in some races. The red deer has been deeply involved in the progress of civilization in Europe, first as a source of food and later as an object of sport. In consequence, interest in the size, branching, and number of points of the antlers has been great, and numerous museums are devoted to collections of fine examples, often of ancient origin. Lydekker (1898a) notes that in the collection at Moritzburg, near Dresden, Germany, there are antlers measuring 50 inches on the outside curve, with points numbering up to fifty.

There is great variation in size and color of red deer in various localities, possibly related to food supply. The introduction of the species into New Zealand from 1851 on resulted in great early success, with production of remarkably fine heads. Later, as their numbers increased, the animals were found to be damaging both natural vegetation and farm crops, and an intensive control program was begun. At the same time, there was marked physical deterioration in the animals themselves, related by some authorities to diminishing availability of food. Others, however, considered the cause to be the introduction of "undesirable strains" rather than lack of nourishment (Wodzicki, 1950).

Red deer in the New York Zoological Park are established in an inclosure of about 1 acre, well shaded by large forest trees, mostly beech and oak, so spaced as to allow grass to grow freely. The overflow from the drinking trough gives rise to a small marshy area, permitting the deer to enjoy the mud bathing which is one of their characteristic habits. This area supports a herd buck, eight to ten females, and their immature offspring, the balance being maintained by regular, judicial removals. The foundation of this herd consisted of eleven animals presented by William Rockefeller in 1900 and 1902, new stags having been introduced on two later occasions. Herd bucks will not endure the presence of younger males during the rut, so that the latter must be removed as antlers begin to harden. Hinds care for their fawns well, and few are lost. Some years ago several young fawns were killed, and efforts to discover the culprit failed. However, an elderly, fawnless hind was suspected, and after her removal losses ceased. Whitehead (1950:144) reports a similar occurrence.

Antlers are usually dropped in March, dates noted here being March 6, 8, 10, and 14 and April 1. The rut takes place in September and October, when the stag's neck swells and his belling or roaring can be heard at considerable distances. The births of 218 fawns recorded here occurred as follows: May, 76; June, 109; July, 19; August, 5; September, 7; October, 2. No instances of twinning were noted, although Whitehead (1950) reports several such occurrences. Asdell (1946) gives the gestation period as 234 days, while averages listed by Kenneth (1953) run from 225 to 246 days.

A female born here on June 23, 1914, died on February 9, 1934, after 19 years, 7 months, 17 days. Brown (1925) reports that a male received at the Philadelphia Zoological Garden on May 30, 1904, lived until June 14, 1923, or 19 years, 15 days. Jones (1958) lists a specimen received at the National Zoological Park on September 22, 1914, as having died on March 24, 1941, 26 years, 6 months, 2 days later.

Several of the large races of *Cervus elaphus* found in the broad expanses of Asia have been kept in zoological gardens but for the most part are now seldom seen. The hangul (*Cervus e. hanglu*) of the mountains of Kashmir approximates the red deer in size, with small differences in color and the branching of the antlers. Three males and one female were received here on April 21, 1909, as the gift of the Duke of Bedford. None of these animals lived for more than 4 years, but a male fawn born on August 15, 1909, lived until March 20, 1917, when he was killed by becoming entangled in a wire tree brace.

The maral (*Cervus e. maral*) is a larger animal than the hangul, with long, heavy, but rather simple antlers in which the bez tine may be lacking. Ward (1922) gives the average weight as 560 pounds. The range includes the Crimea, Asia Minor, northern Persia, and the Caucasus (Ellerman and Morrison-Scott, 1951). A pair purchased from Carl Hagenbeck arrived here on October 17, 1902. They lived for approximately 6 years but failed to produce young. Zuckerman (1953) reports the births of sixteen fawns of this race between 1840 and 1870 in the Zoological Gardens of London.

The Altai wapiti (*Cervus e. asiaticus*) of Western Mongolia, while smaller than the American wapiti or elk (*Cervus canadensis*), approaches that species in size and appearance. Hornaday (1904), in writing of a pair in our collection, says that "they are a constant source of wonder, because of their well-nigh perfect similarity, at all points, to our own Wapiti." A pair of Altai wapiti was received here from Carl Hagenbeck on September 23, 1903, but the female died soon after and was replaced on March 4, 1904, by two further females from the same source. Five single young were produced, three births occurring in June and two in July. A female racial intergrade was born on June 25, 1908, to an Altai female by a Tashkent wapiti (*Cervus e. bactrianus*), the latter a single animal presented by the Duke of Bedford in 1905. This hybrid lived until September 25, 1928, a span of 20 years, 3 months. A line in my notebook of 1908 says she was redder in summer coat than her mother, so that in that season, at least, she was easily recognized. The best longevity here for an Altai of pure blood was established by a male born here on July 15, 1914, which lived until July 2, 1930, or 15 years, 11 months, 17 days.

The Manchurian wapiti or Bedford's deer (*Cervus e. xanthopygus*) is a large animal with a wide distribution in Manchuria, Mongolia, and southeastern Siberia. This form has not been kept here but has been shown fairly extensively in Europe. Its only appearance in this country, as far as I know, was at the National Zoological Park, where four specimens were received in 1916 and from which four young were bred (Mann, 1930).

Jones (1958) reports that an animal born in this herd on July 6, 1917, lived until August 18, 1938, or 21 years, 1 month, 12 days.

The American wapiti or elk (*Cervus canadensis*), once found over much of the United States and southern Canada, is now confined to the mountainous regions of the west. The typical race (*Cervus canadensis canadensis*), which was the eastern representative of the species, is now extinct and its characters have never been clearly defined (Murie, 1951). The range of the Rocky Mountain wapiti (*Cervus canadensis nelsoni*) lies in the Rockies from northern New Mexico to Alberta and British Columbia, the principal herd being that of the Yellowstone Park area. Animals of this form have been reintroduced in parts of its range where it had been exterminated and in other localities in the United States. The wapiti of Saskatchewan and Manitoba has been distinguished as *Cervus canadensis manitobensis*, while the large, dark Roosevelt's or Olympic wapiti (*Cervus canadensis roosevelti*) inhabits the humid western slopes of the mountains from Vancouver Island south through Washington and Oregon to northern California. All these races are sometimes considered to be subspecies of *Cervus elaphus* (see Ellerman and Morrison-Scott, 1951), but we here follow Hall and Kelson (1959) in retaining *canadensis*.

Since most of our experience with wapiti here has had to do with the Rocky Mountain race, the following notes, unless otherwise stated, relate to that form. The normal antlers are very large and typically six-pointed on each side, with brow, bez, trez, and fourth well developed and the tip bifurcated, the last division usually with a downward trend. The greatest length along the main beam listed by the Boone and Crockett Club (1958) is $63\frac{7}{8}$ inches for a specimen from Wyoming now in the National Collection of Heads and Horns, while Mochi and Carter (1953) say that antlers up to 66 inches have been recorded. In summer pelage the back and sides are tawny gray, with head, neck, legs, and underparts dark brown. The large rump patch is yellowish brown. The heavy winter coat is darker, the long hair of the neck and throat forming the characteristic mane. Fawns are tawny spotted with white. Murie (1951) gives the average weight of thirty adult males at Jackson Hole and Yellowstone National Park as 631 pounds; for thirty-eight females, 520 pounds; maximum weight of male, 1,032 pounds, of female, 608 pounds. A mature bull from Jackson Hole, kept in the New York Zoological Park for nearly 12 years, was killed in a crating accident and found to weigh 840 pounds; a 9-year-old cow, born here, weighed 520 pounds at death. Murie (*loc. cit.*) gives the shoulder height as 49–59 inches, with a report of a male of more than 64 inches. Females, of course, are smaller than males.

The first Rocky Mountain wapiti to arrive here were three animals received from the Park Department of Brooklyn, New York, on September 9, 1899. This nucleus was soon reinforced on October 11, 1899, by the gift of six superb specimens from the Catskill Mountain estate of George J. Gould. A magnificent bull from Idaho, the then famous "Stanley," came on October 1, 1901, and with a group of ten from the private preserve of William C. Whitney, near Lenox, Massachusetts, completed the foundation of a herd that was to endure for nearly sixty years. Stanley and a huge animal known as the "Whitney Bull" were alternated as breeding males and when not so occupied were segregated in strongly reinforced bull pens. This continued until the deaths of both animals in 1913, when their duties were taken over by younger males, notably "Stanley II." In 1947 the herd was reinforced by five wapiti brought directly from the Jackson Hole Wildlife Park at Moran, Wyoming, and continued to thrive until 1958, when it was disposed of because of pressing need for the space it had occupied so long.

The Elk Range was an undulating, well-grassed area of perhaps 2 acres with several shade trees, well protected by metal guards. A rustic building and an open shed provided shelter from wind and severe storms. At one side of this building were several pens, well separated from each other and reinforced with heavy iron pipes, where bulls not in use could be confined during the breeding season. Several small corrals permitted occasional segregation of mothers with young or others in need of isolation. One inclosed a small pond, much used for bathing by the wapiti in summer, but since it was finally suspected of implication in the infestations of internal parasites with which regular users were constantly afflicted, it was eventually filled in. All these inclosures were surrounded by the usual open-mesh wire netting, 7 feet high, over which no wapiti ever jumped.

In early days food consisted of clover or mixed clover and timothy hay and crushed or rolled oats. Wapiti will eat timothy if they have to but like most deer, prefer clover or alfalfa. More recently, alfalfa has been fed exclusively and the grain ration has consisted of the pellets already referred to. In feeding it is essential to distribute both hay and grain at well-separated points to make certain that it is available to all. Wapiti graze heavily in summer, when grass is available, so that less dry food is then required. In winter the supply must be increased, even though the animals will scrape away snow to reach the dead grass beneath it.

No one who has ever seen a rutting bull wapiti at close quarters would question the necessity for caution in managing such an animal. Even cows may be dangerous, especially when caring for calves. Males here usually drop their antlers in March, recorded dates running from March 9 to 31, with one each on April 17 and 18. Successive dates for one individual were: 1947, April 18; 1948, March 31; 1949, March 26; 1950, March 28; 1951, March 20; 1952, March 19; 1953, not recorded; 1954, March 19; 1955, March 19; 1956, March 17; 1957, March 18; 1958, March 21. All these notes were for the dropping of the first antler; as in all deer, while both antlers may drop almost simultaneously, the second may not follow for a day or two. The new antlers are hard and clean again by late August or early September, and the main rut follows in September and October, when the bugling of the bulls, whether running with the herd or held in seclusion, typifies the autumn season. Long before this time has been reached, the herd bull has been selected and all others, including spikes from the previous season, have been removed. By early December, when all the cows should have been bred and are no longer cyclic, it has been our practice to remove the bull from the herd, for the no longer responsive cows and their spring calves may be seriously persecuted, injured, or even killed by a persistent bull, particularly in heavy snow.

Average gestation periods given by Kenneth (1953) are 250 and 255 days, while Asdell (1946) gives the period as about $8\frac{1}{2}$ months. Morrison, Turner, and Wright (1959) record a full-term gestation, in a controlled instance, of 247 days. A total of 168 births here occurred as follows: April, 1; May, 6; June, 98; July, 42; August, 9; September, 4; October, 5; November, 3. One pair of twins was recorded. Zuckerman (1953) reports the occurrence of one set of twins in 67 births in the Zoological Gardens of London. It is of interest to note that one of the Gould cows received here as an adult in 1899 produced a calf annually from 1900 to 1917, missing only 1913, to a total of 17. She appears not to have been bred again but lived until September 23, 1922, or 22 years, 11 months, 12 days, our best longevity for a wapiti. Flower (1931) gives 22 years, 1 month, 8 days for an animal born in the Jardin des Plantes, Paris, while Jones (1958) lists a specimen as having lived in the National Zoological Park from September 5, 1912, to January 5, 1936, or 23 years, 4 months.

Roosevelt's or the Olympic wapiti (*Cervus canadensis roosevelti*) is considered to differ from the Rocky Mountain form in being larger and darker, with heavier but shorter antlers. Schwartz and Mitchell (1945) give the following details: shoulder height of a 5-year-old male, 60 inches, of a 4-year-old female, 59 inches; weight of mature males, 700–1,000 pounds, of females, 400–700 pounds, two specimens in poor condition weighing 405 and 425 pounds respectively; average beam length of thirteen sets of five-point antlers, 38.2 inches. The greatest antler length listed by Ward (1922) is 52 inches.

While Roosevelt's wapiti was received at the Zoological Gardens of London as early as 1863 (Flower, 1929), this race does not appear to have been kept generally by American institutions. A pair received here on April 20, 1903, as the gift of the city of Tacoma, Washington, failed to become established and soon passed on without leaving offspring. No further specimens were received until 1955, when, through the co-operation of the Department of Fish and Game at Fortuna, California, a female calf was picked up and hand-reared for us. This calf arrived here in good condition on July 27, 1955, and was kept isolated, save for brief companionship with a young male of the Rocky Mountain race. In 1959, again with the full co-operation of the authorities, a young bull and two cows were crated at the Madison Grant Elk Forest Refuge in Prairie Creek Redwood State Park, California, and safely transported to New York, where they arrived on April 21. The bull was plainly a yearling, his spikes just budding, but while the cows were comparable in size, we were undecided whether they were yearlings or 2-year-olds. After a few days' detention for physical checking, the animals were released in an inclosure already occupied by the 1955 cow.

This area, recently reconditioned after occupancy by other species, includes about 2 acres of well-shaded grass and is protected at one side by a high wall, at the other by a moat 12 feet across, well supplied with running water. Under the wall is an inclosed barn, with a shelter room adjoining a bull pen, a feed room, and another shelter for the use of animals on the range. Adjoining this is an open overhang, 30 feet long, with hay racks and grain mangers. This service area adjoins a small, paved paddock, to which the animals can be confined when required. All wire fences are of the regulation 7-foot type.

The winter feeding schedule provided 20 pounds of alfalfa hay and 7 pounds of pellets for each animal. In spring these quantities were reduced to 15 and 5 pounds, respectively, since grass was in good supply.

During the rutting season of 1959 the young bull did not bugle and while he showed more than usual interest in the females, was not actually seen to cover one. However, on June 14, 1960, one of the young cows produced a weakly calf which died 2 days later. On June 20 the 1955 cow gave birth to a sturdy youngster that developed in normal fashion. The second young cow failed to calf. Yearling male wapiti under natural conditions have little chance of mating, since they cannot compete with older and heavier bulls and have sometimes been considered incapable.

However, the studies of Conoway (1952) have demonstrated active spermatogenesis in yearling males of the Rocky Mountain race and the experience noted above leaves no doubt of the ability of at least one yearling Roosevelt's wapiti. By 1963, the herd had been firmly established, with annual births.

The Tule wapiti (*C. nannodes*) is a small, pale-colored species, once abundant in the San Joaquin and Sacramento valleys of California but now reduced to a few hundreds living under protection. The Tule wapiti has never been shown here but has been kept and bred to at least three generations in the San Diego Zoological Garden (Stott, 1954).

The American wapiti and the red deer hybridize freely, producing fertile offspring. Numerous references to this and other matings involving *canadensis* and various forms of *elaphus* are given by Gray (1954).

Père David's deer (*Elaphurus davidianus*), apparently once a resident of the plains of northeastern China, is now known only in captivity. In 1865, when the French missionary-naturalist Père Armand David peered over the wall of the great Imperial Hunting Park near Peiping, he became the first native of the Western world to view the herd of this curious deer that must have been preserved there for a very long period. In 1866 Père David was able to send prepared specimens to the Museum of Natural History in Paris, where the species was described in the same year by Milne-Edwards. On August 2, 1869, a young pair was received at the Zoological Gardens of London (Flower, 1929). These animals, the gift of Sir Rutherford Alcock, British Minister at Peiping, were the first living specimens to be seen in Europe. In the following years there were further arrivals at London, Paris, Berlin, and perhaps elsewhere on the Continent. During the Boxer uprising in 1900 the remainder of the herd in the Imperial Park were slaughtered by European soldiers, the only survivors being the scattered specimens in European institutions and a few that had been taken to Peiping, where the last one died in 1921 (Ellerman and Morrison-Scott, 1951).

According to Whitehead (1950), it was in 1898 that the eleventh Duke of Bedford, foreseeing the coming tragedy, gathered together the few examples living in Europe and established them at Woburn Abbey. Here, at liberty in the great inclosed park of approximately 4,000 acres, the Père David's deer prospered and in spite of the vicissitudes of two world wars were considered to number three hundred in 1948, when I first saw them.

Père David's deer is not a handsome or graceful animal, at least when judged by the standards usually applied to deer. It is above average in size,

Lydekker (1913–16:4) giving the shoulder height as 3 feet, 9 inches. The legs are heavy, the ears small in proportion to the narrow, extended face, and the long tail is heavily haired toward the tip. Hoofs are long and broad. The large antlers fork just above the burr, one branch extending directly backward, the other continuing up and slightly forward, dividing near the tip. There are sometimes further small divisions in mature animals. The fine summer coat is reddish brown in both sexes, while the heavy winter pelage is dark brown, particularly in males, with a thin mane of longer hair. Adult males are conspicuously light gray about head and face in the winter coat. Fawns are reddish, well spotted with white.

The first examples of Père David's deer to be seen in this country were four young animals picked up as fawns at Woburn Abbey in the spring of 1946 by special arrangement with the Duke of Bedford and hand-reared for us at Whipsnade through the kindness of the Zoological Society of London. These animals, two males and two females, were received here on December 27, 1946, their excellent condition being due to the attention, in transit, of Frank Fooks, director of Jean Delacour's park at Clères, France. Liberated in an inclosure of about $1\frac{1}{2}$ acres, they have since proved indifferent to the extreme variations of the New York climate and have established their ability to thrive on our usual feeding schedule.

All four were left together in the summer of 1947, but there was no indication of breeding activity and no fawns were born in 1948. When antlers hardened in the latter season, the animals had become sexually mature. There was active rivalry between the males, one becoming strongly dominant, and a sturdy fawn was born in 1949.

In that year, as the breeding season approached, the dominant male became actually savage and was removed for the safety of keepers and the rival stag. The result of this move was no fawns in 1950. In that year, while visiting Whipsnade, I was told that a similar situation had developed there, and an aggressive male was being introduced to replace a quieter one. We quickly made a similar move here, providing a shifting gate to protect the keepers from the dangerous stag. Two fawns were born in 1951, and it is my recollection that a similarly good result was achieved at Whipsnade. Regular breeding, with emphasis on aggressive herd bucks, has continued since.

Our little group here bears much the same relation to the Woburn herd as most captive deer do to those in the wild. The Woburn animals are practically at liberty, roaming the great park at will. Except for the rutting period, males and females form a large principal herd, grazing in unison or soaking in the bordering lagoons. His Grace considered this to be essential to the welfare of the animals, although here we have not found the lack to be detrimental. In May, when the fawns are afoot, the great herd may sometimes be seen moving from one area to another, stags and hinds forming a straggling ring, fawns capering inside it. The main rut is said to occur in June and July (Whitehead, 1950) and as this period comes on, the males begin the gathering of harems of perhaps a dozen or fifteen females with much fighting and bawling, the stronger ones, of course, being the most successful. These small groups are kept carefully segregated by their masters, for there is space for all, the Père David's paying no heed to the large numbers of red, fallow, sika, and other deer that share the great expanse.

Since our first Père David's were sent to us in 1946, the Woburn policy of judicial distribution has been broadened. The species is now found in numerous European zoological gardens, as well as in North America, South Africa, Australia, and China. In the latter instance four specimens were sent from Whipsnade to the Peiping Zoological Garden in 1956, a fawn being born there in the following year (Tong, 1958). Records of the present distribution of Père David's deer are maintained by E. H. Tong, director of Whipsnade Park, and the results for 1955, 1957, 1958, and 1959 have been published (Tong, 1957b, 1958, 1960). The total number known to be living in December, 1957, was 443; this had increased to 456 by 1959.

Lydekker (1898a) says that at Woburn antlers are shed in November and December, the rut occurring in June and July. Whitehead (1950) confirms the rutting season, but gives the season for the dropping of antlers as "from October on" and adds that fawns are born in April and May. Both Asdell (1946) and Kenneth (1953) give the gestation period as 250 days, which appears to originate with Jennison (n.d.). Olivier (1954) suggests that the period is actually 10–10½ months, which seems more in accord with known seasons of rut and birth.

Normal shedding of antlers takes place here in January, the only noted exception being December 24. The production of two sets of antlers in one year is reported by Hastings, Duke of Bedford (1949), to have been common at Woburn before 1914, when winter feeding was reduced, and one such instance has been reported here. Our herd stag dropped his antlers on January 7, 1954, grew a new set, and rutted in the usual sequence. On September 24 and 25 he shed these and proceeded to grow a very small pair, which he dropped on February 8, 1955. The replacements were of full size and hardened in time for the onset of rut in June.

The principal rut take place here, as elsewhere, in June and July.

Since possible rivals have been removed before this time, the herd buck is free to attend to his duties without distraction. Having found a receptive female, he drives her relentlessly, bawling and roaring, paying no attention to any animal that may accidentally intervene, so that fawns at foot or even other females are subject to occasional injury.

As with most deer, dates of birth indicate an extension of breeding both before and beyond the principal rutting period. Sixteen Père David's fawns have been born here, as follows: March, three; April, three; May, two; June, seven; July, one. Hastings, Duke of Bedford (1949), mentions a birth at Woburn in October. No instances of twinning have been recorded here.

Actual longevities of Père David's deer seem to have seldom been recorded. All four of the animals received here on December 27, 1946, having been born at Woburn in April of that year, were still living in 1963, the two males having been transferred to other collections. Incidentally, no Père David's deer has died from disease since the arrival of the species here.

Most abundant of the native deer of North America are the members of the genus *Odocoileus*. These include the many races of the white-tailed deer (*O. virginianus*) and of the mule deer (*O. hemionus*), the Columbian black-tailed deer (*O. h. columbianus*) being one of the latter group. Antlers are proportionately heavy and well forked, while coloration is in shades of gray or brown without spotting in adults, such markings being typical of fawns. The range of the genus extends from southern Alaska and western and southern Canada throughout most of the United States and Mexico to northern South America.

As pointed out by Hershkovitz (1948), it appears that the valid name for this genus was *Dama*, and it was so used by Hall and Kelson (1959), rather than *Odocoileus*, as commonly applied. Since this transfer would result in serious confusion, the matter was referred to the International Commission on Zoological Nomenclature and was discussed by Hershkovitz (1949), Morrison-Scott (1951), and Ellerman and Morrison-Scott (1951). In a decision dated January 8, 1960, and published in the *Bulletin of Zoological Nomenclature* (**17**, triple part 9–11, 267–75, September 16, 1960), the Commission used its plenary powers to validate the use of *Odocoileus* for the American genus and to restrict *Dama* to the fallow deer of the Old World. These names are used here in the sense of this decision.

The mule deer (*O. hemionus*) is found in the Rocky Mountain and coastal areas of western North America from southeastern Alaska and British Columbia southward to Baja California and northern Mexico.

Eleven races are listed and described by Cowan (1956). The mule deer is a stout, comparatively heavy-bodied animal with suggestively large ears, for which it is named. The summer coat is yellowish brown, with a blackish patch on the forehead, the throat and caudal disk white, the underparts dark, and the rather long tail white with black tip. The winter pelage is dark gray. There is much variation between the races, of course, in both color and size. Cahalane (1947) gives shoulder heights as 36–42 inches and weight from 145 to a maximum of 400 pounds. The antlers usually bear a small snag near the burr, dividing shortly above this into two prongs, each of which again divides so that the typical number of points on each side is five.

The mule deer is more or less migratory in habit, usually spending the summers at considerable elevations and descending into valleys or lowlands to winter. As described in detail by R. R. Hill (1956), the diet consists mainly of browse and leafy plants of many kinds, certain grasses being taken in spring. Much of the habitat is both high and dry and while neither of these conditions is constant, it appears that one or both may be involved in the difficulty so far experienced by most zoological gardens in maintaining this species. Diet may play a part, but the problem here does not seem to present special difficulties.

In the early years of the present century determined efforts were made here to establish the Rocky Mountain mule deer (*O. h. hemionus*). These attempts were unsuccessful, even fawns produced in the course of the trials thriving little better than their parents. Of eleven fawns born, three in May, six in June, and two in August, including four sets of twins, only one lived for just over 2 years. All of these deer were kept in large, grassy inclosures and fed on the diet of that era, consisting of clover hay, crushed oats, and any available browse.

After attempts to establish the mule deer on a going basis here had been abandoned, two adult bucks were obtained from the state of Washington on April 10, 1906. These animals were placed in separate yards of small size, with bare earth floors, and given the diet previously used. One lived until May 5, 1913, or 7 years, 25 days, the other until April 4, 1916, or 9 years, 11 months, 25 days. On December 3, 1921, an adult male was received from Montana and installed in one of the small yards that had been occupied by his predecessors. Fed on the same diet, this animal lived until February 22, 1934, or 12 years, 2 months, 19 days. Flower (1931) lists 12 years, 2 months, 15 days for a male in the Zoological Gardens of London, and Mann (1930) reports an example as having lived for 13 years, 11 months in the National Zoological Park. In neither case are conditions stated, but it seems probable that they approximated those of our own later experience. The over-all impression is that at the altitude of New York and under similar climatic conditions the mule deer is difficult to maintain in large, grassy runs but that, on the other hand, if kept in bare, well-drained inclosures and provided with clover or alfalfa hay, grain, and abundant cut browse, the species can be expected to give satisfactory results.

The Columbian black-tailed deer (*O. h. columbianus*) inhabits the forested western slopes of the mountains of the Pacific coast of western North America from British Columbia to central California. It is a slender, graceful animal, less bulky in body and with smaller ears than either the Rocky Mountain mule deer (*O. h. hemionus*) or the California mule deer (*O. h. californicus*). The upper surface of the tail is entirely dark, instead of white with dark tip, as illustrated by Cowan (1956). Cahalane (1947) gives the shoulder height as 38 inches and the maximum weight as 310 pounds.

Early experiences here with the Columbian black-tail were as disappointing as were those with the Rocky Mountain mule deer. Liberated in large, grassy ranges, animals received in 1900 and 1901 failed to thrive, and the experiment was dropped for a time. However, it was resumed on January 5, 1908, with the arrival of a young pair of black-tails. These animals were established in a corral similar to those used successfully for mule deer and placed on a similar diet. Here the male lived for just over 7 years, the female for roughly 11. On June 4, 1911, twin female fawns were born and successfully reared by the mother. One was killed 6 years later by striking the fence in a sudden fright, but the other lived until October 5, 1922, when it died, without having shown symptoms of illness, after 11 years, 4 months, 1 day. Mann (1930) gives 11 years, 3 months for a black-tailed deer in the National Zoological Park.

In the course of controlled investigations conducted with animals under seminatural conditions in the state of Washington, Golley (1957) found the gestation period of the black-tailed deer, in five instances, to range from 199 to 207 days, with an average of 203 days.

Both mule deer and Columbian black-tails have thrived and bred well in the San Diego Zoological Garden (Stott, 1954), where conditions would appear to be especially favorable. The black-tail has done reasonably well at the Chicago Zoological Park and has been successful at the Highland Park Zoological Garden, Pittsburgh. At the latter institution, at least, the animals are kept on bare earth with rocky outcroppings and fed clover hay, crushed oats, and browse.

The white-tailed deer (*O. virginianus*) is found from southern Canada southward through most of the United States save for an area in the west-central region, Mexico, except Baja California, and Central America, to northern South America. Thirty races from North and Central America are listed and described by Kellogg (1956), and seven South American subspecies are listed by Cabrera (1961). Size seems to decrease from north to south, ranging from northern races which may stand 42 inches at the shoulder and weigh 400 pounds or slightly more down to tiny creatures such as the Florida key deer (*O. v. clavium*) and the Coiba Island race (*O. v. rothschildi*), less than 30 inches in height and weighing no more than 50 pounds.

Typically, the antlers produce a small, upright tine, just above the burr, the main beam then turning forward and inward with three or four tines rising almost perpendicularly from it. In the northern races, at least, the summer coat is reddish bay, the winter pelage gray, with the throat and underparts white and indistinct bands across the nose and around the eyes. The rather long and bushy tail is dark on the upper surface and white below, so that when raised in flight it becomes a conspicuous signal. Fawns are spotted with white.

While the white-tail may frequently be found in heavy forest, it seems to prefer broken country, where cover is interspersed with small clearings. Extremely important in the economy of earlier days, the white-tail was slaughtered almost to extinction in many areas by the beginning of the present century. Then, however, protective laws were enacted so that in the favorable conditions provided by development of the land, deer have increased almost to the nuisance point, particularly in the eastern parts of their range. So well have they adapted to environmental changes that they frequently invade village gardens and are not at all uncommon even in the northern suburbs of New York City.

The food choices of the white-tail are wide, including browse of great variety, nuts, fruits, and grasses, as given in extensive detail by Hosley (1956). White-tails are usually solitary in habit, groups generally consisting of mother and young. However, in winters of heavy snow the sexes may join in "yards," making available food more readily accessible.

Perhaps because the area of New York is within the natural range of the white-tail, the species has always done well here, as it has in most American zoological gardens. Although white-tails are certainly able to clear a fence 8 feet high without much difficulty, undisturbed animals will seldom make the effort, and our standard of 7 feet has always provided effective restraint. On the other hand, white-tails are especially proficient at digging under fences or squeezing through small spaces below the bottom strand, so that tightness here is really of more importance than height. Shelters are provided, more for their value in occasional catching than for protection. Once fed on clover hay, crushed oats, and browse, which seemed to form an adequate diet, our white-tails now receive alfalfa hay, pellets, and browse (when available). Some grass is eaten, of course, but white-tails are not heavy grazers.

In the course of years, various members of this group have been kept here. These have included the Virginia white-tail (*O. v. virginianus*), which ranges from Virginia to Mississippi, the northern white-tail (*O. v. borealis*), the resident form in southeastern Canada, New Brunswick, and Nova Scotia and in the United States south to Maryland and west to Illinois, the Arizona or Coues white-tail (*O. v. couesi*), found from southern Arizona and New Mexico to northwestern Mexico, the Sinaloa white-tail (*O. v. sinaloae*), from the Pacific coast region of northwestern Mexico, and the Florida coastal white-tail (*O. v. osceola*), which inhabits the upper western coast area of Florida westward to Mississippi.

Our principal experience, of course, has been with the Virginia and the northern, but the Florida coastal race was carried here from 1902 to 1941, when we disposed of the last pair. During this time thirteen fawns were born, nine in June, two in May, and one each in February and April. A male born February 14, 1903, lived until September 7, 1921, or 18 years, 6 months, 24 days. Our single pair of Coues white-tails, received in 1939, was released in exchange two years later without having bred, while a male and female of the little Sinaloa white-tail lived here for 9 years, 5 months, 15 days and 11 years, 8 months, 17 days, respectively, without producing young. The latter were treated as tender and housed indoors in winter, which may have disrupted their reproductive cycle.

White-tails of the northern and Virginia races have been kept here continuously since 1900, when eight specimens of *borealis* were received from the Blue Mountain Forest Association through Austin Corbin. These animals were the foundation of a herd that continued to 1959 and, on a smaller scale, to the present day. Numerous additions of members of this race, with occasional specimens of the somewhat smaller but otherwise similar Virginia white-tail, have been made from time to time, the herd remaining predominantly representative of *borealis*. These animals thrived well enough, it must be said, in open grassy runs on a diet of clover hay, crushed oats, cut browse, and grass. Best results were obtained, however, when the herd was transferred in 1941 to the large inclosure later devoted to Roosevelt's wapiti, as described above (p. 583). At that time the area contained not only numerous large forest trees, principally oak and beech, but a heavy stand of varied undergrowth. The latter, of course, was soon eaten or destroyed by the deer, but the success of the herd, which continued until 1959, when it was removed to make room for the Roosevelt's wapiti, confirmed my own feeling that captive white-tails give best results under a canopy of trees. The herd usually numbered from twenty to thirty adults, including four or five mature bucks and, seasonally, numerous fawns.

Antlers are usually shed by northern white-tails sometime after January 1, specific dates noted here being February 19 and March 9. The new growth has hardened by September, and the swelling necks of bucks indicate the approach of rut, which occurs in October, November, and early December. White-tail bucks do not gather harems but move about in search of does in estrus, which they appear to find by scent. Fierce battles often occur at this season, sometimes resulting in locking of antlers, which may cause the eventual death of both participants.

In our large inclosure fighting between rutting bucks was never serious, for one seemed always able to establish dominance and there was sufficient space for lesser males to keep clear. On one occasion, two of the latter that were engaged in a skirmish managed to lock antlers and were pried apart, with some difficulty, by their keepers.

Spike white-tail bucks in their second autumn are perfectly capable of breeding, though they may seldom have opportunity. Most does probably experience their first estrus in their second autumn, but female fawns not infrequently become pregnant when less than one year old (Severinghaus and Cheatum, 1956). The same authors give the gestation period as approximately 201 days. Does usually produce single fawns at the first birth, followed by twins or occasionally triplets in later years, although this rule is by no means infallible. As many as four fetuses have been found in dead females (Severinghaus and Cheatum, 1956). A remarkable history of a tame female northern white-tail at liberty in the vicinity of a Maine camp that produced thirty-one known fawns in 14 years, including six sets of twins and five of triplets, is given by Palmer (1951).

Of 177 fawns born here, consisting mostly of northern white-tails but including some Virginias, 42 appeared in May, 101 in June, 25 in July, 8 in August, and 1 in September. No record of multiple births could be kept because of the difficulty of establishing identities in large groups.

The greatest longevity for a northern white-tail here was established by a particularly fine buck that was received on March 17, 1905, and died on September 22, 1922, after 17 years, 6 months, 5 days.

Largest of the South American deer is the marsh deer (*Blastocerus dichotomus*), which ranges from Brazil through the Mato Grosso to the Chaco of Argentina, in areas where water is abundant and cover available. This is an animal of good size, its bulk comparing with that of the red deer (Lydekker, 1913–16:4). The general coloration is reddish, with the lower parts of the legs black. The rather heavy antlers lack a basal prong but form two divisions, each of which again forks. The species has been represented sparingly in European collections but there appear to be no records of its having been kept in this country.

The pampas deer (*Blastoceros bezoarticus*), which inhabits the open pampas of South America from Brazil to Argentina, is a much smaller animal than the marsh deer. In color it is light reddish brown, with eye ring, chest, and underparts white. The antlers fork simply, the posterior one dividing again, so that the usual pattern is three points on each side. While certainly never a common species in captivity, the pampas deer has been more generally seen in European gardens than the marsh deer and, according to Flower (1929), was living as early as 1830 or 1831 in the Jardin des Plantes, Paris. A pair received here in 1905 lived for only a short time but Hastings, Duke of Bedford (1949), says a female lived for several years at Woburn Abbey, provided only with an unheated shelter. Single young were born at the Zoological Gardens of London in May, 1875, and August, 1881 (Flower, 1929).

The guemals (*Hippocamelus*) are creatures of the mountains, living in the Andes of western South America at elevations of 14,000 feet or more, descending in winter to lower levels. Two species are known: the Peruvian guemal (*H. antisensis*), found in the heights of Ecuador, Bolivia, Peru, and northern Chile, and the Chilean guemal (*H. bisulcus*), which ranges from central Chile to southwestern Argentina. The generally coarse, heavy coats of both are yellowish gray. Antlers fork simply, the tines not usually dividing, so that the normal number of points on each side is two. Lydekker (1913–16:4) gives 34 inches as the shoulder height of the Peruvian guemal and $39\frac{1}{2}$ inches for the Chilean. The latter has a black Y-mark on the face, lacking in its smaller relative. The guemals have always been rare in collections, although the Chilean, at least, has occasionally been kept in Europe. The only arrival in the United States, as far as I know, was a female Peruvian received here on May 16, 1938. She was a charmingly tame animal, obviously hand-reared, so that the thick, resilient character of her grayish coat could readily be tested. Fed the usual diet with some supplements of fresh vegetables and greens, she lived here until November 30, 1943, or 5 years, 6 months, 14 days.

The brockets (*Mazama*) are small, shy creatures ranging in tropical and subtropical America from Mexico to Paraguay and northern Argentina, usually in densely forested areas. Most of the great number of forms that have been described seem to fall into three species: the red brockets (*M. americana*), the brown brockets (*M. gouazoubira*), and the rufous brockets (*M. rufina*), as listed by Hershkovitz (1958). The first two, with their numerous races, are found from southern Mexico to South America, while *rufina* is confined to the latter continent. A fourth species, *M. chunyi*, a diminutive form from the Andes of southeastern Peru and northwestern Bolivia, has been described by Hershkovitz (1959). General coloration is in shades of brown and gray, fawns being spotted with white. Antlers are unbranched spikes only a few inches long. Shoulder heights, as given by Lydekker (1913–16:4) range from 19 to 27 inches. Brockets apparently representing all of the first three species have been kept fairly frequently by European institutions but much less often in this country. The only examples received here were a pair of red brockets that arrived in 1904 and lived for less than a year. Better results were obtained in the National Zoological Park, where a red brocket lived for 2 years, 6 months and a brown for 2 years, 1 month (Mann, 1930). A red brocket is reported to have lived 9 years, 5 months, 13 days and a brown 9 years, 7 months, 1 day in the Philadelphia Zoological Garden (Jones, 1958). A brocket of unstated species was born in the Zoological Gardens of London in September, 1860 (Zuckerman, 1953). The average gestation period is given by Kenneth (1953) as 217 days for *M. rufina*. The brockets require heated quarters in winter, and the fact that they are chiefly browsers undoubtedly has a bearing on the difficulty of carrying them through the winter months in northern climates. Enders (1930) reports that a captive male on Barro Colorado Island, Canal Zone, had a particular fondness for both fruit and skin of bananas, a quite possibly useful point.

The tiny pudus (*Pudu*) live in the Andes of South America from Ecuador and Colombia to southern Chile. There are two species: the Chilean pudu (*P. pudu*), occupying the southern part of the range, and the Ecuadorian pudu (*P. mephistophiles*), which extends northward to Ecuador and Colombia. In both the general coloration is reddish brown, the antlers are unbranched and very short, and the tail much abbreviated. The Chilean pudu is the smallest of all the deer, Cabrera and Yepes (1940) giving the shoulder height as 35 centimeters (approximately 13.75 inches). This little creature has been kept occasionally in Europe, and Ulmer (1959) reports that a specimen, presumably of this species, was received in 1877 at the Philadelphia Zoological Garden. Single births of the Chilean pudu occurred in the Zoological Gardens of London on May 23, 1932, and May 29, 1933 (Zuckerman, 1953). Jones (1958) reports that an animal of this species received at the Zoological Gardens of London on February 14, 1866, lived until February 17, 1875, or 9 years, 3 days. There appear to be no records of the Ecuadorian pudu in captivity.

Largest of all the deer is the great creature known in America as the moose, in Europe as the elk, but in either case a member of the species *Alces alces*. One form or another is found in heavily forested boreal regions of North America, Europe, and Asia south of the limits of tree growth. As revised by Peterson (1952), there are four North American races: the eastern moose (*A. alces americana*), found from Nova Scotia and Maine to central Ontario, where it meets the northwestern moose (*A. alces andersoni*) which extends westward across northern Michigan and Minnesota to British Columbia and the eastern Yukon; the Yellowstone or Shiras moose (*A. a. shirasi*), inhabiting the Yellowstone region in portions of British Columbia, Alberta, Wyoming, Montana, and Idaho, and the great Alaskan moose (*A. a. gigas*), native to Alaska and contiguous areas of the Yukon and British Columbia. The European elk (*A. a. alces*) extends in forested areas across northern Europe and Asia, from Scandinavia to south-central Siberia, while according to Ellerman and Morrison-Scott (1951), eastern Siberia, Mongolia, and Manchuria are occupied by the Manchurian elk (*A. a. cameloides*), with which these authorities have synonymized *A. a. pfizenmayeri* of various authors.

Moose in general are characterized by great size, high shoulders, broad, overhanging muzzle, long legs, and short tail. A fleshy dewlap or "bell" that hangs from the throat of both sexes is usually longer in males. The heavy beams of the antlers extend outward almost horizontally from the forehead for a short distance, then form two main divisions, which divide again. In adult males the antlers become so broadly palmate that the tines may be distinguishable only as points along the edges. Color varies from almost black to shades of brown, with muzzle, belly, and legs usually paler. The reddish-brown calves are unspotted.

Largest of all forms is the Alaskan moose. The shoulder height of 7 feet, 8 inches given by Seton (1909) is usually quoted as the maximum and the greatest weight as 1,800 pounds. Comparable figures for the eastern moose given by Seton (*loc. cit.*) are 7 feet, 4 inches and an estimated 1,400 pounds. Ward (1922) gives 5 feet, 9 inches at the shoulder for the European elk, with an estimated weight of 1,500 pounds for a Lithuanian specimen. Allen (1938, 1940) says that the Manchurian elk "may stand $5\frac{3}{4}$ to $6\frac{3}{4}$ feet at the shoulder," but weights for this race do not appear to be available.

The widest spread of antlers of the Alaskan moose listed in *Records of Big Game* of the Boone and Crockett Club (1958) is 77⅝ inches, for the eastern moose 71⅝ inches, and for the Yellowstone or Shiras moose 62⅜ inches. Ward (1922) gives 49 inches for both the European elk and the Manchurian. While palmation is usually well developed in adult males of all the American forms, it is less pronounced in the European moose and apparently almost absent in the Manchurian race. In the office of the Zoological Gardens at Skansen, Sweden, hangs a progressive series of antlers grown by a bull European elk that had lived there for 15 years. Beginning with the first simple spikes, the antlers increase in size to the well-palmated pairs of the eighth and ninth years, then show gradual retrogression until those on the mounted head of the animal are only a few inches long, with a single fork.

Moose are basically solitary in habit, although small groups may sometimes gather. The preferred habitat is in heavy growth, usually near water, since leaves, stems, and roots of water lilies are important summer food items. Leaves and twigs of willow, birch, maple, aspen, and balsam, as well as the bark of poplars, are staples. The antlers of males are shed in winter and their replacements have hardened in time for the rutting season in September and October. At this time both sexes call, often to the advantage of hunters. Fierce battles between rival bulls may result, but once dominance has been attained, the victor remains with the cow during her estrus, after which he may seek another mate. The normal calving season is late May or June, the first birth usually being that of a single calf, with twins being common thereafter and even triplets appearing on rare occasions (Hosley and Glaser, 1952). The gestation period is given by Asdell (1946) as 240–50 days.

Moose in this country and elk in Europe have always been notoriously difficult to keep in zoological gardens. Our own efforts with American moose here began in 1899 with the arrival of a young cow from Minnesota. This animal lived for only a few months, and no better results, with one exception, were achieved in the two following years. The single success obtained concerned a bull received from Manitoba on December 5, 1900, that lived until June 1, 1906, or 5 years, 5 months, 27 days, a really creditable record. However, over-all results were discouraging, all the American races, except only the Alaskan, having been tried, so that, beyond one or two chance arrivals, efforts to establish moose here were abandoned until 1942. In that year, on September 25, we received a bull calf and a cow, "Maude," from the Department of Lands and Forests, Nova Scotia, and on October 17, a cow named "Minnie" from the Bureau of Information and Tourist Travel, New Brunswick.

These animals were installed in a large run attached to the spacious inclosure already described under Roosevelt's wapiti (p. 583) and with equal facilities, including access to a pool and abundant shade. Later, this adjunct was used only for animals requiring temporary isolation, and the moose were allowed to run with the white-tailed deer then occupying the larger inclosure. Neither species interfered with the other in any way, except for strict defense of their individual feeding boxes by the moose. The diet provided included alfalfa and clover hay, the grain mixture now used in pellet form but then not compressed, potatoes, carrots, and other vegetables and greens, occasional bananas, for which moose seem to have a special liking, and as much browse as could be obtained. When this was scarce, as it often was, we added a supplement of dried beet-root pulp to the grain for bulk as well as an increase of corn (maize) meal in winter. This diet seemed entirely suitable but pointed up the necessity for browse. This is really a required item and often had to be brought for us from considerable distances.

The bull calf received in 1942 died in the following spring from a perforated ulcer of the stomach, and the two cows lived with only the deer for company until March 3, 1947, when a young bull, "Jerry," was received as a gift from the Maine Department of Inland Fisheries and Game. Jerry had been picked up as a "deserted" calf in the spring of 1945 and hand-reared on whole cow's milk at one of the Department's forest stations. He was completely tame and gentle and at the approximate age of 20 or 21 months weighed 615 pounds, with a shoulder height of 5 feet, 7 inches.

Jerry came into rut in September, 1947, when about 27 months old, and we presumed that both cows were bred. However, Maude died on November 30, 1947, after 5 years, 2 months, 5 days here and was found not to have been pregnant. Her weight at death was 575 pounds. Minnie remained in good health and on June 2, 1948, produced her first calf. Moose calves are well known to begin nibbling solid food at an early age— Dr. Monique Meyer-Holzapfel, in a paper cited on page 600, reported captivity-bred European elk calves as eating for themselves at 21, 13, and 7 days—and we made every effort to induce Minnie's offspring to take fresh browse, but without success. Although Minnie continued to allow her calf to nurse, there was no assurance that her supply of milk was sufficient, and the youngster died, apparently of malnutrition, on July 10. Minnie gave birth to further single calves on June 3, 1949, June 2, 1950, and May 27, 1951, but while one lived for $2\frac{1}{2}$ months, none was successfully reared. Minnie died on June 15, 1952, after 9 years, 7 months, 29 days here.

Minnie was afflicted with overgrown toes or "snowshoes" when she came to us, and this condition undoubtedly hampered her activities in caring for her calves. She was far from gentle, laying back her ears and extending her head in typical moose warning if approached, so that her toes could be trimmed only by means of a hack saw cautiously extended on a lengthy handle while her attention was concentrated on her feeding box.

The problem of overgrown toes in captive moose is a serious one. If the animals are kept on a hard, smooth surface or in an entirely soft-bottomed inclosure, "snowshoes" are bound to result. Our moose inclosure seemed actually to provide ideal conditions, for it contained a pool, some soft areas, and a high, rocky outcropping. The animals made use of all sections, and those received here with normal hoofs were able to keep them in proper condition during their lifetimes.

On February 23, 1948, a cow moose called "Molly," born in 1947, was received from the Maine Department of Inland Fisheries and Game. Molly, like Jerry, had been bottle-reared at a forest station and was a gentle animal with sound feet. She lived until April 3, 1955, or 7 years, 1 month, 11 days, but produced only a single calf. This was born on June 24, 1950; like the others, it failed to survive.

Jerry seemed to be a normal animal and followed the course to be expected of a bull moose. Dates of the dropping of antlers became irregularly earlier as he aged: 1947, March 13 and 17; 1948, February 4 and 6; 1949, January 11 and 12; 1950, January 31 and February 2, and again on December 25 and 27; 1951, December 13 (both); 1953, January 1 (both), and again on November 21 and 24. In both 1950 and 1953 the antlers were shed twice, while the year 1952 was missed altogether by a single day. Regardless of the dates when antlers were dropped, regrowth did not begin until April or May, so that the replacements were always hard and dry by the onset of rut in early September. At this time Jerry, ordinarily quiet enough, became aggressive, even savage, in moose fashion and each day had to be enticed into a bull pen whose fence was reinforced with heavy iron pipes while the range was being serviced. By mid-November he had usually calmed sufficiently to make removal unnecessary. Jerry died on February 20, 1955, after 7 years, 11 months, 17 days here.

An early success in the keeping and breeding of American moose in captivity was accomplished by the Detroit Zoological Park at Royal Oak, Michigan. This was based on a pair obtained in Quebec, apparently in 1928, when the institution was opened to the public, and a female received from New Brunswick in the same year. The latter cow gave birth to a female calf in 1929 which was safely reared. In 1932 this young cow, in turn, produced a calf which lived for 10 days, probably the first instance of reproduction by a captivity-bred American moose (Anon., 1932). These animals were kept in a moated inclosure of good size, provided with a pool but with what seemed to be insufficient shade. When seen in 1931, they appeared to be in excellent condition, but all later succumbed to a reported outbreak of tuberculosis.

Undoubtedly the most noteworthy results with American moose so far achieved are those of the Washington Park Zoological Garden at Milwaukee, Wisconsin. This project began on September 27, 1951, with the arrival from Ontario of a pair of hand-reared calves approximately 4 months old. These animals were installed in a well-shaded inclosure of about 1 acre, provided with a pool and an overhead spray. Fresh browse was available in abundance and a supply for winter was placed in cold storage. A meal mixture, fresh vegetables, greens, and bananas were also furnished. On May 7, 1953, a female calf was born. It was noted that the mother lay on her side and raised one leg to allow the calf to nurse (Bierworth, 1954). This habit was not observed in our own moose, but Hediger (1955a:89) states that the female European moose may sometimes suckle her young in this manner. This calf was reared, with some difficulty (Anon., 1953b), but developed a deficiency in locomotion. It was finally removed to a large wooded tract, where it died in 1956.

To George Speidel, director of the Washington Park Zoological Garden, I am indebted for the complete history of this herd up to September, 1960. The original pair, "Christie" and "Harriet," produced eight calves as follows: May 7, 1953, when the parents were approximately 2 years old, a single female noted above; May 16, 1954, twin females; May 17, 1955, twin males; May 20, 1957, twin females; May 25, 1958, a single male. Of these, six were fully reared. One of the females born on May 16, 1954, "Hilda," gave birth to a single male calf on May 23, 1956, twin females on May 18, 1957, and a single female on May 16, 1958. Of these four calves, two were reared. "Matilda," twin sister of Hilda, produced twin females on May 13, 1957, and a single female on May 15, 1959. Two of Matilda's calves were reared. One of Matilda's female calves born May 13, 1957, called "Lucky," produced a male calf on July 29, 1959, that did not live. Of these sixteen calves, ten were successfully reared by their mothers. Beyond these facts, it is worthy of note that Christie was able to breed at approximately eighteen months, that three of the females were receptive at the same age, and that in each case twins were of the same sex.

Christie, father of all, died on November 2, 1959, presumably of oak poisoning, after 8 years, 1 month, 6 days; Harriet died on August 19,

1958, after 6 years, 10 months, 23 days. In September, 1960, only four adult females of the original stock were living: Matilda, Lucky and her twin sister, and Hilda's daughter, born May 16, 1958. Unfortunately, all the male calves reared had been sold to other institutions because of lack of holding space. However, a young bull was received from Canada on April 13, 1959, and another from Alaska on June 19, 1960, perhaps the first of this race of which there is a captivity record, so it is presumable that successful propagation will continue.

The 8 years, 1 month, 6 days reported for Christie at Milwaukee, Minnie's span of 9 years, 7 months, 29 days here, and 12 years, 7 months, 17 days noted for the Lincoln Park Zoo, Chicago, by Jones (1958) appear to be the most noteworthy longevities so far recorded for American moose in zoological gardens.

The European elk has never been a universally successful zoological-garden animal although, like the American moose, it has given good results in a few isolated instances. In a paper read at the meeting of the International Union of Directors of Zoological Gardens held at Rome, September 15–18, 1952, and included in the minutes of that meeting, Dr. Monique Meyer-Holzapfel reported that up to 1952 only the zoological gardens of Skansen, Berne, Berlin, and Rotterdam had been successful in breeding the European elk. An account of the elk herd at Berlin is given by Heck (1934), and the first two of nine births at Berne have been reported in detail by Hediger (1942, 1949).

The greatest success with the European elk appears to have been accomplished by the Zoological Gardens of Skansen, Stockholm. When seen in 1950, the elk at Skansen were kept in a wedge-shaped wire inclosure, approximately 50 feet at the base, where there was a rustic open shelter, and 30 feet on the sides. It was thinly grassed, shaded at one end only, and provided with a small pool. At that time the group consisted of a 3-year-old bull, a 6-year-old cow which Captain Gustave Lilliehook, the deputy director, said appeared to be barren, and an aged cow. Captain Lilliehook told me that the latter, born at Skansen in 1935 and so aged 15 years, was no longer breeding. In her lifetime she had produced twenty-three calves, including eleven pairs of twins, most of which had been fully reared. The animals were fed some grain but relied chiefly on great sheaves of willow browse, hung daily on the wire of the inclosure. The calves were said to begin nibbling willow at the age of about 2 weeks, so there was no weaning problem, and they were practically independent by November.

Dr. Meyer-Holzapfel, in the paper referred to above, basing her figures on exact observations made at Skansen and at Berne, gave an average gestation period for the European elk in captivity of 236 days, with a minimum of 226 days and a maximum of 249 days. She also confirmed the statement of Hediger (1955a:89) that the female European elk may nurse her young while lying down.

The caribou of North America and the reindeer of the Old World, inhabiting arctic and subarctic regions of North America, Europe, and Asia, are usually considered to form a single species, *Rangifer tarandus*. Hall and Kelson (1959) list fourteen North American subspecies, including two from Greenland, while Ellerman and Morrison-Scott (1951) recognize eight forms in Europe and Asia. Typically, antlers are large but subject to much variation, with both brow and bez tines, above which the main beam turns forward, sometimes giving off a rear tine and ending in several points, usually expanded. Both brow and bez tine may be broadly palmate, in a more or less perpendicular plane, although one of the former may be a simple point. Antlers are generally borne by both sexes, those of females being smaller, and fawns normally produce spikes a few months after birth (Harper, 1955). Hoofs are broad and flat, with the lateral hoofs at least partially functional. A clicking sound, apparently caused by a movable tendon in the foot, is made when the animal moves. Color varies from nearly white in Peary's caribou (*R. t. pearyi*), from northeastern Greenland and the Canadian arctic islands, to the more typical dark brown, with neck, including a long lower fringe, underparts, rump, and hoof rings, whitish. Fawns are unspotted. Shoulder heights are given by Hall and Kelson (1959) as ranging from 680 to 1,397 millimeters (approximately 27 to 55 inches) and weights up to 600 pounds, females being smaller than males. Asdell (1946) gives the rutting season in Siberia, presumably for *R. t. sibericus*, as September and October and the gestation period as from 7 to 8 months. For the woodland caribou (*R. t. caribou*) and the Barren Ground caribou (*R. t. arcticus*), rut is said to occur in October.*

Caribou and reindeer are strongly gregarious, often living in herds of considerable size. The diet in summer consists largely of browse, grasses, and sedges, while for winter food the animals depend chiefly on ground lichens (*Cladonia*), known as reindeer moss, for which they may dig through several feet of snow. Long seasonal migrations are made, particularly by the more northerly races, usually to more favorable feeding grounds.

The great herds of caribou that once existed in the northlands of America and were a basic component in the economy of Eskimos and northern Indians have become greatly reduced and have been exterminated in the

*See Addenda, p. 737.

eastern United States (Lincoln, 1958), with remnants in the west (Flinn, 1959). A similar fate seems to have overtaken the wild reindeer of Europe and Asia, which exist sparingly if at all in most areas of their former range. In those regions domestication has filled the gap left by the vanished herds.

Domestication of the reindeer in northern Europe and Asia must have begun at a very early period—Goodwin (1954) says the earliest reference appears to be one from A.D. 499. At any rate, the tame herds became a fundamental factor in the lives of the Lapps of northern Europe and the Samoyeds and related tribes of Siberia. The animals were and in some areas still are relied upon to supply food, winter garments, and transportation. The herds are moved seasonally as range and weather conditions require, so that overgrazing is avoided.

No attempt seems to have been made by either Eskimos or northern Indians, even to the present day, to domesticate the caribou of North America. An effort to compensate for this lack was begun in 1891, when sixteen domesticated reindeer, presumably *R. t. sibericus*, followed by 171 more in 1892, were brought to Alaska from Siberia. More shipments were added, so that by 1902 the total number of animals imported reached 1,280 (Leopold and Darling, 1953). Under the care of Lapp herders in Government service and later in private hands, the herds increased rapidly and yielded important crops of meat and skins. By 1932 the number of animals was estimated at from 625,000 to 650,000. However, apparently largely because of overgrazing and the inability or unwillingness of Eskimos to adapt themselves to a pastoral life, deterioration began, and by 1952 only 26,735 reindeer were estimated to remain in Alaska (Leopold and Darling, *loc. cit.*). Many of the animals have become feral and hybridized with local caribou, presumably with results detrimental to the latter (Harper, 1955). In a remarkable trek that took more than 5 years, beginning in 1929, a herd of reindeer was driven from Alaska to the Mackenzie region of northwestern Canada, where the animals appear to be thriving. Various introductions of Scandinavian domesticated reindeer into North America have apparently been unsuccessful (Anderson, 1947).

In spite of the statement by Flower (1931) that the reindeer "does well and breeds freely in Zoological Gardens," the general impression, both in this country and in Europe, is undoubtedly to the contrary. Until fairly recent years reindeer were seldom imported into this country, and on these rare occasions results were seldom satisfactory. Even in Europe, reindeer do not seem to be commonly kept, and an aged male with surprisingly large antlers was once a very special attraction in the Zoological Gardens of Antwerp. The Zoological Gardens of London have been more successful than most, at least periodically, in maintaining and breeding reindeer, which may account for Major Flower's optimistic expression.*

Domesticated reindeer first reached the New York Zoological Park on October 17, 1902, when a pair of Siberian origin was received from Carl Hagenbeck. One of these animals lived for only a few months and the other for just over a year. In 1906 two Scandinavian reindeer were obtained, but neither survived for as long as a year. No further effort to solve this problem was made until December 12, 1941, when a male and three female Scandinavian reindeer were obtained from a local source. All three females produced fawns in the following year, one of which was fully reared. The original animals lived for varying periods, the longest just over 3 years, but throughout they never seemed to reach really good condition. They were heavily parasitized on arrival and intensive efforts to clear them were never fully successful, a situation presumably contributory to short duration.

In the fifties restrictions on the importation of ruminants into this country were relaxed in the case of Norway, because of the absence of hoof-and-mouth disease from that area, and reindeer in some numbers became available here. On November 14, 1956, we purchased a pair of these animals; the male was in poor condition and was replaced on February 15, 1957. Up to this time our reindeer had been kept in large inclosures, either wooded or grassy. Indifferent results suggested a change, so one of a series of rather small yards, floored with bare soil, well packed and well drained, was used for the new pair. This has proved successful, for up to 1963 the animals have maintained excellent condition, their offspring have overflowed into adjoining corrals, and the parasite condition has been brought under control.

In spite of the well-known ability of reindeer to withstand severe weather, our animals make regular use of their shelters when snow and deep cold are prevalent, as well as for protection from flies during the heat of summer. They are fed alfalfa hay and the usual pellets, with some browse and occasional vegetables. They have not been provided with reindeer moss, for which there seems to be no real necessity once the animals have become accustomed to a more conventional diet, as pointed out by Pocock (1914) and Hediger (1950:126–27).

While domesticated reindeer are usually considered to be completely gentle, rutting bucks may still be dangerous. A keeper here, attacked without warning, was able to seize the animal's antlers and, although a heavy and powerful man, was pushed backward until he reached a fence,

*See Addenda, p. 737.

up which he managed to scramble. Also, in our small inclosures bucks in antler will not tolerate other males.

Successive dates of the dropping of antlers by an adult buck here are February 25 and 26, 1958, February 12, 1959 (both), and February 16, 1960 (both). A male fawn born May 12, 1958, shed his baby spikes March 22, 1959. Dates for adult females here are February 12, March 4, and March 19. Bucks are in hard antler for the rutting season, which runs here from late August through September. Nine births of single fawns have occurred here, three in April, six in May, the earliest date being April 15, the latest May 16. A female fawn born in 1957 was injured by her father, perhaps accidentally, and was kept separately. She was joined later by a brother born on May 12, 1958, and on May 1, 1960, produced her first fawn, the young male having become sexually functional at about 16 months. The greatest longevity given by Flower (1931) for a domesticated reindeer is for an animal born June 5, 1914, in the Basel Zoological Gardens and which lived there until September 14, 1926, or 12 years, 3 months, 9 days.

Results with caribou in captivity, with rare exception, have so far been unsatisfactory. However, since this was the case with the reindeer until very recently, there is reason to expect better results from efforts now under way. On August 25, 1899, a woodland caribou (R. t. caribou) was received here from Quebec, followed by two specimens from Maine in 1901. The Quebec animal lived for nearly 2 years, one of those from Maine for nearly 3, a result that should not have been too discouraging. In 1900 and 1901 nine young Newfoundland caribou (R. t. terraenovae) were obtained. Most of these animals lived for only a few months, but one individual survived from October 8, 1901, to September 10, 1904, or 2 years, 11 months, 2 days. No caribou of any sort have been received here since that time. Mann (1930) reports 9 years, 11 months for a Newfoundland caribou in the National Zoological Park, a creditable longevity for any *Rangifer*. This animal was kept in a bare, dry inclosure similar to those now in use here for reindeer. The implication, at least as far as zoological gardens are concerned, is unavoidable.

The roe deer (*Capreolus capreolus*) are small, graceful creatures, found in Great Britain and across Europe and northern Asia to the Pacific. As listed by Ellerman and Morrison-Scott (1951), there are three races: the European (*Capreolus c. capreolus*), ranging from England and Scotland to Persia; the Siberian (*Capreolus c. pygargus*), which extends from the Urals and the Volga to the Altai Mountains of Mongolia, and the Manchurian (*Capreolus c. bedfordi*) of central China, Korea, Manchuria, and southeastern Siberia. General coloration is reddish brown in summer, with or without a black mark on the muzzle, and grayish brown in winter, when a large white or yellowish caudal disk becomes conspicuous; fawns are spotted with white at birth. The tail is rudimentary. The small antlers fork simply, the posterior branch again dividing, so that the typical number of points on each side is three. The main beam may be heavily "pearled" with small, rounded excrescences or tiny spurs. The greatest antler length for a British roe given by Ward (1922) is $12\frac{1}{8}$ inches and for a Continental specimen, 14 inches; $13\frac{3}{8}$ inches are recorded for the Manchurian, and for the considerably larger Siberian, $17\frac{3}{4}$ inches. Shoulder heights, as given by Lydekker (1913–16:4), are 26–27 inches for the European, slightly more for the Manchurian, and 28–34 inches for the Siberian. The maximum weight for the European roe is about 60 pounds.

Roe deer usually live in small family parties consisting of male, female and young, territory appearing to be of great importance in their economy (Delap, 1957). Whether or not the mated pair remains constant seems to be in question. The usual habitat is dense or broken cover where special foods are available, including the foliage of trees and shrubs, nuts, fruits, berries, and grasses (Tegner, 1951).

In the European roe antlers are dropped in November or December and the new ones are clean by April. The rut takes place in July and August, and it is thought that the "fairy rings," small, beaten circles or figure of eights, usually surrounding a tree or other object, are made at this time, when the buck is driving his mate. Births, which may consist of one, two, or rarely three fawns, occur in May or early June. The abnormally long gap between fertilization and birth is accounted for by delayed implantation, the ova not becoming attached to the wall of the uterus until December, thus reducing the true gestation period to the area of five months (Asdell, 1946; Matthews, 1952).

Roe deer have been introduced into Texas, but apparently failed to become established (de Vos, Manville, and Van Gelder, 1956). Roe are also reported to have been liberated on the estate of Walter Teagle, Jr., in Dutchess County, New York, about 1900. On a visit to the estate in April, 1956, Manville (1957) sighted two or three animals "that appeared to be true Roe Deer." The descendants of the original importation were thought, at the time of Dr. Manville's visit, to number about six.

Roe deer of all three forms have been exhibited by various European zoological gardens, the local form naturally being most commonly seen. However, results have generally not been satisfactory, and the species is usually considered to be difficult in captivity. Mitchell (1911) reports the average longevity of nine specimens in the Zoological Gardens of London as 24 months, with a maximum of 52 months. For ten specimens received at the National Zoological Park, Mann (1930) gives 1 year, 7 months as the greatest span. Three specimens of the European roe that arrived here on June 16, 1908, were the only representatives of the species that we have exhibited. One of these, a female, lived until September 7, 1912, or 4 years, 2 months, 22 days.

More recently, better results have been obtained with the European roe, at least in Continental zoological gardens. In 1951 there was a small herd, including two recently born fawns, in the Zoological Gardens of Antwerp. These animals were kept in a rather small, open inclosure, floored with coarse sand, and appeared to be in excellent condition. Walter Van den bergh, the director, informed me that their principal food was ivy, with some supplement of alfalfa hay and grain. This group was still thriving in 1954. The late Axel Reventlow told me that he was using the same diet for roe in the Copenhagen Zoological Gardens, with the addition of raspberry canes, the leaves of which were eaten eagerly. It appears that better understanding of the necessity for leafy browse as the principal item in the diet of captive roe deer, as well as their reluctance to take dry food, may account for the improvement in maintenance.

In 1959 six young animals were imported by Roland Lindemann of the Catskill Game Farm, New York, and liberated in a large, brushy inclosure. With natural food thus available, they gradually became reconciled to a supplement of clover and alfalfa hay and feeding pellets as well. Mr. Lindemann informs me that four fawns born in 1961 were all fully reared.

FAMILY GIRAFFIDAE

GIRAFFES AND OKAPI

This remarkable family, confined entirely to Africa, includes but two genera: *Giraffa* and *Okapia*, each containing a single species. Dissimilar in appearance though the members of these groups are, they still have numerous points in common. The elongated neck, more exaggerated in the giraffes than in the okapi and containing only the normal mammalian number of seven vertebrae, is a feature unlikely to be overlooked. However, a more fundamental distinguishing character is found in the short, unbranched, permanent, skin-covered bony horns, borne by both sexes in the giraffes and by males only in the okapi. A short, stiff mane, extending from nape to shoulder, rises from the neck of both sexes in the giraffes but is absent in the adult okapi. Lateral hoofs are lacking, the tongue is extensile and prehensile, and both giraffe and okapi females have four mammary nipples. The normal gait in both is the "pace," the legs of each side moving in unison. The canter or the gallop is used at greater speeds. Descriptions of the gaits of the giraffe, with illustrative drawings, are given by Dagg (1962).

The giraffes (*Giraffa camelopardalis*), certainly among the most spectacular of living mammals, are native to most of Africa south of the Sahara, except the great rain-forest regions of the west. The preferred habitat is dry, open wooded areas or tree-dotted plains, where the great height of the animals makes the leaves of the various acacias, the principal item of diet, readily accessible. Giraffes usually live in groups of females and young, dominated by a single adult male, the herd numbering perhaps a dozen animals. Unattached males may live together or at times several groups may join to form a larger band. In some more remote regions giraffes still persist in fair numbers; in more settled areas they have disappeared entirely or are found only in the great national parks or preserves.

All of the several kinds of giraffes generally recognized are now usually considered to be races of *G. camelopardalis*. The classic review of the group is that of Lydekker (1904), while later revisions have been made by Allen (1939) and, for the southern subspecies, by Ellerman, Morrison-Scott, and Hayman (1953). Only four of the many forms are usually seen in zoological gardens: the Nubian (*G. c. camelopardalis*), of the eastern Sudan and Ethiopia; the reticulated (*G. c. reticulata*), of northern Kenya and southern Ethiopia; the Uganda or baringo (*G. c. rothschildi*), of northwestern Kenya and southeastern Uganda, and the Masai (*G. c. tippelskirchi*), of Kenya and Tanganyika. There appears to be some intermingling of adjacent forms in nature (Stott, 1959), and certainly there is much interbreeding in zoological gardens, so that racial distinctions are not always easily discernible in captive animals.

In general the markings consist of blotches, ranging from pale yellowish brown to nearly black, surrounded by a network of white or yellowish tone. The dark-reddish coloration and narrow netting, extending to the head, of the reticulated, the tightly netted body and openly marked neck of the Uganda, the irregular "leaf" markings and sooty face of the Masai, and the large, quadrate brown patches with broad yellowish separations of the Nubian should serve to distinguish animals typical of these races.

In all giraffes, both male and female, a pair of short, conical horns rises from the crown. They are covered with fine hair and carry a longer tuft at the tip. A large, bony protuberance on the forehead, more strongly developed in the northern races, is sometimes referred to as a third horn. In some, notably adult males of the Uganda and the reticulated, a second, smaller pair of horns rises behind the primary ones, so that the horns may then be said to number five. None of these appendages is ever shed.

The height giraffes may reach is naturally a subject of primary interest. It is known to be greater in males than in females, but accurate figures are difficult to obtain. In order to satisfy the usually incredulous curiosity of our visitors and to gauge our own judgement of height, our indoor giraffe stalls carry at the front a plainly marked perpendicular scale of inches and feet, against which reasonably accurate sighting measurements of standing animals can be made. The greatest height for a giraffe recorded here by this means is 15 feet, 6 inches for a male Nubian born here on January 21, 1929, and measured in 1940. Our tallest female was a Uganda that stood 13 feet, 8 inches, with a shoulder height of 9 feet, 2 inches, when she had lived here for 14 years. Figures quoted by Shortridge (1934) for giraffes in nature run from 16 feet to 19 feet, 3 inches for males and an average of 15 feet, 6 inches to 16 feet for females.

Estimates of weight are given by Shortridge (1934) as 1–2 tons for males, but, as with most large mammals, actual weights are seldom available. Shortridge (*loc. cit.*) quotes Pocock (*The Field*, February 8, 1917) as giving the weight of a female that died in the Zoological Gardens of London as 1,142 pounds, while Talbot and Talbot (1961) give the actual weight of a female Masai, in the field, as 1,760 pounds. An adult male Nubian giraffe weighed 1,650 pounds at death here, and a female of the same race, aged about 10 years, had a living weight of 1,335 pounds.

The extremely long neck and high shoulders of the giraffe make it impossible for the animal to drink or to feed from the ground without spreading its legs sideways or fore and aft. This it accomplishes with some difficulty, although apparently with no concern. Giraffes in nature appear to be able to go for considerable periods without drinking, and in fact are said (Shortridge, *loc. cit.*) to avoid large bodies of water. Rivers seem to provide impassable barriers. Shortridge (*loc. cit.*) says "they may resemble Camels in being bad waders and in being unable to swim." Goodwin (1954) says definitely: "It is a poor wader and unable to swim." Apropos of this point, on September 26, 1960, a giraffe that had just been unloaded from a ship at a New York dock, escaped from its crate, ran to the end of the pier, and fell into the water. Observers reported that the animal sank from sight almost at once without making effective efforts to swim.

While the giraffe in nature has few enemies, its chief protection, when needed, lies in flight. At close quarters the giraffe, awkward though it may seem, is able to defend itself with powerful weapons. It can kick or strike either forward or backward with its heavy, sharp-edged hoofs, while the great head can be swung with lethal force, the effort appearing to be directed toward the delivery of a blow with the side of the head, rather than with the horns. I once saw a bull giraffe strike a female on the lower back, in this manner, with such force as to drive her to the ground, from which she rose with difficulty.

The giraffe, though often considered to be mute, is actually capable, apparently under stress, of making small vocal sounds. Some instances are quoted by Shortridge (1934), who says that a young giraffe "blared" like a calf when captured and "it has been stated that a cow Giraffe occasionally gives vent to a low call note when its young strays too far away." A Masai calf that was born here in 1960 repeatedly uttered a soft, rumbling bleat when separated temporarily from its mother. The latter invariably became agitated at such times but was never heard to make vocal response. A definite instance of the uttering of a vocal sound by a female reticulated giraffe in our collection, has been recorded (Anon., 1943). This animal, suffering from arthritis, was unable to rise from the usual lying position, with legs folded beneath her. When an attempt was made to lift her, she emitted a low mooing sound, distinctly heard by all present, including myself.

Whether or not the giraffe lies down to sleep has long been a controversial subject. Many observers have agreed with the view expressed by Roberts (1951) who says that "their long legs are such that normally they do not lie down to rest but remain standing all the time, even when sleeping." A more moderate position is that expressed by Roosevelt and Heller (1914): "In the land through which we traveled we found that the Giraffes slept standing; but, as is the case with elephants, some individuals, and in some localities all the individuals, habitually lie down to sleep." Observations in nature are not easily made, since a sleeping giraffe is difficult to approach. Even in the zoological garden the situation is much the same, for accustomed to captivity though the animal may be, it always retains its natural timidity. However, caution and persistence have enabled observers to determine that captive giraffes, at least, do lie down to sleep. Hediger (1955b) not only says that giraffes sleep while lying down with heads erect but presents a photograph of what appears to be a young animal with its head folded over its back, presumably in deeper sleep. Grzimek (1956) gives a photograph of an adult giraffe lying down with its neck arched backward, so that its muzzle appears to be resting on the ground. Dr. Grzimek calls this the position of "deep sleep," maintained for an average of only 6½ minutes perhaps five times during the night.

The mere act of lying down with head erect during daytime can often be observed in zoological gardens where the animals are undisturbed. I have frequently seen our own giraffes in this position in their outdoor yards. Whether or not they were sleeping I cannot say, but one of our keepers reports seeing an adult male Masai lying with his neck folded over his back. All three of our present adults have been seen lying down in their stalls at night with heads erect, but usually an approach results only in the sounds made by the rising animals, long since alerted.

Although the giraffe was known to the ancient Egyptians as a captive animal as early as the Eighteenth Dynasty and to the Romans at least during the reign of Julius Caesar (Loisel, 1912), it was not until the nineteenth century that it became fully established in European zoological gardens. In 1826 a single giraffe arrived in France (Loisel, *loc. cit.*), in 1827 another reached England (Mitchell, 1929), and in 1828 a third was received at Schönbrunn, Austria (Kronfeld, 1936). Apparently, each of these animals was the first to be seen, respectively, in these countries and naturally received great acclaim. The latter two arrivals, unfortunately, did not survive for long, but the first lived at the Jardin des Plantes, Paris, for over 18 years (Flower, 1931), an excellent omen for the future.

In 1836 the Zoological Society of London received three males and one female from the Sudan. These animals thrived, and the female produced a number of young, the first in 1839 (Flower, 1929). Following this experience, giraffes were imported into Europe with increasing frequency and were seen in most of the larger collections. In fact, Hagenbeck (1910) says that in 1876 alone he received thirty-five specimens, while a rival importer brought in twenty-six, with the result that the market was temporarily glutted. It seems probable that a giraffe received in 1873 at the Central Park Menagerie in New York was the first to reach America. Five males and one female arrived at the Philadelphia Zoological Garden in 1874 (Ulmer, 1959) and a pair was purchased by the Cincinnati Zoological Park Association in 1878 (Stephan, 1925). The latter author says there were only five giraffes in the United States in 1925, while Cully (1958) found a total of fifty in twenty American zoological gardens in 1958 and adds that twelve of these institutions reported a total of fifty-seven births up to that time.

The first giraffes received by the New York Zoological Park were a pair purchased from Carl Hagenbeck on October 17, 1903. Since that time we have never been without representatives of the group, six further specimens having been acquired by purchase, two by deposit, and six having been born, of which only two were fully reared. All of the four races usually seen, as designated above, have been represented.

Giraffes here are kept in our Antelope House. This building, completed in 1903, is now (1963) outmoded as compared with more elaborate installations. Nevertheless, it is still successfully operating, and its basic plan remains functional, so a description is given here. The building is 142 feet long and 78 feet wide. Stalls are arranged along each side, the smaller ones housing antelopes and okapis, while two larger rooms for giraffes occupy the center of each side—four in all. These stalls measure 19 by 24 feet and are 18 feet high. The separating walls, 10 feet high, are of brick, and at the front there is a 12-inch coping to prevent the animals' hoofs from slipping through the barrier. From this coping rise 2-inch iron bars, 4 feet apart, that join a heavy steel cross-member 8 feet above the floor. Strong wire netting, its oblong meshes ranging from 3 by 6 inches at the bottom to 6 by 6 inches at the top, is fastened across this structure. Netting of larger mesh is unsafe; I was told by F. S. van Reesema, former director of the Zoological Gardens of Rotterdam, that a giraffe there had pushed its head through mesh 1 foot square and, being unable to withdraw, had broken its neck in its struggles. Above the cross-member, a lighter wire-covered section extends upward for another 4 feet, the total of 12 feet being sufficiently high to prevent the animals from extending their heads to within the reach of the public.

There has been much discussion concerning types of flooring for giraffe stalls and, of course, much dissension. The reason for these differences of opinion is the fact that the great hoofs of giraffes are especially subject to overgrowth, and unless the necessary attrition takes place, they may reach prodigious lengths, so that surfaces too smooth or too soft are entirely unsuitable. There is also the point that the timid nature and great weight of the animals make it imperative that the floor provide protection against slipping. Wood, stone, concrete, earth, and sand all have their advocates. Stephan (1925), on the basis of long experience, recommends a complicated structure of concrete, sand, wood, and straw. Various materials and compositions have been tried here, including several abrasive flooring compositions, but we finally reverted to concrete, swept when freshly laid with a coarse broom. This is drawn from all sides to a central drain, leaving narrow furrows from $\frac{1}{8}$ to $\frac{1}{4}$ inch deep, insuring proper runoff of liquids and providing both abrasive and anti-slip qualities. There would be risk of reducing the hoofs to the point of tenderness, of course, if this floor were kept perfectly bare, but an attentive keeper can control this situation perfectly by spreading straw thinly when required. During the 15 years this flooring type has been in use here, the animals' hoofs have kept in perfect condition and none has been injured by slipping.

Access to the outer yards is provided by double doors 11 feet, 6 inches high to the center of the arched top and 7 feet, 4 inches wide. Since giraffes much in excess of 10 feet in height are seldom shipped, these clearances are quite sufficient at first, and as the animals grow, they readily learn to lower their heads, so that there seems to be no real necessity for the doors of 15 or 18 feet sometimes provided.

The yards extend from the building approximately 128 feet to the public walk, where they have a frontal width of about 35 feet, narrowing to 20 feet at the inner end. The outer barrier consists of a concrete coping 12 inches high supporting a row of $\frac{3}{4}$-inch steel rods, 3 feet high, set on $2\frac{1}{2}$-inch centers, surmounted by a section of the same rods, set on 5-inch centers and 4 feet high—8 feet in all. Even giraffes are inveterate beggars, and to keep feeding by visitors at a minimum, 4 feet of wire netting have been added above the fence line or sections have been run across the yards, 15 feet from the perimeter.

Each partition, also 8 feet high, consists of two fences of 6-gauge American Standard wire netting with a space of 3 feet between them. This is planted with privet, providing an excellent screen. These yards were paved originally with macadam. This, however, has long since disintegrated and been replaced by bare, hard-packed earth over the sound foundation of paving stones set on edge that once underlay the paving, providing perfect drainage. In accordance with generally accepted practice, grass is eliminated. Shade is provided by large trees, their branches now beyond the reach of the tallest giraffe.

Usually, animals that have become especially adapted to particular feeding habits are difficult to care for in captivity, but certainly the giraffe cannot be so included, for it presents no difficulties not easily surmounted. Substitutes for the natural diet are taken readily and appear to provide all essential items. The average daily ration for an adult animal here consists of approximately 20 pounds of alfalfa hay, 10 pounds of the feeding pellets described under "Cervidae" (p. 559), and 5 pounds of rolled oats mixed with cut apples, carrots, potatoes, cabbage, and bread. Bananas, reserved as a special treat, are usually fed by hand. There is much variation, of course, in quantities, which must be adjusted to the requirements and preferences of individual animals. Clover hay, if a good quality is available, is an excellent alternative for alfalfa, although only the dried leaves and blossoms are usually eaten. Hay is placed in a feeding rack of pliable iron rods, hung with the bottom about 7 feet above the floor. There is little wastage, since firm footing enables the animal to retrieve from the floor desirable wisps that may fall. Grain is fed in removable mangers which are hung on a wall also about 7 feet above the floor. Water and salt bricks are provided in a partitioned enamel container which rises 4 feet from the floor. In summer fresh, leafy branches are hung on the fences at convenient heights and of course are greatly relished.

Young giraffes require assured supplies of calcium and vitamin D for proper bone growth, and if these are lacking the animals are likely to develop rickets. An extreme case of this condition is figured by Iles (1957). Enlarged joints of the legs in a pair of young Masai giraffes received here after long confinement in quarantine suggested the onset of such difficulty. They were furnished a supplement of irradiated yeast and fine bone meal, which they took readily, so that by the time they had reached maturity there was no indication of a former deficiency.

The temperature in the building is maintained during the winter at about 70° F. When the outside temperature is not less than 50° F. and there is neither high wind nor rain, the giraffes are allowed to go out for up to 2 hours, the period of liberty increasing as the thermometer rises. During rainy periods they are kept indoors unless the temperature is 65° F. or higher, and largely because of the danger of slipping, the animals are never allowed to go outside if ice or snow is present in the yards.

Female giraffes, once they have become familiar with each other, ordinarily will live quietly together, indoors or out. When the greater space of outside runs is available, a single male is usually well behaved with one or more females. However, when the animals are confined to indoor quarters, we follow here the usual practice of separating the male to avoid the constant persecution to which the females might otherwise be subjected.

Fortunately for zoological garden budgets, giraffes breed well in captivity, although the young are not always reared. The first birth of a giraffe in a zoological garden appears to be that referred to above as having occurred in London in 1839—Street (1956) gives the date as June 19. This calf lived for only a few days, but between that year and 1914 there were twenty-two births of giraffes in the Zoological Gardens of London (Zuckerman, 1953). Similar successes have been achieved in many European collections, and by 1960 the threat of oversupply seemed actually to be looming.

The first birth of a giraffe in America seems to have been that of a calf born at the Cincinnati Zoological Gardens on October 20, 1889 (Stephan, 1925). Since that time, breeding results in this country have paralleled those of Europe, all the larger institutions, at least, having been successful.

In nature giraffes appear to have fairly definite breeding seasons (Shortridge, 1934), but in captivity there seem to be no restrictions. A female Uganda here has been noted to be in estrus in every month except January. A compilation of birth dates including those in the Zoological Gardens of London, as charted by Zuckerman (1953), in the Zoological Gardens of Antwerp, as listed by Gijzen (1958a), and in our own records here show at least one such event in every month but December. It is true that births are more numerous during the spring and summer months, but this is largely due to carefully planned matings, designed to avoid the appearance of young while the mothers are confined indoors in winter.

Nouvel (1958) says that the non-pregnant female giraffe comes into estrus at intervals of 14 days. Six successive periods in the female Uganda mentioned above were observed here as occurring at intervals of 19, 16, 14, 16, 17, and 16 days, respectively. Duration has not been found here to exceed 24 hours. During this period many mountings may occur, although pregnancy does not always result. The gestation period is usually given as roughly $14\frac{1}{2}$ months; Asdell (1946) says "between 14 and 15 months," while the several authorities quoted by Kenneth (1953) give figures ranging from 420 to 468 days. In reporting on a remarkably successful breeding season at the Cheyenne Mountain Zoo at Colorado Springs, Colorado, in which each of four reticulated cows produced a viable calf in 1960, D. G. Davis (1960) gives the respective gestation periods as 450, 455 (two), and 461 days.

Parturition has so often been reported in detail (Hediger, 1955a; Pournelle, 1955; Iles, 1957; Gijzen, 1958a) that lengthy repetition is unnecessary. The birth of a Masai calf here on October 2, 1959, was typical. Early on the morning of that day the mother was unusually restless, and enlargement of the udder and vulva was noted. At 10:45 A.M. the forelegs of the calf appeared, soon followed by the head. The mother moved continuously, and at 11:40 A.M., as she assumed a partially squatting but upright position, the calf dropped to the deep straw on the floor. The female licked and cleaned it assiduously. Within an hour, the calf attempted to rise but was unable to do so. The cow passed the afterbirth at 3:07 P.M., and although it was left in the stall overnight, she did not eat it.

Events, up to this point, were in accord with the usual sequence. The normal calf, after several attempts, finally achieves a standing position, wobbles uncertainly to its mother, fumbles about for the udder, and, sometimes assisted by nudges of the dam's head or forefeet, eventually finds it. Once this has been accomplished, there is usually no further difficulty, as the giraffe cow is generally an excellent mother.

Unfortunately, this calf was unable to stand without assistance from the keepers, even with the benefit of cross-hobbles that prevented its legs from spreading. When on its feet it nursed well but became gradually weaker and died on October 7, when its kidneys were found to have been congenitally non-functional. Its height at birth was 70 inches and its weight at death 107 pounds.

On March 4, 1962, after an observed gestation period of 457 days, a second male calf, standing 67 inches, was born to the same female. He was soon on his feet and searching for his mother's nipples. Reluctant at first, she permitted intermittent nursing, but by the next day her udder was swollen and apparently tender, as she avoided the calf's efforts to approach. Under the direction of Dr. Charles Gandal, our veterinarian, a tranquilizer was injected via a Capchur pistol, and a diuretic, Diuril, was administered orally to reduce edema in the udder tissues. This medication proved fully effective, for the calf was nursing again on March 6 and continued to do so normally. On March 17 it was seen to nibble both hay and rolled oats.

It is obvious that the crucial test of a giraffe calf's viability comes with its efforts to stand. If it succeeds, all should be well, but if it fails in its attempts, some weakness or defect is to be suspected. Efforts are often made to hand-rear such calves, seldom with successful results, although Hediger (1955a) reports that a calf accidentally injured by its mother was brought up on cow's milk given from a nursing bottle. A detailed account of successful hand-rearing in the Bristol Zoo is given by Zellmer (1961).

Births of giraffes are usually of single young; Shortridge (1934) reports twins in two instances. The skin and hair tufts that will later cover the still undeveloped horns are present at birth. Heights of newly born calves in the Zoological Gardens of Antwerp are given by Gijzen (1958a) as follows: males, 1.85 meters (approximately 72½ inches) and 1.82 meters (approximately 71½ inches); female, 1.68 meters (approximately 66 inches). The following birth heights have been recorded here: males, 67 inches (approximately 1.70 meters), 68 inches (approximately 1.73 meters), 69 inches (approximately 1.75 meters), and 70 inches (approximately 1.78 meters); female, 66 inches (approximately 1.68 meters). Hediger (1955a) considers that the normal weight at birth is about 110 pounds. A male calf that died here on the day after its birth weighed 87 pounds.

The following heights of giraffes born at Antwerp, measured at the known age of 12 months, are given by Gijzen (1958a): male, 3.15 meters (approximately 10 feet, 4 inches); females, 2.87 meters (approximately

9 feet, 5 inches) and 2.95 meters (approximately 9 feet, 8 inches). A male Nubian born here on January 21, 1929, stood 5 feet, 8 inches at birth. Measurements of height made in January of ensuing years gave the following results: 1931, 11 feet, 9 inches; 1933, 12 feet, 5 inches; 1935, 12 feet, 8 inches; 1938, 14 feet; 1940, 15 feet, 6 inches. Although this animal lived until December 22, 1950, with a life span of 21 years, 11 months, 1 day, he showed no increase in stature after January, 1940, when he was 11 years old. His weight at death was 1,650 pounds, as already noted.

Available information indicates that sexual maturity in the giraffe is attained during the fourth year. The late Axel Reventlow, former director of the Zoological Gardens of Copenhagen, informed me that in a female of known age in his collection first estrus occurred at the age of $3\frac{1}{2}$ years. Gijzen (1958a) says that a female born at Antwerp on April 29, 1953, produced her first calf on March 11, 1958, when she was just under 5 years old. Broadly considered, conception certainly occurred in the second half of the animal's fourth year. Reuther (1961) reports that a male and two females received at the Cleveland Zoological Park on October 22, 1955, were under 10 feet in height and therefore presumably not more than 1 year old. On March 23, 1959, one of these females gave birth to a calf which, estimating the gestation period at about 455 days, would have been conceived early in the parents' fourth year.*

The greatest longevities achieved by giraffes in our collection are that of a male Nubian that was received here on November 22, 1913, and lived until May 13, 1935, or 21 years, 5 months, 21 days, and the span of 21 years, 11 months, 1 day, noted above. Many individuals have equaled or even exceeded these records, but the 27 years, 10 months, and the 28 years given by Flower (1931) for two female giraffes in the Zoological Gardens of Antwerp, presumably still head the list.

The okapi (*Okapia johnstoni*) is found only in the dense rain forests of the [Belgian] Congo. Its distribution, as shown by Schouteden (1947), lies largely to the north and east of the Congo River, although scattered records (see also Harper, 1945) suggest that the okapi may be more abundant on the left bank of the river than previously supposed. Like its much larger relative, the giraffe, the okapi feeds chiefly on foliage, although naturally this is sought at considerably lower levels. Lists of preferred food plants are given by de Landsheere (1957) and by Gijzen (1959a). In the dense cover of their habitat the animals are difficult to observe, so that their numbers and ways are still obscure. Apparently the individuals live solitary lives, the sexes meeting only for brief mating periods, with no herding behavior. The total population may be as sparse as the rarity of

*See Addenda, p. 737.

the species in both preserved and living collections suggests or it may be as great as the "tens of thousands" suggested by Grzimek (1957:220).

Several races of *O. johnstoni* have been described but none is now generally recognized (Allen, 1939). The body color is dark brown, sometimes approaching black, with the sides of the head paler. Horizontal white stripes mark the buttocks and the upper parts of the legs, which are white below with a dark ring above the hoofs and a perpendicular dark line on the fronts of the fore pair. The hair is short and fine, the coat being suggestive of that of a well-groomed thoroughbred in summer. As already stated, there is no mane in the adult.

Horns are borne by males only, and in the adult, unlike those of the giraffe, are bare of skin at the tip, where they may be sharply pointed. Gijzen (1959a) gives a pictorial record of the development of the horns in a growing animal. While male giraffes are larger than females of the same race, the condition is reversed in the okapi. Lydekker (1913–16) says that the female okapi is larger than the male, and measurements given by de Landsheere (1957) confirm the statement. In an adult pair now (1963) living here, the male stands 4 feet, 6 inches (1.37 meters) at the shoulder, the female an even 5 feet (1.52 meters). A male received here in 1937 weighed 500 pounds at death in 1952; the female mentioned above, received here in thin condition in 1956, weighed 465 pounds on arrival.

In defense or offense the male okapi swings its head much as the giraffe does but of course with much less force. The blow has a slight upward direction, bringing the horns into play, so that severe wounds may be inflicted. Both sexes are able to kick with great force, too often without warning.

There are few references in the literature concerning the utterance of vocal sounds by the okapi. Pocock (1946) refers to native reports that the okapi has "a voice like a cow" but adds that "the one now living in the Gardens [London] is as silent as the Giraffes." Its keeper had noted only one exception when, after having been moved to new quarters, the animal made a sound "as much like a bleat as anything." H. Lang (1918), discussing an experience with a young okapi in the Congo, says, "Had it not bleated from time to time like a sheep and walked about in quest of its mother. . . ." In a photograph published later (H. Lang, 1919) this calf is shown with open mouth, over the caption, "Bleating for his mother." Late on a dull winter afternoon in 1943, as I was talking with George Kress, the very experienced keeper then in charge of our Antelope House, I heard a sound that was strange to me. Queried, Kress said it was made by our male okapi, which often called when hungry or thirsty. As Kress hastened to look after the animal's needs, I made a note which I have before me. It describes the sound as a "low, soft but penetrating whistle." On numerous future occasions I heard and saw this okapi call but never could devise a better description—not really a whistle, of course, and certainly not a bawl. I have never heard our present (1963) pair make any sound, but Joseph A. Davis, Jr., curator of mammals, and Neil Dapolite, the keeper, both assure me that they have often heard them call to each other when separated, although their descriptions of the sound are no better than mine. In any case, while the okapi is certainly not a loquacious animal, it is definitely more vocal than the giraffe.

The furor created by the discovery of the okapi in 1901 left an aura of mystery that still surrounds this beautiful animal. That a creature so large and, once in the open, so conspicuous, could have remained so long unknown to any but the primitive inhabitants of the steaming jungles of the Congo even now seems almost incredible. The story of its discovery is of such romantic interest that it has often been repeated (H. Lang, 1918; Pocock, 1946; Gijzen, 1959a). Briefly, Sir Harry Johnston, exploring in the Congo, obtained two strips of the banded skin of an animal unknown to him but called by the natives "okapi." These remnants were forwarded to London, where P. L. Sclater (1901) considered them to represent an unnamed animal which he called *Equus* (?) *johnstoni* in the rather uncertain belief that it was a zebra. Soon afterward, Johnston obtained a skin and two skulls of his new find. In due course these reached London, where Sir E. Ray Lankester, recognizing the affinity with the giraffes rather than with the zebras, devised the generic title *Okapia*.

Naturally, the zoological gardens of the world were deeply interested in this startling discovery and were eager to secure living specimens. H. Lang (1918) gives an absorbing account of his efforts to obtain an okapi for the New York Zoological Park during the Congo Expedition of the American Museum of Natural History, beginning in 1909, in company with James P. Chapin, discoverer of the Congo peacock (*Afropavo*). Lang did succeed in securing a newborn calf, but unfortunately it died after 10 days, following exhaustion of the condensed-milk supply. Apparently the first recorded success in rearing an okapi calf by hand was accomplished by Mrs. Landeghem, wife of the district commissioner at Buta in the Uele District of the Congo, as reported by H. Lang (1919). This young animal, which safely arrived at the Zoological Gardens of Antwerp on August 8, 1919, was the first okapi to be seen alive outside Africa. Unfortunately, it lived for only 51 days (Gijzen, 1959a).

In following years there was a gradual acceleration of arrivals, but mostly of animals obtained by chance. It was not until a station for the capture, study, and supply of living okapis was established in 1946, by the Fish and Game Administration of the Belgian Congo, that animals became more readily available. This center, located at Epulu in the Ituri Forest, was under the direction of Captain J. de Medina. Through his efforts, specimens were furnished to accredited zoological gardens in many parts of the world. Complete records of all the okapis that have been captured or born in captivity before and after the establishment of the Epulu station, up to the dates of publication, are given by Gijzen (1958b, 1959a). The total shown in the latter reference is 137, with seventeen institutions listed as recipients.

The Epulu station relied on the use of the pitfall for the capture of okapis, a method long practiced by the Pygmies. Once trapped, the animal was induced to walk up a camouflaged incline into a crate in which it was transported, sometimes for many miles, to the station. Here it was eventually liberated in a large inclosure, where it quickly settled down. The placid nature of the okapi, as compared with that of the more active giraffe, made accommodation to captivity fairly simple, even fully adult animals quickly becoming perfectly tame. Details of capture and care at the Epulu station are given by de Landsheere (1957) and Gijzen (1959a).

Up to 1963, three okapis have been received here. The first of these was "Congo," number ten on Dr. Gijzen's lists, who arrived here on August 3, 1937 (Bridges, 1937). Congo had been bottle-reared at the Mission of the Premonstratensian Order, at Buta, by Brother Joseph Hutsebaut, pioneer in the care of okapis (Bridges, 1947a, 1947b). A shipment of three male okapis arrived at Antwerp on July 20, 1937, by special arrangement with the Belgian Ministry of the Colonies, and Congo was personally selected by W. Reid Blair, then director of the New York Zoological Park. The choice was based largely on the fact that examination showed the animal to be relatively free of the internal parasites with which freshly imported okapis are too frequently infested (de Landsheere, 1957; Gijzen, 1959a). Congo remained a quiet, steady animal and reigned until his death on September 5, 1952, as the only member of his species to have been seen alive in America up to that time.

Our second okapi was a male called "Biloto," received here on June 15, 1949. He had been sent from Epulu to Leopoldville, where he was added to a large living collection that had been gathered for us by Charles Cordier. Biloto was brought to us in good faith as a female (Cordier, 1949), and it was not until he reached his stall here that his true sex was revealed, the darkness of his crate having prevented previous observation of his very obvious horns. Biloto was a fully grown, wild-caught animal, certainly not young, yet he was almost as steady as the bottle-reared Congo. His arrival found us, of course, with two males, and it was not until November 1, 1956, that we received the female "Muyoni" as the gift of the Belgian Congo Government (Graham, 1956). Again a wild-caught adult, Muyoni was even more docile that either of the males. She had been through 90 days of quarantine before delivery to us and was in thin condition with a heavy infestation of parasites. However, she responded well to intensive treatment and was soon in robust health.

Our okapis are kept in the Antelope House, already described (p. 611), occupying available giraffe stalls or slightly smaller adjoining ones. Feeding is similar to that of the giraffes (p. 612). The male, Biloto, takes 7–8 pounds of alfalfa hay daily, with about 5 pounds of feeding pellets and perhaps 1 pound of rolled oats. Muyoni, the female, has approximately the same allowance, except that she will not eat rolled oats. In addition, both animals are given greens, vegetables, and fruits, particularly bananas, and in summer an abundance of fresh foliage. Okapis received directly from the Congo may have some difficulty in accommodating to dry foods and must be well supplied with greens until they have bridged the gap. Hay racks, of course, are hung at lower levels than they are for giraffes, since the okapi has no difficulty in feeding, even from the ground. Trusting and docile though they may be, okapis here have never solicited food from visitors, as giraffes are inclined to do, so that internal barriers in outdoor runs have not been necessary. Pocock (1946) says that an okapi in the Zoological Gardens of London, apparently fed entirely on fresh leaves, greens, and vegetables, never drank water, the food presumably supplying the required moisture. Our animals, fed largely on dry materials, drink water freely. Salt blocks, impregnated with phenothiazine, are always available.

So great were the difficulties encountered in early experiments in the capture and transportation of okapis that progress in breeding in captivity was slow. Early reports of success at the Epulu station proved to have been based on the production of calves by females pregnant when captured. Several of these calves were successfully reared, sometimes with the help of okapi foster mothers (de Landsheere, 1957; Gijzen, 1959a). Grzimek (1957) says that no young had actually been bred at the station up to that time, but Gijzen (loc. cit.) records one birth in 1956 and two in 1957, three different females at the station having been impregnated by the same captive male.

The first recorded impregnation of a female okapi in captivity occurred in the Zoological Gardens of Antwerp and resulted in the production of a premature fetus, found dead on the morning of January 4, 1953. The female, "Dasegala," is reported to have been rebred 5 days after this event (Anon., 1953c). On the night of September 17–18, 1954, this female gave birth to an apparently normal calf which, unfortunately, she promptly trampled to death. A second seemingly viable calf born on July 3, 1956, met a similar fate (Anon., 1956a). In the face of these misfortunes, it was decided that the next youngster should be separated from its mother and reared by hand. This birth occurred on January 22, 1958, and the calf was promptly picked up. It appeared to be thriving on the bottle, but following a drop in the temperature of its stall to 15°C. (59°F.), it died on February 14, 1958, from meningitis and pulmonary congestion. Its weight at birth is given as 21 kilograms (46.2 pounds) (Van den bergh, 1958). This experiment was repeated, with a more satisfactory result, following the fourth birth of an okapi at Antwerp on April 24, 1959. The calf was removed at once and an attempt was made to persuade a lactating donkey to allow it to nurse. This arrangement proved mutually unsatisfactory, and resort was had to the bottle. First feedings consisted of milk drawn from the donkey, diluted with water, and later supplemented with a feeding preparation called Nutricia. As the donkey's supply waned, sheep's milk was substituted. The calf gained in weight from 18 kilograms (39.6 pounds) at birth to 34 kilograms (74.8 pounds) on June 14, when it was 51 days old. On September 13 the young animal was seen to eat chestnut leaves, its first solid food, and could be considered as safely reared (Van den bergh, 1959). This happy result brought the series to an end, for "Besobe," the sire of all these calves, died on July 22, 1958, 9 months before the birth of his final offspring (Gijzen, 1959a).

On June 6, 1957, the first okapi to have been bred and reared in a zoological garden was born at the Parc Zoologique du Bois de Vincennes, Paris, as reported in detail by Nouvel (1958). The parents were introduced on September 15, 1955, and copulation was first observed on October 8. Repetition was noted at intervals of from 3 to 120 days, up to February 1, 1957, so that no regular estrus cycle could be determined, although Gijzen (1959a) reports a period of about 3 weeks for the female okapi Dasegala at Antwerp. At the time of cessation, movements of the fetus could be observed, and birth followed on June 6, 1957, the period of gestation naturally being indeterminable. Since there appeared to be a delay in the delivery, the keeper managed to complete it by means of a loop of cord but was immediately driven from the stall by the female. Previously gentle, she became so aggressive after parturition that even a familiar keeper could not enter the stall during the first month. The calf was well cared for by the mother, progressed normally, and was fully reared. A second calf, born to the same parents on March 6, 1959, is reported to have died in the following December.

Also in 1959, the first birth of an okapi in the United States occurred on September 17 at the Chicago Zoological Park (Anon., 1959b), followed by a similar event at the New York Zoological Park on October 17 (J. A. Davis, Jr., 1959). The year 1960 was marked by three okapi births in European zoological gardens: February 12, Rotterdam (van Bemmel, 1960); March 2, Basel (E. M. Lang, 1960), and September 9, Frankfurt (Anon., 1960a). In 1961 a second calf was born to the Chicago female on June 6, while in Europe births occurred at Vincennes on April 25 and June 14, and at Copenhagen on June 23. The June 14 birth at Vincennes is of particular interest, for the mother was "Ebola," born at Vincennes on June 6, 1957 (Brouard, 1961). Taking the gestation period as roughly $14\frac{1}{2}$ months, Ebola obviously was bred by her father about April 1, 1960, when she was aged approximately 2 years, 10 months. Early in 1962 there were okapi births at Rotterdam, January 6, and at San Diego, February 8, with the year barely begun. A calf born here on May 31, 1962, after a gestation period of 439 days, sustained double hip dislocations and failed to survive. In each case the mothers appear to have reacted normally, except for Antwerp's Dasegala, who now must be considered as exceptional. It is possible that an initial upsetting experience established a behavior pattern which affected her reaction at subsequent births.*

Some features of the New York birth, already reported by J. A. Davis, Jr. (1959), should be noted here. While male okapis in captivity ordinarily live quietly with females, our male, Biloto, could not be trusted to do so. On several occasions, when the animals had been left together without close observation, he had cut the female, Muyoni, with his sharply pointed horns. Consequently, they were separated at night and allowed to be together only for varying periods during the day, when they could be watched. Testing by Biloto occurred each morning but it was not until August 2, 1958, that Muyoni proved receptive. Between 12:30 P.M. and 7:30 P.M. of that day there were many apparently successful mountings. The animals were left together overnight, but at 6 A.M. on August 3, Muyoni was no longer receptive and had already received several small cuts from Biloto's horns. Daily testing with separation at night showed no renewal of response from Muyoni, so that the experience of recurring irregular periods, reported for the Vincennes female by Nouvel (1958), was not repeated in this instance.

*See Addenda, p. 737.

Since the only statements of the gestation period of the okapi that were known to us were the curiously approximate 426 days given by Jennison (n.d.) and the estimate of about 10 months derived by Nouvel (1958) from the data obtained preceding the first birth at Vincennes, we could only wait, from the tenth month on. With the early Antwerp experiences in mind, a stall adjoining that of Muyoni was darkened and provided with peepholes, while the floors of both stalls were well padded with straw, sand, and dry, sterile sugar-cane residue. On October 15, 1959, enlargement of the vulva with a slight viscous discharge was noticed. The udder had increased in size, and Muyoni had become restless, lying down for a few seconds, then moving from stall to stall. Soon after midnight of the seventeenth, watchers noticed that one foreleg of the calf had appeared. Muyoni then entered the darkened stall and lay down. When she rose again at 1:45 A.M., the faint beam of a flashlight revealed that the calf had been born. Forty-five minutes later he was on his feet and at 4:33, when he was less than 3 hours old, he found his mother's nipples.

Since there could have been no other date of conception than August 2, 1958, the birth on October 17, 1959, definitely establishes the gestation period, in this instance, as 441 days as given by J. A. Davis, Jr. (1959). E. M. Lang (1960) reports the gestation period for the okapi born at Basel on March 2, 1960, as 446 days.

On the morning of the birth, Muyoni permitted her keeper and others of the staff to enter her stall with none of the defensive display shown by mother okapis elsewhere. The calf was somewhat darker in color than Muyoni, and its standing height at the shoulders was found to be $29\frac{3}{4}$ inches (75.57 centimeters), well within the range of 72–83 centimeters given by de Landsheere (1957). A narrow, stiff mane of black hairs about $1\frac{1}{2}$ inches in length ran down the neck from between the ears to the shoulders.

On December 1, when the calf was about 6 weeks old, it was seen nibbling alfalfa hay and nuzzling the feeding pellets. On January 4, 1960, he somehow managed to injure one of his shoulders in such a way that he was unable to assume a proper nursing position and had to rely solely on an increased intake of solid food and water. The condition soon corrected itself, but in the meantime Muyoni's udder became so swollen as to cause her apparent distress. After some experimenting, the keepers were able to draw off a quantity of milk totaling approximately $7\frac{1}{2}$ fluid ounces (222 cc.). As reported by Charles P. Gandal and Joseph A. Davis, Jr., in a mimeographed circular of the Zoo Veterinarians' Association, this sample was submitted to the Central Laboratory of the Sealtest Foods Division of the

National Dairy Products Corporation, which, on January 20, 1960, submitted the following analysis:

Fat	1.975%
Total solids	18.470
Total protein	9.920
Casein	5.704
Albumin	1.172
Lactose	5.138
Ash	1.398

The sample, of course, gathered in two milkings, did not represent total stripping of the udder, a point perhaps explanatory of varying results of analyses of the milk of many non-domesticated species.

On January 19, 1960, Biloto and Muyoni were together for the first time following the birth, the calf being temporarily separated. This was repeated daily, but it was not until April 22 that she first showed receptivity and was bred. She was indifferent following separation overnight, and there was no repetition until May 21, when the same pattern was repeated, followed by complete cessation. Muyoni and her calf spent the afternoon of October 21 together in the outside yard and were returned to the indoor stall at 4:30 P.M. The next morning at 8:00, a dead fetus was found on a defecation heap in the yard, evidently having been aborted on the twenty-first. Muyoni was suspected of estrus, and when Biloto was admitted there was immediate mounting, repeated frequently until separation for the night. This was resumed on the next morning, continuing until 4:30 P.M. Receptivity then recurred at intervals of from 4 to 49 days, an irregular pattern similar to that reported at Vincennes by Nouvel (1958). Interest usually endured through 1 day only, occasionally continuing on the next day, but never longer.

By July 17, 1960, when the calf was 9 months old, he was practically sustaining himself with solid food, although he still nursed occasionally. On October 22, at the time of the abortion of a fetus by his mother, the calf was permanently separated, his age being just over 12 months. At this time his mane had almost entirely disappeared, only scattered long hairs on the shoulders remaining.

The greatest longevities so far established by captive okapis up to January 1, 1963, are those of "Tele," received at Antwerp on September 15, 1928, and died on October 25, 1943, after 15 years, 40 days (Gijzen, 1959a), and Congo, received at New York on August 3, 1937, and died on September 5, 1952, after 15 years, 33 days. On January 1, 1963, four okapis then living in zoological gardens had been more than 10 years in these institutions. These were Esayo, received at Copenhagen April 30,

1948; Dolo, Vincennes, June 2, 1948; Biloto, New York, June 15, 1949, and Dasegala, Antwerp, September 29, 1950.*

On January 1, 1962, there were fourteen living okapis in America, including five potential breeding females. These animals, with at least six pairs and their offspring in the zoological gardens of Europe, would seem to insure the future of the okapi in captivity, whatever may be its fate in nature.

FAMILY ANTILOCAPRIDAE

PRONGHORN

The pronghorn (*Antilocapra americana*), often known as pronghorn antelope or simply antelope, is not an antelope at all but is assigned to a family of its own. Typical of the broad, often arid, prairie regions of western North America, the pronghorn has become greatly reduced in numbers in many parts of its range, although fairly large populations persist in some areas. Five subspecies are recognized (Hall and Kelson, 1959): *A. americana americana*, which once covered most of the plains from Saskatchewan, Alberta, and Manitoba south to the southwestern tier and from the Missouri River area to California; *A. americana mexicana*, from Arizona, New Mexico, and Texas to northern Mexico; *A. americana oregona*, from eastern Washington and Oregon; *A. americana peninsularis*, of Baja California, and *A. americana sonoriensis*, of southern Arizona and western Sonora. Small differences in color, size, and cranial structure distinguish the races.

There are no lateral hoofs and the tail is very short. General coloration is reddish or yellowish brown; the short mane and, in males, a patch below the ears, are black; the cheeks, two bands across the foreneck, the underparts, and the rump patch being white. The long hairs of the latter are erectile, forming a large "rosette" that presumably serves as a warning signal in times of danger.

The horns of females are usually inconspicuous, seldom extending beyond the ear-tips, but in males they may reach a considerable length, the longest recorded in the Boone and Crockett Club's *Records of North American Big Game* (1958) being 20⅛ inches. The horns are hooked sharply backward at the tip, with a short prong projecting from the front edge, about one-third of the distance from the base. In structure, the horns consist of a short, skin-covered permanent core of bone, supporting a sheath

*See Addenda, p. 737.

of keratinous material with which some hairs are incorporated. The prong is formed by the sheath only and has no bony support. The sheaths are shed annually in late autumn, after the breeding season, and are replaced as outgrowths of the skin covering the bony core, as described by Bailey (1920) and in greater detail by Noback (1932). Shoulder height is given by Palmer (1954) as 35–41 inches, and weight of males as 100–140 pounds, of females, 80–105 pounds.

The pronghorn is an inhabitant of open, rolling plains, although in some areas fencing and development have forced it into lightly wooded country. When unimpeded, it is noted for its speed which, while often exaggerated, has been accurately recorded by Einarsen (1948) at 61 miles per hour. While sagebrush of various species appears to be the staple food item, a great variety of other plants, including young grasses and forbs (weeds), as listed in detail by Einarsen (*loc. cit.*), complete the diet.

In late summer and early autumn males gather small bands of up to four or five females for the breeding season. When this has passed, horn sheaths are shed and the groups may join to form herds of some size. The gestation period is usually given as 230–40 days; Skinner (1922) says it is "a little over 8 months." The period of births varies with latitude, beginning in late February in Texas and about the middle of May in southeastern Oregon (Einarsen, *loc. cit.*). Births may be of one or two young.

For reasons still not fully understood, the pronghorn has generally proved unsatisfactory in captivity, particularly in Europe and the eastern United States. Mann (1930) says, "We have never had much success in maintaining the prong-horned antelope in Washington." Nevertheless, he reports a longevity of 5 years, 3 months and the birth of six young in the National Zoological Park, both worthwhile achievements. R. Marlin Perkins informs me that a very large single male kept in the Lincoln Park Zoo, Chicago, and well known to zoo visitors, lived there for 8 years under his care.

The first pronghorns received by the New York Zoological Park were two young females that arrived from Kansas on September 28, 1899, followed on October 11 of the same year by a male and three females from North Dakota. None of these animals lived for more than a few months, and of forty further individuals received here up to 1936, when our efforts to establish the species were abandoned, 3 years, 3 months, 7 days was the greatest longevity attained. Twin young were born on June 2, 1903, but neither was fully reared.

These experiences with the pronghorn are typical of the situation in this country generally up to only a few years ago, when experiments were undertaken by zoological gardens in the west and southwest. A herd of from five to seven animals has been maintained at the San Antonio Zoological Park, Texas, for a number of years, and Director Fred W. Stark has provided the following information concerning them. The animals are confined by a sloping or "ha-ha" moat with an outer wall 7 feet high. This has proved adequate, as anticipated, for while pronghorns are capable of lengthy horizontal leaps, they seldom undertake the clearing of high obstacles. The earthen floor of the inclosure is entirely bare. Mr. Stark considers that wire netting should never be used for pronghorns because they may strike it when running. The diet used at San Antonio consists of alfalfa hay, calf pellets, and rolled oats. This herd was based on bottle-reared animals; the young born and reared annually are distributed to other institutions, in order to keep the herd at the desired maximum.

The Dallas (Texas) Zoo and Aquarium has also had excellent results with the pronghorn, and Pierre Fontaine, the director, has given me (*in litt.*) an outline of his experience. In 1956 a "tame," hand-reared male, then 2 years old, was obtained from a ranch near Amarillo. In the same year, five 3-day-old young were collected in southwestern Texas and four were safely reared. Some additional young were obtained later, so that in December, 1960, the herd consisted of the original male, then over 6 years old, three females of 1956, and two of later vintage. Three young born in 1960 were sent in exchange to another institution, in order to keep the herd in numerical balance. The diet includes $\frac{1}{4}$ pound of commercial grain pellets with a vitamin and mineral supplement for each animal daily, with a constant supply of alfalfa hay. In summer fresh leaves of hackberry, elm, oak, and willow are fed, a procedure considered essential by Mr. Fontaine. Salt blocks are always available. Sagebrush is not obtainable in the Dallas area, a lack that appears to be unimportant.

Successful maintenance of the pronghorn at the Rio Grande Zoo at Albuquerque, New Mexico, is reported by Poglayen-Neuwall (1959). Principal foods used are a commercial grain mixture with minerals and molasses added, game bird pellets, carrots, apples, and alfalfa hay, with no sagebrush. Dr. Poglayen-Neuwall considers that the high humidity and frequent precipitation of the eastern United States and Europe are basically responsible for the difficulty experienced in maintaining the pronghorn in those areas and that neither altitude nor diet is an important factor. However, the high protein content of both sagebrush, the predominant natural food, and alfalfa, the most readily available substitute, suggests a relation of probable consequence (Einarsen, 1948).

The importance of acquiring hand-reared or captivity-bred specimens for the foundation of a projected herd is emphasized in the preceding accounts. Many of the animals received here in earlier days were captured as well-grown young, which are now known to be especially difficult. Nichol (1942) reports a successful experiment in hand-rearing, conducted near Flagstaff, Arizona. The young animals were given $2\frac{1}{2}$–3 ounces of a mixture of six parts of evaporated milk, ten parts of limewater, and one part of Karo syrup, heated to approximately 100° F., fed from a nursing bottle at 4-hour intervals. This was continued for 10 days, after which the Karo was slowly reduced and finally discontinued at 4 weeks. At 9 weeks milk-feeding was stopped, as the animals were fully on solid food. This consisted of alfalfa hay, calf meal, and rolled oats, with a supplement of salt and bone meal. Seven of nine normal young pronghorns were fully reared by this method and were liberated in a suitable area where restocking was desired. An analysis of pronghorn milk given by Einarsen (1948) shows it to be much richer in fats (13.0 to 3.7 per cent) and protein (6.9 to 3.5 per cent) in ratio to cow's milk. A report quoted from William Anderson concerning the rearing of young pronghorns at the Hart Mountain National Wildlife Refuge, in Oregon, refers to the use of cod-liver oil as a fat supplement in the fluid diet.

"Abandoned" young pronghorns are frequently picked up and reared by ranchers in the sagebrush country. Such animals make engaging pets while young, but males especially are likely to become obstreperous as they develop, so that new homes must be found. The foundations of most going pronghorn herds now kept in captivity have been formed by such animals.

FAMILY BOVIDAE

ANTELOPES, WILD CATTLE, GOATS, AND SHEEP

Except for some breeds of domesticated cattle, goats, and sheep, all the members of this huge and economically important group carry horns, which may be borne by both sexes or by males only. These paired appendages are formed by horny, unbranched, hollow sheaths growing over permanent bony cores rising from the skull and are never shed. There are no upper incisors or canines, and lateral toes are rudimentary or missing altogether. The family is represented in Africa, Asia, Europe, and North America but is absent from South America, Australia, New Zealand, and Madagascar. All the included species are herbivorous. Because of the great number and diversity of the forms included, it seems best to treat them here under the five subfamilies designated by Simpson (1945), as follows: Bovinae, Cephalophinae, Hippotraginae, Antilopinae, and Caprinae.

As a group, the Bovidae thrive and breed well in captivity, so that they have an important place in the composition of most large collections. While there are great variations in the requirements of the many forms involved, some general observations applying largely to antelopes, made here before more detailed consideration of the subgroups, will save repetition.

Our Antelope House, intended for the exhibition of animals requiring heated quarters in winter, represents the conventional style usual in colder climates and has been described in detail in the section devoted to "Giraffes" (p. 611). In addition to the four large compartments assigned to these animals, there are eight stalls measuring 12 by 16 feet and twelve that are 10 by 16, arranged along the sides of the public space. Partitions consist of sheet iron, 4 feet high, surmounted by $\frac{3}{4}$-inch rods of round steel, 3 feet high, set on 4-inch centers. Fronts are closed by similar rods alone, access for keepers being provided by swinging doors of the same construction. As originally built, there were no connecting doors, so essential in operation; some have since been installed. A particular objection to the use of bar fronts for antelopes is that, when confined in winter, the males of many species are likely to rub the sides of their horns against them, sometimes actually cutting them off, so that they are reduced to mere stumps, an unfortunate habit seldom practiced by females. The only remedy so far found helpful is the provision of solid bases, from 3 to 4 feet high, below the bars, but this so greatly reduces the visibility that the method has not been attempted here.

The choice of floor material presents another basic problem. At first concrete, simply smoothed, mixed with round pebbles, or cut into 2-inch squares, was used. All these surfaces, particularly when wet, proved to be slippery and dangerous for hoofed animals, and substitutes were sought. Many compositions were tried, but the majority proved vulnerable to dampness and constant wear. Most successful has been a material known as Tremco, which can be applied over a concrete base. This provides a non-slip surface, and when used for animals of less weight than giraffes and buffaloes, keeps in good condition for periods of up to 5 years. Each stall is provided with a permanent receptacle for food and water and racks for hay. Salt blocks, plain or medicated, are always available.

Chain-operated sliding doors provide access to the outdoor runs, already described, for use during the summer months. During mild winter periods, when the yards are free of ice and deep snow, most of the inmates of the building can be liberated for the brief period required for servicing, although shifting to an adjoining stall for this purpose is practiced where possible.

When the larger antelopes are confined in winter, it is usually necessary to separate the sexes, as males are likely to injure or even kill females. Males and females of many of the smaller species may safely remain together.

In recent years there has been a general tendency to the keeping of antelopes in large outdoor areas, when space is available, housing them in winter, when necessary, in quarters secluded from the public. An example of this system is seen in our African Plains, now largely devoted to a herd of nyala with some large birds for diversity. This area, opened to visitors on May 1, 1941 (Osborn, 1941), is about 1 acre in extent and inclosed by a concave wall of concrete averaging 8 feet in height. From its base the interior slopes upward for about 20 feet to eye level. It is well grassed and provided with a shallow, paved pool as well as several shade trees. It was opened with a varied collection of antelopes, including nyalas (*Tragelaphus angasi*), bushbuck (*Tragelaphus scriptus*), waterbuck (*Kobus ellipsiprymnus*), zebras, elands (*Taurotragus oryx*), and others. However, all but the nyalas and bushbuck soon proved unsuitable for one reason or another and were removed (Crandall, 1945). The principal point derived from this effort is the fairly obvious one that more than a single male antelope, at least of the larger species, cannot be kept in such an inclosure without risk of injury through fighting. Even the male bushbuck had to be segregated and allowed to run with the females only at night, in a small adjoining corral. Females of various sorts, however, can be run together with little danger.

Winter quarters for these animals are provided in a low, partly concealed building containing a large stall for the nyala herd, with several smaller ones for the herd bull and expectant mothers. There is less difficulty than might be supposed in controlling these animals, for we have found that before a single keeper, moving cautiously, they will walk into the shelter as quietly as cattle.

Most antelopes prefer alfalfa or clover hay to timothy but will take the latter if pressed to do so. The general diet used here consists of alfalfa, the feeding pellets described under the "Cervidae" (p. 559) sometimes mixed with rolled oats, and cut vegetables and greens. Many species also receive fresh foliage when this is available. When hand-rearing of calves is necessary, it is usually accomplished with little difficulty by the use of whole cow's milk, preferably homogenized, or reconstituted evaporated milk, fed from a nursing bottle.

SUBFAMILY BOVINAE

Kudus, Sitatunga, Bushbucks, Nyalas, Elands, Bongo, Nilgai, and Wild Cattle

The species included in this group are animals of medium or large size. Their general distribution is that of the family, but there is a marked concentration of forms in Africa. Horns are always carried by males and may be present or missing in females.

The kudus, greater (*Tragelaphus strepsiceros*) and lesser (*Tragelaphus imberbis*), are among the handsomest of antelopes, their long, openly spiraled horns, borne by males only, being special points of attraction. The greater kudu, in several forms, inhabits heavy bush country, usually in hilly areas, and is spottily distributed in East Africa, from Ethiopia to the Cape. The general coloration is pale brown, adult males tending to become grayish. The body is marked by transverse stripes of white and a white bar across the face below the eyes. The neck and shoulders are maned and the throat is handsomely fringed. The height at the shoulder is given by Sclater and Thomas (1894–1900, 4:170) as 50–52 inches. An adult male kept here weighed 460 pounds at death. The weights of three males collected in Kenya are given by Meinertzhagen (1938) as running from 584 to 604 pounds. The greatest horn length given by Ward (1922) is 64 inches on the outer curve, 41 inches in a straight line.

The lesser kudu is a much smaller animal with a shoulder height of 40 inches (Sclater and Thomas, 1894–1900, 4:185). The greatest length of the more tightly twisted horns listed by Ward (1922) is $35\frac{1}{4}$ inches on the outer curve and $26\frac{1}{4}$ inches in a straight line; the weight is given as about 230 pounds. The lesser kudu is somewhat darker in coloration than the greater, making the body stripes more conspicuous; it has the white nose-band as well as white patches on throat and chest. The lower legs are chestnut, and there is no fringe on the throat. Its haunts are the open bush of low country, from Tanganyika to Ethiopia and Somaliland.

Although the greater kudu was received by the Zoological Gardens of London as early as 1861 (Flower, 1929) and by most of the larger institutions since that time, it has never been commonly available. In spite of constant efforts on our part to secure the species, it was not until 1909 that our first greater kudu was obtained. Only six further specimens have since been received here, up to 1963. Our first calf, born on June 19, 1932, was a female which, in turn, produced a calf on September 22, 1946. The latter was sired by a bull approximately 18 months old that had been reared in the Chicago Zoological Park. The species has also been bred by the St. Louis Zoological Park and perhaps by others. The gestation period is given by Asdell (1946) as from 7 to 8 months. The greatest longevity listed by Flower (1931) is 11 years, 3 months, 5 days in the Zoological Gardens of London. The female noted above as having been born here on June 19, 1932, lived until November 7, 1947, or 15 years, 4 months, 19 days. Rabb (1960) lists a duration of 23 years for a greater kudu in the Chicago Zoological Park.

The lesser kudu, although much less frequently seen in zoological gardens than the greater, has still been shown by a considerable number. While less spectacular than the larger species, the slender grace of the lesser is ample compensation. The first specimen to be received here was a female on October 1, 1957, followed by a male on July 18, 1959, both hand-reared young animals. The species has been bred sparingly in European gardens and in this country by the Chicago, St. Louis, and San Diego zoological parks. The gestation period and longevity in captivity appear not to have been recorded.

The sitatunga (*Tragelaphus spekei*) is an antelope of medium size, especially adapted to life in the dense swamps it inhabits, the hoofs being greatly lengthened for added support on soft surfaces. It takes readily to water, swimming and diving freely. Seven races are listed by Allen (1939), ranging from Rhodesia to the southern Sudan in the east and from the Congo to Senegal in the great forests of the west. Males are usually grayish in tone, females brown, but there is much variation in racial distinctions. Body stripes are sometimes present but may be faint or missing. The horns of males are loosely spiral in form, usually with yellow tips. The longest listed by Ward (1922) are of the Zambesi race (*Tragelaphus spekei selousi*) and measure $35\frac{7}{8}$ inches on the curve, 24 inches in a straight line. Shoulder heights as given by Lydekker (1913–16, **3**:186) range from 32 to 42 inches. The hornless females are smaller than males.

Never a common animal in zoological gardens, the sitatunga has probably become more generally represented in recent years than was previously the case. Our first specimens were received here in 1909, and young were born on September 12, 1909, and December 5, 1910. The species has also been bred by the National Zoological Park (Mann, 1930) and perhaps also by others, but the greatest success with the sitatunga in this country has been that of the Chicago Zoological Park. There a large herd, usually numbering as many as thirty specimens, is maintained. In Europe the Zoological Gardens of Antwerp have been able to build up a thriving herd from which a number of animals have been released to other collections

(Gijzen, 1959b). No specific gestation period appears to have been recorded for the species. The best longevity for a sitatunga here is 8 years, 3 months, 18 days. Mann (1930) gives 11 years, 6 months for a specimen in the National Zoological Park, while Flower (1931) lists 17 years, 5 months, 5 days for a racial intergrade bred in the Zoological Gardens of London.

The bushbucks or harnessed antelopes (*Tragelaphus scriptus*) are found over most of Africa except for open plains or desert areas, no less than twenty-eight races being listed by Allen (1939). Coloration ranges from the bright chestnut of the typical race, with longitudinal and transverse stripes and interspersed spots of white, to almost black with scant markings in the Abyssinian *Tragelaphus s. meneliki*. The latter is among the larger races, its shoulder height being $29\frac{1}{2}$ inches (Lydekker, 1913–16, 3:160). A short mane extends down the back from the nape. The greatest length of the spiraled horns, carried by males only, given by Ward (1922) is $21\frac{3}{4}$ inches, for the Cape bushbuck (*Tragelaphus scriptus sylvaticus*).

Bushbucks have been kept and even bred, though sparingly, both in Europe and in this country. Our only experience here has been with the Cape race. We have found them nervous and excitable but were able to achieve good results when they were given the freedom of our African Plains in summer, with carefully secluded heated quarters in winter. A male and two females purchased in June, 1942, were treated in this manner, and young, all successfully reared, were born on May 28, 1943, November 28 and December 23, 1944, February 13, 1946, and January 6, 1947. The gestation period for the species is given by Asdell (1946) as $7\frac{1}{2}$ months. Flower (1931) lists a longevity of 9 years, 3 months, 14 days for a bushbuck in the Zoological Gardens of London; a female born here on May 28, 1943, lived until January 7, 1956, or 12 years, 7 months, 10 days.

The nyala (*Tragelaphus angasi*), larger relative of the bushbucks, is surely among the most beautiful of the antelopes. The adult male is dark gray in general, with the lower parts of the legs and an area on the crown tawny. Narrow stripes of white mark the sides, with a chevron on the nose and other scattered white markings. An erectile mane of dark, white-tipped hairs runs from nape to tail, while a long fringe depends from the foreneck and the sides of the body. The greatest length of the horns recorded by Ward (1922) is $31\frac{1}{2}$ inches measured on the curve, 26 inches in a straight line. The hornless females and the young are bright bay in color, with transverse body stripes of white and a narrow black dorsal line. Meinertzhagen (1938) gives the weights of two males collected in the field in Nyasaland as 252 and 269 pounds, respectively. An adult male kept here weighed

195 pounds at death. The shoulder height is given by Lydekker (1913–16, 3:180) as about 42 inches. The species has a rather limited distribution in southeastern Africa, from Natal north to Nyasaland, where it has become greatly reduced in numbers. Like the bushbuck, it is a forest-dwelling animal, usually seen in the open only at twilight.

On September 5, 1939, we received a young pair of nyalas directly from Africa. After a short stay in our Antelope House, they were installed in the African Plains (p. 630), where they proved most prolific, the female producing her first calf in 1941. As the herd grew in size, young females were retained and males, because of the intolerance of the adult bull, were released to other institutions. The original male lived until 1949, when he was replaced by a son that had been held in reserve, a process since repeated. On January 1, 1963, the herd numbered seventeen animals, not including a reserve bull. Sixty-three births have occurred, as follows: January, twenty-seven; February, six; March, three; April, two; May, three; June, two; July, one; November one; December, eighteen. Concentration in December and January resulted from sequestration of the herd bull during the winter months to prevent his damaging the females in close quarters, so that breeding took place, in general, after liberation on the Plains in spring. Scattered births during the summer were due to late impregnation of young females and the precocious activities of young males not separated from the herd in winter. Pregnant females are segregated in individual compartments and returned to the group after their calves have become well established. The close inbreeding has so far resulted in no detectable loss in strength or vigor. The female nyala, mother of our herd, noted above as having arrived here on September 5, 1939, died on July 14, 1955, after 15 years, 10 months, 9 days.

The mountain nyala (*Tragelaphus buxtoni*) is a rather large animal with a shoulder height of about 52 inches (Lydekker, 1913–16, 3:183). It is grayish brown in color, with scattered patches of white and faint body stripes. There is a scant dorsal mane but no throat fringe. It is found only at high altitudes in southern Ethiopia (Carter, 1959). This rare and little-known species appears to have been shown only by the Zoological Gardens of Berlin, where a male was received in 1931 and a female in 1934, both figured in the guide books of the period. According to Jones (1958), these animals were killed during an air raid in 1944.

Largest of the antelopes are the elands (*Taurotragus*), of which two species are known: the common (*Taurotragus oryx*) and the giant (*Taurotragus derbianus*). The common eland, a grazing animal, is found in the plains area of Africa from the Cape north to Angola and Kenya, although in the south it now exists only in preserves. Five races are recognized by Allen (1939), differing chiefly in points of coloration. In general the body is pale tawny or grayish, with narrow transverse stripes of white on the sides, except in the typical race, *Taurotragus o. oryx*, from the Cape, which lacks them entirely. A short, dark mane runs from the nape over the back. There is a heavy mat of hair, usually dark in color, between the horns in adult males, and a heavy, fleshy dewlap ending in a tuft of dark hair depends from the neck. The shoulder height is given by Lydekker (1913–16, **3**:210) as 5 feet, 7 inches or perhaps 6 feet. Both sexes bear horns, those of the female often being longer, though slimmer, than those of the male. The greatest length of male horns given by Ward (1922) is 37 inches, for the Zambesi race (*Taurotragus o. livingstonei*); for a female of unknown origin, $39\frac{1}{2}$ inches. A male that had lived in our collection for more than 10 years weighed 910 pounds at death; a female of approximately the same age weighed 950 pounds. The weights of four males collected in East Africa ran from 1,604 to 2,078 pounds (Meinertzhagen, 1938).

The common eland is kept so generally by zoological gardens that racial distinctions are seldom discernible. Usually quiet, almost lethargic in nature, it thrives and breeds freely in captivity. Even old bulls are seldom truculent. A mature cow reputed to have gored several herd mates before she came to us proved harmless enough here. The eland is so suggestive of an ox that many attempts have been made to domesticate it, none with real success. The species is also sometimes considered to be cold resistant, but we have found that in the climate of New York some heat is required in winter.

Eighteen common elands have been born here, up to 1963, births having occurred in every month of the year except January, February, and October. The young usually have been reared without difficulty. The gestation period is given by Asdell (1946) as from 255 to 270 days. A female eland presented by the eleventh Duke of Bedford arrived here on June 22, 1910, and lived until October 5, 1928, or 18 years, 3 months, 13 days. Rabb (1960) gives 25 years for a common eland in the Chicago Zoological Park.

The giant eland is a somewhat larger animal than the common, with longer and heavier horns, the greatest length recorded by Ward (1922) being $42\frac{1}{2}$ inches for a bull of the Congo race (*Taurotragus d. congolanus*). Distribution of the species extends from Senegal eastward across Nigeria, northern (former) French Equatorial Africa, and northeastern [Belgian] Congo to the Sudan. Five races are recognized by Allen (1939). Adult bulls develop a pad of hair between the horns, and the origin of the dewlap is farther forward than in the common eland. Coloration varies from reddish to fawn, with white striping on the body. In bulls the sides of the neck are dark brown or black, followed by a white stripe.

The giant eland appears to be a browser rather than a grazer, feeding largely on the foliage of forest trees. It has become reduced in numbers in many parts of its range, but Blancou (1958*a*) estimates the population in what was French Equatorial Africa as 10,000. The species has seldom been kept in zoological gardens, the only representatives that have reached America up to 1963 being two females of the Sudanese race (*Taurotragus d. gigas*) received in 1937 by the Chicago Zoological Park, followed later by a male. These animals bred successfully for a number of years. A photograph of a pair is reproduced in the *Guide Book* of that institution for 1941 and another of mother and young in the edition of 1947. Unfortunately, this incipient herd survived for but a few years. The only giant eland to arrive in Europe appears to have been an example of *Taurotragus d. cameroonensis*, received by the Frankfurt Zoological Gardens in 1958.

The bongo (*Boocercus eurycerus*) must be numbered among the rarest and least well known of the antelopes, as well as among the most beautiful. The adult male is dark brown in color, with fore- and underparts approaching black. Narrow transverse body stripes, a chevron across the nose, and a patch on the chest are white. The female and young are bright chestnut and similarly marked with white. There is no throat fringe or dewlap, but a thin mane extends along the back in adults. This mane is considerably longer in the young, the white body stripes carrying through. Spiraled horns are borne by both sexes, the greatest length given by Ward (1922) being 39½ inches for a specimen of the eastern race, *Boocercus e. isaaci*. Shoulder height is given by Lydekker (1913–16, **3**:204) as 48–50 inches. The only specimen kept here, a female, weighed 440 pounds at death. Four races are listed by Allen (1939), the range of the species extending in forested areas from Sierra Leone to western Kenya. The bongo is a dweller in deep forests, where it is difficult to observe, so that its habits are imperfectly known. It appears to feed chiefly on foliage and seldom comes into the open.

Up to 1963, only nine specimens appear to have reached zoological gardens: two at London, two at Rome, two at Antwerp, two at Cleveland, and one at New York. A female received at Rome in 1935 seems to have been the first arrival in Europe, followed soon afterward by a male. A female shipped to the Zoological Gardens of London from East Africa in 1936 gave birth to a calf on the voyage; mother and young are pictured in the *Illustrated London News* of April 17, 1937. It is of special interest to note that this female, pregnant when captured, cared well for her calf and was perfectly steady when I had the pleasure of viewing the pair in the Gardens in 1938. This is in accord with the report of Cordier (1949) concerning an adult male captured in the Congo that became tame enough, after a week in a stockade, to come up to anyone for proffered food. This animal, unfortunately, was eventually lost through mishandling by native carriers. Walter Van den bergh says (*in litt.*) that a bongo arrived at the Antwerp Zoological Gardens in July, 1937, and that it died between June and October, 1940. A second specimen, a male, was received in 1960 from the okapi station at Epulu in the [Belgian] Congo (Van den bergh, 1961). A young female collected in the Aberdare Mountains of Kenya at an elevation of 8,900 feet on May 31, 1958, was hand-reared and delivered to the Cleveland Zoological Park, where it was first exhibited to the public on June 3, 1959 (Anon., 1959c). This calf was given cow's milk diluted with water and fortified with glucose, fed from a bottle (Root, 1959). L. J. Goss, director at Cleveland, reports (*in litt.*) that this animal became cyclic in December, 1959, the following intervals being approximately 3 weeks and duration about 3 days. A young male, reported to have originated in Ghana, was received at Cleveland in June, 1963, and was readily accepted by the female as a companion (L. J. Goss, *in litt.*).

The New York bongo, "Doreen," appears to have been the first to reach a zoological garden. Captured in the Aberdares as a well-grown calf on June 6, 1932, by Colonel E. Percy-Smith, she was introduced to a domestic cow and calf and soon learned to usurp the latter's place at the udder. Later, she drank milk from a pan and then advanced to solid food (Percy-Smith, 1933). Loaded aboard ship at Mombasa on November 26, 1932, she made the trip safely via London, finally reaching us on January 4, 1933 (Leister, 1933). Doreen was a lovely animal, both physically and temperamentally. She lived here peacefully until her death on March 23, 1951, after 18 years, 2 months, 19 days.

The nilgai (*Boselaphus tragocamelus*) is the largest of the Asiatic antelopes, Blanford (1888–91) giving the shoulder height as 52–56 inches. A short mane extends down the neck and back, and there is a tuft of hair on the chest of the male. Short, simple, slightly recurved horns are borne by males only, the greatest length listed by Ward (1922) being $9\frac{15}{16}$ inches. The adult male is bluish gray, with white areas about the mouth and chin, the chest, the inner sides of the thighs, the rump, and just above the hoofs. The light bay of female and young is similarly marked with white. An adult male received here weighed 295 pounds on arrival; two adult females weighed, respectively, 240 and 290 pounds. Distribution is in open or lightly wooded areas of the Indian peninsula from the base of the Himalayas to Mysore.

The nilgai seems particularly well adapted to zoo life and has been widely kept and bred over a long period, few institutions having failed to exhibit the species. The blue bull, particularly, is especially attractive and usually tractable, although truculent individuals sometimes occur. We have made several attempts to keep the nilgai without heat in winter but have always had to revert to its use. Eight births have occurred here, scattered from January to November, and always of single young. On the other hand, Zuckerman (1953), in reporting sixty-one births in the Zoological Gardens of London, occurring in every month, says that "on an average, twins were born in every alternate birth." Brown (1936) gives the gestation period as "not more than 8 months and 7 days." Flower (1931) records a nilgai as having lived 12 years, 4 months, 8 days in the Jardin des Plantes, Paris, and a less well authenticated duration of about 21 years in the Antwerp Zoological Gardens. A nilgai born in the National Zoological Park on February 15, 1918, is reported by Jones (1958) to have lived until November 7, 1939, or 21 years, 8 months, 23 days. Our best longevity here is 15 years, 4 months, 7 days for an animal received on October 5, 1926, and sold as surplus on February 12, 1942.

The four-horned antelope (*Tetracerus quadricornis*) is a small creature, suggestive in appearance of the duikers of Africa. It is found over most of India, seeming to prefer hilly, lightly wooded country to open plains. In color it is brownish with light underparts and no distinctive markings. Blanford (1888–91) gives the shoulder height of the male as $25\frac{1}{2}$ inches and the weight as 43 pounds. The outstanding character of the species is the possession of four horns by adult males, the females being hornless. The posterior pair are the longer, the greatest length given by Ward (1922) being $4\frac{3}{4}$ inches. The forward pair may be mere knobs or lacking altogether, perhaps an indication of age, Blanford (1888–91) stating that in a captive animal they did not appear until the third year.

The four-horned antelope has been kept, irregularly, by various European zoological gardens but for some reason has never become firmly established. It has been bred occasionally, Zuckerman (1953) reporting five births in the Zoological Gardens of London between 1882 and 1890, including three pairs of twins. The gestation period is given by Asdell (1946) as 183 days. Three specimens received by the New York Zoological Park in 1905, followed by another in 1906, appear to be the only examples so far to arrive in this country. One of these animals lived for 3 years, 1 month, 17 days, while Flower (1931) gives 7 years, 6 months, 26 days for a specimen in the Zoological Gardens of London and 10 years for another in Pretoria.

Of all the mammals that have been developed in captivity and modified to meet the needs of man, none have been so economically important as the domesticated cattle, for the European breeds of which the name *Bos taurus* was provided by Linnaeus in 1758. These, at least, are believed to be descendants of the aurochs (*Bos primigenius*), the great wild ox that once roamed most of Europe and North Africa. The last known survivor of this giant species is said to have died in a Polish preserve in 1627 (Harper, 1945) but its descendants serve man as an indispensable source of meat, milk, and leather. The zebu (*Bos indicus*), kept in many distinct breeds and varieties widely spread in Asia and Africa, differs from European cattle in several important details (Antonius, 1943). The large, fleshy hump on the shoulders, the well-developed dewlap, the drooping ears, the form of the horns, which reach enormous size in some of the African breeds, and the grunting voice are all points of distinction. The ancestry of the zebu has not been definitely determined. Whether the aurochs is solely responsible or whether the banteng (*Bos banteng*) may in some way be concerned (Frechkop, 1955) are still matters of conjecture.

Largest of the living wild cattle is the gaur (*Bos gaurus*). Lydekker (1898*b*) gives 6 feet, 4 inches as an exceptional shoulder height for this huge species, even noting some measurements in excess of this figure. The typical race inhabits India, Assam, and Nepal. *Bos g. readei* is found in Burma, Tenasserim, and Indochina, while *Bos g. hubbacki*, the "seladang," is the gaur of the Malay Peninsula. Males are dark brown to black, with the lower legs white, females and young being inclined to reddish. A high, fleshy ridge surmounts the back from the shoulders midway to the tail. The heavy horns of both sexes turn upward, then in, with a haired, bony ridge between them. The greatest length, on the curve, given by Ward (1922) is 31½ inches, the widest spread 44¾ inches. Weights of gaur taken in Mysore are given by Meinertzhagen (1938) as 1,720 and 1,870 pounds for two males and 1,546 pounds for a female. Heavily forested hills are the usual habitat, although gaur sometimes enter open, grassy areas to feed.

The gaur is seen infrequently in zoological gardens. Regarding a belief, apparently once generally accepted, in the difficulty of maintaining gaur in captivity, Blanford (1888–91) says, "The calves appear always to die in captivity, none, it is said, having been known to attain their third year." However, in spite of this pessimistic view, some very good results have been obtained. A fine herd that numbered five members when seen in 1941 lived and bred for some years in the St. Louis Zoological Park. The finest success with gaur in this country is that of the National Zoological Park. A pair obtained in Mysore, India, in 1937, bred regularly up to the death of the male on May 26, 1957, after approximately 20 years. An account of these animals is given by Reed (1959). Thirteen young were born in the period from 1940 to 1956, most of the calves being safely reared. A female born in 1947 was paired with a brother born in 1948 and up to 1958 had produced three young, bringing the total number of births to sixteen. Single young were born in every month except January and April. The original female, received in 1937, died on July 17, 1961, after approximately 24 years. Asdell (1946) gives the gestation period as 9 months.

A young pair of gaur received here from Germany in April, 1941, were both found dead in September of the same year. At necropsy, their stomachs were found to contain quantities of nightshade (*Solanum nigrum*) that had carelessly been allowed to invade their inclosure and which was believed to have caused their deaths.

The gayal (*Bos frontalis*) is generally believed to be a domesticated form of the gaur. The two animals are similarly colored, although Blanford (1888–91) says mottled or even white individuals of the gayal may sometimes be seen. Antonius (1932) gives a photograph of a white-faced female. The gayal is a somethat smaller animal than the gaur, although definitely stockier. The horns, instead of turning upward, project almost horizontally with only a slight curve. The greatest length given by Ward (1922) is $22\frac{3}{4}$ inches.

The gayal is kept by the hill people of the Assam–Upper Burma area. The village herds roam by day but return at night. Mr. E. P. Gee has told me that the cows are never milked and that the animals are slaughtered only on special occasions, their use being chiefly for dowries or wife purchase. The greatest weight recorded for a male in our collection is 1,670 pounds; for a female, 1,190 pounds.

Many institutions have kept and bred the gayal. Unlike the gaur, it is ordinarily steady and quiet, even phlegmatic. Our first specimens, a pair received on September 18, 1928, lived for 6 and 7 years, respectively, but produced no offspring. A second pair, purchased on September 28, 1939, gave much better results. From them and their descendants there have been sixteen births of single calves, all between January and August. These dates correspond with those shown by Zuckerman (1953) for a similar number of births in the Zoological Gardens of London, except for an extension of the period into September. A male calf born here on March 7, 1954, weighed 13 kilograms (28.6 pounds). Calves may be reddish, like those of the gaur, or dark gray, without regard to sex. At birth, the lower legs are colored like the body, but the beginning change to white is evident by the age of two months. The present (1963) descendants of this herd consist of a single bull and cow, with a gray bull calf born in July, 1962.

The adult gayal is hardy here and can endure our winters if provided with a dry, unheated shelter. However, calves are less resistant, and we have been most successful when pregnant females have been kept indoors and provided with mild heat until the calves are well established. There is close attachment between members of a herd, which are most impressive when lying together, usually with the herd bull at the back. I have seen the gaur at St. Louis in the same pyramidal formation. Bulls are most tolerant of younger members of the herd, but maturing males must be removed.

Gayals are heavy grazers, of course, when grass is available and also will take any foliage within their reach. We have found them to take timothy hay only sparingly but to feed well on clover or alfalfa hay, with an evident preference for the latter. Feeding pellets are used as a grain ration.

The banteng (*Bos banteng*) is smaller and lighter than the gaur, with the dorsal ridge reduced in size. The horns in both sexes are slender and curved upward, the greatest length listed by Ward (1922) being $34\frac{1}{2}$ inches on the outside curve. The ridge between them is horny and roughened. The shoulder height is given by Lydekker (1898b) as ranging from 5 feet to 5 feet, 9 inches.

In the typical race, found in Java, the adult male is very dark brown or black, with the lower legs and caudal disk white. Females and young are reddish brown, with similar markings. In the mainland race, *Bos banteng birmanicus*, found in Burma, Thailand, and Indochina, both sexes are reddish, adult males being darker than females. The Bornean race has been designated as *Bos banteng lowi*. The banteng is kept in a domesticated state by the people of the island of Bali, and animals of this type have sometimes been seen in zoological gardens.

The banteng has seldom been brought into this country, and the only specimen we have had here was an animal received in 1929. Of two pairs of the Javan race imported in 1959 by Roland Lindemann of the Catskill Game Farm, one was retained by himself and the other released to the Philadelphia Zoological Garden. The females of both pairs produced young in 1961. Javan bantengs are fairly well established in European zoological gardens. Members of the fine herd at Rotterdam are described and figured by Appelman (1952). Whenever I have had the pleasure of seeing these animals, the superb black, white-rumped bull and bright red cows and calves have always been most impressive. Surplus animals produced by this herd have been distributed among other institutions.

Few longevities of banteng appear to have been recorded. Jones (1958) lists 8 years, 5 months, 28 days for a specimen in the Zoological Gardens of Berlin.

The kouprey (*Bos sauveli*) appears to be known only from Cambodia. First described by Urbain (1937) from a young specimen received at the Parc Zoologique du Bois de Vincennes, Paris, in 1937, it was made better known by Coolidge (1940), who gives a complete description of the adult and discusses the animal's relationships. The kouprey is very large, with a shoulder height of 6 feet, 3 inches and a horn length, on the outer curve, of 810 millimeters, or nearly 32 inches (Coolidge, *loc. cit.*). Adult males are black or very dark brown in general, while females and young are grayish; in both sexes the lower parts of the legs are white. There is a well-developed hump and a heavy dewlap which, in males, reaches huge proportions. In this sex shredding of the horns, below the tip, is characteristic. Following a survey made in Cambodia in 1937, Edmond-Blanc (1947) expresses the belief that the kouprey is really a hybrid between two or more of the bovid species found in the area. Under the auspices of the Coolidge Foundation, Charles H. Wharton visited Cambodia in 1951–52. A thorough study of the kouprey and its ecology was made, no indication of mixed ancestry being found (Wharton, 1957). Those who have been privileged to see the remarkable films made by this expedition will realize the difficulties that hamper investigation, for a total population of perhaps five hundred koupreys is associated, more or less loosely, with banteng, gaur, water buffalo (*Bubalus*) and native cattle. Numerous records of cross-breeding between various species of wild cattle in captivity are given by A. P. Gray (1954), the water buffalo not being included.

The range of the wild yak (*Bos grunniens mutus*) is given by Lydekker (1913–16, 1:33) as extending from Ladak, Kashmir, to Kan-su in western China, at elevations between 14,000 and 20,000 feet. This distribution, however, has been reduced by constant hunting, so that the animal is now found only in the most remote areas. The coloration is very dark brown or black, with some white about the muzzle. A heavy fringe of hair depends from the sides of the body, and the tail is long and fully haired. Lydekker (1898b) gives the height at the shoulder hump as from 5 to 6 feet and a weight estimate of from 1,100 to 1,200 pounds. The greatest horn length given by Ward (1922) is 38¼ inches on the outer curve. Females are greatly inferior in body size and length of horns.

The domesticated yak (*Bos g. grunniens*) is of indispensable service to the people who are resident at high altitudes in central Asia. They are used as riding and pack animals, and their milk, flesh, and hides are economically important. The domesticated animals are smaller than their wild forebears and may vary in color from black, reddish brown, or pied to pure white. Some are entirely hornless. They cross freely with domestic cattle (A. P. Gray, 1954), the hybrids being useful at lower altitudes where pure-bred yaks do not endure work well.

Yaks are kept by most zoological gardens. Lydekker (1898*b*) says that only the domestic breeds from lower elevations are exhibited in Europe, but whatever their origin may be, yaks seem to experience no difficulty with either high temperatures or low levels—at least as long as they are not required to work! On November 22, 1913, we received a pair of yaks from Carl Hagenbeck. These animals were deep black with whitish muzzles and were believed to be of wild stock. In any case, they were said to be the first black yaks seen in this country (Leister, 1943). A total of forty-two young was produced by the original pair or their descendants, and none showed any variation in color. The survivor of this herd died in 1937 and animals since purchased, while themselves sound in color, occasionally produce a reddish-brown calf.

Yaks, of course, are indifferent to cold and are kept here in open inclosures with open-fronted shelters that are seldom used. Bulls, however large and imposing, have been tolerant of each other—at one time, our herd consisted of six adult males and a single female living peacefully together. They were very antagonistic toward horses, however, and toward neighboring male bovids of other species.

Of forty-eight yak calves born here, twenty-two appeared in June, nine in July, and eight in August, with scattered births in most other months of the year. The gestation period quoted by Asdell (1946) is 258 days.

Of many long-lived yaks kept here, the greatest span was established by the female received on November 22, 1913, which died on August 26, 1934, after 20 years, 9 months, 4 days. Flower (1931) gives 22 years, 8 days for an animal in the Dublin Zoological Gardens and 22 years, 3 months, 23 days for one at Rotterdam.

The Indian or water buffalo (*Bubalus bubalis*) is a very large animal, Lydekker (1898*b*) giving its shoulder height as from 5 feet to 6 feet, 2 inches. Typically, the coat is close to black and is usually very thin in adults; the lower legs may be whitish. The sweeping horns sometimes reach prodigious lengths, the greatest given by Ward (1922) being $77\frac{3}{8}$ inches on the outside curve. The range of the typical race includes the plains of India and northern Ceylon, east to Indochina. A dun-colored form

(*Bubalus bubalis fulvus*) is found in Assam, and a smaller subspecies, *hosei*, is known from Borneo. The species has been kept in domestication for so long and has so often become feral that it is now difficult to establish the status of presumed wild herds. Harper (1945) gives much information on this point.

As a domestic animal, the Indian buffalo has become widely distributed in the warmer regions of Asia, Europe, and Africa, as well as in other parts of the world. It has changed little in either form or color from its wild ancestors, although I well remember that the first example I ever saw was a pure white individual living in the Central Park Menagerie, New York, in 1907. As a working animal, the Indian buffalo is quiet and amenable in the care of familiar herders but may be hostile and even dangerous to strangers.

Because of a long-established but not always logical policy that has prohibited the showing of some domesticated animals here, we have never kept the Indian buffalo. It has, of course, been included in many other collections, where it lives and breeds well. It presents no special difficulties but does require winter protection in cold areas. Gestation periods given by Kenneth (1953) range from 287 to 340 days. According to A. P. Gray (1954), no hybridization involving the Indian buffalo has been recorded. The greatest longevity listed by Flower (1931) is that of an animal that lived in the Adelaide Zoological Gardens from April 12, 1886, to August 1, 1915, or 29 years, 3 months, 20 days.

The small buffaloes of the genus *Anoa* occur in two species: *A. depressicornis*, the anoa of Celebes, and *A. mindorensis*, the tamarao, of the island of Mindoro in the Philippines. The common anoa (*A. d. depressicornis*) inhabits heavily forested areas, where it is difficult to observe, although it has acquired a reputation for being dangerously aggressive. Two other races, known as mountain anoas, have been described: *A. d. fergusoni* and *A. d. quarlesi*. Their status is not entirely clear, but both are listed provisionally by Laurie and Hill (1954).

The common anoa is the smallest of the buffaloes, Lydekker (1913–16, 1:48) giving the shoulder height as 3 feet, 3 inches. The short horns are nearly straight and sharply pointed. The coat, which may be very thin in adults, is dark brown or black, usually marked with white on throat and lower jaw.

Although not well known in nature, the common anoa is rather familiar in zoological gardens. Its reputation for aggression in nature is well sustained by its behavior in captivity. At close quarters, at least, it may be dangerous, and only the agility of our keepers has prevented serious incidents here. At the Catskill Game Farm at Catskill, New York, Roland Lindemann has been able to maintain anoas in winter with only an unheated shelter. However, attempts to do so here have invariably come to an end when the starey coats of shivering animals indicated a need for warmth.

The common anoa has been bred frequently in this country as well as in Europe. Births here, four in number, occurred in March, July, and August, all the young having been fully reared by their mothers. Average gestation periods given by Kenneth (1953) are 276 and 315 days. Miss Hattie Ettinger (*in litt.*) informs me that a female anoa lived in the St. Louis Zoological Park from July 25, 1927, to February 14, 1951, or 23 years, 6 months, 20 days. Jones (1958) reports that an anoa received at the Zoological Gardens of London on July 13, 1927, died on April 4, 1953, after 25 years, 8 months, 22 days. A male born here on March 13, 1927, died on March 23, 1948, after 21 years, 10 days; a female born on July 16, 1928, lived until January 10, 1957, or 28 years, 5 months, 25 days (Anon., 1957*a*).

The tamarao (*A. mindorensis*) is a somewhat larger animal than the common anoa, with a shoulder height of "about 3½ feet" (Lydekker, 1913–16, **1**:47). Color and markings are similar to those of the anoa. It inhabits the deep jungles of Mindoro, and little seems to be known of its habits beyond the point that it is much feared by the local inhabitants. The tamarao appears to have no captivity history.

The buffaloes of Africa (*Syncerus*) show wide diversity, ranging from the great black Cape buffalo of the plains of the south and east to the much smaller red or forest buffalo of the west. Many races have been described, and the nomenclature is much confused. For present purposes, it seems expedient to use *Syncerus c. caffer* for the Cape group and to follow Hill and Carter (1941) and Ellerman, Morrison-Scott, and Hayman (1953) in applying *S. c. nanus* to the red or forest buffalo, although the latter is considered by some authors (Allen, 1939) to be a distinct species.

The Cape buffalo (*S. c. caffer*) is a large and heavy animal, with a shoulder height of from 4 feet, 10 inches to 5 feet (Lydekker, 1898*b*). The hair, thin in adults, is usually black, although there may be a brownish tone in some areas of the range. The horns curve out and down, then up and in, their ridged and roughened bases almost meeting on the forehead. The greatest width given by Ward (1922) is 56¼ inches, for a specimen from Kenya. Weights of six males taken in East Africa, given by Meinertzhagen (1938), ran from 1,496 to 1,841 pounds. An adult female kept here weighed 1,290 pounds at death.

Because of its great size and strength as well as its traditional aggressiveness, the Cape buffalo is not overly popular among those responsible for zoological-garden operation. It has been kept and even bred, of course, by many, although seldom on a continuing basis. At the present time (1963) the only breeding group in this country is a small herd in the San Antonio Zoological Park, Texas.

Only four Cape buffaloes have been kept here, three bulls and one cow. Two of the males were reasonably quiet animals and caused no particular difficulties. However, a cow received in 1940 and a bull obtained in 1941 were both less amenable. The cow, reared in East Africa as a farm pet, had been banished after reportedly killing two domestic cows. The bull, aged about 2 years when received here, was tractable at first but became irascible and finally dangerous as he aged. Because of mutual aggression, regardless of season, these animals were kept in separate but adjoining stalls in our Antelope House. Curiously, when out of doors in summer, they were reasonably quiet and made no effort to damage the wire netting of their inclosures. But during the winter months, when they were confined indoors, they constantly battered the bars of their cage fronts, which had to be strongly reinforced with steel cross-members.

The Cape buffalo is a grazer, and since the outdoor runs chosen for our animals were well grassed, they were able to follow their natural bent in summer. At this season a small supplement of timothy hay, rolled oats, and feeding pellets seemed to satisfy their requirements. In winter, however, their appetites seemed insatiable. They not only consumed immense quantities of hay but, this finished, ate the straw of their bedding. Even the dry, heavy stalks of clover hay, taken by hardly any other herbivore, were not overlooked. On this basis, the usual allowance of grain, hay, greens, and vegetables of the winter diet seemed as nothing.

Because of the incompatibility of the only pair we have owned, the Cape buffalo has never been bred here. Zuckerman (1953), in reporting fourteen single births in the Zoological Gardens of London, notes their occurrence in every month except April and September. The gestation period is given by Kenneth (1953) as 330 days. The greatest longevity given by Flower (1931) is for a bull sold by the Zoological Gardens of London after 15 years, 5 months, 27 days. The female noted above lived here from September 5, 1940, to February 10, 1959, or 18 years, 5 months, 5 days. Jones (1958) reports that a specimen received at the Philadelphia Zoological Garden on October 8, 1929, lived until January 30, 1956, or 26 years, 3 months, 22 days.

The red or forest buffalo (*S. c. nanus*) is a comparatively small animal, as wild cattle go, its shoulder height being about 3 feet, 6 inches (Lydekker, 1898*b*). Blancou (1958*b*) says the weight does not exceed 660 pounds. The general coloration is bright reddish bay, usually with a darker dorsal stripe, although there is some local variation, ranging from dark brown to yellowish. The drooping ears are fringed with long hair. The range includes the densely forested areas of west and central Africa, from Angola northward.

The forest buffalo has recently been imported into this country by Roland Lindemann of the Catskill Game Farm, Catskill, New York, his animals deriving from the breeding herd in the Zoological Gardens of Lisbon. They have bred well, and a young pair, our first representatives of the form, was released to us in 1963. The forest buffalo is also exhibited at both Antwerp and Vincennes.

The bisons (*Bison*) are tall, heavy animals, with marked shoulder humps and hind quarters sharply sloping away. The head and shoulders are more or less maned, the horns are short and incurved, and the rather brief tail carries a well-developed brush at the tip. The general coloration is from light brown to brownish black. Distribution is confined to Europe and North America, now much restricted on both continents. There are two living species: *Bison bison* of North America and *Bison bonasus* of Europe.

The American bison or buffalo (*Bison bison*) is heavily haired over the head, shoulders and forelegs, and the depth of the proportionately large head is emphasized by a long beard, these growths being more strongly developed in males than in females. The remainder of the body is clothed in short, thick, woolly hair in winter, but after this has been shed in spring, the covering is fine and thin. The body hair is brown, usually paler in winter, particularly toward spring, while the longer pelage of the face-parts is very dark, often approaching black. Calves are reddish at birth. Lydekker (1913–16, 1:38) gives the shoulder height of the male as 5 feet, 9 inches; females are considerably smaller. Weight is usually given as about 2,000 pounds for males and about 1,000 pounds for females, but these figures are sometimes exceeded by exceptional animals. Cahalane (1947) says that a wood bison (*Bison b. athabascae*) killed and accurately weighed on the spot was recorded at 2,402 pounds. Garretson (1938) reports a record of 3,000 pounds for a plains bison (*Bison b. bison*) but informed me personally that this was an estimate, not made by himself. The greatest horn length listed in the Boone and Crockett Club's *Records of North American Big Game* (1958), is 22⅔ inches on the outer curve, with a spread of 35⅜ inches, for a bull taken in Yellowstone Park, Wyoming, in 1925.

The American bison is known in two forms: the plains bison (*Bison b.*

bison) and the larger and darker wood bison (*Bison b. athabascae*). Formerly, the range of the plains bison extended from western New York across most of the United States as far as the foothills of the Rockies, south into northeastern Mexico and north into the south-central provinces of Canada. The greatest concentration of the plains bison was in the broad prairie regions of the west, where its numbers have been estimated at as many as sixty million (Seton, 1927). The wood bison occurred from western Colorado north to the Yukon and southern Alaska, perhaps even farther north.

The wholesale slaughter of the plains bison reached a climax in 1867, when the Union Pacific Railroad was completed to Cheyenne, Wyoming. The railroad, for some reason not entirely clear, separated the animals into two groups, known as the northern and southern herds, at the same time making them readily accessible to the hordes of commercial hunters. The southern herd was first to go, and the northern group endured but little longer. Seton (1927) estimates that by 1895 no more than 800 animals existed in the world. A census of living American bison as of January 1, 1934, prepared by Garretson (1934), shows a total of 21,701 then in Government preserves, zoological gardens, or private hands. A similar compendium gathered by Collins (1952) brought the number to 23,340, and the total has undoubtedly increased since that time.

This happy recovery of an animal that once seemed about to vanish forever was brought about by the tardy awakening of various conservation forces, both in this country and in Canada. In the forefront was the American Bison Society, organized at a meeting held in the Lion House of the New York Zoological Park on December 8, 1905, William T. Hornaday, first director of the Zoological Park, being elected president and Martin S. Garretson, secretary. Under the inspiring leadership of its officers, the Bison Society took a leading part in securing the future of the American bison, and its Annual Reports have detailed the advancement of the project. Among the many accounts of the history of the American bison are those of Hornaday (1889), Seton (1927), Garretson (1938), and Roe (1951). An important study of behavior and ecology has been contributed by McHugh (1958).

The first American bison to be received here arrived on October 1, 1899, just before the Zoological Park was opened to the public on November 8 of that year. The shipment consisted of four bulls and three cows purchased from C. J. Jones, better known as "Buffalo" Jones. Two of these animals had been obtained by Jones from the famous Goodnight herd maintained by Colonel Charles Goodnight on his ranch in the Texas

Panhandle. The bison was at low ebb at the time, and, determined to aid in its possible resuscitation, the Zoological Society continued to increase its stock at every possible opportunity. The final establishment of our herd on a firm basis came with the arrival of twenty-six bison late in 1903, as the gift of the Honorable William C. Whitney. Births, the first on July 6, 1900, had increased the number of bison already on hand, so that the Whitney group brought the herd up to approximately forty animals.

In 1905 the New York Zoological Society offered to the Government of the United States a nucleus herd of bison for installation in the Wichita Forest Reserve in Oklahoma, provided that a suitable area would be fenced. The offer was accepted, a range of about 6,200 acres was inclosed, and fifteen animals were transported and liberated in October, 1907 (Sanborn, 1908). Halloran (1957a), in reporting on the status of the Wichita herd, says that in 1955 it numbered 973, more than 3,600 calves having been born and over 2,000 animals slaughtered or released to zoological gardens. With the exception of four bulls from the Fort Niobrara National Wildlife Refuge in Nebraska, no additions to the original stock had been made. Increase in the size of the herd necessitated enlargement of the range, and it was extended to include 59,000 acres. Statistics of both live and dressed weights of bison at the Wichita Range, listed according to sex and known age (Halloran, 1957b), show the heaviest animal to have been a 7-year-old bull that weighed 1,525 pounds.

In 1913 the New York Zoological Society offered to present to the American Bison Society, of which Professor F. W. Hooper was then president, a herd of fourteen bison for shipment to the Wind Cave National Park in South Dakota. The Department of Agriculture having agreed to accept the gift, the animals, seven males and seven females, were crated and shipped from the Zoological Park on November 25, 1913 (Hornaday, 1914). With the exception of a single cow from the Whitney herd, received in 1903, all these animals had been born and reared in the Zoological Park.

Following the Wind Cave shipment, our bison herd was allowed to wane, the principal reason for its establishment having been satisfied. The last birth from the older stock was that of a bull calf born on May 24, 1934. This magnificent animal lived until November 5, 1954, or 20 years, 5 months, 12 days, the best longevity recorded here for a bison. At the present time (1963) we have only a single pair, purchased in the late fifties, with five of their descendants.

When the bison-breeding project was in its heyday it was an undertaking of some magnitude, one that could not ordinarily be maintained by an urban zoological garden. The main range embraced an area of at least 10 wire-inclosed acres of open grassland. Adjacent but concealed was a low, unheated shelter, suitably divided into useful compartments. It adjoined a large feeding corral, with many scattered feeding boxes placed on the ground and hay racks under the eaves of the shelter. The herd was drawn into this inclosure after the food had been put out and usually was not released until morning. There also was a strongly reinforced bull pen, generally containing a huge male that had become too overbearing to be allowed to run with the herd. The main group averaged from thirty to forty animals, consisting largely of cows with their calves and three or four bulls. The latter were closely watched to make certain that the established order of dominance was maintained. Separated from the main range was a large corral devoted to bulls only that usually contained a dozen or more males not immediately required. This group lived quietly, with little serious disturbance. On the higher ground of the main inclosure, the bison had excavated a number of wallows, used year after year. In dry summer weather clouds of dust rose from the area as the animals rolled in the fine dry earth. During periods of rain the wallows filled with water, providing mud baths as a welcome respite from biting flies.

Timothy, alfalfa, or clover hay were fed, apparently without particular choice on the part of the animals. Grain fed at the time consisted of rolled oats; nowadays, our feeding pellets are used instead. In summer there was always an abundance of grass which seemed never to suffer from overgrazing.

This great area is now devoted to our African Plains, the old shelter having been remodeled as a winter Antelope House, the Lion Rock with its concealed shelter, and the African Plains Annex, the latter containing aoudads and elands. South of all this are numerous inclosures for cranes, emus, vicuñas, llamas, and yaks, with a low stone shelter. One of these sub-divisions is devoted to our present American bison—reminders of older times.

Bison usually mature at 3 years, occasionally earlier. The breeding season in nature is usually given as July to September, with April to June as the calving months. Average gestation periods as given by Kenneth (1953) run from 270 to 285 days. Hediger (1950) points out that abundant food and propinquity may often result in variations in breeding periods. This is supported by our own records in the case of the American bison, for while the majority of births here have occurred at the normal season, there are many exceptions. A total of ninety-one calves, in single births, have been born here, as follows: April, twenty-one; May, thirty-three;

June, fourteen; July, eight; August three; September, four; October, five; November, three.

Bison and domestic cattle interbreed readily, domestic bull on bison cow being more successful than the reciprocal mating. The production of such hybrids, known as cattalos, has proved not to be commercially worth while, largely because of limited fertility. According to A. P. Gray (1954), male hybrids of the first generation are sterile and females only partially fertile, reproductive ability improving in both sexes of further generations as the percentage of domestic blood increases.

As already noted, the greatest longevity recorded here for an American bison is 20 years, 5 months, 12 days. Flower (1931) gives 22 years, 10 months, 25 days for an animal in the Rotterdam Zoological Gardens, and Jones (1958) reports that a bison received at the National Zoological Park on August 19, 1906, lived until August 16, 1932, or just 3 days short of 26 years. This presumably is the animal listed by Mann (1930) as having been in the National Zoological Park for 22 years, 6 months and still living.

The history of the wood bison (*Bison b. athabascae*) has been briefly recapitulated by Banfield and Novakowski (1960). Once fairly well distributed in the western United States and Canada, it had become reduced by 1891 to about 300 animals in the Great Slave Lake area. It was then taken under the protection of the Canadian Government, and at the time of the establishment of Wood Buffalo Park in northeastern Alberta and southern Mackenzie in 1922, the estimated population had increased to between 1,500 and 2,000. However, between 1925 and 1928, 6,673 plains bison were introduced to relieve the population pressure in Wainwright Buffalo Park. This resulted, of course, in cross-breeding, so that the existence of pure wood bison eventually became doubtful. In 1959 a herd of about 200 wood bison was located in a remote area in the northwestern section of the Wood Buffalo Park, isolated from the nearest range of other bison by 75 miles of almost impassable terrain. It is believed that these animals are the undiluted remnants of their race. While it seems possible that specimens of the wood bison may have been kept in zoological gardens, I have been unable to find a record of such an event.

The European bison or wisent (*Bison bonasus*) is a taller animal than the American species, with shorter mane and beard and less pronounced development of hump and shoulders, giving it a more rangy appearance. The general coloration is an almost uniform dark brown. The greatest length of the rather slender, incurved horns given by Ward (1922) is 20 inches on the outer curve. The same author records a weight, presumably of a male, of 2,001 pounds. Lydekker (1913–16, 1:35) gives the shoulder height as from 6 feet to 6 feet, 2 inches. Detailed accounts of the history of the wisent are given by Harper (1945), Mohr (1952) and, of course, many others.

Once found over most of Europe with possible extension into Siberia, the wisent was gradually eradicated from much of its range, increasing development of the land and destruction of the forests bringing about the inevitable result. The typical or Lithuanian race (*Bison bonasus bonasus*) became restricted to the Bialowieza Forest of Poland, where, in 1803, according to Zabinski (1960), a herd of from three hundred to five hundred animals came under the protection of the czar of Russia. After undergoing a series of fluctuations and disasters caused by political disturbances and apparently adversely affected by overbrowsing, the Bialowieza herd had become exterminated by 1921, and it was not until 1929 that re-establishment was begun (Zabinski, *loc. cit.*). Almost concurrently, the few remaining wisents of the somewhat smaller and darker Caucasian race (*Bison bonasus caucasius*) living in the mountains of southern Russia met a similar fate. Zabinski (*loc. cit.*) says that the last Caucasian wisent was killed in 1927.

Fortunately, in better times numerous wisents had been sent from Bialowieza to various zoological gardens and private preserves, so that at the end of World War II at least these scattered animals and the remnants of the rebuilt Bialowieza herd remained alive. Some of these included in their ancestry a Caucasian bull received by Hagenbeck in 1907 as the gift of the Russian czar (Zabinski, 1960), so that the otherwise extinct eastern stock is still faintly represented. Zabinski, apparently dating his estimate as of 1960, believes there were then over three hundred wisents living and that the species had been saved from extinction. Much of the credit for this apparent success must go to the International Society for the Protection of the European Bison, originated in 1923 and modeled after the older American Bison Society. In spite of a rather uneven career, the Society has managed to maintain its records and to publish its *Pedigree Book*, the first in 1932, the latest available here appearing in 1953 under the editorship of Dr. Zabinski.*

A serious obstacle to clearing the eligibility of individual animals for inclusion in the *Pedigree Book* has been the frequent crossing with the American bison. Such hybrids are readily produced, of course, and at one period, when the plight of the wisent appeared hopeless, interbreeding seemed the only recourse. Freedom from any trace of alien blood in accepted animals insures the purity of those listed, now numerous enough to end the interest in the production of hybrids.

*See Addenda, p. 738.

The first European bison to be seen alive in this country appear to have been a pair received here on April 18, 1904 (Anon., 1904). These animals came to us as the gift of Norman James, having been purchased from the Duke of Pless, whose herd originated with stock obtained from Bialowieza in 1865. They were placed in a large inclosure adjacent to that occupied by spare American bison bulls and were soon in excellent condition. The bull lived for just over 8 years, the cow for 13, but during this period no calves were born, the general belief being that the bull was sterile.

No further wisents reached America until 1956, when pairs were received by the National Zoological Park, the Chicago Zoological Park, and the Philadelphia Zoological Garden. In 1959 Roland Lindemann of the Catskill Game Farm obtained two pairs, and one pair was received for our own collection. A single bull reached the Milwaukee Zoological Park in 1960, bringing the total number in the United States at that time to thirteen. Unfortunately, the Washington cow died in 1959 after giving birth to a heifer calf. This calf, successfully reared and later transferred to the Catskill Game Farm, was the first wisent to be born in this country. A calf born to the female of the Chicago pair on October 14, 1961, is figured in the *Brookfield Bandar-Log* of November, 1961. One of the two Catskill pairs was lost, but the female of the surviving pair produced calves in 1959 and 1961 and reared both successfully (Heinz Heck, personal communication).*

Our own pair, received here on August 7, 1959, was sent to us as the gift of the Zoological Gardens of Amsterdam. The bull, "Aristo," was born in the fine herd at Amsterdam on May 19, 1957; the cow, "Ardetta," on June 2, 1957. Both contain the blood of the Caucasian bull, No. 100 of the *Pedigree Book*, imported by Hagenbeck in 1907. This is attested by the accompanying pedigrees, carried to the sixth generation on the official forms of the International Society for the Protection of the European Bison, carefully compiled and certified by Dr. Erna Mohr, present custodian of the records. The history of the Amsterdam herd is given by Jacobi (1960).

The animals were placed in a wire-inclosed run of about $\frac{3}{4}$ acre, well grassed and shaded, and provided with an unheated shelter. Food furnished included alfalfa and timothy hay, feeding pellets and fresh browse as available. Ardetta was in estrus for the first observed time on October 16, 1960, and was duly covered by Aristo. Ages at the time were approximately 3 years, $4\frac{1}{2}$ months and 3 years, 5 months, respectively. A male calf that unfortunately lived for only a few hours was born on July 5, 1961, after

*See Addenda, p. 738.

a gestation period of 262 days. A vigorous female calf was born on July 11, 1963.

The findings of Jaczewski (1958), from observations made in Polish reserves and studies of the *Pedigree Book*, indicate that the principal mating season is in August and September, though breeding may occur at any time. Births were noted in every month, the majority in May or June. The gestation period is given as from 260 to 270 days. The wisent is usually said to mature at 3 years, but a male was noted to have bred successfully at 15 months and cows to have produced calves at 32 and 36 months.

The greatest longevity for a European bison given by Flower (1931) is 21 years for a well-known cow in the Duke of Bedford's herd at Woburn Abbey. Jaczewski (1958) lists two females as reaching a maximum of 26 years and a male that lived for 23 years.

Taken over-all, there seems to be good reason for accepting Dr. Zabinski's belief that the future of the European bison is assured, at least as far as that of any species can be assured in captivity. The wisents at Amsterdam, all in superb condition, are kept in pens covered deeply with sand and with snug shelters attached. At Skansen, Stockholm, conditions are similar, with gravel replacing sand in the runs. In the Polish and Russian preserves surroundings are certainly more normal but still not fully natural. Beginning with the return of two animals of the Bialowieza Reserve herd to complete liberty in the forest in 1952, a group of more than a dozen freely roaming wisent had been built up by 1960 (Zabinski, 1960). But unless the forests of Europe can themselves be restored and protected, the future of the wisent as a wild animal, living in a state of nature, seems dim indeed.

SUBFAMILY CEPHALOPHINAE

DUIKERS

The duikers are small, furtive creatures, depending on the protection of dense cover rather than speed in escaping their enemies. Duikers are usually found wherever in Africa, south of the Sahara, there is sufficient herbage to provide the needed shelter, with a natural concentration in the great forested areas of the west. The horns, which may be absent in females, are short, straight, and sharply pointed, often with a tuft of hair between them. Allen (1939) lists fifty-seven forms in the genus *Cephalophus* and twenty-five in *Sylvicapra*, for a total of eighty-two. Technical names used here are largely those of Allen (*loc. cit.*), with some modifications in accordance with Ellerman, Morrison-Scott, and Hayman (1953).

Duikers have not usually been considered as especially desirable zoological-garden subjects, perhaps because of their shyness and apparent psychological need for darkened retreating areas. This urgency may become less pressing, of course, in perfectly tame, hand-reared animals, as shown by the fact that such specimens, kept in small, bare, well-lighted cages in the National Zoological Park have bred well and established outstanding longevity records. I have been informed by their keeper that even then special caution was necessary in caring for them, since they were still subject to sudden panic.

Duikers that have developed in nature are still able to adjust well to captivity if their requirements for shadowy corners, at least, are satisfied. Several species have done well here in indoor pens approximately 6 by 8 feet, one side of which is shielded from light by a solid partition 4 feet high, topped by bars. The flight distance of these little animals is very exacting, and if pressed too closely they are subject to running blindly. For this reason a spare stall is left in the series, so that shifting for daily cleaning is easily accomplished by means of sliding doors, with no risk to the animals. In summer our duikers have access to outdoor runs, but they seldom venture to leave the shadows.

Duikers freshly imported from Africa have usually been fed largely on fresh foliage and other greens, particularly the vines of the sweet potato. Whether received at a quarantine station or directly at a zoological garden, a period of adjustment is generally necessary, during which green food should be supplied in quantity at first and gradually reduced as the animals become accustomed to substitutes. The final feeding schedule here includes alfalfa hay, grain pellets, an allowance of bananas, cut vegetables, greens, and any available foliage, especially that of the Russian mulberry (*Morus*).

Largest of the duikers and certainly one of the most attractive, is the yellow-backed (*Cephalophus silvicultor*) which occurs in two generally accepted races, from Sierra Leone to Northern Rhodesia. The over-all coloration of the adult is dark blackish brown, with some white about the lips and face, a triangular yellowish patch on the lower back, and a reddish tuft between the horns. The hair of the head and neck is short and fine, the length gradually increasing posteriorly. The shoulder height is 34 inches (Lydekker, 1913–16, 2:64). Horns are borne by both sexes, as in most other members of this genus.

Although the yellow-backed duiker was exhibited by the Zoological Gardens of London as early as 1870 (Flower, 1929), it has been shown but rarely since that time. The only arrival in this country of which there appears to be a record was a female brought to us from the [Belgian] Congo by Charles Cordier, received on June 15, 1949. She reached us from quarantine with a broken leg, which fortunately knit well under treatment. A "tic" that developed later in the injured member made it difficult for the animal to maintain footing on the relatively smooth floor, but she was greatly helped by a patch of corrugated hard rubber matting cemented to the floor. This lovely duiker was far steadier than most and eventually learned to allow her silky neck to be stroked. She lived here until November 2, 1956, or 7 years, 4 months, 18 days. Flower (1931) gives 8 years, 11 months, 26 days for a specimen in the Zoological Gardens of Rotterdam.

Of the very large group of medium-sized duikers, generally reddish in color, three species are most likely to be seen in zoological gardens. These are the red or Natal duikers, *C. natalensis*, the bay duikers, *C. dorsalis*, and the black-fronted duikers, *C. nigrifrons*, all of which have been represented here.

The red duikers are widely distributed in East Africa from Natal to the Sudan. Many races have been described, their common character being the clear reddish coloration, free from dark markings. Lydekker (1913–16, 2:68) gives the shoulder height as 17 inches. The only one that has been received here is Weyns's duiker (*C. natalensis weynsi*) from the northeastern [Belgian] Congo, two males of which were brought to us on June 15, 1949, by Charles Cordier. One of these animals was still living here in 1963.

The bay duikers are distinguished by a black dorsal stripe; the shoulder height is given by Lydekker (1913–16, 2:80) as 16 inches. The several races are distributed from Sierra Leone to the [Belgian] Congo. Five specimens of *C. d. castaneus*, the chestnut duiker, came to us from the Congo with the Cordier collection on June 15, 1949. Three were sent to the Chicago Zoological Park, where a number of young were bred. The pair retained here proved equally prolific, ten young having been produced up to 1962 by the original animals or their offspring, single births having been distributed throughout the year. The young are tiny at birth and are kept tucked away in a shadowy corner for the first few days. However, the rate of growth is surprisingly rapid, and in a few months they are almost indistinguishable from the adults. While pairs live quietly together and males have never been seen actually to disturb the young, we have made it a practice to remove them when births have occurred or have been anticipated. Adult males cannot be kept together, but females usually are not antagonistic toward each other. The female of the original pair died on September 24, 1961, after 12 years, 3 months, 9 days.

Also included in the Cordier shipment received June 15, 1949, were a male and two females of the Gaboon duiker (*C. leucogaster*), sometimes considered to be a form of *dorsalis* (Rode, 1943). These animals proved rather short-lived, the survivor dying on October 15, 1954, after 5 years, 4 months. However, they did produce three young, one each in January, February, and November.

The several races of the black-fronted duiker extend across equatorial Africa from the Gaboon to Kenya. A blackish blaze on the forehead and no dorsal stripe distinguish the species; Lydekker (1913–16, 2:72) gives the shoulder height as 18 or 19 inches. Our first real success in the maintenance of duikers here was with the only representative of this species so far received. This animal was a male that arrived on June 3, 1937, and lived quietly until September 2, 1946, or 9 years, 3 months. Three black-fronted duikers were brought from Liberia to the National Zoological Park by the Smithsonian-Firestone Expedition, arriving on August 6, 1940. I am informed (*in litt.*) by Theodore H. Reed, director at Washington, that the first of several young produced was born on May 26, 1942, and lived until April 20, 1960, or 17 years, 10 months, 25 days.

The blue duikers (*C. monticola*), in very many forms, extend from Senegal in the west and Kenya in the east southward through East Africa to the Cape Province, avoiding the desert areas of the southwest. They are tiny, delicately formed animals, with a shoulder height of about 13 inches (Sclater and Thomas, 1894–1900, 1:192); the general coloration is bluish gray, with some infusions of tawny. On June 15, 1949, we received with the Cordier Congo shipment two males and three females of the equatorial blue duiker (*C. m. aequatorialis*) and one male and two females of Simpson's blue duiker (*C. m. simpsoni*). The former, found in the northeastern [Belgian] Congo and Uganda, gives an over-all impression of fairly clear blue-gray, with just a hint of brown. Simpson's, from the central Congo, south of the river, is noticeably smaller and definitely grayish-brown. These little duikers were extremely timid on arrival, and in spite of liberal use of fresh sweet potato vines and leaves of the Russian mulberry, were more difficult than the larger forms to persuade to take dry foods. An equatorial was born on March 1, 1950, but eventually we found ourselves with only a male Simpson's and a female equatorial. This pair had become steady and confiding, and from them and their offspring sixteen young were produced, single births occurring in every month except November. They agreed well together, even males not being unduly aggressive, and when removed in summer to a small, sheltered inclosure floored with sand but provided with ample cover, made a most charming exhibit. In two of three females living in 1963, the oldest of which was born on August 17, 1951, the tiny horns barely protrude beyond the hair of the crown; in the third the horns, though present, are not visible.

Perhaps most interesting and curious of the members of the genus *Cephalophus* is the zebra or banded duiker (*C. zebra*), of Liberia and Sierra Leone. This remarkable and little-known species is rufous in general, with a series of narrow black bands crossing the back; its shoulder height is given by Lydekker (1913–16, 2:90) as about 16 inches. This striking duiker appears to have been kept first in the old Zoological Gardens of Hamburg and is included by Bolau (1904) in a list of the specimens living there in 1903. Its next appearance, as far as known, was in 1958, when two females, followed later by a male, were obtained from Liberia by the Frankfurt Zoological Gardens—a unique exhibit.

The gray duikers (*Sylvicapra grimmia*) are found in broken bush or open areas from Ethiopia and Senegal to the Cape. Coloration varies in the many races through shades of brownish gray to yellowish, more or less grizzled with black and with dark markings on the face and forelegs. The shoulder height of the Cape duiker (*S. g. grimmia*) is given as from 23 to 25 inches (Lydekker, 1913–16, 2:110). The slender, upright horns of the male may reach a length of 6 inches; females are usually hornless. Many of the races have been kept by zoological gardens, but only the Cape form has been received here. For some reason, this duiker has never really thrived here, our best longevity being only 3 years, 2 months. Better results have been achieved elsewhere, Jones (1958) giving 11 years, 10 months, 20 days for a specimen in the Zoological Gardens of London. Zuckerman (1953) lists five single births of gray duikers in London between 1854 and 1857. The gestation period is given by Asdell (1946) as about 4 months.

SUBFAMILY HIPPOTRAGINAE

WATERBUCKS AND KOBS, REEDBUCKS, ROAN AND SABLE ANTELOPES, ORYXES, ADDAX, BLESBOK AND BONTEBOK, HARTEBEESTS, AND GNUS

The members of this admittedly heterogeneous group, which Ellerman and Morrison-Scott (1951) consider to be doubtfully definable, are almost entirely African in distribution, the single exception being the Arabian oryx (*Oryx leucoryx*). The nomenclature used here is largely that of Allen (1939) with some changes as suggested by Ellerman and Morrison-Scott (*loc. cit.*) and Ellerman, Morrison-Scott, and Hayman (1953).

The waterbucks and kobs (*Kobus*) are large or medium-sized animals in which long, ridged, and generally lyre-shaped horns are borne by males only. In the waterbucks the hair is long and coarse, usually developing a mane, but in the kobs the coat is shorter and usually lies more closely. All are typically inhabitants of the great open plains, some showing a preference for swampy areas.

The common waterbuck (*Kobus ellipsiprymnus*), of which Allen (1939) lists five races, is found in eastern Africa from the Transvaal to Somaliland. It is grayish in general, with a white band circling the buttocks and white markings on the muzzle and above the eyes. The shoulder height is given as about 39 inches (Sclater and Thomas, 1894–1900, 2:98); the greatest length of horns listed by Ward (1922) is 36½ inches. The common waterbuck has been kept fairly generally by zoological gardens, but while it has occasionally been bred, it appears seldom if ever to have reached the herd level. The only specimens that have been received here were two males obtained in 1941. Of these, one that arrived on June 9, 1941, lived until November 29, 1957, or 16 years, 5 months, 20 days. He weighed 570 pounds at death.

The defassa or sing-sing waterbuck (*K. defassa*) is a larger animal than the common, Sclater and Thomas (1894–1900, 2:115) giving the shoulder height as 46–50 inches. The general coloration of the typical race is reddish, with a white patch instead of a circular band on the rump, the body color varying in the many subspecies to shades of gray. Distribution as a species covers much of the open regions of central and western Africa, south of the Sahara, from Senegal to western Ethiopia and southward to Northern Rhodesia and Angola. Three specimens of the sing-sing waterbuck, all of which were referred to the Senegal race, *K. defassa unctuosus*, have been received here. Of a pair that arrived on June 29, 1927, the male lived until January 24, 1941, or 13 years, 6 months, 26 days, the female to May 3, 1941, or 13 years, 10 months, 4 days. Flower (1931) lists a female of this form as having lived for 15 years, 2 months, 25 days in the Zoological Gardens of London. The female of our pair gave birth to a calf on July 16, 1931, which she fully reared.

The red lechwe waterbuck (*K. l. leche*) is a smaller and lighter animal than either of the preceding, with rather coarse hair and slightly developed mane. The body color is dull yellowish brown, with the legs dark brown or black. The preferred habitat is reedy swamps, although the herds may sometimes be found on grassy uplands. Distribution is in southern central Africa, from Nyasaland to Angola. The red lechwe was once the most common of the waterbucks seen in zoological gardens but now is less frequently kept. A large herd was maintained in the African Veldt exhibit of the Detroit Zoological Park for a number of years, the females and young having their liberty in summer, the herd male being confined indoors except when required for breeding purposes. This fine group finally declined, but rejuvenation began when a new male was finally obtained (Anon., 1959d). Nine red lechwes have been kept here over the years, the greatest longevity recorded being 10 years, 10 months, 22 days. Jones (1958) reports a specimen as having lived in the Zoological Gardens of London from March 30, 1934, to March 15, 1949, or 14 years, 11 months, 15 days. Three young have been born in our collection, the births occurring in January, April, and August. Asdell (1946) gives the gestation period as 7 months.

The black lechwe (*K. l. smithemani*), a dark form in which the male's coat is suffused with a blackish cast, found in the marshlands of Northern Rhodesia, appears to have no captivity history. But the Nile lechwe or Mrs. Gray's waterbuck (*K. megaceros*), from the wetlands of the southern Sudan, has been sparingly exhibited. This is a comparatively small but handsome species, in which the male is blackish brown with white on the shoulders and underparts and about the head, the female reddish brown. Only a single male has been shown here, an animal which lived for 9 years, 10 months, 7 days.

The kobs are the smallest of the members of the genus *Kobus*, with rather short, smooth hair and no manes. They are found across equatorial Africa, almost from coast to coast, keeping largely to open, grassy areas. Two species are usually recognized: *K. vardoni*, the puku, a plainly colored, brownish animal found from Mozambique to Nyasaland, and *Kobus kob*, the numerous and better known forms of which are more widely distributed. The puku appears not to have been kept in captivity outside Africa, but the races of *Kobus kob* are sometimes seen in European and American collections. Most striking of these is the white-eared kob (*Kobus kob leucotis*) of the Sudan, in which the nearly black adult male, as well as the brownish female, has the sides of the head, the ears, and the underparts white. This kob has not been kept here, but Rabb (1960) reports a longevity of 17 years for an example in the Chicago Zoological Park. However, Dr. Rabb has informed me (*in litt.*) that this duration was actually 16 years.

The only kobs to have been received here were a pair of the Uganda race (*Kobus kob thomasi*) that arrived on August 9, 1935. The subspecies of *Kobus kob* are difficult to distinguish, at least when immature, so that our animals were at first referred to *leucotis*, and it was not until some time later that their true identity was determined. The Uganda kob, in both sexes, is almost uniformly light reddish brown, with whitish areas about the eyes, above the hoofs, and on the underparts, and stripes of black on the fronts of the lower legs. Lydekker (1913–16, 2:256) gives the shoulder height as about 35½ inches. The range extends from the region of Lake Victoria northward through Uganda. A study of the curious territorial mating behavior has been made by Buechner (1961).

Our original Uganda kobs, as well as their offspring, were extremely nervous and excitable, so that their handling and operation required the greatest caution. Nevertheless, they bred well, a total of eleven young having been produced by the first pair and their descendants, single births occurring from January to July, a restriction enforced by the necessary segregation of the sexes during the winter months. The male received August 9, 1935, lived until April 15, 1949, or 13 years, 8 months, 6 days; a female born July 19, 1939, died on October 30, 1955, after 16 years, 3 months, 11 days.

The reedbucks (*Redunca*) are light, graceful animals in which the short, slender horns of the males turn sharply forward; females are hornless. The coat is short and tight, usually gray or brown, and there is a bare, glandular patch below the ear on each side. The reedbucks are widely distributed in Africa, taking their name from the reedy swamps commonly frequented by most of the forms. The small, gray, somewhat woolly-coated vaal rhebok (*Pelea capreolus*) of South Africa is an aberrant relative of the true reedbucks. Its horns turn forward but slightly, and it lacks the bare space below the ears. The vaal rhebok has been kept rarely in European zoological gardens, but there appears to be no record of its importation into this country. On the other hand, the three commonly recognized species of *Redunca* are more generally seen and all have been included in our own collections here.

The common reedbuck (*R. arundinum*) is found in two races: *R. a. arundinum*, distributed from the Cape to Angola and Nyasaland, and *R. a. occidentalis*, restricted to Northern Rhodesia and Tanganyika. The common reedbuck is grayish brown, with the throat and underparts white; Sclater and Thomas (1894–1900, 2:159) give the shoulder height as about 36 inches. Three specimens of the typical race have been kept here, the greatest longevity recorded being 9 years, 10 months, 13 days.

No young have been produced here, but Zuckerman (1953) records seven births in the Zoological Gardens of London, from November to May. The gestation period is given by Kenneth (1953) as 233 days.

The bohor reedbuck (*Redunca redunca*) is a somewhat smaller animal than the common, light reddish brown in color and with the horns turned more sharply forward. Nine races are listed by Allen (1939), ranging from Tanganyika north to Ethiopia and west to Senegal. Three specimens of the bohor, of unknown origin, were received here on October 13, 1903, the survivor living for 9 years, 11 months, 14 days. A male presented to us on December 19, 1952, by the St. Louis Zoological Park, where a herd has been maintained for some years, died on February 17, 1963, after 10 years, 1 month, 29 days.

The mountain reedbuck (*R. fulvorufula*) is predominantly grayish in color, with some infusions of rufous. The several races extend through East Africa from the Cape to Ethiopia. The preferred habitat appears to be in rocky highlands, rather than the swampy regions frequented by other members of the genus. A male received here on May 29, 1937, and a female that arrived on October 13 of the same year were referred to *R. f. chanleri*, Chanler's mountain reedbuck, the Kenya race. These animals were placed together in a roomy stall in our Antelope House, with an outside run in summer. Six young were produced by this pair and their offspring, single births occurring in January, February, June, July, and October. Contrary to usual antelope behavior in close quarters, the male lived quietly with the small herd, the only exception being a strong antagonism toward developing young males, which had to be removed at early ages. The original female lived until February 16, 1950, or 12 years, 4 months, 3 days.

The roan and sable antelopes (*Hippotragus*) are among the tallest of the group, being second in height only to the elands. But size alone is not their only point of attraction, for their grace and beauty are outstanding. Horns, borne by both sexes, are long and sickle-shaped; the neck is maned above and fringed with hair below.

The roan antelope (*Hippotragus equinus*), both male and female, is sandy roan in color, with face and cheeks black marked by a crescentic band of white that extends downward from the base of each horn; the muzzle and underparts are white. The ears are long and sometimes tufted at their tips. Shoulder height is given by Lydekker (1913–16, 3:135) as "56 to 60 inches or even more"; the greatest length of horn listed by Ward (1922) is 37¼ inches. Distribution of the seven races recognized by Allen (1939) extends from the Orange River area of South Africa northward to the Sudan and westward to Angola and Senegal, in broken scrub or even open plains, sometimes at rather high altitudes.

The roan has never been widely kept, and at the present time (1963) there are only scattered specimens in captivity, at least outside Africa. Single examples of Baker's roan antelope (*H. e. bakeri*), the Sudan race, were received here in 1903 and 1904. One lived for 6 years, 12 days, the other for 6 years, 8 months, 27 days. Flower (1931) reports a roan antelope as having lived for 14 years in the Zoological Gardens of Pretoria.

The sable antelope (*H. niger*) is a slightly smaller animal than the roan, its shoulder height being 52–54 inches (Lydekker, 1913–16, 3:142). The fully adult male is black or very nearly so. The face is white, with a black median stripe and another on each cheek. The throat, belly, and buttocks are white. Females and young are brown, similarly but less sharply marked with white. The curved horns are considerably longer than those of the roan, Ward (1922) listing 52½ inches for a specimen of the typical race from Northern Rhodesia. The range of the four races of Allen (1939) extends from the Transvaal to Kenya and west to Angola, wherever open forest offers both protection and grazing areas. The giant sable (*H. n. variani*), though only slightly larger than the related races, is remarkable for the great length of its horns. Blaine (1922) gives the record as 64 inches and the shoulder height of a large male as 55½ inches. The giant sable is confined to Angola, where it is now strictly protected. In describing the measures taken for the preservation of this magnificent animal, Frade (1958) estimates the number then living as about five hundred.

There appears to be no record of the giant sable in captivity, but other forms of the species have been widely kept. Since World War II the sable has been at low ebb in European collections, but in this country it is fairly well established, a small breeding herd being maintained at the San Diego Zoological Garden and perhaps elsewhere. Since 1909 the species has been represented in our own collections by a total of eight examples. The best longevity established here is 10 years, 9 months, 27 days. Flower (1931) lists 16 years, 8 months, 22 days and left alive for a specimen in the Giza Zoological Gardens. The gestation period is given by Asdell (1946) as 270–81 days.

The oryxes (*Oryx*) are stout-bodied antelopes of medium size, with long, nearly straight or beautifully curved horns in both sexes. There are wide differences in general coloration, but the typical facial markings—a patch between the horns, a nasal stripe, and a streak through each eye—

are more or less traceable in all. Open or even desert areas are the usual habitat.

Best known of the group in zoological gardens is the beisa oryx (*Oryx beisa*) found, in several races, on the plains of East Africa, from Tanganyika to the Sudan. The beisa is tawny gray, with the usual markings on the head, a stripe on the sides delimiting the white of the belly, a band above the knees and tail-tuft black. Sclater and Thomas (1894–1900, **4**:66) give the shoulder height as about 46 inches. The greatest length of the nearly straight horns given by Ward (1922) is 39 inches for a female of the typical race from Somaliland, the horns of females usually exceeding those of males.

The beisa is fairly well established as a breeding species in Europe as well as in this country, where the zoological gardens of San Diego, St. Louis, and Chicago, at least, have been able to report a number of births. Only three beisas of the typical race have been kept here, the best longevity recorded being 11 years, 7 months. Flower (1931) lists a specimen as having lived 18 years, 4 months, 7 days in the Jardin des Plantes, Paris. A female beisa received at the Chicago Zoological Park in 1934 was reported as still living in 1956 (Anon., 1956*b*). Jennison (n.d.) gives the gestation period as 260-300 days.

The fringe-eared beisa (*O. b. callotis*), the Tanganyika representative of the species, is readily distinguished by the long black tufts on the ear-tips. Two males only have been received here, one of which lived from July 16, 1914, to January 7, 1931, or 16 years, 5 months, 22 days. A male and two females of this race were received at the San Diego Zoological Garden on October 2, 1961 (Anon., 1962). Each of these females gave birth to a calf in 1963 (Anon., 1963).

Largest of the oryxes is the gemsbok (*O. gazella*), for which Sclater and Thomas (1894–1900, **4**:58) give a shoulder height of 48 inches. Its markings differ from those of the beisa principally in the extensive black areas of the upper legs and rump; there is also a small tuft of black hair on the throat. The horns, which are almost straight, may reach a length of 48 inches (Ward, 1922). The gemsbok lives in the open, arid areas of southwestern Africa, north to southern Angola, where a paler race, *O. g. blanei*, is distinguished. The gemsbok has never become firmly established as a zoo animal and seems to have been exhibited only sporadically. Two specimens are currently (1963) living in the Cheyenne Mountain Zoological Park, Colorado, and four at the Lincoln Park Zoo, Oklahoma City, while a male and two females were received here on September 7, 1962. A single example received here on October 25, 1930, lived until October

27, 1936, or 6 years, 2 days. Flower (1931) lists a specimen as having lived in the Zoological Gardens of London for 10 years, 4 months, 7 days, and Jones (1958) reports that an animal received at the Philadelphia Zoological Garden on September 3, 1920, died on October 10, 1938, after 18 years, 1 month, 7 days. Haagner (1920) says that a pair in the National Zoological Gardens, Pretoria, bred well, the female producing a calf in each of three successive years.

The scimitar-horned oryx (*O. tao*) is an inhabitant of the desert regions of North Africa from Nigeria to Libya and the Sudan. The body coloration is whitish, more or less suffused with brown, more pronounced on shoulders and neck; the typical facial markings are evident. The slender, beautifully curved horns may be as long as 45 inches (Sclater and Thomas, 1894–1900, **4**:44). In the desolate areas of its habitat the scimitar-horn is said to follow the rains seasonally, feeding on the newly sprouting herbage. The species undoubtedly has become reduced in both numbers and range but nevertheless does not appear to be immediately threatened.

The scimitar-horned oryx seems to have been kept in zoological gardens almost as frequently as has the beisa, and small breeding stocks are still held here and there. Nouvel, Rinjard, and Pasquier (1960) report a herd of six in the Parc Zoologique du Bois de Vincennes, Paris, on December 31, 1959, four young having been born and two successfully reared during that year. A newborn calf in the Zoological Gardens of Antwerp is figured with its mother by Gijzen (1959*b*). In this country the scimitar-horn is still among the great rarities, yet there exists a photograph of a sturdy calf born in the Chicago Zoological Park in 1955 (Anon., 1956*c*). Zuckerman (1953) reports twelve births of this species in the Zoological Gardens of London between 1852 and 1933, with occurrence in every month except February and August.

A female scimitar-horn was received here on October 13, 1903, and a male on March 25, 1904. Two young were produced, one in March, the other in December; both were fully reared and eventually sent to the National Zoological Park. A further male that arrived on June 30, 1925, lived here until February 13, 1940, or 14 years, 7 months, 14 days. Flower (1931) reports 18 years, 1 month, 8 days for an animal that died in the Zoological Gardens of London in 1871.

The Arabian oryx (*O. leucoryx*) is the smallest member of the genus, with a shoulder height of about 35 inches (Sclater and Thomas, 1894–1900, **4**:52). The body color is white, with patches of blackish brown on the forehead, nose, and cheeks. The tail-tip and legs, except for a white ring above each hoof, are also dark brown, and there may be a faint indication of the usual flank stripe. Horns are short and almost straight; record lengths, as listed by Ward (1922) are up to $27\frac{1}{4}$ inches. The name "white oryx" has been applied so indiscriminately to both this animal and the scimitar-horn that much confusion has resulted.

The Arabian oryx once had a fairly extensive range in the desert areas of the Arabian peninsula and nearby areas. Constant hunting, in recent years by means of motor cars and airplanes, has reduced the animals to a point where according to Talbot (1960) no more than two hundred then existed in a remote and desolate region in southern Saudi Arabia. More recent reports indicate further onslaughts, and it appears likely that the dwindling herds will soon have disappeared entirely. An extended history of the Arabian oryx is given by Harper (1945).

In earlier days, when we knew the Arabian oryx as the beatrix antelope, it was a fairly common zoological-garden exhibit, as noted by Ulmer (1959). It lived and bred well, but unfortunately no one then realized the necessity for establishing it firmly. A male purchased from Carl Hagenbeck was received here on October 17, 1903, and on September 27, 1906, a female was obtained from the Bostock Menagerie, then at Coney Island, New York. Four young were born to this pair, one birth occurring in March, three in April, all the young being fully reared. The original female lived until March 19, 1924, or 17 years, 5 months, 20 days. Jones (1958) reports a specimen as having lived in the Zoological Garden of Philadelphia from April 24, 1909, to April 22, 1926, or 2 days less than 17 years.

In 1962 a project for the capture of Arabian oryxes for transfer to a protected area was organized by the Fauna Preservation Society (*Oryx*, 6 (4):208–10), and as a result two males and one female were captured and safely transported to temporary holding quarters in Kenya (Grimwood, 1962). Later, these three animals, with a female supplied by the Zoological Society of London, were shipped to New York, where they entered quarantine on May 23, 1963. After thirty days in seclusion they were forwarded to the Arizona Zoological Society at Tempe, Arizona, where they were placed in the permanent quarters in which it is hoped that they will thrive and breed, in the last stand of a sorely threatened species. The experiment started well, with the birth of a calf on October 26, 1963.*

The addax (*Addax nasomaculatus*) appears to be closely related to the oryxes but differs markedly, in both sexes, in the spiral form of the horns that, as recorded by Ward (1922), may reach a length of $39\frac{5}{16}$ inches. Sclater and Thomas (1894–1900, 4:38) give the shoulder height as 38

*See Addenda, p. 738.

inches. The addax is a nearly uniform grayish brown above, with a flat, rounded tuft of black on the forehead and a white stripe descending from the eyes and crossing the nose below it. The hind quarters, underparts, legs, and tail are white, the latter with a dark tip, and the "knees" are marked with brown.

The addax is a desert animal, its hoofs broad and flattened in keeping with the soft footing of such regions. Its range is the same as that of the scimitar-horned oryx, extending across the Sahara from Río de Oro to the Sudan.

Like most of the oryxes, the addax has never been commonly kept in zoological gardens, although a pair was received by the Zoological Gardens of London as early as 1849 (Flower, 1929). The best continuing success with the species in Europe probably has been that of the Parc Zoologique du Bois de Vincennes, Paris, where a small herd has been maintained since its opening in 1934, with three survivors on December 31, 1959 (Nouvel, Rinjard, and Pasquier, 1960). An animal received there in 1935 is reported by Urbain, Nouvel, Bullier, and Rinjard (1955) to have lived until March 15, 1954, this period of 19 years appearing to be the longest so far recorded for a captive addax. A female received into our own collection on October 17, 1903, may very well have been the first representative of the species to be seen alive in this country. This animal lived until July 6, 1921, or 17 years, 8 months, 19 days.

A pair of addax received from Khartoum by the Chicago Zoological Park in 1937 seems to have been the first couple to be exhibited in America. This pair proved to be notably prolific and produced a number of young, the herd reaching a total of seven animals in 1957 (Anon., 1957b).

A young pair from the Chicago herd was received here on July 25, 1946. These animals were assigned to small individual stalls in our Antelope House because of the risk of injury to the female by the male in close quarters. Here they were confined during the colder months but were allowed to run together in the large outdoor yard in mild weather. From 1948 to 1955 five young were produced, single births occurring in February, May, June (two), and September. All were safely reared and released to other institutions, save one, which appeared to have been injured at birth. Its weight was 12 pounds. Breeding, for no apparent reason, ended with the 1955 birth, and both animals died during 1961.

The blesbok (*Damaliscus dorcas phillipsi*) and the bontebok (*Damaliscus dorcas dorcas*) are closely related and very similar forms, once common in South Africa but now greatly reduced, the bontebok, at least, to the verge of extinction. In the blesbok the back is rufous, the extremities being somewhat darker. The face is white, crossed by a dark bar between the eyes. The lower parts are white, continued down the legs, which are marked with dark brown on their outer surface; a small caudal disk is light brown. In the bontebok the contrast between the shades of brown is more distinct, enhancing the saddle effect on the back; the white blaze on the forehead is continuous, the lower legs are more clearly white, and there is a large white rump patch. The shoulder height of the bontebok is given as 40 inches (Sclater and Thomas, 1894–1900, 1:74); that of the blesbok is similar. The maximum length of the heavily ringed, partially lyrate horns given by Ward (1922) is 18⅝ inches for the blesbok, 16¾ for the bontebok.

Once numerous on the plains of South Africa from Cape Province to the Transvaal and Bechuanaland, the blesbok has now become restricted to nature reserves in the Orange Free State and the Transvaal and to private farms, where it is propagated for the production of venison (Knobel, 1958). The bontebok, abundant in better days from the Cape to the Orange River, is now, according to Knobel (*loc. cit.*), reduced to perhaps one hundred and fifty animals in the Bontebok National Park, Cape Province, with a few still on private farms.

The blesbok has long been kept and bred by zoological gardens generally, and in spite of its increasing scarcity, is still shown by many, both in Europe and in this country, where there are breeding herds at San Diego, San Antonio, and undoubtedly elsewhere. A herd of fourteen imported in 1960 by Roland Lindemann of the Catskill Game Farm, New York, and seven animals received here in December, 1962, should be important assets.

Since the arrival of our first specimen here in 1903, the blesbok has been represented continuously in our collection. Four young have been born here, one each in May and August and two in June. Average gestation periods given by Kenneth (1953) run from 225 to 240 days. The best longevity recorded here is that of a male born on June 10, 1946, which died on September 12, 1961, after 15 years, 3 months, 2 days. Jones (1958) reports a specimen as having lived in the Philadelphia Zoological Garden from April 24, 1909, to February 16, 1926, or 16 years, 9 months, 23 days. Flower (1931) gives 17 years and still alive for a blesbok in the Zoological Gardens of Antwerp.

The bontebok, unlike the blesbok, seems to have been kept only occasionally by zoological gardens and at the present time probably is not represented outside Africa. Only three specimens have been received here, one in 1909 and two in 1914. No breeding results were achieved, and none of these animals survived for more than a few months over 2 years. Jones (1958) lists a bontebok as having lived at the Philadelphia Zoological

Garden from September 3, 1920, to April 24, 1936, or 15 years, 7 months, 21 days.

Several close relatives of the blesbok and the bontebok, all with faces black instead of white, have figured rarely as zoological-garden exhibits. The korrigum or Senegal hartebeest (*Damaliscus k. korrigum*), found from Lake Chad to Senegal, was described from an animal living in the Zoological Gardens of London (Ogilby, 1836). The topi (*D. k. jimela*), of Uganda, Kenya, and Tanganyika, the tiang (*D. k. tiang*), from the Sudan, and the sassaby or tsesseby (*D. lunatus*), which ranges from the Transvaal and Bechuanaland to Northern Rhodesia, have all been represented occasionally. The only member of this group received here was a tiang that arrived on May 25, 1925. This animal lived until April 13, 1930, or 4 years, 10 months, 19 days. Jones (1958) reports a sassaby as having lived in the National Zoological Gardens, Pretoria, from February 12, 1931, to June 24, 1940, or 9 years, 4 months, 12 days.

The hartebeests (*Alcelaphus*) are tall, slender animals, with shoulders higher than hips. The head is long and narrow, a condition emphasized by the extension of the skull to form a pedicel for the horns. These appendages, present in both sexes, are strongly ridged and abruptly double-curved, the tip turning backward. The numerous forms occur in varying shades of brown, sometimes with blackish markings on face and legs. Distribution is widespread on the open, grassy plains of Africa.

Striking and curious though the hartebeests are, they have usually appeared in zoological gardens as single exhibits, and breeding records are few, although many of the races of *Alcelaphus buselaphus* have been shown. The bubal hartebeest (*Alcelaphus b. buselaphus*), the typical subspecies, formerly found in North Africa from Morocco to Egypt, is now considered to be extinct, the last known living specimen having died in the Jardin des Plantes, Paris, in 1923 (Flower, 1931). Another specimen of this form is reported by Bourdelle and Mouquet (1930) to have lived at the same institution from July 10, 1897, to June 14, 1916, or 18 years, 11 months, 4 days, probably the greatest longevity recorded for any captive hartebeest. The bubal was shown in earlier days at the Philadelphia Zoological Garden, the last specimen there dying in 1905 (Ulmer, 1959).

Three specimens of Coke's hartebeest or kongoni (*Alcelaphus b. cokii*), the Kenya and Tanganyika race, were received at London's Whipsnade in October, 1952 (Kelham, 1953), and were reported as still living there in 1958. A pair of kongoni arrived at the Chicago Zoological Park in 1960 and produced a calf on June 28, 1961, pictured in the *Brookfield Bandar-Log* for November, 1961. The female of a pair of the same form at the Highland Park Zoological Gardens, Pittsburgh, gave birth to single young in 1960 and 1961 (Edward J. House, personal communication).

The Cape hartebeest (*Alcelaphus b. caama*), formerly found in the Cape area, is now considered to be extinct. A close relative, *Alcelaphus b. selbornei*, ranges from the western Transvaal across Bechuanaland to South West Africa, where it appears to exist in some numbers. It is probable that animals kept in recent years and referred to *caama* may actually have represented *selbornei*. Six specimens imported in 1960 by the Catskill Game Farm, New York, were assigned to the latter race. A pair living in the Chicago Zoological Park from 1938 to 1945 produced a number of young, unfortunately all males, for which no mates could be found (Anon., 1960*b*). Four specimens, two males and two females, have been kept in our own collection, but a potential breeding pair was never included. A male lived from May 6, 1940, to October 17, 1948, or 8 years, 5 months, 11 days. A specimen in the Philadelphia Zoological Garden, recorded as *selbornei*, is reported by Jones (1958) to have lived there for 12 years, 12 days.

Besides these animals, the only other hartebeest received here up to 1963 was a lelwel (*Alcelaphus b. lelwel*), a race noted for its particularly elongated face and elevated pedicel. Its range extends from western Kenya and Uganda across the Sudan to the former French Equatorial Africa. This animal, which arrived here in 1913, lived for just under 3 years. It is hoped that four specimens of Jackson's hartebeest (*A. b. jacksoni*), of East Africa, received here on October 17, 1963, will be the nucleus of a future herd.

The gnus or wildebeests (*Connochaetes*) are characterized by large heads, recurved horns, high shoulders and flowing tails, suggestive of both cattle and horses. Natural distribution covers the open plains of southern and eastern Africa.

The white-tailed gnu (*C. gnou*) is the smallest of the group, its shoulder height being about 3 feet, 10 inches (Lydekker, 1913–16, 2:52). The body is very dark brown to black, the long hair of the tail white. There are tufts of hair on the nose and chin as well as between the forelegs, and a well-developed mane extends from nape to shoulders. The horns, in both sexes, turn downward and forward, ending in an upward curve. These appendages are straight in young animals; their growth and development have been described and figured by Blaauw (1889). Large herds of this striking species once lived on the open veldt from the Cape to the Transvaal, but it has been so nearly exterminated that Knobel (1958) estimates its numbers at no more than five hundred animals, living in reserves or on private farms.

By good fortune, the white-tailed gnu, once generally kept by zoological gardens, is still holding its own in captivity, at least in Europe, where several small breeding herds are maintained, notably at Whipsnade. In this country the species has never been really common. In 1960 thirteen specimens were imported by Roland Lindemann of the Catskill Game Farm, New York, and there, together with an elderly female bred in our own collection, formed a potential breeding herd of important size. Although no young had been produced through 1961, two were born in 1962 and five up to July, 1963.

From 1903 to 1940 eight specimens were received here, although it was not until 1940 that a breeding pair was obtained from South Africa. Their first offspring, a female, was born on July 7, 1942. This female and her mother each produced single calves in 1947 and 1949, two of these five births occurring in June, three in July, all the calves being fully reared. Gaps in breeding were caused by the extremely savage nature of the male, a trait that seems to be characteristic of this species. The original female and her first daughter lived and even reared their calves together but the male could be allowed to run with them only at intervals, when close supervision could be maintained. The death of this male in 1951 put a stop to breeding, no replacement being available. The female of a pair received here in 1962 gave birth to a sturdy calf in January, 1963.

The gestation period of the white-tailed gnu is given by Asdell (1946) as 8–8½ months. A specimen is reported to have lived in the Jardin des Plantes, Paris, from January 31, 1912, to November 21, 1926, or 14 years, 9 months, 21 days (Flower, 1931). A male received here on October 17, 1903, died on July 25, 1921, after 17 years, 9 months, 8 days; the female that arrived on May 6, 1940, lived until April 14, 1960, or 19 years, 11 months, 8 days. Her first daughter, born here on July 7, 1942, died on February 7, 1962, after 19 years, 7 months.

The blue or brindled gnu (*C. taurinus*) is a larger animal than the white-tailed, its shoulder height varying from 4 feet, 3 inches to 4 feet, 4½ inches (Lydekker, 1913–16, 2:55). There are several races, the best known being the typical one, *C. t. taurinus*, which ranges from the Orange River northward to Angola in the west and Northern Rhodesia in the east. The general coloration is bluish gray, with vertical stripes of a darker shade on the sides; the nasal tuft, neck fringe, mane, tail, and face are blackish. The horns, borne by both sexes, grow outward almost horizontally from the skull, the points then curving upward and inward. The blue gnu is still fairly abundant over most of its range, the herds frequently intermingling with those of other antelopes and zebras.

The typical blue gnu is frequently to be seen in zoological gardens. While it is by no means a calm or trustworthy animal in captivity, it seems less inclined to actual ferocity than the white-tailed. Five specimens were received here between 1920 and 1941, but only a single calf was born, on June 28, 1932. Asdell (1946) gives the gestation period as 8–9 months. W. C. O. Hill (1957) reports that an animal born in the Zoological Gardens of London lived there for 18 years. A male blue gnu that arrived here on August 8, 1941, died on November 6, 1957, after 16 years, 2 months, 29 days and a female received on September 4, 1920, was sold on August 26, 1940, after 19 years, 11 months, 22 days.

The white-bearded gnu (*C. t. albojubatus*) is similar to the typical race but is paler in color, with the throat fringe white or yellowish. This is the common wildebeest of the plains of central Kenya and Tanganyika, where it appears to be in no more immediate danger than other hoofed inhabitants of this troubled area.

The white-bearded gnu is fairly well established in this country at the present time, largely due to the efforts of the Chicago Zoological Park, where a breeding herd has been maintained for some years. In Europe, too, this is the most commonly seen of the gnus. A female of this race received here on October 17, 1903, lived until August 25, 1917, or 13 years, 10 months, 8 days. Rabb (1960) reports that a white-bearded gnu lived for 20 years in the Chicago Zoological Park, while Flower (1931) lists a female as having lived in the Philadelphia Zoological Garden from June 5, 1908, to July 27, 1928, or 20 years, 1 month, 22 days. Steinbacher (1959) gives the gestation periods in three pregnancies in the Augsburg Tiergarten as 249, 251, and 255 days, respectively.

SUBFAMILY ANTILOPINAE

KLIPSPRINGERS, DIK-DIKS, BLACKBUCK, DIBATAG, GERENUK, GAZELLES, ETC.

This subfamily includes a large number of medium-sized to very small antelopes, a few well known in zoological gardens, others extremely rare. Distribution is concentrated in Africa, a few species being confined to Asia and several having representatives on both continents. Horns are usually carried by males only but in a few cases by females as well. Lateral hoofs may be present or absent. The nomenclature used here for African forms is largely that of Allen (1939) with some changes suggested by Ellerman, Morrison-Scott, and Hayman (1953) and Ellerman and Morrison-Scott (1951). The latter authorities have been followed for Asiatic antelopes.

The klipspringer (*Oreotragus oreotragus*), as its name implies, is a dweller on high rocky prominences, where it is as sure-footed as any goat. The functional hoofs are small and rounded and so arranged that the animal stands upon their very tips with the lateral hoofs well above. The klipspringer is a small animal, with a shoulder height of 20–22 inches (Lydekker, 1913–16, 2:125). The thick, heavy coat is grizzled in yellow and black, with the underparts sometimes white. Variations in shade are used largely in differentiating the races, of which Allen (1939) lists twelve, ranging from Cape Province to Angola and northward through East Africa to Somaliland, Ethiopia, the Sudan, and Nigeria. Small, straight horns are carried by males and not usually by females, although a Tanganyika race, *Oreotragus o. schillingsi*, is said to be an exception.

The klipspringer has been shown infrequently by various zoological gardens, too often with indifferent results. The greatest success with this species in captivity in this country and quite possibly anywhere has been achieved by the St. Louis Zoological Park. A number of young were reared from animals obtained in 1935, and a considerable stock was built up. After some years, however, vitality seemed to wane, so that the herd finally disintegrated.

A pair of newly imported klipspringers was added to our collection on August 27, 1940. The female gave birth to a single youngster soon after arrival but failed to rear it. This animal survived her mate but still lived for only 17 months. In 1941 we received a pair of klipspringers from the St. Louis herd. The female produced single young on May 1, 1942, and on December 11 of the same year, but the first lived for only a few days, the second for just over 3 months. These animals were kept in a roomy stall in our Kangaroo House during the winter and given access to a large paved yard in summer. A tall kiosk of rough stone was erected here, and while the klipspringers did make use of it, climbing was less frequent than we had expected it to be. Food consisted of crushed oats, feeding pellets, alfalfa and clover hay, apples, bananas, fresh foliage in summer, and lettuce in winter. In spite of our efforts, the animals seemed to "fade" gradually, the survivor dying after 2 years, 1 month, 17 days. Jones (1958) reports a klipspringer as having lived in the National Zoological Park from October 8, 1942, to July 20, 1947, or 4 years, 9 months, 12 days. Miss Hattie Ettinger, administrative assistant at St. Louis, has informed me (*in litt.*) that a member of the herd there, born in 1938, lived until 1953, approximately 15 years.

The oribi (*Ourebia ourebi*), colored in shades of yellow, reddish, or gray with white underparts, is readily distinguished by the tufts of hair that decorate its "knees," and the bare patches below the ears. A large number of races inhabit open grasslands or broken bush country from Cape Province to Angola, north to Ethiopia and Senegal. Shoulder heights, as given by Shortridge (1934) run from 21 to 26 inches. Oribis have been kept very rarely by zoological gardens. Two received here in 1928 lived for only a few months, but Flower (1931) reports a specimen as having lived for 8 years, 10 months, 6 days in the Zoological Gardens of London and another for 13 years, 8 months, 19 days in the Basel Zoological Gardens.

The steinbok (*Raphicerus campestris*) is a smaller animal than the oribi, the shoulder height being 21 or 22 inches (Lydekker, 1913–16, 2:148). The general coloration is sandy red with the underparts white, and sometimes faint markings of black and white about the head. Small, straight horns occur in males only, and lateral hoofs are absent. Six races, as listed by Allen (1939), are found in long grass or open bush from the Cape to Angola and Kenya. The grysbok (*R. melanotis*) approximates the steinbok in size. The rather coarse hair is reddish, grizzled with white, and lateral hoofs are retained. This monotypic species appears to be confined to southern Cape Province, where, according to Knobel (1958), its position is fair. Sharpe's grysbok (*R. sharpei*) closely resembles *melanotis* but lacks lateral hoofs. The species, in two races, inhabits open country from the Transvaal to Tanganyika. All these small creatures are extremely rare in zoological gardens. Even when they have been obtained, few have survived for more than a few months. Single specimens of both steinbok and grysbok were received here together in 1940, but only the latter lived as long as 5 weeks.

Closely allied to the steinbok and the grysbok but very much smaller is the suni (*Nesotragus moschatus*), for which Lydekker (1913–16, 2:160) gives a shoulder height of 13–14 inches. The usual coloration is grayish brown with the underparts white. There are no lateral hoofs, and only the males carry the short, straight horns. The suni is distributed, in five presently recognized races, from Natal to Kenya. Preferred habitat is tangled bush. The suni has rarely been kept in captivity; Haagner (1920), speaking of his experience in the National Zoological Gardens, Pretoria, says that it seldom lives longer than a year.

Justly famed as the smallest of the antelopes is the royal (*Neotragus pygmaeus*), with a shoulder height of only 10 inches (Lydekker, 1913–16,

2:170). This delicate little creature, rufous in color, with throat and under-parts white, is native to the deep forests of West Africa from Sierra Leone to Gaboon. The tiny horns of males may measure less than an inch in length. The royal antelope seems to have no real captivity history, although it was represented in the Zoological Gardens of London in 1914 (Flower, 1929), and again by a pair received in 1962.

The dik-diks (*Madoqua*) are well known by name, though seldom in the flesh, for while occasional specimens have reached zoological gardens, these arrivals have been few indeed. The dik-diks are tiny, fragile creatures, the shoulder height of *Madoqua saltiana*, of Ethiopia, being 14–15 inches (Lydekker, 1913–16, 2:175). Coloration is in shades of brown and gray; there is an upright tuft of hair on the crown and the muzzle is extended and mobile. The slender horns of males may reach a length of 4 inches (Ward, 1922). Twenty-two forms, found in South West Africa and Angola and from Kenya to Ethiopia and Somaliland, are listed by Allen (1939). The favorite haunts of the dik-diks seem to be dry, tangled scrub, from which the animals emerge in the evening to feed (Shortridge, 1934).

No example of this group had been received here up to 1963. Mann (1930) reports a specimen of *Madoqua kirki nyikae*, from Kenya, as having lived for 10 days in the National Zoological Park, and a female referred to *Madoqua g. guentheri*, received at the Chicago Zoological Park, has been figured and described (Anon., 1957c). This animal was fed lettuce, carrots, apples, bananas, grapes, raisins, grain, bread, and hay, presumably alfalfa. A female included in a trio of Kirk's dik-dik (*Madoqua k. kirki*) received at the Philadelphia Zoological Garden on August 25, 1961, gave birth to a sturdy youngster early in the following month (Frederick A. Ulmer, Jr., personal communication).

An extensive account, profusely illustrated, of two specimens of *Madoqua kirki*, kept in the Zoological Gardens of Basel, is given by Ziegler-Simon (1957). A female received from Tanganyika in November, 1947, was joined by a male obtained in the summer of 1953. These animals, hand-reared and quite tame, were kept at semi-liberty and fed lucerne (alfalfa) hay, raw rice, rolled oats and corn (maize), greens, potatoes, nuts, and fruit. Sexual behavior was noted but no young resulted. Both animals were still living in 1956, when the female had reached the age of 9 years.

From an intensive study of 412 specimens of *Madoqua kirki thomasi* shot in Tanganyika as well as of 23 young animals kept in captivity, Kellas (1954–55) concludes that in this form, at least, sexual maturity is reached at about 6 months. The gestation period is estimated to be approximately 6 months, most females breeding twice yearly. A report of a female, said to have been born in captivity, that had lived to the age of 9 years, 2 months is quoted, although survival in nature is estimated to average 5 years or less. The longest survival of an animal kept in captivity in the course of Kellas's work was 16 months.

The blackbuck (*Antilope cervicapra*) lives on the plains of India from the Punjab in the west and East Pakistan in the east, south to Cape Comorin, at the very tip of the peninsula. Four races are recognized by Ellerman and Morrison-Scott (1951). Young males and females are light brown, with markings about the face white, as are the underparts. Males become gradually darker, the brown areas, usually except for the shoulders, finally assuming a shade close to black. There is much variation in this process, some animals requiring several years to complete the change, while some fail altogether to accomplish it. Lydekker (1913–16, **3**:26) suggests that the black pelage in males may be seasonal, but observation of our own animals here does not confirm this. The handsome, spiraled horns, borne by males only, have been recorded as reaching a length of $28\frac{7}{8}$ inches (Ward, 1922). The shoulder height is given by Lydekker (1913–16, **3**:25) as 30 inches. A male here weighed 92 pounds at the age of 6 years, when crated for shipment.

Certainly the blackbuck is kept by zoological gardens more commonly than any other antelope and it is also seen as a park animal at semi-liberty on many estates in France and England. Its hardiness, of course, is a principal factor, for the blackbuck endures temperatures well below 0°F. ($-17.8°$C.) when provided with an open, unheated shelter. Kept in small quarters, the blackbuck does well enough, but males so confined are likely to become savage, and breeding is greatly restricted. When released in a large, grassy inclosure where natural herd behavior can have full play, results are much more satisfactory.

In 1941 a small herd was established here in an open range of about $1\frac{1}{2}$ acres, well grassed and including several shade trees. This area was shared with Reeves's muntjacs (*Muntiacus reevesi*) as already described under that species. The two groups have never interfered with each other nor with various cranes and geese sometimes kept in the inclosure. An open shelter containing grain boxes and hay racks is provided for general feeding, and there is an inclosed barn for occasional shelter. The latter is particularly useful for catching, the animals being enticed to enter by means of special feeding. The door is then closed by a concealed operator and windows covered, leaving the interior in darkness, so that wanted individuals can be selected by hand without difficulty. A small "pop-hole" is used to release them, one at a time, into crates set up outside. This method, of course, is followed for many sorts of hoofed animals, but blackbuck on range are so very difficult to secure by other means that this simple solution is mentioned here. There is also the point that removals are accomplished without undue disturbance.

Feeding, schedules include the usual alfalfa hay and grain pellets. During the summer there is an ample supply of grass, which the animals never crop too closely, and in winter some greens are provided.

The herd here usually consists of from six to eight females with such young as may be about, a single dominant male, and perhaps two or three younger males. The latter are kept at a distance from the group by the herd male, constantly on the alert. It is necessary to watch these developing males carefully, for while they usually retreat when approached by the herd male, one that has gained sufficient size and weight will eventually challenge him, usually with fatal results.

Up to 1962, ninety-seven young were born here, as follows: January, one; February, six; March, ten; April, eleven; May, eight; June, thirteen; July, seven; August, eight; September, six; October, eight; November, twelve; December, seven. All births were of single young, no case of twinning having been noted. The gestation period is given by Brown (1936) as 6 months.

A female born here on October 9, 1904, lived until May 16, 1920, or 15 years, 7 months, 7 days, while under close control. Somewhat longer spans for range animals have been recorded here but with natural possibility of error. Flower (1931) gives 15 years, 1 month, 25 days and left alive for a specimen in the Antwerp Zoological Gardens.

The impala (*Aepyceros melampus*), noted for its grace as well as for its running and leaping ability, is found in several races from South West Africa and Angola east to Mozambique and north to Kenya and Uganda. The body color is warm brown, sometimes with the face blackish; the throat and underparts are white. There is a patch of stiff black hair on the lower part of each hind leg, and lateral hoofs are missing. The undulating, lyrate horns, absent in females, may exceed 30 inches in length. Lydekker (1913–16, **3**:6) gives the shoulder height as about 39 inches.

Although the impala seems to be maintaining its numbers comparatively well and is still numerous in many areas, it remains uncommon in collections. The only specimens received here before 1963 were four animals that arrived between 1939 and 1941. All were reasonably quiet and docile, but the longest survival was 2 years, 2 months. Jones (1958) reports a specimen of *Aepyceros m. suara*, from East Africa, as having lived in the National Zoological Park from November 9, 1926, to January 14, 1937, or

10 years, 2 months, 5 days. An account of the capture of this animal with others in East Africa is given by Mann (1930).

Trying again to establish an impala herd, we received 3 specimens on October 17, 1963.

The impala seems to thrive in captivity within its natural area, for Haagner (1920), in writing of his experience in the National Zoological Gardens of South Africa at Pretoria with wild-caught animals, says, "They bred quite well and soon got tame." This seems to have marked the beginning of a continuing success, for R. Bigalke (1961) reports three single births of impala at Pretoria in December, 1960. Breeding outside South Africa has been less frequent, though births have occurred at the Zoological Garden of San Diego (Anon., 1961a), St. Louis, and London. The gestation period is given by Asdell (1946) as from 6½ to 7 months.

The dibatag or Clarke's gazelle (*Ammodorcas clarkei*), of Somaliland, is a slender animal, with neck and legs greatly lengthened. It is dark brown in color, with an area about the eyes, a conspicuous streak along each side of the face, underparts, and caudal disk white. The horns, borne by males only, curve forward, much as in the reedbuck, and may reach a length of 12 inches. The shoulder height is given by Lydekker (1913–16, 3:3) as about 31 inches. Apparently the first dibatag to leave Africa was a female received at the Zoological Gardens of Naples in October, 1954 (Cuneo, 1955). A male and two females obtained later by the same institution are figured in *Giardino Zoologico* (2 (4):34, July–August, 1960) and were reported as still living in 1961.

In the gerenuk (*Litocranius walleri*) the neck and legs are so elongated that the animal is somewhat suggestive of a miniature giraffe. The resemblance is borne out, at least to a degree, by its feeding habits, for like the giraffe it subsists largely on foliage. Unlike the larger species, however, the gerenuk is able to increase its feeding range by standing upright on its hind legs, supporting itself by bracing its front feet against a tree trunk or strong branch. Feeding attitudes in a captive animal have been well described and figured by Priemal (1930).

The gerenuk is light brown in color, with a darker area extending along the back. There is a whitish eye ring as well as a short facial streak and narrow stripes bordering the tail. The underparts are white. Small "knee" tufts are black or brown. The heavily ringed horns, in males only, are roughly lyrate, with a marked forward hook at the tip. The maximum length on the front curve given by Ward (1922) is 17 inches; shoulder height is 39 inches. The species extends, in two generally recognized races, from Tanganyika to Ethiopia and Somaliland.

Although apparently fairly abundant in most parts of its range, the gerenuk was an extremely uncommon zoo animal until within fairly recent years. At the present time (1963) a small number of charmingly tame, hand-reared specimens are sometimes available, and there seems to be an excellent possibility that the species may at last become established in captivity. Early arrivals in Europe were scattered and none appear to have survived for long. The first representative to have reached America apparently was a specimen received at the National Zoological Park in 1934 (Mann, 1934:4) but this animal lived for less than 1 year. Later arrivals were recorded at the zoological parks of St. Louis, Chicago, and San Diego, all with more encouraging results.

Experience with the gerenuk in our own collection did not begin until October 1, 1957, when a young pair was received. The female died suddenly, less than 2 years later, and a replacement met a similar fate after a few months. Autopsy in neither case gave fully satisfactory causes of death, although nightshade (*Solanum nigrum*) was suspected as the lethal agent in the first instance.

In June, 1961, two further females were received and readily accepted as companions by the male. These animals took alfalfa hay and feeding pellets freely, these staples being supplemented with bananas, fresh foliage in season, and greens. The younger of the two females, although apparently fully grown, still took milk from a bottle in addition to solid food. The male, after 6 years with us, still remained completely tame and gentle. A sturdy female calf was born on September 30, 1963, the first in the Western Hemisphere.

The finest success so far attained with the gerenuk is undoubtedly that of the Zoological Gardens of Frankfurt. The female of a pair received there on July 12, 1956, gave birth to a single calf on March 1, 1957, presumably the first to have been born in captivity (Anon., 1957d). Births continued in following years, so that by December 31, 1960, breeding had progressed to the fourth generation, the original male had become a great-grandfather, and a second herd had been established. The total stock on that date numbered two males and four females (Grzimek, 1961).

Marvin Jones (*in litt.*) reports that a gerenuk received at the Zoological Gardens of London on July 31, 1956, died on January 12, 1961, after 4 years, 5 months, 12 days. This appears to be the best longevity so far completed by a captive animal of this species. However, the original male at Frankfurt that arrived on July 12, 1956, and was still living in 1963, as well as our own male, had already exceeded this span.

The gazelles of the genus *Gazella* have all the qualities of grace and beauty popularly attributed to the group, although it must be admitted that these are seen to less advantage in the zoological garden than in nature, since broad space is required for their full display. For the most part, the gazelles are small, delicate creatures, shoulder heights ranging between 2 and 3 feet. A list derived from Allen (1939) and Ellerman and Morrison-Scott (1951) shows that eight species are confined to Africa and one to Asia, while three are found on both continents. When recognized subspecies are considered, the total number of forms exceeds fifty.

Typically, the gazelles are colored in shades of brown, with the under-parts and caudal disk white. There is often a white stripe on either side of the face from above the eye to the muzzle, bordered below by a dark streak, and there may be a blackish spot near the tip of the nose. A dark band with a lighter one above it often separates the brown of the upper parts from the white of the belly, and a perpendicular streak may border the white rump-patch. A small "knee" tuft is usually darker than the body color. In all forms, except only the Persian or goitered gazelle (*G. sub-gutturosa*), both sexes carry lyrate horns, usually smaller in females than in males.

Gazelles of many kinds are commonly kept in the zoological gardens of Europe—eight forms are listed as living in the Parc Zoologique du Bois de Vincennes, Paris, as of December 31, 1959 (Nouvel, Rinjard, and Pasquier, 1960). Such a series as this is not to be seen in this country. Where small, delicate species of ruminants are concerned, necessarily strict federal importation and quarantine regulations impose risks and costs that are almost prohibitive. However, in spite of these difficulties, gazelles of one sort or another are still to be seen in most of our larger institutions.

Probably best known in captivity of all the gazelles is the dorcas (*G. dorcas*), which, in several races, extends across northern Africa from Río de Oro to Ethiopia and northward through the Sinai peninsula and Palestine to Arabia. This is one of the smaller species, with the shoulder height about 24 inches (Lydekker, 1913–16, 3:68). The general color is very light, the lateral body stripe and the facial markings only faintly indicated; the nasal spot is usually absent. The slender horns of males may reach a length of $13\frac{1}{2}$ inches (Ward, 1922).

Dorcas gazelles are frequently hand-reared in many parts of the range, and as such animals are delightfully tame, they are often brought home by European travelers. For this reason they are commonly seen in European zoological gardens and, to a lesser extent, are sometimes seen in this country. The first specimens to be included in our own collection were a pair received on April 10, 1900, the female of which gave birth to a single calf on August 2, 1904. We have always treated the dorcas as delicate and have provided our specimens with heated quarters at the onset of cool weather. Hagenbeck (1910:208) gives a photograph of dorcas gazelles that "gambolled about at temperatures several degrees below freezing." Concerning the treatment of a male and three females received at the Detroit Zoological Park in 1948, Frank McInnis informs me that the animals were allowed the freedom of a large grassy inclosure until early winter, when temperatures were as low as 20° F. (−6.7° C.). As winter closed in, the gazelles were taken indoors, where the male had to be segregated; in restricted quarters he disturbed the young, a number of which were bred.

The male noted above as having been received here on April 10, 1900, lived until October 15, 1912, or 12 years, 6 months, 5 days. Flower (1931) gives 11 years, 5 months, 8 days for a female in the Giza Zoological Gardens. George H. Pournelle, curator of mammals at the San Diego Zoological Garden, has informed me (*in litt.*) that a specimen of the Isabella gazelle (*G. dorcas isabella*), of Ethiopia, lived at San Diego for 13 years, 6 months, 21 days.

Tallest of the gazelles is *G. dama*, found in several races across the deserts of northern Africa from Senegal to the Sudan. In this species, for which Lydekker (1913–16, **3**:103) gives a shoulder height of 36–37 inches, there is a progressive invasion of the dark areas with white, so that the addra (*G. d. ruficollis*), of the Sudan, is almost entirely white, save for a rufous infusion on the neck and upper back. A pair of addra gazelles received here on May 25, 1925, proved completely amenable and most attractive. The male lived in our Antelope House until July 11, 1937, or 12 years, 1 month, 16 days. Flower (1931) reports that a female of this race, born in the Giza Zoological Gardens in 1912, died in 1923 after 11 years, 1 month, 11 days.

The Persian or goitered gazelle (*G. subgutturosa*) is an Asiatic species, its several races ranging from Asia Minor to the Gobi Desert of Mongolia. The color is rather dark brown, the facial markings and lateral body stripes indistinct. As already noted, the female is exceptional in that the horns are rudimentary or entirely lacking. Males develop a swelling on the throat at the breeding season. This species has bred particularly well in the Zoological Gardens of London, Zuckerman (1953) reporting twenty-three births in that institution between 1875 and 1936, twins occurring about every third birth. Jones (1958) reports a specimen as having lived at London from May 31, 1933, to March 25, 1948, or 14 years, 9 months, 25 days.

Speke's gazelle (*G. spekei*), of the highlands of Somaliland, approximates the dorcas in size and color, with facial and lateral markings darker and a distinct nasal spot. Its chief distinction is a raised, fleshy area on the median line of the face, just above the nostrils. Speke's gazelle is rarely seen in collections, but in the Lincoln Park Zoo, Chicago, where three specimens were still living in 1961, single young were born on May 24, 1958, and November 12, 1959 (Anon., 1960c).

Grant's gazelle (*G. granti*) is a comparatively large animal, its shoulder height being about 34 inches (Lydekker, 1913–16, 3:86). Five subspecies, ranging from the plains of Kenya northward to the Sudan and Ethiopia, are listed by Allen (1939). The general color is light brown, with the usual facial markings and a dark nasal spot. There is a large white caudal disk, bordered in front by a dark perpendicular line; the lateral stripe of the body varies in distinctness. The lyrate horns are the largest among the gazelles; Ward (1922) gives 30 inches for a specimen of the typical race from Kenya and a spread of $36\frac{1}{2}$ inches for *G. g. robertsi* of Tanganyika. Grant's gazelle has never been kept here but it has done well and bred at the San Diego Zoological Garden (Anon., 1960d).

Thomson's gazelle (*G. thomsonii*), ubiquitous resident of the plains of East Africa, ranges, in four races (Allen, 1939), from Kenya to the Sudan. It is among the smallest of the gazelles, with a shoulder height of about 25 inches (Lydekker, 1913–16, 3:84). The facial markings are typical, including a black mark on the nose; the lateral body stripe is usually well developed but the markings bordering the tail are narrow or sometimes absent. The "Tommy" is among the most familiar of the plains antelopes of East Africa; Swynnerton (1958) considers that in the Serengeti area of Tanganyika it is exceeded in abundance only by the wildebeest. The first Thomson's gazelles to be kept here were received in 1960, with additional arrivals in 1961, all in the hope that a going herd might be established. That this is possible is shown by experience at London's Whipsnade Park, where in each of the years from 1951 to 1960 from one to five Thomson's gazelles were born, as recorded in the *Annual Report* of the Zoological Society of London for those years. Of three young born in our own herd in 1962, two were fully reared, as were three born in 1963. A male of the Sudan race (*G. t. albonotatus*) is reported by Flower (1931) to have lived in the Giza Zoological Gardens for 9 years, 9 months, 11 days and still alive.

Our most extensive experience with gazelles here has been with the Arabian (*G. gazella arabica*), from the Sinai peninsula and Arabia. It is comparable to the dorcas in size but is darker in color, with the body stripe and dark nasal spot well marked. A young male and two females, all completely tame, reached us on October 31, 1950, as the gifts of Dr. and Mrs. Frank J. Zukowski, of Beirut, Lebanon, the animals having derived from Saudi Arabia. They readily accepted the usual diet of alfalfa hay, feeding pellets, greens, and vegetables, and appeared to be thriving. However, in early March, 1951, symptoms of acute rickets developed, and within a few days all had died. We attributed this to an undersupply of calcium and vitamin D, a situation often confronting young ruminants confined indoors in winter and presumably especially dangerous for desert species. Following this loss, Dr. and Mrs. Zukowski set about obtaining replacements, as described by Mrs. Zukowski (1951). The duplicate shipment reached us on July 12, 1951, and this time a supplement of fine bone meal and cod-liver oil was added to the previous diet. It is true that many ruminants will reject food containing either or both of these items, but the young gazelles took it freely. The supplement was discontinued in the spring of 1952, when the animals were placed in an outdoor inclosure, no indication of rickets having appeared. At the approach of autumn an unheated shelter, the entrance provided with a wind-baffle, was made available and here the gazelles wintered well, using the shelter only when temperatures were well below the freezing point or when snow was deep. Eleven young were born to this trio or their descendants, ten in March, one in June. Two instances of twinning occurred, with one birth of triplets. The latter were born on March 24, 1955, and one, a female, picked up and reared by hand, was still living in 1963. A female born here on March 16, 1953, gave birth to a normal calf on March 28, 1954, when she was just over 1 year old.

The springbok (*Antidorcas marsupialis*) is closely allied to the gazelles and, in fact, represents that group in South Africa. It is intermediate in size, with a shoulder height of 31–32 inches (Lydekker, 1913–16, 3:111). In color it is reddish brown, with a dark lateral band on the body and less distinct stripes on the hips. The face is white, with dark lines on the sides and sometimes with a brown mark on the forehead. The most striking character is a patch of erectile white hairs on the lower back adjoining the extensive white area surrounding the tail. The underparts and the inner surfaces of the legs are white also. The horns, in both sexes, are of the lyrate form seen in *Gazella*. Three races, ranging from the Cape to Angola and the Transvaal, are recognized by Ellerman, Morrison-Scott, and Hayman (1953).

In earlier days the springbok often moved in herds of immense size from one area to another, presumably in search of food or water; such invasions, known as "treks," often involved thousands of animals

(Shortridge, 1934). According to R. C. Bigalke (1958), this phenomenon still occurs periodically in South West Africa, although the herds are
considerably reduced in size. In the Union of South Africa the springbok
appears to be confined largely to the national parks and reserves and to
private farms, where it is found in fair numbers.

While the springbok has been quite generally kept by zoological gardens,
it appears that general experience has not been entirely satisfactory.
Since 1912 fifteen specimens have been received here, and lives have
generally been of short duration, although spans of from 3 to 7 years have
been recorded. Flower (1931) gives 9 years, 11 months, 13 days for a male
in the Zoological Gardens of London. A single calf was born in our own
collection on November 29, 1941, and was fully reared. Breeding successes
with the springbok have been particularly notable at the St. Louis Zoological Park and at the San Diego Zoological Garden, where three single
young were born in July, 1960 (Anon., 1960e). The only statement
regarding the gestation period seems to be that of W. L. Sclater (1900–1901,
1:213) who quotes 171 days in the Zoological Gardens of Cologne.

SUBFAMILY CAPRINAE

Saiga, Goral, Serows, Rocky Mountain Goat, Chamois, Takin, Muskox, Goats, and Sheep

This group is essentially northern in distribution, being represented by
indigenous forms in Europe, Asia, North Africa, and North America only.
Domesticated goats and sheep, of course, are found in most parts of the
world and have frequently become feral. Horns are borne by males of all
species included but are sometimes absent in females. The arrangement
followed here is that of Simpson (1945); nomenclature has been derived
from Ellerman and Morrison-Scott (1951) for Old World forms and from
Hall and Kelson (1959) for those of North America.

The saiga (*Saiga tatarica*) is a thick-bodied, medium-sized animal
with comparatively short legs; Lydekker (1913–16, 3:15) gives the shoulder
height as 30 inches. The trim summer coat is light brown, with indistinct
head markings, and the underparts are whitish; the long, thick hair of
winter is much paler, almost white. The most arresting feature is the great
expansion of the nasal area, which ends in a down-turned, proboscis-like

muzzle in both sexes, giving the creature a most bizarre appearance. The lyrate, amber-colored horns of males have been recorded as reaching a length of 14⅜ inches (Ward, 1922); females are hornless.

The saiga is an animal of the open steppes, moving seasonally to avoid the most severe winter weather or irregularly as the needs for food and water demand. Once abundant from the area of the Volga across southwestern Siberia to western Mongolia, the saiga was hunted so persistently, largely because of the demand for the horns in China, that the great herds became reduced to scattered fragments. However, Bannikov (1958*b*), in discussing the status and biology of the species, says that following prohibition by the Russian Government in 1919 of all hunting of the saiga, there has been a remarkable increase in both distribution and numbers, which he estimates to have reached approximately two million.

In captivity the saiga has never been found fully satisfactory, duration usually being short. Of four specimens that have been received here, the longest survival was 2 years, 8 months, 18 days, while one that arrived at the National Zoological Park on August 26, 1955, lived until September 14, 1959, or 4 years, 19 days. This animal, as a representative of a notably hardy species, was kept out of doors the year round with only an unheated shelter in winter. The principal difficulty with captive saigas appears to be a dietary one, a subject discussed in detail by Mohr (1943), and until the problem has been solved, optimum results can hardly be expected. A list of food plants is given by Bannikov (1958*b*), and the solution may well derive from it. Saigas here have received the usual regimen of alfalfa or clover hay, rolled oats or feeding pellets, and any available greens.

The saiga has occasionally been bred in captivity. Single births occurred in the Zoological Gardens of London in 1956 and 1960, as recorded in the *Annual Report* of the Society for those years and two young were born at the Dallas, Texas, Zoo in 1963. The gestation period is given by Bannikov (1958*b*) as 5 months.

The closely related chiru or Tibetan antelope (*Pantholops hodgsoni*), which lives high on the plateaus of eastern Kashmir and Tibet, appears to have no captivity history. The chiru and the saiga form the tribe Saigini of Simpson (1945).

While the relationships of the members of the four following genera—*Nemorhaedus*, the goral, *Capricornis*, the serows, *Oreamnos*, the Rocky Mountain goat, and *Rupicapra*, the chamois—are not entirely clear, they are assigned by Simpson (1945) to the tribe Rupicaprini and are sometimes known as "goat-antelopes." In all, horns are present in both sexes.

The goral (*Nemorhaedus goral*) is a small, goatlike animal, with a shoulder height of 26–28 inches (Lydekker, 1913–16, 1:204). The several races extend, in mountainous areas, from Kashmir eastward through the Himalayas across China to Korea, Manchuria, and southeastern Siberia. Color varies in shades of brown or gray, with a yellowish throat-patch; dark stripes may mark the back and forelegs. The short, black horns curve slightly backward. The goral has been kept occasionally by European zoological gardens but appears not to have been brought to this country. Flower (1931) reports that two specimens lived in the Zoological Gardens of London for 11 years, 5 months and 17 years, 7 months, 23 days, respectively.

The serow (*Capricornis sumatraensis*) is much larger than the goral, with a shoulder height of up to 37 inches and weight over 200 pounds (Blanford, 1888–91). It is found from the mountains of southern China west to Kashmir and south through Burma and the Malay States to Sumatra. The long, rough coat may vary from black to rufous, the legs being sometimes whitish or reddish. There is a distinct mane, more or less white, as is well shown in photographs of captive specimens by Mohr (1934; 1936). The ears are long, almost donkey-like, and the pointed horns, lightly curved, may reach a length of $12\frac{1}{4}$ inches (Ward, 1922). Like the goral, the serow, in several forms, has been shown rarely in Europe but apparently never in this country.

The Japanese serow (*Capricornis crispus*) is found, typically, in the mountains of Japan, with a race in Formosa. This is a smallish animal, approaching the goral in size. The coat is thick and gray to brown in color with some white about the cheeks and underparts; the mane is less strongly developed. At one time brought close to extinction by overhunting, the Japanese serow has been given complete protection and appears to be recovering (Harper, 1945). Outside Japan the species has been shown at least at the Zoological Gardens of London, where it was received in 1879 (Flower, 1929).

The New World representative of the "goat-antelopes" is the Rocky Mountain goat (*Oreamnos americanus*). In four recognized races (Hall and Kelson, 1959), this distinctive species is found in the high mountain ranges of western North America from southern Alaska and Yukon south through British Columbia and western Alberta to Washington, Idaho, and western Montana. In 1924 six animals from Alberta were taken to the Custer State Park, in the Black Hills of South Dakota, where they were placed in an inclosure. Two soon found their way to liberty, and in 1929 the remaining herd, then increased to eight, also escaped. The new environment proved favorable, for a study made in 1942 showed over two hundred mountain goats in the area (Harmon, 1944). Various other transfers, usually within the natural range, have been made successfully.

The Rocky Mountain goat is a short-bodied animal, with the shoulders noticeably elevated. The thick, woolly undercoat and the long, shaggy guard hairs are white, sometimes with a yellowish tint; both sexes are bearded. Cahalane (1947) gives the shoulder height as 35–40 inches and the weight as up to 300 pounds. The horns of both sexes, each with a bare, black glandular area behind it, are black in color and are curved slightly backward. The greatest horn length listed in the Boone and Crockett Club's *Records of North American Big Game* (1958) is $12\frac{4}{8}$ inches and the widest spread $11\frac{6}{8}$ inches, both for females taken in British Columbia.

Great heights and bare ledges form the natural habitat of the Rocky Mountain goat, which rarely descends to lower levels. It browses extensively on such leafy food as is available and also takes mountain grasses, mosses, and lichens, many specific items being listed by Harmon (1944).

For many years American zoological gardens have striven to establish the Rocky Mountain goat in captivity, but while some encouraging results have been obtained, this purpose has never been fully accomplished. In a general account Grant (1905) says: "In captivity we have had, on the Atlantic Coast, only eight immature specimens, two in Boston in 1899, two in Philadelphia in 1893 and the four now living in the New York Zoological Park. One well grown male is living at this time in the London Zoological Gardens." The latter is presumably the animal listed by Flower (1931) as having lived at London from June 6, 1900, to January 19, 1909, or 8 years, 7 months, 13 days. Since these earlier dates, of course, a fair number of specimens have reached our zoological gardens, and in 1963 two were living in the National Zoological Park and four in the St. George's Island Zoo and Natural History Park, Calgary, Alberta, Canada. A kid was born in the latter group on May 23, 1963.

The Rocky Mountain goat was first received here in 1904, when two kids arrived from British Columbia on October 23 (Anon., 1905). These animals were placed on our Mountain Sheep Hill, where they failed to thrive, neither quite living the year out. On March 18, 1905, another young pair arrived from the same locality, followed by five more in October of the same year. A valuable account of the capture and rearing of the latter animals as very young kids in May, 1905, is given by Chapman (1910). This time the mountain goats were kept in a wired inclosure paved with asphalt, about 75 feet in each dimension, with an unheated rustic shelter attached. The roof of this structure provided a playground for the goats, access being furnished by a series of ramps (illustrated in Anon., 1907).

The diet used consisted of clover and alfalfa hay, rolled oats, diced raw white potatoes, carrots, and apples, with fresh browse as available. The animals thrived under this treatment, and on May 20, 1908, a vigorous kid was born, presumably the first instance of captivity breeding. I find among my notes an entry made in August, 1908: "The kid, which is now nearly three months old, and strong and vigorous, is the first to be born in captivity." My optimism concerning the young animal's vigor proved well founded, for it was fully reared by the mother. The gestation period was 4 days less than 6 months, the shoulder height of the kid was $13\frac{1}{2}$ inches, and its weight was $7\frac{1}{4}$ pounds (Anon., 1908). A further note of special interest records the general belief that the mountain goat should never be exposed to rain because of the presumed difficulty of drying a saturated coat. In any case, I can certify that our goats were never allowed to become thoroughly wet, their keeper often returning at night to make certain that they were indoors when there was a sudden threat of rain.

Further single births of mountain goats occurred here on June 8, 1910, and May 30, 1911. Both kids, like the first, were safely reared. Hollister (1921) records the birth of a mountain goat in the National Zoological Park on May 20, 1921, while Mann (1930) says that two births occurred in that institution, one of the kids having been reared on the bottle following the death of its mother.

In addition to the specimens already mentioned, eleven further mountain goats have been received here, the last a single female that arrived on January 26, 1928. For some reason, this female achieved our best longevity for the species, having completed 9 years, 5 months, 26 days here when she died on July 22, 1937. Jones (1958) lists a specimen as having lived in the National Zoological Park from February 11, 1923, to May 20, 1934, or 11 years, 3 months, 9 days.

The chamois (*Rupicapra rupicapra*) is famous in legend and in fact for its sure-footed ability in leaping from crag to crag in the mountain fastnesses where it makes its home. Nine races listed by Ellerman and Morrison-Scott (1951) are found in the great ranges of Europe from Spain east to the Caucasus of southeastern Russia. The typical coloration in summer is reddish brown, the winter coat being much darker; there is a whitish patch on the throat and there may be more or less distinct light facial markings as well as a dark dorsal band. The shoulder height is given by Lydekker (1913–16, 1:181) as about 32 inches. Horns, in both sexes, rise almost vertically, then hook sharply downward and backward; the greatest length recorded by Ward (1922) is $12\frac{5}{8}$ inches for a female specimen. There is no beard in either sex.

While the chamois has been maintained in zoological gardens for reasonably long periods, it has never become firmly established and is commonly kept only in some institutions of Continental Europe. Even there most of the specimens observed have seemed not well adapted to their new surroundings. Single animals received here in 1902 and 1904 were fed clover and alfalfa hay, rolled oats, diced vegetables, and greens, but one lived for only just over 2 years, the other for 4 years, 3 months, 20 days. The species has not been tried here since that time. Mann (1930) says that two young were bred from a herd of five received at the National Zoological Park in 1909 as the gift of the Swiss Government; this appears to be the only breeding record for the chamois in this country. Births in Europe, of course, have been more frequent, Zuckerman (1953) reporting five such occurrences in the Zoological Gardens of London between 1864 and 1911. Gestation periods quoted by Kenneth (1953) range from a low average of 153 days to a maximum of 210 days. Mann (1930) reports a chamois as having lived 5 years, 11 months in the National Zoological Park, while Flower (1931) lists the following records for European Zoological Gardens: Basel, 13 years, 7 months, 21 days; London, 15 years, 8 months, 1 day, and the Jardin des Plantes, Paris, 16 years, 10 months, 19 days.

The takin (*Budorcas taxicolor*), sometimes considered as a member of the "goat-antelope" group, is included by Simpson (1945) in the tribe Ovibovini, along with the muskox (*Ovibos moschatus*). The takin is a heavy, stout-bodied, short-coupled animal with high shoulders and comparatively short legs. It lives in mountainous areas of southeastern Asia, often above tree line, from Bhutan northeastward to Shensi in central China. In the typical race, found at the western end of the range, the coloration is largely blackish, the back, save for a dark dorsal stripe, being grizzled brown. The Szechwan race, *B. taxicolor tibetana*, is much more yellowish in color, while in *B. t. bedfordi*, from Shensi, sometimes known as the golden takin, the dark markings have almost entirely disappeared, leaving the animal largely yellow or buffy. For the typical race, Lydekker (1913–16, 1:217) gives the shoulder height as about $3\frac{1}{2}$ feet. Allen (1938, 1940) quotes the weights of two males of the golden takin as 435 and 635 pounds, respectively. The heavy horns, in both sexes, grow outward from the head, then backward and slightly inward at the tip. The greatest length given by Ward (1922) is $23\frac{1}{4}$ inches measured on the outer curve, for a male of the typical race.

Heavy and cumbersome though the takin may be, it is agile enough in negotiating steep mountainsides and sufficiently powerful to force its way through tangled thickets of bamboo and rhododendron. The takin is a social animal, living in small herds and feeding on both foliage and grass (Allen, 1938, 1940).

Up to 1959 the only living takins known to have left Asia were two specimens received at the Zoological Gardens of London. The first, a male, reached that institution on June 22, 1909, and lived until May 7, 1918; the second, a female, arrived on January 26, 1923 (Flower, 1929), and is stated by van Bemmel (1959) to have died in 1935. The male was assigned to *B. t. whitei*, a race now considered to be of questionable standing; subspecific designation of the female is not given. Seen several times in November and December of 1912, the male was in excellent condition and appeared to me to be indifferent to the cold drizzle likely to prevail in London at that season. Pang-Chieh (1957) briefly describes and figures a male golden takin (*B. t. bedfordi*) shown at the Peking Zoological Park in 1957.

On October 30, 1959, the first takin to reach America was received here. After 60 days in quarantine at Hamburg, Germany, and 30 days more at the port of New York, she still was strong and sturdy. Captured in the Mishmi foothills on the north Burma border by Burmese villagers in July, 1958, while very young, she was found running with the local cattle in the capacity of village pet by Oliver M. B. Milton, leader of the Burma Wild-life Survey team, and with the co-operation of the Kachin State Government was finally secured for us (Estes, 1959). With great difficulty the animal was transported to the Zoo at Rangoon and finally to Hamburg (Milton, 1959). On arrival here one horn was found to have been damaged, but by 1963 this had been almost entirely corrected by continuing growth. "Gracie" was perfectly tame and gentle, seeming to welcome human companionship. However, she eventually became too frolicsome for the comfort of her keepers, who had some difficulty in avoiding her apparently well-intended demonstrations. Placed in one of the yards of our Antelope House, she was quickly at home and made no effort to scale the 8-foot fences, although while in quarantine at Athenia, New Jersey, she was reported to have negotiated a stall wall 9 feet high. During the first summer a water spray was provided in Gracie's stall and she spent much time under it. Later, an air conditioner was installed and the pen was inclosed in heavy Plexiglas, so that in really hot weather the temperature could be held between 60° and 70°F. (approximately 15.5° and 21°C.). A small hut erected for winter shelter went unused; she has remained out of doors through the most severe weather, only occasionally seeking the protection of the overhanging eaves of the building. Her food here has consisted of from 8 to 10 pounds of alfalfa hay, about 3 pounds of feeding pellets, and rolled oats, bananas, apples, carrots, sweet potatoes, cabbage, and fresh foliage, especially that of Russian mulberry, when available.

The muskox (*Ovibos moschatus*) is a sturdy, heavily haired animal, well adapted for survival in the frozen wastes in which it lives. Once found across the Arctic and subarctic regions of North America from Alaska to Hudson Bay and northeastward through the islands to northern Greenland, its range has now become greatly restricted. Tener (1958) says that in 1917, when protection was established by the Canadian Government, only scattered remnant populations still existed on the mainland, largely in the Thelon Game Sanctuary, northeast of Great Slave Lake, and in an area south of Coronation Bay, farther to the west. At the time of his writing, the mainland population was estimated to be fifteen hundred and that of the islands where the animals still existed about thirty-five hundred. In Greenland distribution extends northward on the eastern coast from above 70° N., then west along the northern coast and south on the western side to about 81° N. (Miller and Kellogg, 1955). Vibe (1958) considers muskoxen in Greenland to number between five and ten thousand, their increase, despite Government protection, being limited by the climate, which permits frequent icing of the feeding grounds with resulting starvation of the animals.

Typically, the muskox is dark brown above, with the underparts nearly black. There is usually a light-colored saddle, and the legs are white. The underwool is soft and dense, the outer coat long and stringy, often touching the ground and hiding the rudimentary tail. Horns, in both sexes, grow out and down, recurving sharply at the tips, and with thickened bosses, particularly in males, at their bases. The greatest length of horn recorded in the Boone and Crockett Club's *Records of North American Big Game* (1958) is 29 inches for a male from the Northwest Territories, Canada.

Three races are currently recognized (Hall and Kelson, 1959): the Barren Ground muskox (*O. m. moschatus*), which once occupied most of the mainland area already noted, now greatly restricted; the Hudson Bay muskox (*O. m. niphoecus*), a dark form found in northeastern Keewatin, and the white-fronted muskox (*O. m. wardi*), paler in color and with varying amounts of white about the head and face, that inhabits the Arctic islands, from many of which it has disappeared, and the regions of Greenland already outlined. Average shoulder heights are given by Pedersen (1958) as 1.45 meters (approximately 57 inches) for the male of the typical race and from 1.10 meters (approximately 43 inches) to 1.30 meters (approximately 51 inches) for males of *O. m. wardi*. Actual weights have seldom been recorded and are usually given as 500–900 pounds (Cahalane, 1947). A male white-fronted that had lived here for nearly 8 years weighed 360 pounds, and a female of the same race, after 5 years here, weighed 260 pounds, both at death.

In the hope of re-establishing the muskox in Alaska, from which it had long since been extirpated, an appropriation of $40,000 was granted by Congress in 1930 for the purpose. Following this action, Johs. Lund of Norway was commissioned to secure a group of white-fronted muskoxen in Greenland, and on September 15, 1930, thirty-four animals arrived safely in New York. After completion of a quarantine period at Athenia, New Jersey, they were forwarded to Seattle by train and traveled by ship to College, Alaska, where they arrived on November 4. A detailed account of the capture, care and transportation of the herd is given by Bell (1931). The muskoxen were liberated in a large inclosure providing suitable seasonal feeding grounds. In following years a number of young were born, but several animals were killed by bears or died from disease. In 1935 four were removed to Nunivak Island, in the Bering Sea off the Alaskan coast, and in the next year they were joined by the twenty-seven that had remained at College. Jackson (1958), in recounting the experiment, considers it to have been fully successful, a total of seventy-six animals, including seven calves, having been counted by airplane in 1951.

The muskox is a social animal, living in herds of a dozen or more. Its habit of forming rings of adults facing outward with calves inside as a method of defense is well known. The species is non-migratory, although it does move seasonally between the lowlands where it spends the summer and the higher levels where it winters. Since on the wind-swept heights the snow lies less deeply, the broad hoofs are better able to expose the dry vegetation that forms the meager winter fare. General food items include grasses, sedges, and lichens, as well as the foliage and twigs of willows, birches, and numerous leafy plants, as given in detail by Hone (1934).

The history of the muskox in captivity is much more brief than might be supposed. Writing just before the close of the last century, Lydekker (1898b) expresses belief that up to that time the muskox had not been brought alive to Europe and adds the impression that, in any case, it could not endure transportation from its "icy home." However, in the following year two male calves collected on the east coast of Greenland by a Swedish Arctic expedition reached Europe safely. Hornaday (1902) states that one of these animals went to Woburn Abbey, the other to the Zoological Gardens of Berlin. However, Flower (1939) says, "Two young male Musk-oxen from Claverling Island, East Greenland, were alive at Woburn in 1899," and Hastings, Duke of Bedford (1949), mentions two male calves as having lived at Woburn, one for a few months only, the other to maturity, adding that the latter was a "very bad tempered animal." In any case, there appears to be no doubt that in the words of Dr. Hornaday, "these specimens were the first to reach civilization alive."

On March 22, 1902, a muskox presumed to be the first living example received in this country arrived at the New York Zoological Park. This animal, a female, was the survivor of four calves captured in March, 1901, 30 miles from the shore of the Arctic Ocean, north of Great Bear Lake, Mackenzie Territory, by a party sent out by Captain H. H. Bodfish of the wintering whaler "Beluga." Unfortunately, three of the calves were killed by sledge dogs, but the fourth finally reached San Francisco safely and eventually came to us as the gift of the Hon. William C. Whitney (Hornaday, 1902). No other representative of the Barren Ground race has so far been received here. Placed in an inclosure on our Mountain Sheep Hill, with a rock shelter cooled by ice during hot weather, and fed clover hay, crushed oats, vegetables, and freshly cut grass, she appeared to be thriving but died on August 16, 1902, after less than 5 months here.

On September 21, 1902, this animal was replaced by another female, this time a white-fronted, brought from Greenland by Commander Robert E. Peary and presented to us by the Peary Arctic Club. Unfortunately, her stay here was even more brief than that of her predecessor, for she died on the following October 25 from injuries received in a fall from the rocks in her inclosure. A third female, also a white-fronted, collected on Melville Island by Captain Joseph E. Bernier in the summer of 1909, was received here on November 17, 1909. This animal provided our first successful experience with muskoxen, for it lived until May 15, 1915, or 5 years, 5 months, 28 days.

In 1910 the Arctic expedition conducted by Paul J. Rainey collected six young white-fronted muskoxen, four males and two females, on Ellesmere Island and presented them to us on September 10. According to Bridges (1939), these calves were lassoed while the adults were held at bay by dogs, so that no serious damage was done. These young animals were placed in an inclosure adjacent and similar to that already described for Rocky Mountain goats, although the wire fencing was reinforced with horizontal steel bars. One calf, injured in capturing, survived for only a few months, but the others lived for periods of from 3 years to just over 7. They were fed the established diet of clover hay, crushed oats, cut vegetables, greens, and available browse. As in the case of the Rocky Mountain goats, they never were allowed to become thoroughly wet, their keeper taking great pains to see that this was avoided. In spring, when the thick undercoat is shed, this was carefully combed out as it loosened, although this was a process requiring some caution because of the unpredictable dispositions of the animals.

On January 3, 1921, we received a young pair of white-fronted musk-oxen from Greenland, shipped to us by Johs. Lund, of Norway, noted above as the supplier of the animals for the successful Alaskan experiment of 1930. This pair lived only about 18 months, but a further shipment of two males and three females that reached us from Mr. Lund on November 14, 1922, produced the best results so far obtained here with this species. All these animals lived for from 3 years upward, the survivor, a male, dying on September 20, 1930, after 7 years, 10 months, 6 days, the best longevity recorded here. On September 5 and September 14, 1925, single calves were born to two of the females, presumably the first muskoxen to have been bred in captivity. Neither mother appeared to lactate normally, and in spite of all efforts to save them, including the services of a nursing goat, the first calf lived for only 3 days, the second for 4. The latter measured 18 inches at the shoulder and weighed 16 pounds (Hornaday, 1925, illus.; 1926). According to Pedersen (1958), muskoxen in Greenland breed in July and August, the majority of births occurring in April and May, after a gestation period of about $8\frac{1}{2}$ months.

Our efforts to establish the muskox firmly in captivity continued with the importation of two pairs from Mr. Lund in October, 1929, and the purchase of a further two pairs lassoed in Greenland by Captain Bob Bartlett and received here on September 14, 1939. Most of these animals seemed to thrive but none survived for more than 4 years. Up to 1963, no resumption of these experiments had been undertaken.

At the present time (1963) no muskox is known to be living in an American zoological garden, although small herds of the Barren Ground race are kept by A. F. Oeming of the Alberta Game Farm, Edmonton, Alberta, and John J. Teale, Jr., of Huntington Center, Vermont, both in co-operation with the Canadian Wild Life Service. A calf born at the Alberta farm on June 6, 1962, was thriving on July 17, 1962, in the mother's care (A. F. Oeming, *in litt.*).*

Andersen and Poulsen (1958) give an account of muskoxen in the Zoological Gardens of Copenhagen from 1900 on, with details concerning a young pair received in August, 1954, from Danish meteorological stations in eastern Greenland. The male of this pair was still living at Copenhagen in 1963. This animal and a second male received at Copenhagen in 1960

*See Addenda, p. 738.

and transferred to the Zoological Gardens of Antwerp (Argus, 1961; Gijzen, 1961) appear to be the only muskoxen presently living in European zoological gardens.

That muskoxen have not so far given entirely satisfactory results in captivity must be admitted. Buckley, Spencer, and Adams (1954) report recovery of the body of a female muskox floating off Nunivak Island, Alaska, in late May, 1953. This animal bore an ear-tag indicating that she had been born in Greenland in the spring of 1930. On the presumption that she had died during the winter of 1952–53, her age at death would have been nearly 23 years. In the light of this natural span, captivity records indicate that, although some progress has been made, full possibilities have not yet been realized. Flower (1931) gives 10 years, 2 months, 1 day for a muskox in the Zoological Gardens of London, and Jones (1958) lists 11 years, 3 months, 23 days for an animal that died in the same institution in 1936. Mohr (1951) says that of a pair of muskoxen received in Boston from Greenland in 1925, the male lived 11 years, 6 months, 12 days, the female 14 years, 9 months, 9 days. Russell L. Grant, assistant director of the Franklin Park Zoological Gardens, has informed me (*in litt.*) that these animals were received at Boston from Greenland via Norway on February 7, 1925, the male living to August, 1936, the female to November 16, 1939, thus confirming Dr. Mohr's figures. Miss Hattie Ettinger, administrative assistant at the St. Louis Zoological Park, advises me (*in litt.*) that a female muskox received there on October 24, 1924, died on July 27, 1941, after 16 years, 9 months, 3 days, apparently the greatest longevity so far recorded for a captive animal of this species.

The goats and sheep form a natural group designated by Simpson (1945) as the tribe Caprini. Distribution is confined to the mountainous regions of Europe, Asia, North Africa, and western North America, sheep alone occurring in the latter area. Horns, generally massive, are borne by males of all species but may be present or absent in females. Mammary nipples are usually two, although there appears to be an exception in the case of the tahr (*Hemitragus*), in which, according to Lydekker (1913–16, 1:174), there are four. So closely are the goats and sheep related that assignment of some intermediate species is more or less arbitrary. Distinctions between the typical genera, *Capra*, the goats, and *Ovis*, the sheep, are listed by Ellerman and Morrison-Scott (1951:412). There are a number of anatomical differences in the skull, but the most obvious are that male goats have the chin bearded while sheep do not and that goats lack the gland below the eye, present in sheep. In *Capra* the horns curve backward in scimitar form, often with knobs on the forward edges, or spiral upward, while in *Ovis* they turn along the sides of the head, points directed slightly outward or twisting more or less widely. A further characteristic, unlikely to be missed, is the strong odor of male goats, not noticeable in sheep.

Rather curiously, while goats and sheep of many forms when mated with others within their own groups have produced fertile hybrids or intergrades, no instance of successful crossing of goats and sheep is listed by A. P. Gray (1954). In matings between domestic goats and sheep it has been found that while conception frequently occurs, young have not been known to reach full term (Warwick and Berry, 1949). The explanation probably lies in the disparity in the chromosome count, which Berry (1938) gives as 60 for the domestic goat, 54 for the domestic sheep, and 57 for hybrids, all for cells from the amniotic tissues of 30-day embryos.

Both goats and sheep are basically gregarious in habit. They frequent mountainous areas, in these days usually remote, the goats being more venturesome than sheep in resorting to the higher crags and escarpments. Principal food items include grasses, either fresh or dried, the foliage of trees and shrubs, various alpine plants, and even lichens. Domesticated descendants of both groups are valuable as producers of food and clothing.

Principal quarters for goats and sheep here are a series of six inclosures, each 50 by 100 feet, known as Sheep Hill. Along one side of this installation there is a beautiful, glacially scored rock outcrop, from the base of which the terrain slopes sharply to a lower level, originally grassy. Cavelike shelters of stone have been blended with the natural formation, although it seems probable that more simple, uninclosed overhangs might have served the purpose better. Fencing is of woven wire netting, the mesh running from 3 by 6 inches at the bottom to 5 by 6 inches at the top, partitions being double with a separation of 3 feet. This netting, strung between steel posts set in concrete at intervals of 10 feet over a base of stone, is only 7 feet, 6 inches high. There is no overhang, but in spite of the well-known jumping ability of both goats and sheep (Hediger [1955a] says that in an emergency an ibex can clear a fence 12 feet high), I cannot recall an instance in which an animal has leaped over these barriers. This is in accord with common experience indicating that while many animals may attempt to surmount solid obstacles, such as walls, the impulse seems to be baffled by one through which they can see, especially if the upper limit is not heavily marked.

Food items used here for both goats and sheep include alfalfa hay and feeding pellets, as described under "Cervidae" (p. 559). In addition, fresh vegetables, especially white potatoes and carrots, and greens, such as cabbage and lettuce, are fed as available. Because both goats and sheep seem especially susceptible to invasions of internal parasites, salt blocks containing phenothiazine are always available. In addition, regular fecal examinations are made by the veterinarian, so that further steps may be taken if this medication proves to be not fully effective.

This brings up the question of proper footing for inclosures used for these animals in order to keep the risk of parasitism at the minimum. General experience has shown that, as pointed out by Meyer-Holzapfel (1958), the area should be floored with stone, concrete, or asphalt so that it can be thoroughly flushed and drained, with no remaining pools of water. Results with our own Sheep Hill serve well to emphasize this necessity. While the higher parts are entirely suitable, the lower levels cannot be fully drained, so that hosing is not practical. It is to this condition that we attribute the impossibility, at least in the past, of using the installation for many of the species for which it was intended. Rather recently, crushed stone to a depth of 6 inches has been spread over the lower sections, and while this is less effective than a permanent surface would be, it enables us to maintain some species that previously could not be kept in these inclosures. In our experience, the aoudad (*Ammotragus lervia*) and the Himalayan tahr (*Hemitragus jemlahicus*) have proved highly resistant to parasitism, the mouflon (*Ovis musimon*) somewhat less so. On the other hand, all the goats of the genus *Capra* and all the sheep except those noted, as well as the Rocky Mountain goat (*Oreamnos*) and the muskox (*Ovibos*), have been really successful here only on paved surfaces.

There are other methods than ours, of course, for exhibiting goats and sheep. Among the more spectacular is one to be seen in the Parc Zoologique du Bois de Vincennes, Paris. A beautifully fashioned pinnacle of concrete 350 feet high, serving as a water tower, dominates the area. Well above the base a sharply pitched, inserted plateau provides space for a herd of aoudads which are visible, to great effect, for considerable distances.

A simulated mountain of rock or concrete surrounded by a dry or water-filled moat is frequently used and has great popular appeal. A structure of this sort, used for aoudads in the Detroit Zoological Park at Royal Oak, Michigan, has a moat wall 9 feet high, the exhibit floor sloping to its base from a point about 15 feet back. In the Zoological Gardens of Buffalo, New York, a similar installation accommodates a herd of tahr living peacefully with a number of red and silver foxes. All these exhibits are provided with hard floors and all are highly successful.

Only two genera are included in the group commonly designated as goats: *Hemitragus*, the tahrs, and *Capra*, the true goats, ibexes, and markhors. The tahrs, of which three species are listed by Ellerman and Morrison-Scott (1951), lack the beard of the more typical goats, but the characteristic odor is produced by males. The only member of the genus ordinarily seen in zoological gardens is the Himalayan tahr (*H. jemlahicus*), found in the middle ranges of the Himalayas from Kashmir to Sikkim. This is a narrow-faced, stout-bodied animal with rather long, rough coat and a heavy mane, in males, on shoulders, throat, and chest. The general coloration is brownish gray, sometimes appearing nearly black in adult males. The short, laterally compressed horns curve backward, those of females nearly equaling those of males. Shoulder height is given by Lydekker (1913–16, 1:174) as 36–40 inches.

The Himalayan tahr has been fully successful here, a going herd having been maintained continuously since the importation of a single female in 1901 and a pair in 1902, all from Carl Hagenbeck. These animals bred prolifically, and their young have been distributed widely in this country as well as in Europe. No new blood was added until a male was obtained in 1922, again from the Hagenbecks. Further additions were made from 1940 on, mostly of animals descended from our own stock. Up to 1961 a total of 181 had been born here, as follows: May, 31; June, 103; July, 38; August, 8; September, 1. These birth periods are in accord with those of Zuckerman (1953), who reports 115 births in the Zoological Gardens of London as having occurred from May to October, with the greatest number in June and early July. He adds that twins were born in each 12 births, but only one pair has been definitely recorded here. Hodgson, cited by Blanford (1888–91), gives the gestation period as 6 months. Tahr kids are usually vigorous and easily reared by their mothers. Adult males here have been less tolerant of others of the same sex than is usual in this group.

The greatest longevity of a Himalayan tahr recorded by Flower (1931) is 16 years, 11 months, 16 days for a female in the Zoological Gardens of London. A male born in our own collection in 1905 lived until June 10, 1925, or approximately 20 years. Jones (1958) lists a specimen as having lived in the National Zoological Park from August 2, 1919, to January 29, 1940, or 20 years, 5 months, 27 days.

The genus *Capra*, the characteristics of which have already been noted, includes the goats, ibexes, and markhors. There appear to be six valid species (Ellerman and Morrison-Scott, 1951; Allen, 1939), distributed in Europe, Asia, and northern Africa. In all, males are bearded and odorous; horns are borne by both sexes, those of females usually being smaller than those of males.

Typical of the goats is the domestic animal, to which Linnaeus in 1758 assigned the name *Capra hircus*. Widely spread in domestication and feral in many areas, the common goat is found in most parts of the habitable world. The Persian wild goat (*Capra h. aegagrus*) of the Greek islands (notably Crete), Asia Minor, Persia, and the Caucasus, is believed to be the ancestor of the domestic breeds. A smaller race, *Capra h. blythi*, ranges westward to Baluchistan and Sind. The body color is reddish brown, grayer in winter, with the underparts white; the dorsal stripe, a collar across the shoulders, the chest, and the fronts of the legs are dark brown approaching black. Horns are of the scimitar type, with narrow front edges and the terminal portion knobbed. Ward (1922) gives the greatest length of horn for *C. h. aegagrus* as 55½ inches and the shoulder height as 37 inches.

Once well known in zoological gardens, the Persian wild goat is now seldom seen in captivity. The only specimens living in this country in 1963 were a pair at the Catskill Game Farm, New York. Examples of this race were first received in our own collection on June 16, 1908, when a male and two females were obtained. Eleven young were born, ten in April, one in May. Two pairs of twins were included. Jennison (n.d.) gives the gestation period as 150 days. A female of the original trio lived until August 22, 1917, or 9 years, 2 months, 6 days. Jones (1958) lists a specimen as having lived in the Zoological Gardens of London from April 27, 1913, to January 29, 1934, or 20 years, 9 months, 2 days.

In the ibexes (*Capra ibex*) the horns of males sweep backward in a great semicircle, their forward surfaces broad, with heavy transverse knobs. Four races are listed by Ellerman and Morrison-Scott (1951) as ranging from North Africa to central Asia, always, of course, in high mountainous areas. Three of these forms are well known in captivity: the European or Alpine ibex (*Capra i. ibex*), the Siberian or Asiatic ibex (*Capra i. sibirica*), and the Nubian ibex (*Capra i. nubiana*). The Abyssinian ibex (*Capra walie*) of north-central Ethiopia, listed by Allen (1939) as a full species, seems to have no captivity history.

The European ibex is brownish gray, the underparts darker. Lydekker (1913–16, 1:141) gives the shoulder height as 32–34 inches; the greatest length of horn on the outer curve listed by Ward (1922) is 34½ inches.

Once common in the Alps of central Europe, particularly in Switzerland, Austria, and Italy, the European ibex was so constantly pursued by sportsmen that by the sixteenth century it had become greatly reduced in numbers (Lydekker, 1898b). Eventually, only a protected herd in the Parco Nazionale del Gran Paradiso in the Italian Alps and a few scattered animals elsewhere remained. During the present century, introductions into Switzerland and Austria have been made successfully, activities with which the Zoological Gardens of Berne and Schönbrunn have been associated (Meyer-Holzapfel, 1958; Antonius, 1929).

The European ibex has never been kept here but has been exhibited by several other institutions in this country, including the National Zoological Park, the Philadelphia Zoological Garden, and the Chicago Zoological Park. A male and two females at the Catskill Game Farm, New York, produced one kid in 1960 and two in 1961, all living together in the latter year. Meyer-Holzapfel (1958) reports forty-six births in the Zoological Gardens of Berne between 1938 and 1957, forty-two of which occurred between May 21 and June 16, four between June 22 and July 5. Asdell (1946) gives the gestation period as 150–80 days. Antonius (1929) says that two females in the Schönbrunn Zoological Gardens, Vienna, were destroyed at the age of 17 years because of senility.

The Siberian or Asiatic ibex is the largest and finest of the forms of this species, Lydekker (1913–16, 1:143) giving the shoulder height as about 42 inches. The body color is in shades of brown, varying seasonally; there is a dark dorsal stripe and sometimes a pale saddle. The outer hair is long and coarse but there is a dense woolly undercoat, much sought for the weaving of cloth. The greatest length of the massive horns listed by Ward (1922) is 55 inches on the front curve. Distribution is in the great mountain ranges of Asia, from Afghanistan east to central Siberia.

The Siberian ibex has long been greatly sought by zoological gardens and has been kept and bred by many, although it seems never to have become firmly established. The best results in this country were those obtained by the St. Louis Zoological Park, where this animal was kept and bred for a number of years before finally running out. In 1961 the largest stock in America was at the Catskill Game Farm, New York, where three adult pairs with two kids of the year were living together on a high cliff of shale.

The first Siberian ibex received here was a male purchased from Carl Hagenbeck in 1902, followed in the next year by a female that had been born in the Zoological Gardens of Berlin. These animals, quartered on our Sheep Hill, failed to thrive. The female of a second pair, obtained in 1940, produced a kid on June 29, 1942, but both mother and young died during the same year. The male, in poor condition due to a heavy infestation of internal parasites, was removed to a high, well-drained inclosure in another area. Here the parasites yielded promptly to treatment but quickly revived when the animal was returned to his former quarters. The transfer was soon repeated, and the ibex lived healthily for seven years in the smaller but more suitable yard. Our present group, consisting of an adult pair and a kid born in June, 1960, seems to be maintaining good health on the reconditioned Sheep Hill.

The greatest longevity so far reported for a captive Siberian ibex appears to be 22 years, 3 months, 19 days, as listed by Flower (1931) for a female in the Zoological Gardens of London.

The Nubian ibex is considerably smaller than the Siberian, with a shoulder height of about 33 inches (Lydekker, 1913–16, 1:153). It is, however, a spectacular animal, for the slender, well-knobbed horns may reach a length of 46⅛ inches (Ward, 1922). The body color is brown, with dorsal stripe, throat, chest, and outer surfaces of legs black, the underparts white. A white band around each leg, just above the hoofs, is distinctive. Distribution is from the mountains of Nubia and Upper Egypt to Arabia.

The race has never been represented here and appears to be uncommon in European collections, though it is maintained at the Khartoum Zoological Gardens. There are at least two strong breeding herds in this country, one at the Catskill Game Farm, New York, and a larger group at the Cleveland Zoological Park, Ohio. Dr. L. J. Goss, director at Cleveland, has been good enough to supply me with an account of this herd which on November 4, 1961, numbered seventeen animals. Of two pairs received on January 17, 1955, one male was kept in reserve and died in 1959 from accidental injuries. The three others were placed in a wire-inclosed area approximately 275 by 225 feet, the terrain consisting principally of a high, steep embankment of shale, topped by a small, fully drained plateau of the same formation. The only shelter provided was an open-fronted shed to which the animals resorted during stormy weather. The diet was composed of alfalfa hay and commercial feeding pellets, eked out in autumn with considerable quantities of falling leaves. Each female produced a kid in 1956, the number of annual births gradually increasing thereafter as the young females matured. Up to 1961 a total of twenty-eight young were born, as follows: March, nine; April, thirteen; May, two, with one each in June, July, September, and October. Most of these kids were fully reared, the total being reduced by occasional losses and releases to other institutions. While twinning was suspected in a number of cases, only one instance was confirmed. On November 4, 1961, the herd consisted of ten males and seven females, but a more suitable ratio in the breeding herd was established by the removal of several of the males.

In the Spanish ibex (*Capra pyrenaica*) the flattened, cross-ridged horns rise from the forehead and flare outward then backward over the neck in a partial spiral, the tips rising. Four races have been recognized from the mountains of Spain and Portugal (Ellerman and Morrison-Scott, 1951), but of these, two are considered to have become extinct and the third greatly reduced, only *Capra p. hispanica* still existing in some numbers in scattered areas of southern Spain (Harper, 1945). The typical coloration is light brown, the males having dorsal stripe, beard, chest, and outer surfaces of legs black and a dark line on the sides above the white of the underparts; females and young are less distinctly marked. The shoulder height is given by Lydekker (1913–16, **I**:139) as 27–32 inches.

The Spanish ibex is now, of course, extremely rare in zoological gardens and may even be nonexistent in collections. Two males and one female were received here on January 11, 1902, and a second female on April 5, 1905. Five births occurred, one in March, four in April. The greatest longevity recorded here was that of a female born on April 10, 1906, which died on June 23, 1921, after 15 years, 2 months, 13 days.

Among the largest of the goats is the markhor (*Capra falconeri*), of which seven races are listed by Ellerman and Morrison-Scott (1951) as extending, in the great ranges, from southern Russian Turkestan east to Kashmir and south through Afghanistan to Baluchistan. This is a heavy, powerful animal, with a shoulder height of 41 inches (Lydekker, 1913–16, **I**:162). The general coloration is brown in summer and gray in winter, adult males then becoming very pale. The coat is long and thick, with a heavy fringe of hair, in adult males, on shoulders, throat, and chest. Points of distinction are found in the long horns, which vary from an open spiral in the Astor markhor (*Capra f. falconeri*) at one extreme, to the nearly straight, tightly twisted form seen in the Suleman markhor (*Capra f. jerdoni*).

While the markhor has been kept and occasionally bred in zoological gardens over many years, it is still rare in collections. The first specimens received here, two males, arrived on May 27, 1904. One survived for only 2 years, but the other and a third male obtained in 1908 each lived for just over 8 years. These animals were kept in our Kangaroo House, already described (p. 36), where both indoor and outdoor compartments are hard-surfaced. They made no effort to clear the fences, 7 feet, 6 inches high, certainly well within their leaping ability. A fourth markhor, again a male, received here on June 8, 1932, lived until December 23, 1942, or 10 years, 6 months, 15 days, our best longevity for the species.

All these animals had tightly twisted horns and were referred to *Capra f. jerdoni*, the Suleman markhor. A beautiful herd seen in 1961 at the Catskill Game Farm, New York, consisted of three adult males, five adult females, and five kids of the year, all living together in a large inclosure on a cliff of shale. One of these males was obviously a Suleman, but the horns of the two others were of the open spiral type seen in the Astor markhor.

Our first female markhor, received with a male in February, 1956, produced stillborn female twins on June 12, 1957. Zuckerman (1953), in reporting twelve births in the Zoological Gardens of London in April, May, and June, says that all were of single young. Asdell (1946) gives the gestation period as 153 days.

The Caucasian tur (*Capra caucasica*), with a shoulder height of only 36 inches, still gives an impression of great strength and power. Usually considered as monotypic, the species is confined to the Caucasus Mountains of southeastern Russia. Its color is grayish brown, with markings of black on the back, chest, and legs. The beard is shorter than that of most related forms. The massive, cross-ribbed horns of males turn outward, then back and in, the tips rising. Ward (1922) gives 46 inches as the length of horns of a specimen from the eastern Caucasus.

There appears to be no record of the importation of the tur into this country, except for a pair received in 1960 by the Catskill Game Farm, New York. Seen in 1961 with a well-grown kid of the year, they appeared to be in excellent condition and made a most impressive exhibit. The species has been kept and bred in various European zoological gardens. Zuckerman (1953) reports the birth of twenty-four young in the Zoological Gardens of London in May and June. A male is listed by Flower (1931) as having lived at London from January 16, 1908, to September 29, 1922, or 14 years, 8 months, 13 days. An excellent account of turs kept in the Zoological Gardens of Halle, Germany, is given by Petzsch and Witstruk (1958).

Those members of the tribe Caprini that are known as sheep are found in three genera: *Pseudois*, the blue sheep or bharal, *Ammotragus*, the aoudad or Barbary sheep, and *Ovis*, the typical sheep. Beards are lacking in all species, but while facial glands are present in *Ovis*, they are absent in *Pseudois* and *Ammotragus* (Lydekker, 1913–16, 1:73).

The blue sheep (*Pseudois nayaur*), found in two races from Kashmir to the mountains of western China, is bluish or brownish gray, with underparts white. In adult males the face, chest, and stripes on the flanks and legs are black. The shoulder height is given by Lydekker (1913–16, 1:127) as about 36 inches. The nearly smooth horns of males turn outward, then back and in, with the tips rising, much as those of the Caucasian tur; in fact, it has been suggested (Lydekker, 1898b) that a bridge between the goats and the sheep may be formed by these two species. The greatest length of horn listed by Ward (1922) for the blue sheep is 31½ inches.

Once fairly well represented in zoological gardens, the blue sheep has now become extremely rare in collections. The first specimen to be received here came from the Zoological Gardens of London in 1902, "in exchange for two Brown Pelicans and some reptiles." Of a male and two females obtained in 1904 from William Jamrach, a well-known London dealer of that era, one female lived here for 6 years, 8 months, our best longevity for the species. Flower (1931) gives 16 years, 14 days for a female in the Zoological Gardens of London. No young were produced here, but Zuckerman (1953) records the births of forty-three lambs in the Zoological Gardens of London between 1882 and 1908 as having occurred from May to September. Asdell (1946) gives the gestation period as 160 days.

In this country the best results with the blue sheep have been achieved by the National Zoological Park, where a small herd was developed from a pair received in 1937. The survivor of this group, which died in 1962, was believed to have been the only representative of the species remaining in a Western zoological garden.

Certainly most abundant of this group in zoological gardens is the aoudad or Barbary sheep (*Ammotragus lervia*), which ranges, in a number of races, across the mountainous areas of North Africa from Mauritania to Egypt and south to the Sudan and the former French Equatorial Africa. Practically uniformly light brown in color, the greatest attraction of the species lies in the mass of long hair developed on the throat, chest, and forelimbs, particularly in adult males. The horns follow the form of those of the bharal, the greatest length listed by Ward (1922) being 33¼ inches. Lydekker (1913–16, 1:123) gives the shoulder height as about 39 inches.

In many parts of its range the aoudad has become greatly reduced in numbers; the status of the various forms has been reviewed by Harper (1945). On the other hand, the species is so hardy and so prolific in captivity that it is absent from few collections and takes a prominent position in most surplus lists. As already noted, experience here indicates a particularly high resistance to parasitism.

In earlier days our aoudad herd occupied an inclosure on Sheep Hill, showing no adverse reaction to conditions which related species found difficult. Since 1940 the animals, usually numbering from fifteen to twenty, have run in an area of about 2 acres, mostly in grass and shared during the summer months with a small group of elands (*Taurotragus oryx*). A low but fairly long outcropping of rock that bisects the inclosure is less used by the aoudads than might be expected. The fencing is of open-mesh wire, 7½ feet high; replacement with a moat is planned. While adult males spar frequently, such encounters are seldom serious, so that several may safely be kept with the herd. The "creep" mentioned earlier in this section seems to be of special importance with this species, since young of the year are likely to have difficulty during their first winter unless food is freely available.

Our aoudad herd was founded on six animals purchased from Carl Hagenbeck in 1901, 1902, and 1904, with a pair from the National Zoological Park in 1905. Since that time, there have been no introductions and the herd continues with vigor unreduced.

From 1902 to 1961, inclusive, 194 lambs have been born, as follows: January, 4; February, 22; March, 95; April, 39; May, 9; June, 5; July, 1; August, 5; September, 6; October, 4; November, 2; December, 2; 32 sets of twins were included. The occurrence of births in every month is in accordance with the findings of Zuckerman (1953), who records 190 births in the Zoological Gardens of London, similarly distributed. The gestation period is given by Asdell (1946) as 154–61 days.

The greatest longevity for a captive aoudad listed by Flower (1931) is 15 years, 5 months, 12 days in the Zoological Gardens of London. Our own specimen cards show many spans in excess of this figure, but in large groups of animals not readily identifiable the risk of error is so great that a record of 13 years, 3 months, 25 days is the longest for which we can vouch. Jones (1958) reports an aoudad as having lived 13 years, 4 months, 6 days in the Zoological Garden of Philadelphia, and one specimen is listed as having been kept in the Calgary Zoo, Calgary, Alberta, for 24 years (Anon., 1955b).

The typical sheep of the genus *Ovis* are confined to North America, Europe, and Asia, six species being currently recognized (Hall and Kelson, 1959; Ellerman and Morrison-Scott, 1951). Horns are present in females of most forms but are usually absent in females of the mouflon (*Ovis musimon*) and in those of some of the races of the red sheep (*Ovis orientalis*) (Lydekker, 1913–16, 1:74).

The bighorn sheep (*Ovis canadensis*) is found in the mountains of western North America and in similar regions of northeastern Siberia and Kamchatka. The average coloration is grayish brown, with white rump patch and underparts; there is much local variation to darker or paler shades. Males of the typical race have a shoulder height of 38–42 inches and may weigh up to 300 pounds (Anthony, 1928); females, of course, are smaller, and there are size differences among the forms. Horns of males are massive and closely turned along the sides of the head, the tips pointing outward. The greatest length of horn listed in the Boone and Crockett Club's *Records of North American Big Game* (1958) is 49$\frac{4}{8}$ inches for a specimen of the typical race from British Columbia. Horns of ewes are short and nearly straight.

The seven American races, as listed by Hall and Kelson (1959), were once well distributed in the mountains of the west, from Alberta and British Columbia to northern Mexico and Baja California. However, ranges have now become restricted to scattered, remote areas, as indicated by Buechner (1960), and one race, *Ovis c. auduboni*, of eastern Montana and Wyoming, the Dakotas, and western Nebraska, is considered to have become extinct. None of the five Asiatic subspecies recognized by Ellerman and Morrison-Scott (1951) appears to have a captivity history, but work with North American forms has been fairly extensive.

The first bighorn to be received here arrived on March 14, 1902. This animal, presented by W. M. Harriman, had been captured as a lamb east of San Quintin, Baja California, and presumably represented the Peninsular bighorn (*Ovis c. cremnobates*), a form not described until 1904. Following this specimen, ten bighorns assigned to the typical race were received here up to 1937, when our efforts to establish the species ceased. The earlier arrivals were placed on Sheep Hill and did not give satisfactory results, although four lambs were born, three in May, one in August. Animals received at later dates were kept in hard-floored inclosures in other areas which, as anticipated, proved far more suitable. A female that arrived on March 22, 1921, lived in a corral paved with macadam until August 7, 1936, or 15 years, 4 months, 16 days, our best longevity for a bighorn. A fine adult male Nelson's or desert bighorn (*Ovis c. nelsoni*), received on December 12, 1912, was installed in a paved yard at our Zebra House, where he lived until September 20, 1920.

Exceptionally good results with bighorns have been obtained at the National Zoological Park, as described by Mann (1930). Kept in a high dry inclosure floored with natural rock and concrete, the herd made a striking exhibit. Mann (*loc. cit.*) lists twenty births in the collection and gives a maximum longevity of 9 years, 8 months.

Bighorns have also been particularly successful in the San Diego Zoological Garden, where Stott (1954) reports three races—*canadensis*, *cremnobates*, and *nelsoni*—as having been bred. A vigorous, hardy group of bighorn by mouflon (*Ovis musimon*) hybrids has also been established (Anon., 1953*d*). Sheep at San Diego, where rainfall is light and infrequent, are kept in bare, well-drained ranges, where conditions approximate those of paved inclosures in areas of heavier precipitation.

The gestation period of the bighorn is given by Spencer (1943) as approximately 180 days. Births of single young seem to predominate. In experiments in the hand-rearing of bighorn lambs at the Desert Game

Range, Nevada, Deming (1955) found goat's milk to be an excellent substitute for that of the mother.

The captivity span of 15 years, 4 months, 16 days established by a female bighorn here has already been noted. Jones (1958) reports that a specimen lived in the Zoological Gardens of London from November 25, 1929, to February 20, 1944, or 14 years, 2 months, 26 days.

The white or Dall's sheep (*Ovis d. dalli*) is the most northerly in distribution of the three presently recognized races of this species (Hall and Kelson, 1959). The over-all distribution extends from the mountains of northern Alaska through the Yukon and western Mackenzie to northern British Columbia. In the typical subspecies of the north the coat is white, becoming darker or "saddle-backed" toward the south, gradually merging into the pale-faced, dark gray Stone's or black sheep (*Ovis d. stonei*) of the southern Yukon and northern British Columbia. The Kenai Peninsula is occupied by *Ovis d. kenaiensis*, an isolated white form distinguished principally by cranial characters.

This species in general is smaller than the bighorn, Cowan (1940) giving shoulder heights of 37 and 40 inches and weights up to 200 pounds for males of Dall's sheep. The horns of males are long, slender, and inclined to spiral outward; they are amber colored in the white forms. The greatest length listed in the Boone and Crockett Club's *Records of North American Big Game* (1958) is 51⅝ inches for a Stone's sheep. The numerical status of the races has been reviewed by Allen (1942).

Early efforts to secure living specimens of Dall's sheep were discouraging. Probably the first really serious attempt was made by the New York Zoological Society, which in 1902 sent an expedition to Alaska, headed by J. Alden Loring, expressly for the purpose. Working inland from Cook Inlet, Loring did succeed in capturing three lambs but was unable to keep them alive (Loring, 1902). Better results do not seem to have been achieved until 1958, when a ewe lamb was received on July 25 at the National Zoological Park. This animal was followed on January 4, 1959, by a second female (Theodore H. Reed, *in litt.*). In 1959 three lambs arrived at the Chicago Zoological Park (Bean, 1959). These proved to be two males and one female, the latter producing a vigorous female lamb herself in 1961, presumably the first of the species to be born in captivity (Anon., 1961b). A series of exchanges between the two institutions left Washington, at the end of 1961, with an adult pair and Chicago with an adult male, two adult females, and the female lamb, providing hope for the firm establishment of the beautiful Dall's sheep in captivity.*

*See Addenda, p. 738.

The argali (*Ovis ammon*) is an Asiatic species of large size, distributed in the mountains from eastern Russian Turkestan through the Pamirs and the Himalayas to Sikkim and across the Tibetan Plateau east to Mongolia. Fifteen races are listed by Ellerman and Morrison-Scott (1951). The upper parts in general are grayish brown, with the rump, underparts, legs, chest, and face white. In winter the coat is heavy and darker, with a whitish ruff developing on the throat and chest in adult males. The horns of males curve forward along the sides of the head, then flare outward, sometimes to great lengths. The horns of females are much smaller.

Few of the races have been kept in zoological gardens, and even these have so far failed to become established, although, according to Flower (1929), the Zoological Gardens of London received a specimen as early as 1829. In referring to argalis received at Woburn Abbey soon after the turn of the present century, Hastings, Duke of Bedford (1949), says that while the animals did well in yards and even bred, they "went to pieces very quickly" on grass, which is in accord with general experience.

Best known in captivity is the Siberian argali (*Ovis a. ammon*), found from eastern Russian Turkestan to the Altai Mountains. This form is considered by Lydekker (1913–16, 1:95) to be the largest of all the wild sheep, with a shoulder height of about 48 inches. The greatest length of the heavily ridged, widely spread horns given by Ward (1922) is $62\frac{1}{4}$ inches, measured on the front curve. The Siberian argali has been kept sparingly by zoological gardens, usually with little success. The first specimen seen by me was a female in the Zoological Gardens of Amsterdam in 1951, and I well recall being impressed by her great size. She was kept in a pen deeply bedded in sand, after the Amsterdam custom, and appeared to be in excellent condition. This race has not been represented in our collection, but L. J. Goss, director of the Cleveland Zoological Park, has informed me that a female received there on January 17, 1955, lived until August 10, 1960, or 5 years, 6 months, 24 days, certainly beyond the common experience. The only specimen known to be living in this country at the present time is a female seen in September, 1961, at the Catskill Game Farm, New York, where she shared a rocky inclosure with a small group of bighorns.

Marco Polo's sheep, or the Pamir argali (*Ovis a. polii*), is found on the Pamir Plateau of Russian Turkestan, where, according to Van Gelder (1957), it may range in summer as high as 18,000 feet. The remarkable flaring horns of males have made Marco Polo's sheep much sought by sportsmen, Ward (1922) giving the greatest length as $70\frac{3}{4}$ inches on the front curve.

A young male and two females of this superb race were received here on September 4, 1956. However, they were in poor condition on arrival, with heavy, unyielding infestations of internal parasites, and the survivor lived for only just over 1 year. Specimens received at the Cleveland Zoological Park at the same time thrived no better. More encouraging results have recently been obtained at the Zoological Gardens of Rotterdam, where a lamb was born in 1957, followed by a second in 1958, as recorded and figured by van Bemmel (1958). A further birth in 1959 at the Georg von Opel Institute at Kronberg, Germany, is reported in the *International Zoo Yearbook,* 1959, published by the Zoological Society of London.

The red sheep (*Ovis orientalis*), sometimes known as the Asiatic mouflon, is a comparatively small animal, found in mountain ranges from Cyprus and Asia Minor east to the Punjab and Kashmir. Several forms once considered as distinct species are listed by Ellerman and Morrison-Scott (1951) as races of *orientalis*, bringing the total number of subspecies to fifteen. There is much variation in color, but the upper surface is usually reddish, the underparts white, with small, scattered markings of black. Old males may develop a long throat fringe, white in some forms and varied with black in others; there may be a pale saddle-mark on the back. Horns, proportionately very large, may curve outward and back or forward along the sides of the face, seldom exceeding a full circle. They are absent in females of some of the races. Shoulder heights, as given by Lydekker (1913–16, 1) vary from $26\frac{1}{2}$ to 36 inches.

Red sheep of several forms have been kept by zoological gardens, and while they have seldom bred, have established better longevities, as a group, than have argalis. Ten specimens have been received here; the race of four, unfortunately, cannot now be determined. Six, however, were definitely assigned to *Ovis orientalis cycloceros*, the Afghan wild sheep. Of these, three were received from Carl Hagenbeck on October 17, 1902, and a fourth from William Jamrach in 1904. Twin lambs, one of which was fully reared, were born on May 9, 1903. A pair of the same race arrived from the Hagenbecks on January 21, 1928, the female giving birth to a single lamb on September 7 of that year. The male lived until November 20, 1937, or 9 years, 10 months, our best longevity for the species. Flower (1931) lists a specimen of the urial or shapo (*Ovis orientalis vignei*), of Kashmir, as having lived in the Zoological Gardens of London from January 27, 1896, to October 17, 1907, or 11 years, 8 months, 20 days. The only red sheep known to be living in this country at the present time are five specimens of the typical race, from Iran, seen at the Catskill Game Farm, New York, in September, 1961.

The mouflon (*Ovis musimon*), of Sardinia and Corsica, is among the smallest of the wild sheep, its shoulder height being given as about 27 inches (Lydekker, 1913–16, 1:76). The over-all color is reddish brown, darker in winter, a black stripe on the flanks limiting the white of the underparts. The hind neck, throat, chest, and shoulders are blackish and the muzzle gray or white. A light saddle marking is typical of adult males. The horns of males curve rather closely around the head, the points usually turning outward. In some captive individuals, however, they may turn inward and actually reach the sides of the head. In such cases the tips must be cut back periodically to avoid damage. Schneider (1932) describes and illustrates a mechanical "horn-spreader" used successfully in the Zoological Gardens of Leipzig for the correction of this condition in the mouflon. The greatest length of horn listed by Ward (1922) is 38½ inches. Ewes are usually hornless, although horned females are reported as occurring occasionally (Lydekker, 1898b:156).

As already noted, the mouflon appears to be more resistant to internal parasites than other members of this genus, and with reasonably close supervision can be maintained where related species may fail. Presumably for this reason, the mouflon far outnumbers all other wild sheep in general collections and is missing from few.

There is wide variation in the temperaments of mouflon males, some being tolerant of rivals, others persistently antagonistic. Some herd rams here have so persecuted young males that removal of one or the other has been necessary, while others have proved so indifferent that several lesser rams were allowed to remain with the herd.

Our first mouflon were a pair received on July 17, 1901, as the gift of Maurice Egerton of London. A second female, purchased from Carl Hagenbeck, arrived on October 17, 1902, and a third, from the same source, reached us on March 9, 1904. These four animals founded a going stock that continued without reinforcement until the death of the final survivor on March 24, 1941. Renewal was not established until 1948, when a pair was obtained from the Catskill Game Farm, New York, followed by a male from the same source in 1955 and another from the Highland Park Zoo, Pittsburgh. The herd in January, 1962, numbered ten animals, including one adult male, six adult females, and three lambs of 1961. The total number of young born here up to 1961 is ninety-four, as follows: February, three; March, fifty-nine; April, twenty-five; May, two; June, one; September, two; October, two. Eight pairs of twins were included. The gestation period is given by Asdell (1946) as 150 days.

The best longevity definitely established by a mouflon here was that of the female received on March 9, 1904, which lived until January 5, 1921, or 16 years, 9 months, 27 days. Flower (1931) reports a female as having lived in the Zoological Gardens of London from March 16, 1868, to June 8, 1887, or 19 years, 2 months, 23 days.

The readiness with which the mouflon accepts the conditions of captivity lends credence to the belief held by many that it entered largely into the ancestry of the domestic sheep, although this, actually, is totally unknown (Lydekker, 1898*b*:151–52). The domestic sheep was designated as *Ovis aries* by Linnaeus in 1758 and thus is the type of the genus, even though its origin remains a mystery. The soft, heavy wool borne by many breeds is not a distinguishing character, for this is merely a development of the undercoats found in most natural species, the long guard hairs having been eliminated; in fact, many primitive breeds still are clothed in hair. It is possible that the ancestry may have been a mixed one, involving the mouflon, the red sheep, and even others; on the other hand, there is some evidence to support the theory that a now extinct and unknown species was responsible. But whether or not a final solution is reached, the fact remains that the genus *Ovis* has produced a domestic animal of the greatest economic importance to mankind.

· REFERENCES

AITCHISON, JAMES.
  1946–47. Hinged teeth in mammals: a study of the tusks of muntjacs (*Muntiacus*) and Chinese water deer (*Hydropotes inermis*). Proc. Zool. Soc. London, **116**:329–38.

ALLEN, GLOVER M.
  1938, 1940. The mammals of China and Mongolia. American Museum of Natural History, New York. 2 vols. 1350 pp.
  1939. A checklist of African mammals. Bull. Mus. Comp. Zool., Harvard, 83. 763 pp.
  1942. Extinct and vanishing mammals of the Western Hemisphere. Spec. Pub. 11. American Committee for International Wildlife Protection, New York. 620 pp.

ANDERSON, R. M.
  1947. Catalogue of Canadian Recent mammals. Bull. Nat. Mus. Canada, **102**:1–238.

ANDERSEN, SVEND, and HOLGER POULSEN.
  1958. Two musk-oxen (*Ovibos moschatus* Zimm.) in captivity. Zool. Garten, Leipzig (N.F.), **24** (1/2):12–23.

ANON.

1904. European bison. Bull. New York Zool. Soc., No. 14, pp. 170–71.
1905. At last the mountain goat. *Ibid.*, No. 16, p. 204.
1907. The mountain goat herd. *Ibid.*, No. 24, p. 317.
1908. The mountain goat breeding in captivity. *Ibid.*, No. 30, pp. 429–30.
1932. The bull moose and family. Detroit Zoo-Life, Zoo-Life Publishing Co., Detroit, Mich. 30 pp.
1943. The giraffe has a voice. Animal Kingdom, 46 (6):141.
1953a. The peaceful end of "Pete." *Ibid.*, 56 (2):61.
1953b. Young moose dislikes Milwaukee weather; too hot and humid. Milwaukee Zoo News, 3 (5):3.
1953c. La reproduction des okapis en captivité. Zoo, Anvers, 19:20.
1953d. Ram without a country. Zoonooz, 26 (4):5.
1954. Nos collections zoologiques. Zoo, Anvers, 19:78.
1955a. Nos collections zoologiques. *Ibid.*, 20:77.
1955b. Longevity records. Internatl. Zoo News, 2 (4):66.
1956a. Pour le deuxième fois "Dassegela" a tué son nouveau-né. Zoo, Anvers, 22:57–58.
1956b. Old timers. Brookfield Bandar-Log, 15:6.
1956c. Desert oryx baby growing nicely. *Ibid.*, 15:4.
1957a. Longevity record. Animal Kingdom, 60 (1):32.
1957b. Note. Brookfield Bandar-Log, 17:8.
1957c. Dik-diks, otters, etcetera, etcetera! *Ibid.*, 16:1.
1957d. Frankfurt am Main—Germany. Internatl. Zoo News, 4 (3):74.
1959a. Note. *Ibid.*, 6 (4):167.
1959b. America's first baby okapi. Brookfield Bandar-Log, 21:3–4.
1959c. Welcome—Bongo or Karen. Cleveland Zoo News, 1 (15):1.
1959d. Curator's corner. Your Detroit Zoo, 14 (1):7.
1960a. Baby okapi in Frankfurt Zoo. Internatl. Zoo News, 7 (4):99.
1960b. *Alcelaphus buselaphus cokii.* Brookfield Bandar-Log, 23:4.
1960c. Notes from Lincoln Park Zoo. Internatl. Zoo News, 7 (2):50.
1960d. Zoo briefs. Zoonooz, 33 (4):6.
1960e. Zoo briefs. *Ibid.*, No. 9, p. 7.
1961a. Caption, *Ibid.*, 34 (5):16.
1961b. Brookfield babies, 1961. Brookfield Bandar-Log, 24:7.
1962. Mammal memos. Zoonooz, 35 (1):15.
1963. Caption. *Ibid.*, 36 (6):16.

ANTHONY, H. E.

1928. Field book of North American mammals. G. P. Putnam's Sons, New York. 674 pp.

ANTONIUS, OTTO.

1929. Über steinwild. Zool. Garten, Leipzig (N.F.), 2 (4/6):95–106.
1932. Beobachtungen an Rindern in Schönbrunn. 2. Banteng, Gaur, Gayal. *Ibid.*, 5 (7/9):178–91.
1943. Beobachtungen an Rindern in Schönbrunn. 5. Über zebus. *Ibid.*, 15 (5/6):185–213.

APPELMAN, F. J.
  1952. Vom Banteng (*Bibos sondaicus*). Zool. Garten, Leipzig (N.F.), **19** (5):189–92.

ARGUS.
  1961. Le boeuf musqué (*Ovibos moschatus* [Zimmermann]). Zoo, Anvers, **27** (1):14.

ASDELL, S. A.
  1946. Patterns of mammalian reproduction. Comstock Publishing Co., Ithaca, N.Y. 437 pp.

BAILEY, VERNON.
  1920. Old and new horns of the prong-horned antelope. Jour. Mammal., **1** (3):128–29.

BANFIELD, A. W. F., and N. S. NOVAKOWSKI.
  1960. The survival of the wood bison (*Bison bison athabascae*) in the Northwest Territories. Nat. Hist. Papers, 8. National Museum of Canada, Ottawa. 6 pp.

BANNIKOV, A.-G.
  1958a. Distribution géographique et biologie du cheval sauvage et du chameau de Mongolie (*Equus przewalskii* et *Camelus bactrianus*). Mammalia, **22** (1):152–60.
  1958b. Distribution géographique actuelle et biologie de la saiga en Europe. Mammalia, *Ibid.*, No. 2, pp. 208–25.

BARTLETT, A. D.
  1899. Wild animals in captivity. Ed. EDWARD BARTLETT. Chapman & Hall, Ltd., London. 373 pp.

BEAN, ROBERT.
  1959. Brookfield—U.S.A. Internatl. Zoo News, **6** (4):168.

BELL, W. B.
  1931. Experiments in re-establishment of musk-oxen in Alaska. Jour. Mammal., **12** (3):292–97.

BERE, R. M.
  1958. The status of ungulate mammals in the Uganda National Parks. Mammalia, **22** (3):418–26.
  1959. Queen Elizabeth National Park: Uganda. The hippopotamus problem and experiment. Oryx, **5** (3):116–24.

BERRY, R. O.
  1938. Comparative studies on the chromosome numbers in sheep, goat and sheep-goat hybrids. Jour. Heredity, **29** (9):343–50.

BIERWIRTH, ROBERT.
  1954. The raising and feeding of moose. Parks and Recreation, **37** (3):21–22.

BIGALKE, R.
  1961. List of animals bred in the collection in the year 1960. Ann. Rept., 1960, National Zoological Gardens of South Africa, Pretoria.

BIGALKE, R. C.
  1958. On the present status of ungulate mammals in South West Africa.
         Mammalia, 22 (3):478–97.

BLAAUW, F. E.
  1889. Letter to the Secretary of the Zoological Society of London. Proc.
         Zool. Soc. London, pp. 2–5.

BLAINE, GILBERT.
  1922. Notes on the zebras and some antelopes of Angola. Proc. Zool. Soc.
         London, pp. 317–39.

BLANCOU, L.
  1958a. Note sur le statut actuel des ongulés en Afrique Équatoriale française.
         Mammalia, 22 (3):399–405.
  1958b. The African buffaloes. Animal Kingdom, 61 (2):56–61.

BLANFORD, W. T.
  1888–91. The fauna of British India. Mammalia. Taylor and Francis, London.
         617 pp.

BOHLKEN, HERWART.
  1960. Remarks on the stomach and the systematic position of the Tylopoda.
         Proc. Zool. Soc. London, 134:207–14.

BOLAU, HEINRICH.
  1904. Jahresbericht über den Zoologischen Garten in Hamburg 1903.
         Zool. Garten (Frankfurt), 45 (7):212–20.

BOONE AND CROCKETT CLUB, SAMUEL B. WEBB, CHAIRMAN.
  1958. Records of North American big game. Chas. Scribner's Sons, New
         York. 264 pp.

BOURDELLE, E., and A. MOUQUET.
  1930. La longévité des mammifères à la ménagerie du Muséum National
         d'Histoire Naturelle. Bull. Mus. Hist. Nat., Paris. 2d ser., 2 (5):
         488–97.

B[RIDGES], W[ILLIAM].
  1936. Another pygmy hippo. Bull. New York Zool. Soc., 39 (2):82–83.

BRIDGES, WILLIAM.
  1937. An okapi comes to the Zoological Park. Bull. New York Zool. Soc.,
         40 (5):135–47.
  1939. Four stubborn babies from Greenland. Ibid., 42 (6):163–71.
  1947a. A visit to Brother Joseph. Animal Kingdom, 50 (2):37–43.
  1947b. Okapi experiences. Ibid., 50 (5):154–57.
  1960. The first baby hippopotamus in sixty years. Ibid., 63 (1):2–6.

BROUARD, PIERRE.
  1961. Notes on Vincennes Zoo okapis. Internatl. Zoo News, 8 (4):112.

BROWN, C. EMERSON.
  1924. Rearing hippopotamuses in captivity. Jour. Mammal., 5 (4):243–46.
  1925. Longevity of mammals in the Philadelphia Zoological Garden. Ibid.,
         6 (4):264–67.

1936. Rearing wild animals in captivity, and gestation periods. *Ibid.*, **17** (1): 10–13.

BUCKLEY, JOHN L., DAVID L. SPENCER, and PAUL ADAMS.
1954. Muskox (*Ovibos moschatus*) longevity. Jour. Mammal., **35** (3):456.

BUECHNER, HELMUT K.
1960. The bighorn sheep in the United States, its past, present and future. Wildlife Monographs, 4. The Wildlife Society. 174 pp.
1961. Territorial behavior in Uganda kob. Science, **133** (3454):698–99.

CABRERA, ANGEL.
1961. Catalogo de los mamiferos de America del Sur. Rev. Mus. Argentina Cienc. Nat. Bernardino Rivadavia, Zool., **4** (2):309–732.

CABRERA, ANGEL, and JOSÉ YEPES.
1940. Historia Natural Ediar. Mamiferos Sud-Americanos. Compañia Argentina de Editores, Buenos Aires. 370 pp.

CAHALANE, VICTOR H.
1947. Mammals of North America. Macmillan Co., New York. 682 pp.

CARTER, T. DONALD.
1959. The mountain nyala. Animal Kingdom, **62** (4): 118–23.

CHAPMAN, CHARLES A.
1910. How our white mountain goats were caught. Bull. New York Zool. Soc., No. 40, pp. 680–82.

COLLINS, HENRY H., JR.
1952. 1951 census of American bison. Blue Heron Press, Bronxville, N.Y. 21 pp.

CONOWAY, CLINTON.
1952. The age at sexual maturity in male elk (*Cervus canadensis*). Jour. Wildlife Management, **16** (3):313–15.

COOLIDGE, HAROLD J., JR.
1940. The Indo-Chinese forest ox or kouprey. Mem. Mus. Comp. Zool., **54** (6):417–531.

CORDIER, CHARLES.
1949. Our Belgian Congo expedition comes home. Animal Kingdom, **52** (4):99–114.

COTTON, W. B.
1936. Note on the giant forest hog (*Hylochoerus meinertzhageni*). Proc. Zool. Soc. London, pp. 687–88.

COWAN, IAN McTAGGART.
1940. Distribution and variation in the native sheep of North America. Amer. Midland Nat., **24** (3):505–80.
1956. What and where are the black-tailed deer? In: The deer of North America. Ed. WALTER P. TAYLOR. The Stackpole Co., Harrisburg, Pa., and The Wildlife Management Institute, Washington, D.C. 668 pp.

CRANDALL, LEE S.
   1945.   Four years of Africa-in-the-Bronx. Animal Kingdom, **48** (3):59–61.

CULLY, WILLIAM.
   1940.   Tribute to Clarence. Bull. New York Zool. So··., **43** (1):30–31.
   1958.   *Giraffa camelopardalis.* Parks and Recreation, **41** (4):197–98.

CUNEO, FRANCO.
   1955.   Rare antelopes. Internatl. Zoo News, **2** (2):36.

DAGG, ANNE INNIS.
   1962.   The role of the neck in the movements of the giraffe. Jour. Mammal.,
           43 (1):88–97.

DAVIS, DON G.
   1960.   Socrates, you're OK! Parks and Recreation, **43** (12):536–37.

DAVIS, JOSEPH A., JR.
   1959.   An okapi is born in the zoo. Animal Kingdom, **62** (6):162–66.

DELACOUR, JEAN.
   1931.   Le cerf *pseudaxis.* La Terre et la Vie, N. S., **6**:373–75.

DE LANDSHEERE, J.
   1957.   Observations concernant la capture, l'élevage et les soins de l'okapi.
           Zoo (Anvers), **23** (1):12–25.

DELAP, PETER.
   1957.   Some notes on the social habits of the British deer. Proc. Zool. Soc.
           London, **128**:608–12.

DE LA TOUR, G. DENNLER.
   1954.   The guanaco. Oryx, **2** (5):273–79.

DEMING, O. V.
   1955.   Rearing bighorn lambs in captivity. California Fish and Game,
           41 (2):131–43.

DE VOS, ANTOON, RICHARD H. MANVILLE, and RICHARD G. VAN GELDER.
   1956.   Introduced mammals and their influence on native biota. Zoologica,
           41 (4):163–94.

DITMARS, RAYMOND L.
   1919.   Our oldest specimens. Bull. New York Zool. Soc., **22** (3):60–65.

DITTOE, GEORGIA B.
   1945.   A pig by another name. Zoonooz, **18** (5):3–4.

DUETZ, GERTRUDE.
   1939.   Revised tables of maximum exhibition periods for animals in the
           Philadelphia collection as compared with available figures from other
           Zoos, together with some data on those now living in the Garden.
           In: Rept. Penrose Res. Lab., Zool. Soc. Philadelphia, 1939. 50 pp.

EDMOND-BLANC, FRANÇOIS.
   1947.   A contribution to the knowledge of the Cambodian wild ox or Kou-
           proh. Jour. Mammal., **28** (3):245–48.

EINARSEN, ARTHUR S.
   1948.   The pronghorn antelope and its management. Wildlife Management Institute, Washington. 238 pp.

ELLERMAN, J. R., and T. C. S. MORRISON-SCOTT.
   1951.   Checklist of Palaearctic and Indian mammals. British Museum (Natural History), London. 810 pp.

ELLERMAN, J. R., T. C. S. MORRISON-SCOTT, and R. W. HAYMAN.
   1953.   Southern African mammals, 1758 to 1951: a reclassification. British Museum (Natural History), London. 363 pp.

ENDERS, ROBERT K.
   1930.   Notes on some mammals from Barro Colorado Island, Canal Zone. Jour. Mammal., 11 (3):280–92.

ESTES, RICHARD D.
   1959.   A visit to our first takin. Animal Kingdom, 62 (2):37–42.

FLINN, PAUL.
   1959.   The caribou of northern Idaho. Idaho Wildlife Rev., 11 (5):10–11.

FLOWER, S. S.
   1929.   List of the vertebrated animals exhibited in the Gardens of the Zoological Society of London, 1828–1927. 1. Mammals. Zoological Society of London. 419 pp.
   1931.   Contributions to our knowledge of the duration of life in vertebrate animals. 5. Mammals. Proc. Zool. Soc. London, pp. 145–234.

FRADE, F.
   1958.   Mesures adoptées pour la protection de l'hippotrague géant en Angola. Mammalia, 22 (3):476–77.

FRECHKOP, SERGE.
   1955.   Ordre de paraxoniens ou artiodactyles. In: Traité de zoologie. Ed. PIERRE-P. GRASSÉ. Vol. 17. Mammifères. Masson et Cie, Paris. 1170 pp.

GARRETSON, MARTIN S.
   1934.   A short history of the American bison. American Bison Society, New York. 66 pp.
   1938.   The American bison. New York Zoological Society, New York. 254 pp.

GEE, E. P.
   1958.   Four rare Indian animals. Oryx, 4 (6):353–58.

GIJZEN, AGATHA.
   1958a. Quelques observations concernant la naissance et la croissance de girafes (Giraffa camelopardalis antiquorum [Swainson]) au Jardin Zoologique d'Anvers. Mammalia, 22 (1):112–20.
   1958b. Notice sur la reproduction de l'okapi, Okapia johnstoni (Sclater) au Jardin Zoologique d'Anvers. Bull. Soc. Roy. Zool. Anvers, No. 8. 82 pp.
   1959a. Das okapi, Okapia johnstoni (Sclater). Die Neue Brehm-Bücherei, 231. A. Ziemsen, Wittenberg Lutherstadt. 120 pp.

1959b. L'élevage en captivité d'animaux où en voie d'extinction. Zoo (Anvers), 25 (1):26–32.

1961. Le boeuf musque (*Ovibos moschatus* [Zimmermann]). *Ibid.*, 27 (2): 41–48.

GLOVER, RICHARD.
1956. Notes on the sika deer. Jour. Mammal., 37 (1):99–105.

GOLLEY, FRANK B.
1957. Gestation period, breeding and fawning behavior of the Columbian black-tailed deer. Jour. Mammal., 38 (1):116–20.

GOODWIN, G. G.
1925. The first living elephant in America. Jour. Mammal., 6 (4):256–63.
1954. Pp. 681–874 in: The animal kingdom. Vol. 2. FREDERICK DRIMMER, Editor-in-chief. Greystone Press, New York.

GRAHAM, RALPH.
1956. Muyoni, our new female okapi. Animal Kingdom, 49 (6):162–69.

GRANT, MADISON.
1905. The Rocky Mountain goat. 9th Ann. Rept., New York Zool. Soc., 1904, pp. 231–61.

GRAY, ANNIE P.
1954. Mammalian hybrids. Commonwealth Agricultural Bureaux, Farnham Royal, Bucks, England. 144 pp.

GRAY, RAYMOND F.
1956. Breeding hippopotomi. Parks and Recreation, 39 (5):24.
1959. Care and breeding of captive hippopotami. Proc. 60th Ann. Conf. Amer. Inst. Park Executives and Amer. Assoc. Zool. Parks and Aquariums.

GRIMWOOD, R. I.
1962. Operation oryx. Oryx, 6 (6):308–34.

GRZIMEK, BERNHARD.
1956. Schlaf von Giraffen und Okapi. Naturwissenschaften, 43 (17):406.
1957. No room for wild animals. W. W. Norton & Co., Inc., New York. 271 pp.
1961. Über den Tierbestand. 102nd Report of the Zoological Gardens of Frankfurt for the year 1960. 15 pp.

HAAGNER, ALWIN.
1920. South African mammals. H. F. and G. Witherby, London. 248 pp.

HAGENBECK, CARL.
1910. Beasts and men. Longmans, Green & Co., London. 299 pp.

HALL, E. RAYMOND, and KEITH R. KELSON.
1959. The mammals of North America. The Ronald Press Co., New York. 2 vols. 1083 pp.

HALLORAN, ARTHUR F.
1957a. The bison returned to the plains. Animal Kingdom, 60 (5):130–34.
1957b. Live and dressed weights of American bison. Jour. Mammal., 38 (1):139.

HALTENORTH, TH.
1958. The rarest zoo animal. Internatl. Zoo News, 5 (1):18.

HANSON, R. P., and LARS KARSTAD.
1959. Feral swine in the southeastern United States. Jour. Wildlife Management, 23 (1):64–74.

HARMON, WENDELL H.
1944. Notes on mountain goats in the Black Hills. Jour. Mammal., 25 (2):149–51.

HARPER, FRANCIS.
1945. Extinct and vanishing mammals of the Old World. Spec. Pub. 12. American Committee for International Wild Life Protection, New York. 850 pp.
1955. The Barren Ground caribou of Keewatin. University of Kansas, Lawrence. 163 pp.

HASTINGS, DUKE OF BEDFORD.
1949. The years of transition. Andrew Dakers Ltd., London. 340 pp.

HEAPE, W.
1901. Quoted by S. A. Asdell. In: Patterns of mammalian reproduction, 1946, p. 328.

HECK, LUTZ.
1934. Vom Elch. Zool. Garten, Leipzig (N.F.), 7 (1/3):1–16.
1936. Nachrichten aus Zoologischen Garten: Berlin. Ibid., 8 (7/9):239–42.

HEDIGER, H.
1942. Zur Elch-Geburt im Berner Tierpark 1940. Zool. Garten, Leipzig (N.F.), 14 (1/2):14–23.
1949. Der zweite Elchgeburt im Berner Tierpark (1941). Ibid., 16 (3/4): 93–110.
1950. Wild animals in captivity. Butterworths Scientific Publications, London. 207 pp.
1951. Observations sur la psychologie animale dans les Parcs Nationaux du Congo Belge. Institut des Parcs Nationaux du Congo Belge, Brussels.
1952. Observations on reproduction in zoo animals. Pp. 74–83 in CIBA Foundation Colloquia on Endocrinology, 3. J. & A. Churchill Ltd., London.
1955a. Studies of the psychology and behaviour of captive animals in zoos and circuses. Butterworths Scientific Publications, London. 166 pp.
1955b. Animal sleeping postures. Animals asleep, Vol. 2. J. R. Geigy S.A., Basle. 8 pp.

HERSHKOVITZ, PHILIP.
1948. The technical name of the Virginia deer with a list of the South American forms. Proc. Biol. Soc. Washington, 61:41–48.
1949. Technical names for the fallow deer and Virginia deer. Jour. Mammal., 30 (1):94.
1958. The metatarsal glands in white-tailed deer and related forms of the neotropical region. Mammalia, 22 (4):537–46.

1959.   A new species of South American brocket, genus *Mazama* (Cervidae). Proc. Biol. Soc. Washington, 72:45–54.

HILL, JOHN ERIC, and T. DONALD CARTER.
1941.   The mammals of Angola, Africa. Bull. Amer. Mus. Nat. Hist., 78:1–211.

HILL, RALPH R.
1956.   Forage, food habits and range management of the mule deer. In: The deer of North America. Ed. WALTER P. TAYLOR. The Stackpole Co., Harrisburg, Pa., and The Wildlife Management Institute, Washington, D.C. 668 pp.

HILL, W. C. OSMAN.
1957.   Report of the Society's prosector for the years 1955 and 1956. Proc. Zool. Soc. London, 129:431–46.

HOLLISTER, N.
1921.   Report of the superintendent of the National Zoological Park for the fiscal year ending June 30, 1921. Ann. Rept., Smithsonian Inst. for 1921, pp. 84–99.

HONE, ELISABETH.
1934.   The present status of the muskox in Arctic North America and Greenland. Spec. Pub. 5, American Committee for International Wildlife Protection, New York. 87 pp.

H[ORNADAY], W[ILLIAM] T.
1902.   The musk-ox. Bull. New York Zool. Soc., No. 7, pp. 33–35.
1904.   Our Asiatic deer collection. *Ibid.*, No. 15, pp. 173–76.
1925.   Two musk-ox calves born in New York. *Ibid.*, 28 (5):131.

HORNADAY, WILLIAM T.
1889.   The extermination of the American bison, with a sketch of its discovery and life history. Ann. Rept., U.S. Nat. Mus. for 1887, pp. 367–548.
1914.   Report of the Director of the Zoological Park. In: Eighteenth Annual Report of the New York Zoological Society, 1913, pp. 67–103.
1920.   Birth of a pygmy hippopotamus. Bull. New York Zool. Soc., 23 (1):11–13.
1926.   Two musk-ox calves born in New York. Jour. Mammal., 7 (1):61.

HOSLEY, NEIL W.
1956.   Management of the white-tailed deer in its environment. In: The deer of North America. Ed. WALTER P. TAYLOR. The Stackpole Co., Harrisburg, Pa., and The Wildlife Management Institute, Washington, D.C. 668 pp.

HOSLEY, N. W., and FRANK S. GLASER.
1952.   Triplet Alaskan moose calves. Jour. Mammal., 33 (2):247.

ILES, GERALD T.
1957.   Giraffes in the Zoological Gardens, Belle Vue, Manchester, 1929–1954. Zool. Garten, Leipzig (N.F.), 23 (1/3):162–77.

JACKSON, HARTLEY H. T.
1958. The return of the vanishing musk oxen. Smithson. Inst. Rept. for 1957, pp. 381–89.

JACOBI, E. F.
1960. De wisent. Artis, 6 (1):4–9.

JACZEWSKI, ZBIGNIEW.
1958. Reproduction of the European bison, Bison bonasus (L.), in reserves. Acta Theriol., 1 (9):333–76.

JENNISON, GEORGE.
N.d. Table of gestation periods and number of young. A. & C. Black, Ltd., London. 8 pp.

JONES, MARVIN L.
1958. Mammals in captivity. Mimeographed MSS (unpublished).

KELHAM, MOIRA.
1953. Recent arrivals at the London Zoo. Zoo Life (London), 8 (1):30–32.

KELLAS, L. M.
1954–55. Observations on the reproductive activities, measurements and growth rate of the dikdik (Rhynchotragus kirkii thomasi Neumann). Proc. Zool. Soc. London, 124:751–84.

KELLOGG, REMINGTON.
1956. What and where are the whitetails? In: The deer of North America. Ed. WALTER P. TAYLOR. The Stackpole Co., Harrisburg, Pa., and The Wildlife Management Institute, Washington, D.C. 668 pp.

KENNETH, J. H.
1953. Gestation periods. Commonwealth Agricultural Bureaux, Farnham Royal, Slough, Bucks, England. 39 pp.

KNOBEL, R.
1958. Present day status of certain ungulates in the Union of South Africa. Mammalia, 22 (3):498–503.

KOFORD, CARL B.
1957. The vicuña and the puna. Ecol. Monogr., (27), pp. 153–219.

KRONFELD, E. M.
1936. Die erste Giraffe in Schönbrunn. Zool. Garten, Leipzig (N.F.), 8 (7/9):214–20.

KUIPER, KOENRAAD.
1943. Der neue Tierpark Blij-Dorp in Rotterdam. Zool. Garten, Leipzig (N.F.), 15 (1/2):59–68.

LANG, E. M.
1960. Ein okapi wurde geboren. Zolli (Basel), 4:11–12.

LANG, HERBERT.
1918. In quest of the rare okapi. Bull. New York Zool. Soc., 21 (3):1601–14.
1919. An okapi reared in captivity. Ibid., 22 (4):71–73.

LANGER, MARCEL.
1959. Note. Internatl. Zoo News, 6 (3):105.

LAURIE, ELEANOR M. O., and J. E. HILL.
   1954. List of land mammals of New Guinea, Celebes and adjacent islands. Trustees of the British Museum, London. 175 pp.

LEISTER, CLAUDE W.
   1933. The bongo comes to the Zoological Park. Bull. New York Zool. Soc., 36 (2):33–37.
   1939. The wild pigs of the world. *Ibid.*, 42 (5):131–39.
   1943. Before Montefiore Joash Sunshine. Animal Kingdom, 46 (3):63–70.

LEONARD, ARTHUR GLYN.
   1894. The camel. Longmans, Green & Co., London. 335 pp.

LEOPOLD, A. STARKER, and F. FRASER DARLING.
   1953. Wildlife in Alaska. The Ronald Press Co., New York. 129 pp.

LINCOLN, FREDERICK C.
   1958. Saving North America's endangered species. Oryx, 4 (6):365–72.

LOISEL, GUSTAVE.
   1912. Histoire des ménageries de l'antiquité à nos jours. Octave Doin et Fils, Henri Laurens, Paris. 3 vols.

LORING, J. ALDEN.
   1902. The quest for *Ovis dalli.* Bull. New York Zool. Soc., No. 7, pp. 46–55.

LYDEKKER, RICHARD.
   1893–96. The royal natural history. Frederick Warne & Co., New York and London. 6 vols.
   1898a. The deer of all lands. Rowland Ward, Ltd., London. 329 pp.
   1898b. Wild oxen, sheep and goats of all lands. Rowland Ward, Ltd., London. 318 pp.
   1904. On the subspecies of *Giraffa camelopardalis.* Proc. Zool. Soc. London, Vol. 1, pp. 202–27.
   1913–16. Catalogue of the ungulate mammals in the British Museum (Natural History). Trustees of the British Museum, London. 5 vols.

MANN, WM. M.
   1930. Wild animals in and out of the zoo. Smithsonian Sci. Ser., Vol. 6. 362 pp.
   1934. Report on the National Zoological Park for the year ending June 30, 1934. Smithsonian Inst. Rept. for 1934, pp. 46–53.

MANVILLE, RICHARD H.
   1957. Roe deer in New York. Jour. Mammal., 38 (3):422.

MATTHEWS, L. HARRISON.
   1952. British mammals. Collins, London. 410 pp.

McCLUNG, ROBERT M.
   1953. Deer: those adaptable animals. Animal Kingdom, 56 (2):35–44.

McHUGH, TOM.
   1958. Social behavior of the American buffalo (*Bison bison bison*). Zoologica, 43 (1):1–40.

MEINERTZHAGEN, R.
1938.   Some weights and measurements of large mammals. Proc. Zool. Soc. London, **108**, Ser. A: 433–39.

MEYER-HOLZAPFEL, MONIQUE.
1958.   Bouquetins en captivité. Mammalia, **22** (1):90–103.

MILLER, GERRIT S., JR.
1924.   A second instance of the development of rodent-like incisors in an Artiodactyl. Proc. U.S. Nat. Mus., **66** (8):1–4.

MILLER, GERRIT S., and REMINGTON KELLOGG.
1955.   List of North American Recent mammals. Bull. 205. U.S. National Museum, Smithsonian Institution, Washington, D.C. 954 pp.

MILTON, ANN M.
1959.   A rarity from Burma—the first takin in America. Animal Kingdom, **62** (6):173–78.

MITCHELL, P. CHALMERS.
1911.   On longevity and relative viability in mammals and birds; with a note on the theory of longevity. Proc. Zool. Soc. London, pp. 425–548.
1929.   Centenary history of the Zoological Society of London. By the Society, Regent's Park, London. 307 pp.

MOCHI, UGO, and T. DONALD CARTER.
1953.   Hoofed mammals of the world. Chas. Scribner's Sons, New York.

MOHR, ERNA.
1934.   Vom Kambing oetan (*Capricornis sumatrensis* Bechst.). Zool. Garten, Leipzig (N.F.), **7** (1/3):24–28.
1936.   Weiteres vom Kambing oetan (*Capricornis sumatrensis* Bechst.). *Ibid.*, **8** (10/12):291–95.
1942.   Das Riesen-Waldschwein, *Hylochoerus meinertzhageni* Thos. *Ibid.*, **14** (4):177–91.
1943.   Eineges über die saiga, *Saiga tatarica* L. *Ibid.*, **15** (5/6):175–85.
1951.   Lebensdauer einiger Tiere in Zoologischen Garten. *Ibid.*, **18** (1/2):60.
1952.   Der wisent. Die Neue Brehm-Bücherei, 74. Geest and Portig K.-G., Leipzig. 75 pp.
1960.   Wilde schweine. Die Neue Brehm-Bücherei, 247. A. Ziemsen Verlag, Wittenberg Lutherstadt. 156 pp.

MONTAGU, IVOR.
1957.   Colour-film shots of the wild camel. Proc. Zool. Soc. London, **129**:592–95.

MORRIS, DESMOND, and CAROLINE JARVIS (EDS.).
1959.   Species of mammals and birds bred in captivity during 1959. Internatl. Zoo Yrbk., **1**:138–60.

MORRISON, JOHN A., CHARLES E. TURNER, and PHILIP L. WRIGHT.
1959.   Breeding season in elk as determined from known-age embryos. Jour. Wildlife Management, **23** (1):27–34.

MORRISON-SCOTT, T. C. S.
    1951.   The technical names of the fallow deer and the Virginia deer. Jour. Mammal., **32** (1):125–26.

MORTON, SAMUEL G.
    1844.   On a supposed new species of hippopotamus. Proc. Acad. Nat. Sci. Philadelphia, **2**:14.

MURIE, OLAUS J.
    1951.   The elk of North America. The Stackpole Co., Harrisburg, Pa., and The Wildlife Management Institute, Washington, D.C. 376 pp.

NEAL, BOBBY J.
    1959.   A contribution on the life history of the collared peccary in Arizona. Amer. Midland Nat., **6** (1):177–90.

NICHOL, A. A.
    1942.   Gathering, transplanting and care of young antelopes. Jour. Wildlife Management, **6** (4):281–86.

NOBACK, CHARLES V.
    1932.   The deciduous horns of the pronghorn antelope. Bull. New York Zool. Soc., **35** (6):195–207.

NOUVEL, J.
    1958.   Remarques sur le fonction génitale et la naissance d'un okapi. Mammalia, **22** (1):107–11.

NOUVEL, J., J. RINJARD, and M. A. PASQUIER.
    1960.   Rapport sur la mortalité et la natalité enregistrées au Parc Zoologique pendant l'année 1959. Bull. Mus. Hist. Nat., Paris, **6**:453–72.

NOUVEL, J., M. A. PASQUIER, J. RINJARD, and G. CHAUVIER.
    1958.   Inventaire actuel des collections d'ongulés vivants du muséum. Mammalia, **22** (2):348–52.

OGILBY, W.
    1836.   Remarks upon two antelopes (*Koba* and *Kob* of Buffon). Proc. Zool. Soc. London, part 4, pp. 102–3.

OLIVIER, GEORGES.
    1954.   Le cerf du Père David. La Terre et la Vie, No. 3, pp. 183–91.

OSBORN, FAIRFIELD.
    1941.   The opening of the African Plains. Bull. New York Zool. Soc., **44** (3):67–73.

PALMER, RALPH S.
    1951.   The whitetail deer of Tomhegan Camps, Maine, with added notes on fecundity. Jour. Mammal., **32** (3):267–80.
    1954.   The mammal guide. Doubleday & Co., Inc., Garden City, N.Y. 384 pp.

PANG-CHIEH, T'AN.
    1957.   Rare catches by Chinese animal collectors. Zoo Life (London), **12** (2):61–63.

PEDERSEN, ALWIN.
1958. Der Moschusochs. Die Neue Brehm-Bücherei, 215. A. Ziemsen Verlag, Wittenberg Lutherstadt. 53 pp.

PERCY-SMITH, E.
1933. The quest of the bongo. Bull. New York Zool. Soc., **36** (2):27-32.

PETERSON, RANDOLPH L.
1952. A review of the living representatives of the genus *Alces*. Contr. Royal Ontario Mus. Zool. and Palaeontol., **34**:1-30.

PETZSCH, HANS, and KLAUS-GÜNTHER WITSTRUK.
1958. Beobachtungen an Daghestanischen Turen (*Capra caucasica cylindricornis* Blyth) im Berg-Zoo Halle. Zool. Garten, Leipzig (N.F.), **25** (1/2): 6-29.

POCOCK, R. I.
1910. On the specialized cutaneous glands of ruminants. Proc. Zool. Soc. London, pp. 840-986.
1914. The keeping of reindeer in captivity. Year Book, Amateur Menagerie Club, pp. 5-22.
1946. The okapi. Zoo Life, **1** (1):3-6.

POGLAYEN-NEUWALL, IVO.
1959. News from Albuquerque, New Mexico. Internatl. Zoo News, **6** (4):142-43.

POURNELLE, GEORGE H.
1955. Notes on the reproduction of a Baringo giraffe. Jour. Mammal., **36** (4):574.

PRIEMAL, KURT.
1930. Die Giraffengazelle. Zool. Garten, Leipzig (N.F.), **3** (4/8):116-34.

RABB, GEORGE B.
1960. Longevity records for mammals at the Chicago Zoological Park. Jour. Mammal., **41** (1):113-14.

REED, THEODORE H.
1959. Report on the National Zoological Park for the year ended June 30, 1958. Smithsonian Inst. Rept. for 1958, pp. 140-79.
1960. Report on the National Zoological Park for the year ended June 30, 1959. Smithsonian Inst. Rept. for 1959, pp. 150-89.

REUTHER, RONALD T.
1961. Breeding notes on mammals in captivity. Jour. Mammal., **42** (3): 427-28.

ROBERTS, AUSTIN.
1951. The mammals of South Africa. Trustees of the Mammals of South Africa Book Fund, Johannesburg. 700 pp.

RODE, PAUL.
1943. Faune de l'Empire français. Vol. 2. Mammifères ongulés de l'Afrique noire. Libraire Larose, Paris. 122 pp.

ROE, FRANK GILBERT.
  1951. The North American buffalo. University of Toronto Press, Toronto, Ontario. 955 pp.
ROOSEVELT, THEODORE, and EDMUND HELLER.
  1914. Life-histories of African game animals. Chas. Scribner's Sons, New York. 2 vols. 798 pp.
ROOT, ALAN.
  1959. Bringing up bongo. Wild Life, 1 (2):9; 30.
SALEZ, M.
  1959. Statut actuel du cerf de Barbarie (Cervus elaphus barbarus). La Terre et la Vie, Suppl., 1959.
SANBORN, ELWIN R.
  1908. The National bison herd. Bull. New York Zool. Soc., No. 28, pp. 400–3; 406–12.
SCHNEIDER, KARL MAX.
  1932. Eine Vorrichtung zum Ausbiegen einwachsender Gehörne. Zool. Garten, Leipzig (N.F.), 5 (7/9):235–37.
SCHOMBURGK, HANS.
  1912. On the trail of the pygmy hippo. Bull. New York Zool. Soc., 16 (52):880–84.
  1913. Distribution and habits of the pygmy hippopotamus. 17th Ann. Rept. New York Zool. Soc., 1912, pp. 113–20.
SCHOUTEDEN, H.
  1947. De zoogdieren van Belgisch Congo en van Ruanda-Urundi. Ann. Mus. Congo Belge, Ser. 2, 3 (1/3):1–576.
SCHWARTZ, JOHN E., II, and GLEN E. MITCHELL.
  1945. The Roosevelt elk on the Olympic Peninsula, Washington. Jour. Wildlife Management, 9 (4):295–319.
SCLATER, PHILIP LUTLEY.
  1873. Remarks on the Liberian hippopotamus. Proc. Zool. Soc. London, p. 434.
  1901. On an apparently new species of zebra from the Semliki forest. Ibid., Vol. 1, pp. 50–52.
SCLATER, PHILIP LUTLEY, and OLDFIELD THOMAS.
  1894–1900. The book of antelopes. R. H. Porter, London. 4 vols.
SCLATER, W. L.
  1900–1901. The mammals of South Africa. R. H. Porter, London. 2 vols.
SETON, ERNEST THOMPSON.
  1909. Life histories of northern animals. Chas. Scribner's Sons, New York. 2 vols. 1267 pp.
  1927. Lives of game animals. Doubleday, Page & Co., New York. 4 vols.
SEVERINGHAUS, C. W., and E. L. CHEATUM.
  1956. Life and times of the white-tailed deer. In: The deer of North America. Ed. WALTER P. TAYLOR. The Stackpole Co., Harrisburg, Pa., and The Wildlife Management Institute, Washington, D.C. 668 pp.

SHORTRIDGE, G. C.
  1934. The mammals of South West Africa. Wm. Heinemann, Ltd., London, 2 vols. 779 pp.

SILVER, HELENETTE.
  1961. Deer milk compared with substitute milk for fawns. Jour. Wildlife Management, **25** (1):66–70.

SIMON, E. S.
  1943. Life span of some wild animals in captivity. Jour. Bombay Nat. Hist. Soc., **44** (1):117–18.

SIMPSON, GEORGE GAYLORD.
  1945. The principles of classification and a classification of mammals. Bull. Amer. Mus. Nat. Hist., **85**. 350 pp.

SKINNER, M. P.
  1922. The prong-horn. Jour. Mammal., **3** (2):82–105.

SPENCER, CLIFFORD C.
  1943. Notes of the life history of Rocky Mountain bighorn sheep in the Tarryall Mountains of Colorado. Jour. Mammal., **24** (1):1–11.

STEINBACHER, GEORG.
  1959. Trächtigkeitsdauer beim weissbartgnu (*Connochaetes taurinus*). Säugetiere Mitteil., **7** (2):75.

STEINMETZ, H.
  1937. Beobachtungen über die Entwicklung junger Zwergflusspferde im Zoologischen Garten Berlin. Zool. Garten, Leipzig (N.F.), **9** (6): 255–263.

STEPHAN, SOL A.
  1925. Forty years' experience with giraffes in captivity. Parks and Recreation, **9** (1):61–63.

STOTT, KEN, JR.
  1954. Baby food for thought. Zoonooz, **27** (6):5.
  1959. Giraffe intergradation in Kenya. Jour. Mammal., **40** (2):251.

STREET, PHILIP.
  1956. The London Zoo. Odhams Press, Ltd., London. 223 pp.

SWYNNERTON, G. H.
  1958. Fauna of the Serengeti National Park. Mammalia, **22** (3):435–50.

TALBOT, LEE MERRIAM.
  1960. A look at threatened species. Oryx, **5** (4/5):153–280.

TALBOT, LEE M., and M. H. TALBOT.
  1961. How much does it weigh? Wild Life, **3** (1):47–48.

TATE, G. H. H.
  1947. Mammals of eastern Asia. The Macmillan Co., New York. 366 pp.

TEGNER, HENRY.
  1951. The roe deer. The Batchworth Press, London. 176 pp.

TENER, J. S.
1958.   The distribution of muskoxen in Canada. Jour. Mammal., **39** (3): 398–408.

TONG, E. H.
1957a.   Recent arrivals at Whipsnade. Zoo Life, **12** (1):16–17.
1957b.   World register of Père David's deer. Proc. Zool. Sc:. London, **129**:343–49.
1958.   Père David's deer, 1957. *Ibid.*, **131**:318–19.
1960.   World register of Père David's deer 1958/1959. *Ibid.*, **135**:315–17.

ULMER, FREDERICK A., JR.
1959.   The golden age of zoo exhibits. America's First Zoo, **11** (1):5–9.

URBAIN, ACHILLE.
1937.   Le kou prey ou boeuf gris Cambodgien. Bull. Soc. Zool. France, **62**:305–7.

URBAIN, A., J. NOUVEL, P. BULLIER, and J. RINJARD.
1955.   Rapport sur la mortalité et la natalité enregistrées au Parc Zoologique du Bois de Vincennes pendant l'année 1954. Bull. Mus. Hist. Nat., Paris, 2d ser., **27** (2):117–34.

V[AN] B[EMMEL, A. C. V.].
1958.   De schapen van Marco Polo. Blijdorp-Geluiden, **6** (7/8):4–5.
1959.   Takins. *Ibid.*, **7** (9):4–5.

VAN BEMMEL, A. C. V.
1960.   Ituri. Blijdorp-Geluiden, **8** (3):3–4.

VAN DEN BERGH, W.
1958.   Succes et échec d'ordre zootechnique. Zoo, Anvers, **23** (4):130–34.
1959.   Nos collections zoologiques. *Ibid.*, **25** (2):46–47.
1961.   L'antilope bongo (*Boocerus euryceros* [Ogilby]). *Ibid.*, **27** (1):7–13.

VAN GELDER, RICHARD.
1957.   The sheep that was a legend. Animal Kingdom, **60** (1):2–5.

VERHEYEN, RENÉ.
1954.   Monographie éthologique de l'hippopotame (*Hippopotamus amphibius* Linné). Exploration du Parc National Albert. Institut des Parcs Nationaux du Congo Belge, Brussels. 91 pp.

VEVERS, G. M.
1926.   Some notes on the recent birth of a hippopotamus (*H. amphibius*) in the Gardens. Proc. Zool. Soc. London, pp. 1097–1100.

VIBE, CHR.
1958.   The musk ox in Greenland. Mammalia, **22** (1):168–74.

WARD, ROWLAND.
1922.   Records of big game. Rowland Ward, Ltd., London. 526 pp.

WARWICK, BRUCE L., and R. O. BERRY.
1949.   Inter-generic and intra-specific embryo transfers in sheep and goats. Jour. Heredity, **40** (11):297–303.

WHARTON, CHARLES H.
  1957. An ecological study of the kouprey, *Novibos sauveli* (Urbain). Monogr.
          Inst. Sci. Technol., 5. Manila. 111 pp.

WHITEHEAD, G. KENNETH.
  1950. Deer and their management in the deer parks of Great Britain and
          Ireland. Country Life Ltd., London. 370 pp.

WISLOCKI, GEORGE B.
  1954. Antlers in female deer, with a report of three cases in *Odocoileus*. Jour.
          Mammal., 35 (4):486–95.
  1956. Further notes on antlers in female deer of the genus *Odocoileus*. *Ibid.*,
          37 (2):231–35.

WISLOCKI, G. B., J. C. AUB, and C. M. WALDO.
  1947. The effects of gonadectomy and the administration of testosterone
          propionate on the growth of antlers in male and female deer. Endo-
          crinology, 40 (3):202–24.

WODZICKI, K. A.
  1950. Introduced mammals of New Zealand. Bull. 98, Dept. of Scientific
          and Industrial Research, Wellington. 255 pp.

ZABINSKI, JAN.
  1960. The European bison (*Bison bonasus*). State Council for Conservation
          of Nature, 9. Warsaw. 26 pp.

ZELLMER, G.
  1961. Hand-rearing of giraffe at Bristol Zoo. Internatl. Zoo Yrbk., 2
          (1960):90–93. Zoological Society of London.

ZIEGLER-SIMON, J.
  1957. Beobachtungen am Russeldikdik, *Rhynotragus kirki* (Gthr.). Zool.
          Garten, Leipzig (N.F.), 25 (1/3):1–13.

ZUCKERMAN, S.
  1953. The breeding seasons of mammals in captivity. Proc. Zool. Soc.
          London, 122 (4):827–950.

ZUKOWSKI, MRS. FRANK.
  1951. The story behind Bambi, Brownie and Baby. Animal Kingdom, 54
          (5):146–50; 160.

ADDENDA

·

Preparations for a second printing of "The Management of Wild Mammals in Captivity" give a welcome opportunity to supplement certain records with new information that has come to me through the literature or the interested kindness of colleagues. There is, of course, no end to the extending of notes on births and longevity records; for the present purpose the cutoff date is December, 1964.

LEE S. CRANDALL

P. 71 par. 5

Two lesser mouse lemurs were born in the Zoological Gardens of London in 1962 (Internatl. Zoo Yrbk., 1962 [1963], 4: 222).

P. 74 par. 3

J. G. Nieuwendijk (*in litt.*, 1964) says that an aye-aye received at Artis, the Zoological Gardens of Amsterdam, on June 3, 1914, lived until September 15, 1937, or 23 years, 3 months, 12 days.

P. 78 par. 3

The first birth of an angwantibo in captivity occurred at Artis, the Zoological Gardens of Amsterdam, on December 14, 1963 (Anon., 1964. Angwantibo's. Artis, 10 [2]: 48–52).

P. 79 para. 2

The first recorded birth of a potto (*Perodicticus*) in captivity occurred at Artis, the Zoological Gardens of Amsterdam, on September 4, 1887. (Anon., 1964. Potto—een "Afschouwelyk Beest"? Artis, 9 [5]: 164–69).

P. 89 par. 1

A red uakari, born at the Monkey Jungle, Goulds, Florida, on June 23, 1963, is believed to represent the first breeding of this species in captivity. (Anon., Newsletter, American Association of Zoological Parks and Aquariums, 4 [2]: 8).

P. 95 par. 3

The male hooded capuchin, known as Irish, received at the San Diego Zoological Garden in 1927, died on May 24, 1964, after approximately 37 years (Clyde A. Hill, 1964. Internatl. Zoo News, 11 [4]: 125).

P. 96 par. 5

At the Mesker Park Zoo, Evansville, Indiana, births of squirrel monkeys are reported to have occurred yearly since 1957, with 3 in August, 1964. The animals are kept in a group consisting of both males and females in about equal numbers (Marvin L. Jones, *in litt.*).

P. 106 par. 3

The Goeldi's marmoset, received at the New York Zoological Park on September 1, 1959, died on March 5, 1964, after 4 years, 6 months, 4 days.

P. 121 par. 3

Clyde A. Hill (*in litt.*, 1963) reports the birth of a proboscis monkey in the Surabaja Zoo, Java. This appears to be the first birth of this species in captivity.

P. 122 par. 3

"Solemn John" or "Big John," the male Kikuyu colobus monkey received at the San Diego Zoological Garden in 1940, died on April 7, 1964, after approximately 24 years in San Diego. He is said to have sired 8 offspring, the last having been born on March 20, 1964 (Clyde A. Hill, 1964. Primate senior citizens. Zoonooz, 37 [5]: 14).

P. 130 par. 1

Dr. Harold J. Coolidge has pointed out to me that the first birth of a gibbon in captivity in Europe or America appears to have been that of a white-cheeked (*Hylobates* [*concolor*] *leucogenys*) at the National Zoological Park, Washington, in 1930, as reported by William M. Mann (1931. Report of the director of the National Zoological Park for the year ended June 30, 1931. Smithsonian Inst. Report for 1931, pp. 86–116).

P. 146 par. 3

Killing and eating of mammalian prey by Schweinfurth's chimpanzee, observed in the Gombe Stream Game Preserve, Tanganyika, is reported by Jane Goodall (1963. My life among wild chimpanzees. Nat. Geogr. Mag., 124 [2]: 272–308).

P. 168 par. 1

A fourth infant was born to the female lowland gorilla at Basel on June 1, 1964, and like the third, was being cared for by the mother (E.M. Lang, 1964. Internatl. Zoo News, 11 [4]: 119).

P. 168 par. 2

A full account of the birth of a lowland gorilla in the National Zoological Park, Washington, D.C., September 9, 1961, has been published by Theodore H. Reed and Bernard F. Gallagher (1963. Zool. Garten, Leipzig [N.F.], 27 [6]: 279–92). A second birth to the same female occurred on January 10, 1964.

P. 238 par. 3

Four living examples of Cuming's giant rat (*Phloeomys cumingi*), 2 males and 2 females, brought from the Philippines by Dr. Alexander Schadenburg in 1890 and deposited in the Zoological Gardens of Dresden, Germany, appear to have been the first to have reached a zoological garden (A.B. Meyer, 1890. Zool. Garten, Frankfurt, 31 [7]: 195–99).

P. 247 par. 4

Mr. Gerald Iles, formerly director of the Belle Vue Gardens, Manchester, England, tells me that a specimen of the Brazilian tree porcupine (*Coendou prehensilis*), received at Manchester May 26, 1950, and transferred later to the Zoological Gardens at Chester, was still living there on August 20, 1964, after 14 years, 3 months, 25 days.

P. 298 par. 1

An innovation in the exhibition of brown bears has been instituted at Skansen, the zoological gardens of Stockholm. By a series of steps, European red foxes were introduced to the enclosure occupied by a group of European brown bears. This arrangement has proved so successful that foxes and bear cubs play freely together. (Kai Curry-Lindahl, 1958. Brown bears [*Ursus arctos*] and foxes [*Vulpes vulpes*] living together in the same enclosure. Zool. Garten, Leipzig [N.F.], 24 [1/2]: 1–8).

P. 315 par. 5

The birth of an olingo (*Bassaricyon gabbii*), presumably the first in captivity, occurred at the Louisville, Kentucky, Zoo on March 7, 1964. It was destroyed by the mother on the following day, as reported by Dr. Ivo Poglayen. (Anon., Newsletter, American Association of Zoological Parks and Aquariums, 5 [4]: 5).

P. 323 par. 4

On September 9, 1963, the first recorded birth of a giant panda in captivity occurred in the Peking Zoo. The baby, well cared for by the
mother, is reported to have weighed 5 ounces at birth. On January 28,
1964, its weight had increased to 21 pounds; it was able to walk at 3
months. (Ouyang Kan and Tung Shu-Hua, 1964. In the Peking Zoo—
the first baby giant panda. Animal Kingdom, **67** [2]: 44–46).

P. 329 par. 1

Three grisons (*Galictis vittata*) were born at the Chester Zoo, England, in
September, 1963, and fully reared.   (Anon., 1963. Zoo babies. Chester
Zoo News, October, 1963: 11).

P. 333 par. 2

A litter of two ratels (*Mellivora capensis*) born in the National Zoological
Gardens of South Africa, Pretoria, on February 27, 1942, appears to
constitute the first captivity breeding record for this species (D.J. Brand,
1963. Mammals bred in the National Zoological Gardens, South Africa,
during the period 1908–1960. Proc. Zool. Soc. London, **140** [4]: 617–
59).

P. 334 par. 2

The birth of 2 Japanese badgers (*Meles m. anakuma*) at the Buffalo (N.Y.)
Zoological Gardens, on March 25, 1964, is reported by Clayton F.
Freiheit, curator (*in litt.*). One was killed by the mother, but the other
was successfully reared by hand.

P. 343 par. 5

An Asiatic clawless otter (*Aonyx cinerea*) received at the New York
Zoological Park on June 20, 1964, plunged freely into water and swam
well, contrary to previous experience with this species.

P. 345 par. 3

The female giant otter (*Pterónura brasiliensis*) received at the New York
Zoological Park on February 22, 1955, was found to weigh 22.9 kilograms (50 pounds, 6 ounces) on March 20, 1964.

P. 383 par. 1

On January 6, 1963, a normally colored male Bengal tiger arrived at the
National Zoological Park, Washington, from the zoo at Ahmedabad,
India. Bred under the direction of the Maharajah of Rewa, this animal is

both half-brother and uncle of the "white" female received in 1960 (Theodore H. Reed, 1964. Report on the National Zoological Park for the year ended June 30, 1963. Smithsonian Inst. Report for 1963, pp. 107–46). These animals were paired and on January 6, 1964, the female gave birth to three cubs, of which one was "white," the others normal. Birth and development were observed by closed-circuit television without risk of disturbance.

P. 389 par. 2

Dacca, the female Bengal tiger born in the New York Zoological Park on February 8, 1944, died on September 10, 1964, after 20 years, 7 months, two days.

P. 396 par. 1

A female snow leopard born at Whipsnade, 1960, died in the New York Zoological Park on August 13, 1964, and was found to weigh 32 kilograms (approximately 70 pounds, 6 ounces).

p. 423, par. 2

Three Guadalupe fur seals, collected by an expedition headed by Professor Carl Hubbs, were received at the San Diego Zoological Gardens in March, 1962. Of these, only one male was retained at San Diego, the others, by prearrangement, being sent to the Mexican Fisheries Department in Mexico City (George H. Pournelle, 1964. Eight species— a new high for seals. Zoonooz, 37 [7]: 3–7). Dr. Pournelle also notes that the first Guadalupe fur seal to be kept in captivity was received at San Diego in 1922.

P. 432 par. 3

Kai Curry-Lindahl, director at Skansen, the zoological gardens of Stockholm, informs me (*in litt.*) that a European harbor seal (*Phoca v. vitulina*) lived for 26 years at his institution.

P. 434, par. 2

Gray seals (*Halichoerus grypus*) were born at the Zoological Gardens of London on October 31 and November 14, 1963 (Anon, 1964. Newsletter, American Association of Zoological Parks and Aquariums, 5 [1]: 5). Births of this species occurred also at the New York Aquarium on January 8 and January 28, 1964 (Anon., 1964. Gray seal pup is born at the Aquarium. Animal Kingdom, 67 [1]: 30). The birth weight of the female pup born on January 8 is given as 27½ pounds; 2 weeks after birth it weighed 109 pounds.

P. 436 par. 1

Three Weddell's seals (*Leptonychotes weddelli*) captured in the Antarctic by Dr. Carleton Ray and received at the New York Aquarium on November 15, 1963, appear to have been the first representatives of this species to reach North America alive (Carleton Ray, 1964. Studying the Weddell seal in Antarctica. Animal Kingdom, **67** [2]: 34–43). The largest of these animals was a female weighing 750 pounds. All seem to have accepted captivity well.

P. 489 par. 3

The fifth issue of the *Pedigree Book of the Przewalski Horse*, edited by Jiří Volf and published by the Zoological Gardens of Prague, 1964, shows that as of January 1, 1964, there were 110 animals living in captivity, an increase of 20 over the total of the previous year.

P. 513 par. 1

Further births to the female Indian rhinoceros at Basel were a male born on August 3, 1962, and a female born in the period May–June, 1964, making a total of four young produced by this remarkable pair (H. Wackernagel, 1964. Internatl. Zoo News, **11** [4]: 133–4). A calf is reported to have been born in August, 1964, at the Hagenbeck Zoo, Stellingen, Germany, to a female Indian rhinoceros that had been sent to be bred by the Basel male (Marvin L. Jones, *in litt.*).

P. 513 par. 2

A white rhinoceros calf was born on April 11, 1964, at the Loskp Dam Reserve in the Transvaal, to a female captured in Zululand a year previously, when presumably pregnant (World Wildlife News, **27** [June, 1964]: 1).

P. 514 par. 3

A male black rhinoceros is reported to have lived in the Municipal Zoological Gardens, Johannesburg, Transvaal, from March 7, 1914, to March 21, 1948, or 34 years, 14 days (Richard J. Reynolds, 1963. The black rhinoceros (*Diceros bicornis*) in captivity. Internatl. Zoo Yrbk., **4**: 98–113).

P. 546 par. 3

That dromedaries may accustom themselves to entering shallow water is shown by a report from James Coder, manager of the Farm-in-the-Zoo in the New York Zoological Park, that a female dromedary and her male calf of 1962 regularly bathed in a pool 4 feet in depth during the summer of 1964.

P. 566 par. 5
Kai Curry-Lindahl, director at Skansen, the zoological gardens at Stockholm, Sweden, has cited (*in litt.*) a longevity of 25 years for a captive fallow deer.

P. 567 par. 1
When visiting the New York Zoological Park on December 3, 1964, Khosrow Sariri, chief game warden of Iran, reported that his department had recently captured 4 specimens of the Persian fallow deer and is holding them for breeding. He believes that about 40 animals are still surviving in Iran.

P. 601 par. 2
The Scandinavian reindeer is designated as the typical race, *Rangifer t. tarandus.*

P. 603 par. 1
K. Curry-Lindahl reminds me (*in litt.*) that a breeding herd of reindeer has been maintained at Skansen, Stockholm, for more than 60 years.

P. 616 par. 2
Paul Breese, director of the Honolulu Zoo until late 1964, reports (*in litt.*) the birth of a giraffe at his institution on October 9, 1964. The father, a reticulated giraffe, was born in Honolulu on November 3, 1960. Estimating the gestation period at roughly 15 months, this male would have been approximately 2 years, 8 months old when conception occurred.

P. 622 par. 2
Further births of viable okapis occurred as follows: San Diego, August 9, 1962, March 22, 1964, and May 6, 1964; Bristol, England, November, 1963; New York, November 23, 1963; Rotterdam, January 3, 1964.

P. 625 par. 1
"Esayo," the male okapi received at the Zoological Gardens of Copenhagen on April 30, 1948, died in November, 1963 (Bent Jorgensen, 1964. Internatl. Zoo News, 11 [4]: 125). This span of approximately 15 years, 6 months is the greatest so far recorded for an okapi.

P. 652 par. 3

In a brief mimeographed report dated January 1, 1964, Dr. Erna Mohr lists 235 European bison known to be living in the world, aside from those in Poland, Russia, Roumania, Bulgaria, and Yugoslavia, the data for which have been gathered by Dr. Zabinski. Dr. Mohr estimates the total as of January 1, 1964, at about 700 animals.

P. 653 par. 2

Further European bison were born at the Philadelphia Zoological Garden on June 1, 1964, and at New York on September 22, 1964.

P. 666 par. 4

After the arrival of the first 4 animals at Tempe, the ruler of Kuwait presented another female, and in 1964, through the intervention of King Saud, 2 males and 2 females from the collection maintained by the municipality of Riyadh in Saudi Arabia, were presented to the U.S. National Appeal of the World Wildlife Fund. After quarantine at Naples and New York, these animals arrived safely at Tempe, greatly strengthening the growing herd already there. A second calf was born on May 22, 1964. At the end of 1964 there were thus 11 animals in the Tempe herd.

P. 694 par. 4

A. F. Oeming tells me that 3 Barren Ground muskoxen were born at the Alberta Game Farm in both 1963 and 1964.

P. 707 par. 5

A. F. Oeming, of the Alberta Game Farm, Edmonton, reports the births of five Stone's sheep (*Ovis dalli stonei*) in 1964.

INDEX